*Test Item File and Instructor's Resource Guide
to Accompany*

Elementary and Intermediate Algebra:
A Combined Course

Third Edition

Larson/Hostetler

Ann R. Kraus
Cheryl A. Leech

Houghton Mifflin Company
Boston   New York

Editor-in-Chief, Mathematics: Jack Shira
Managing Editor: Cathy Cantin
Senior Associate Editor: Maureen Ross
Associate Editor: Laura Wheel
Assistant Editor: Carolyn Johnson
Supervising Editor: Karen Carter
Project Editor: Patty Bergin
Editorial Assistant: Christine E. Lee
Art Supervisor: Gary Crespo
Marketing Manager: Ros Kane, Michael Busnach
Marketing Associate: Erin Dionne
Composition and Art: Meridian Creative Group

Printed in the U.S.A.

ISBN: 0-395-97643-X

123456789-KCO-02 01 00 99

PREFACE

This *Test Item File and Instructor's Resource Guide* is a supplement to the textbook *Elementary and Intermediate Algebra: A Combined Course*, Third Edition, by Ron Larson and Robert P. Hostetler.

This resource guide begins with a section of Notes to the Instructor containing contemporary instructional strategies and ideas that you may find useful in meeting the needs of the students in your algebra course. Topics include assessment, cooperative learning, multi-cultural issues, language issues, flexibility and order of topics, and algebra study skills.

The first portion of this *Test Item File and Instructor's Resource Guide* is a bank of test questions arranged by text section. To assist you in selecting test questions and administering examinations, each question is followed by a two-, three-, or four-item code line. The first item of the code always indicates the level of difficulty of the questions: straightforward (1) or medium difficulty (2). If the solution to the problem requires the use of a graphing utility, the next code is (T) for technology-required. If the test item is used in a chapter test form in the test bank in the second portion of this guide, the next item in the code line represents the sample test form which utilizes this question. By coding test items in this way, all questions appearing on Test Form 3C for example, may be called up, and any or all of them may then be edited as desired. The last item in the code line is always the answer.

The second portion of this supplement contains a bank of test forms. These are three sample tests, two with multiple-choice questions and one with open-ended questions, for each text chapter. In addition, there are two final examinations, one with multiple-choice questions and one with open-ended questions. An answer key for the chapter test and final examination forms follow.

Finally, the last portion of this supplement contains 30 transparency masters that are keyed to the text.

A computerized version of the test bank, with a User Manual, is available for the IBM-PC, IBM-compatible computers, and the Macintosh. For more information, please contact your local sales representative.

We have made every effort to see that the answers are correct. However, we would appreciate very much hearing about any errors or other suggestions for improvement.

Ann R. Kraus
Cheryl A. Leech

CONTENTS

Notes to the Instructor

ASSESSMENT

The purpose of assessment in mathematics is to improve learning and teaching. A key component in contemporary education, assessment must be used to broaden and inform, not restrict, the educational process. This view is well stated in the NCTM *Curriculum and Evaluation Standards for School Mathematics.*

"Assessment must be more than testing; it must be a continuous, dynamic, and often informal process." (p. 203)

According to the Mathematical Sciences Education Board (MSEB), there is a need for mathematics assessments that accomplish several goals.

- Promote the development of mathematical power for all students
- Measure the full range of mathematical knowledge, skills, and processes specified by the National Council of Teachers of Mathematics (NCTM) curriculum standard
- Communicate to students and teachers what mathematics students already know, as well as the mathematics they have yet to learn

Formal Assessment Strategies

Elementary and Intermediate Algebra: A Combined Course, Third Edition, is a comprehensive teaching and learning package. The text and an array of text-tied supplements offer a variety of vehicles for progress assessment.

In the text, Mid-Chapter Quizzes, Chapter Tests, Cumulative Tests, and "Explaining Concepts" in each exercise set are designed to help measure retention and understanding. The "Developing Skills" and "Solving Problems" exercises can also be part of the assessment program.

The supplements package for *Elementary and Intermediate Algebra: A Combined Course,* Third Edition, offers substantial resources to help you prepare formal tests and quizzes. This *Test Item File and Instructor's Resource Guide* contains many test items with answers for each section of the text. The test items are organized by text section and coded as routine or challenging, and technology-required if appropriate. A bank of ready-made Chapter Tests (Forms A through C) and final exams with answer keys completes the *Guide.* The test questions are also available in a computerized format, offering the instructor the opportunity to create customized tests. The *Student Solutions Guide* is particularly useful for student self-assessment.

Alternative Assessment Strategies

In addition to the formal assessment strategies, various forms of alternative assessment may help the instructor (and student) reveal the student's capabilities, as well as gather information to determine what students "know" (understand) as compared to what students "know how to do" in mathematics. Alternative assessment is a means for evaluating student progress using non-traditional assessment tools. The information gathered by alternative assessment can be used in various ways. Students can use it to appraise themselves and their mathematical abilities; instructors can use it to make informed decisions about the instruction of their students.

Some formats for informal and ongoing assessment are:
- student-created problems (problem posing),
- journals and portfolios,
- projects or research assignments, and
- demonstration or performance assessment.

There are several advantages to using a variety of measures of achievement.
- One type of assessment cannot serve all informational needs.
- Receiving information from multiple sources leads to more informed decision making.
- Traditional paper-and-pencil tests may be incomplete measures of achievement.
- Using a variety of assessment methods enables the instructor to obtain a more equitable measure of a student's mathematical progress with less potential for biases than traditional measures.

The goals of alternative assessment are to:
- find out what the student already knows.
- evaluate the depth of the student's conceptual understanding and his or her ability to transfer this understanding to new and different situations.
- evaluate the student's ability to communicate his or her understanding mathematically, make mathematical connections, and reason mathematically.
- plan the mathematics instruction in order to achieve the objectives.
- report individual student progress and show growth in mathematical maturity.
- analyze the overall effectiveness of the mathematics instruction.

Scoring

There are several ways to score alternative assessment assignments. The most simplified scoring involves grading the assignment on a scale of 0–3. If the student gives a clear, coherent explanation with appropriate diagrams or graphs, a score of 3 is given; if the student's work shows understanding of the assignment but contains computational errors and/or minor flaws in the explanation, a score of 2 is given; if the work contains serious conceptual errors in addition to flagrant computational errors, a score of 1 is given; and if little or no attempt is made to complete the assignment, a score of 0 is given.

Formats

Problem Posing

Students can be asked to create their own problems for tests, with answers. They can then exchange questions and check each other's answers. Asking students to create review sheets can also provide a means for you to assess student understanding of the essentials. Note that many of the in-text *Discussing the Concepts* encourage students to create problems or correct solutions.

Journals and Portfolios

Students can keep mathematics portfolios of problems and write journals of attitudes, understandings, and applications of mathematics as part of an instructor's assessment strategy. Students can be asked to write explanations for others; they can identify and explain mathematical ideas; and they can design exercises to find out whether someone understands a mathematical relationship.

Built-in features of the text can be springboards for implementing this type of alternative assessment and allow students to demonstrate individual capabilities. In the Preface of the text, "How to Write Mathematically" is a helpful student reference. The *Discussing the Concept*, at the end of each section, offers students the opportunity to practice and write about mathematical thinking. The last section of each Exercise Set, *Explaining Concepts*, offers the opportunity for oral and written responses. A variety of other exercises also prompt students to explain their reasoning.

Following are additional suggestions for Journal topics.

<u>Attitudes</u> What is the best experience the student has ever had in a math class? What did the student like best/least about math class this week? Of all the resources available to help students understand math (videos, tutorial software, study guide, solutions guide, multimedia projects, and so on), which did they find most useful and why? How would the student evaluate his or her own progress this week? Did any of the applications based on real data interest the student, and, if so, why?

<u>Understanding</u> Ask students to compare and contrast, and explain mathematical relationships as appropriate. For instance, students may be asked to describe the relationship that is necessary among the terms of a trinomial in order for it to factor as a perfect square trinomial. Students could be asked to choose an exercise that has given them trouble, and describe the approaches they used to try to solve the problem. Writing can encourage more active learning.

<u>Applications</u> Students might be asked to create one of each basic type of problem, together with its solution, for a section. Compare and contrast problem-solving strategies used. Some instructors have successfully used concept maps: having students list all the concepts they consider important in a section and draw arrows to indicate the relationships among the ideas.

Explanations Have students explain to a friend, in writing, how to solve a particular problem. What advice would they give to help him or her avoid errors?

Following are additional suggestions for Portfolio topics.

Exercises Ask students to keep all or some instructor-selected homework exercises in a notebook. Collect this Portfolio occasionally, and grade a subset of the problems. You may also choose to give a grade for general effort based on how many of all of the problems were tried.

In-class activities A summary of in-class problems can also be part of the portfolio, as well as review handouts from the instructor.

Projects

Projects provide the student with the opportunity to express his or her mathematical ability in a format other than paper-and-pencil tests. Some sources for projects include the following.

Research Projects In each chapter of the text, there are *Research Projects* that can be assigned to groups, pairs, or individual students.

Reports Students can be asked to research and write a report on the contributions of a mathematician. The *Historical Notes* in the text introduce several mathematicians and their work as well as relevant mathematical artifacts, and students can be asked to elaborate on this material.

Chapter Projects The multi-part *Motivating the Chapter* can be assigned to groups, pairs, or individual students. Students might be asked to present the findings of the project to the class.

Demonstration or Performance Assessment

Instructors can assess student comprehension by affording them the opportunity to explain mathematical concepts in their own words—using manipulatives, diagrams, and examples—for the entire class or within a small-group setting. Students may reveal their level of comprehension, show their ability to transfer skills, demonstrate their computational skills, and so on. Note your observations, and consider recording these facts.

An instructor might look for opportunities to further involve students in the learning process. For example, if technology (calculator, graphing calculator, or computer) is being used in conjunction with an overhead viewing device, consider asking a student to press the keys to help demonstrate simple ideas. This can encourage active class participation, while the instructor monitors the discussion.

In summary, the text and supplements offer the following alternative assessment features.

- *Discussing the Concept*
- *Explaining Concepts* (Exercise Set)
- *Integrated Review* (Exercise Set)
- *Motivating the Chapter*
- *Multimedia CD ROM Projects*
- *Notes to the Instructor* (*Test Item File and Instructor's Resource Guide*)

As you begin to integrate alternative assessment into your course, it is important to start slowly to avoid becoming overwhelmed. Try one form of alternative assessment, then add others to your repertoire. As you select problems from the text or design your own, you might consider characteristics such as open-ended response, multiple correct answers, no stringent time limits, and opportunities for learning during the assessment process. Take your time, and enjoy what you are doing. A combination of formal and informal assessment can help you evaluate each student most effectively.

COOPERATIVE LEARNING

Benefits of Cooperative Learning

Cooperative learning, or small group instruction, is an effective tool for achieving many instructional goals. Group work can be done in pairs, or in groups of as many as six individuals. Often thought of as peer tutoring or teaching, group work can also be used for group investigations and activities. In the text, you will find *Discussing the Concept*, *Motivating the Chapter*, and *Multimedia CD-ROM Projects* that are designed for use in a cooperative learning setting, although some may also be appropriate for individual assignments. In addition, the more challenging exercises, technology-required exercises, and *Explaining Concepts* activities are also good problems for group work.

When making small-group assignments, consider having each group in the class work on the same problem, then join in a class-wide discussion of the results. Alternatively, consider assigning different parts of a multi-part problem to each group, then have the groups share all results for analysis and interpretation by the entire class. The Group Activities on pages 39, 50, and 94, for example, are appropriate for these teaching strategies.

Group work can empower students and enhance self-esteem. When groups are formed at the beginning of the course, students often report that they enjoy getting to know members of the group well. Group members can learn to be responsible for each other, phoning other students to share notes or picking up copies of handouts for an absent classmate. If groups change during the term, students enjoy the opportunity to meet new class members.

Group work encourages students to focus on learning, instead of merely earning grades. Students often feel that they can ask questions or admit confusion to peers in groups. Students may listen better to a peer explanation since they tend to communicate more directly and effectively with each other.

Group work teaches the vital life skills of cooperation, respect for others, listening, and speaking that are used in committees and working groups in the community and on the job. The instructor can monitor in-class group work dynamics, adjusting the focus and mediating as necessary.

Group work can help meet diverse needs within a class. Students working with partners can share complementary skills. For example, a student who is likely to grasp the algebra but for whom English is a second language, can be paired with a student whose English is good, but who may need help with the algebra.

Managing the Cooperative Learning Classroom

Instructors must be aware of two possible characteristics of groups that may make them less effective: the group may have trouble staying on task, and one student may dominate, while others let that student do the work and copy. To eliminate the first problem (if the group work occurs during class), circulate around the room, listen, and adjust the focus of each group as necessary. To help with the second problem, talk to the dominant student leaders. Help them to realize that they learn by explaining to others as they formulate, organize, justify, and express their skills and knowledge. Also give these high achievers recognition for helping others. Let students know that when someone else in their group arrives at a new understanding, all members can be proud of this achievement.

It can help students to give them general guidelines for working together, such as the following.

Teamwork Suggestions

Here are some general guidelines to consider when working on problem solving in groups.

1. Agree on what you have to do.
2. Make a plan.
3. Listen to each other's ideas.
4. Praise each other's ideas and see if you can build on another's idea.
5. Ask for help when you need it; give help when asked. If you finish your part and others are still working, volunteer your help.
6. Finish the project together. Proofread your work.
7. Discuss what you did well together and what you could do differently next time.

MULTI-CULTURAL ISSUES

Students should be aware of the rich cultural heritage of mathematicians throughout the centuries. They also should be aware that mathematics is created and used by people like themselves. Throughout *Elementary and Intermediate Algebra: A Combined Course,* Third Edition, Historical Notes can help promote this awareness. See, for example, the biographical notes about Blaise Pascal on page 281.

LANGUAGE ISSUES

Students for whom English is a second language, or who have limited English proficiency, may need help from the instructor and fellow students to express their interest and abilities in mathematics. As an instructor, consider the following suggestions.
- At the beginning of each class (or during the first class of the week), outline the material you plan to discuss.
- When you use a key math term for the first time, and when you use a key term that you feel should be emphasized, write it on the board.
- When you write a definition or example on the board, review sheet, or overhead transparency, label it.
- A student who is adept at the mathematics, but for whom English is a second language, can benefit from working with a student whose English skills are good, but who may need help with the mathematics.
- Use figures, graphs, and diagrams. Note that the text contains numerous figures, helpful side comments accompanying the solutions to examples, straightforward language, and key terms in boldface type, and that color is used to enhance readability.

FLEXIBILITY AND ORDER OF TOPICS

Elementary and Intermediate Algebra: A Combined Course, Third Edition, was designed to be flexible with respect to the order of coverage of core algebra topics, adapting easily to a wide variety of course syllabi and teaching styles. The text begins with The Real Number System, a thorough review chapter. All or part of this material may be covered or it can be omitted. Graphing is introduced in Chapter 4. The early introduction of graphs make more figures available to illustrate subsequent topics, giving students further insight and opportunities for greater understanding. Factoring can be taught in several locations, corresponding to the desires and needs of an individual college or instructor. Technology is integrated at appropriate points for easy access and for student awareness.

If you have any questions concerning the order of topics, please send a note to the Editorial address in the front of the text. As the text is used over time, the flexibility allows for potential growth and change in the algebra course.

ALGEBRA STUDY SKILLS

Elementary and Intermediate Algebra: A Combined Course, Third Edition, is designed to encourage the development of strong study skills. The general study tips in "How to Study Algebra," located in the preface, help students develop an overall course strategy. In addition, individual Study Tips are interspersed throughout the text offering specific help and insights to improve understanding, learning, and retention. The exercise sets include "Integrated Review" and there are opportunities throughout the text for self-assessment and review in the Mid-Chapter, Chapter, and Cumulative Review Tests.

The supplements package reinforces the text's emphasis on good study skills.
- The *Student Solutions Guide* contains summaries of the highlights of each chapter.
- A multiple-tape set of Videotapes accompanies the text. Keyed to the text, these include full content coverage, animations, and study tips.
- Tutorial Software includes opportunities for additional exercises and diagnostics.

Unit Conversions

Length

Within the English System: Inch (in.), Foot (ft), Yard (yd), Mile (mi)

1 mi = 5280 ft	1 mi = 1760 yd
1 yd = 3 ft	1 ft = 12 in.

Within the Metric System: Millimeter (mm), Centimeter (cm), Meter (m), Kilometer (km)

1 km = 1000 m	1 m = 100 cm
1 m = 1000 mm	1 cm = 10 mm

Between English and Metric Systems (to six significant figures)

Metric to English	English to Metric
1 mm = 0.0393701 in.	1 in. = 25.4000 mm
1 cm = 0.393701 in.	1 in. = 2.54000 cm
1 m = 3.28084 ft	1 ft = 0.304800 m
1 m = 1.09361 yd	1 yd = 0.914400 m
1 km = 0.621371 mi	1 mi = 1.60934 km

Area

Within the English System: Square Inch (in.^{2}), Square Foot (ft^2), Square Yard (yd^2), Acre, Square Mile (mi^2)

1 mi^2 = 640 acres	1 acre = 43,560 ft^2
1 yd^2 = 9 ft^2	1 ft^2 = 144 in.^{2}

Within the Metric System: Square Centimeter (cm^2), Square Meter (m^2), Square Kilometer (km^2)

1 km^2 = 1,000,000 m^2	
1 m^2 = 10,000 cm^2	

Between English and Metric Systems (to six significant figures)

Metric to English	English to Metric
1 cm^2 = 0.155000 in.^{2}	1 in.^{2} = 6.45160 cm^2
1 m^2 = 10.7640 ft^2	1 ft^2 = 0.0929030 m^2
1 m^2 = 1.19599 yd^2	1 yd^2 = 0.836127 m^2
1 km^2 = 0.386102 mi^2	1 mi^2 = 2.58999 km^2

Volume

Within the English System: Cubic Inch (in.^{3}), Cubic Foot (ft^3), Cubic Yard (yd^3), Fluid Ounce (fl oz), Pint (pt), Quart (qt), Gallon (gal)

1 yd^3 = 27 ft^3	1 ft^3 = 1728 in.^{3}
1 gal = 4 qt	1 qt = 2 pt
1 pt = 32 fl oz	1 pt = 16 fl oz
1 gal = 231 in.^{3}	1 ft^3 = 7.48052 gal

Within the Metric System: Cubic Centimeter (cm^3), Cubic Meter (m^3), Milliliter (ml or cc), Liter (l)

1 m^3 = 1000 liters	1 liter = 1000 ml
1 cm^3 = 1 ml	

Between English and Metric Systems (to six significant figures)

Metric to English	English to Metric
1 cm^3 = 0.0610237 in.^{3}	1 in.^{3} = 16.3871 cm^3
1 m^3 = 35.3147 ft^3	1 ft^3 = 0.0283168 m^3
1 m^3 = 1.30795 yd^3	1 yd^3 = 0.764555 m^3

Mass and Force

Within the English System:	(Mass)	Slug
	(Force/Weight)	Ounce (oz), Pound (lb), Ton
Within the Metric System:	(Mass)	Gram (g), Kilogram (kg), Metric Ton
	(Force/Weight)	Dyne, Newton (N)

Conversions (to four significant figures, at sea level for weight/mass conversions)

Mass to Mass	Mass to Weight	Weight to Weight
1 metric ton = 68.52 slug	1 metric ton = 1.102 ton	1 lb = 4.448 N
1 metric ton = 1000 kg	1 kg = 2.205 lb	1 lb = 16 oz
1 kg = 1000 g	1 kg = 35.27 oz	1 ton = 2000 lb
1 kg = 0.06852 slug	1 g = 0.3527 oz	1 N = 100,000 dyne
	1 slug = 32.17 lb	

Problem-Solving Strategies

Following is a summary of strategies that you may find useful in approaching a problem to be solved. This four-step problem-solving process is based on principles first described by George Polya in *How to Solve It* (1945).

1) Understand the Problem

    a) Notice what is being asked.

    b) List the unknowns.

    c) Identify the information and conditions given in the problem and distinguish that which is not needed. Look to see if information is missing. Is the missing information assumed to be general knowledge, *e.g.*, human body temperature, 98.6° F?

    d) Sketch a graph or draw a diagram of the situation.

    e) Write a verbal description of the relationship among all quantities. Assign appropriate notation for both the given and unknown quantities.

    f) Make an estimate of what you think the final solution should be.

2) Plan a Method for Solution

    To proceed with the solution, you must be able to devise a way to find the unknowns from the givens of the situation. The following suggestions, which can be used with analytical, graphical, or numerical approaches to problem solving, may help you to see a relationship among the quantities and to get you started on your solution:

    a) Refer to or enhance your graph or diagram as appropriate.

    b) Write a formula describing the situation.

    c) Decide if technology can help with part or all of the solution.

    d) Construct a table.

    e) Examine similar problems to see if their solution techniques are applicable.

    f) Look for a pattern.

    g) Work backward.

    h) Start with a special or simpler case to gain insight.

    i) Introduce an extra relationship between the givens and unknowns.

    j) Split the problem into nonoverlapping cases and solve for each case individually.

3) Execute the Plan for Solution

    a) Keeping an accurate record of your work, make all necessary calculations according to the plan and write out all details.

    b) Verify each step of your solution and check your final result. (If you choose to solve the problem using a table, try checking the solution with an algebraic approach. Or, if you choose to solve the problem algebraically, try checking the solution with a graphical approach.)

4) Return to the Original Problem

    a) Does your solution answer the original question?

    b) Does your solution make sense in terms of the original situation?

    c) Is there an easier way to solve this problem?

    d) Can you use this technique or result with another problem?

C H A P T E R   1
The Real Number System

Section 1.1   Real Numbers: Order and Absolute Value

1. Determine which numbers in the following set are rational numbers: $\left\{-2, -\frac{1}{2}, 0, 1, 3\right\}$

   (a) $\left\{-\frac{1}{2}\right\}$ (b) $\left\{-2, -\frac{1}{2}, 1, 3\right\}$ (c) $\left\{-2, -\frac{1}{2}, 0, 1, 3\right\}$

   (d) $\{1, 3\}$ (e) None of these

   1—Form: 1A—Ans: c

2. Determine which numbers in the following set are whole numbers: $\left\{-2, -\frac{1}{2}, 0, 1, 3\right\}$

   (a) $\left\{-\frac{1}{2}\right\}$ (b) $\left\{-2, -\frac{1}{2}, 1, 3\right\}$ (c) $\left\{-2, -\frac{1}{2}, 0, 1, 3\right\}$

   (d) $\{0, 1, 3\}$ (e) None of these

   1—Form: 1B—Ans: d

3. Identify the integers in the following set: $\{-4, -1, 0, 1, 4\}$

   1—Ans: $\{-4, -1, 0, 1, 4\}$

4. Identify the integers in the following set: $\{-5, -2, 0, 2, 5\}$

   1—Ans: $\{-5, -2, 0, 2, 5\}$

5. Determine which numbers in the following set are natural numbers: $\left\{-3, -\frac{3}{2}, 0, \frac{3}{2}, 3\right\}$

   1—Ans: $\{3\}$

6. Determine which numbers in the following set are natural numbers: $\left\{-4, -\frac{4}{3}, 0, \frac{4}{3}, 4\right\}$

   1—Ans: $\{4\}$

7. Identify the real number that corresponds to the point plotted on the number line.

   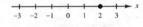

   1—Ans: 2

8. Identify the real number that corresponds to the point plotted on the number line.

   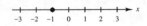

   1—Ans: -1

9. Identify the real number that corresponds to the point plotted on the number line.

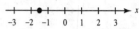

1—Form: 1C—Ans: $-\frac{3}{2}$

10. Identify the real number that corresponds to the point plotted on the number line.

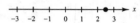

1—Ans: $\frac{5}{2}$

11. For the points marked on the number line, which of the following statements is *false*?

(a) $\frac{3}{2} > 3$ (b) $0 > -\frac{1}{2}$ (c) $-\frac{5}{2} < -\frac{1}{2}$ (d) $3 > \frac{3}{2}$ (e) $-\frac{1}{2} < \frac{3}{2}$

1—Ans: a

12. For the points as marked on the number line, which of the following statements is *false*?

(a) $\frac{3}{2} > -\frac{5}{2}$ (b) $0 < 3$ (c) $3 > \frac{3}{2}$

(d) $-\frac{1}{2} < \frac{3}{2}$ (e) None of these

1—Ans: e

13. Which of the following statements is *false*?

(a) $0 > 3$ (b) $0 > -3$ (c) $-2 < 0$ (d) $0 < 2$ (e) None of these

1—Ans: a

14. Which of the following statements is *false*?

(a) $0 > 4$ (b) $0 > -4$ (c) $-1 < 0$ (d) $0 < 1$ (e) None of these

1—Ans: a

15. Which of the following statements is *false*?

(a) $-1 > -2$ (b) $3 > -4$ (c) $-1 < 2$

(d) $-1 < -3$ (e) None of these

1—Ans: d

16. Which of the following statements is *false*?

(a) $-2 < -4$ (b) $3 > -1$ (c) $-2 < 3$

(d) $-1 > -3$ (e) None of these

1—Form: 1B—Ans: a

17. Which of the following statements is *false*?

(a) $\frac{5}{3} < \frac{5}{2}$ (b) $-\frac{5}{3} < -\frac{5}{2}$ (c) $-2 < 3$

(d) $0 > -\frac{7}{8}$ (e) None of these

2—Ans: b

18. Which of the following statements is *false*?

(a) $-\frac{7}{8} < 0$ (b) $-2 > -3$ (c) $\frac{5}{2} > \frac{5}{3}$

(d) $-\frac{5}{2} > -\frac{5}{3}$ (e) None of these

2—Ans: d

19. Which of the following statements is *false*?

(a) $-\frac{2}{3} < -\frac{1}{3}$ (b) $\frac{2}{3} > \frac{1}{3}$ (c) $-\frac{1}{3} < \frac{2}{3}$

(d) $-\frac{2}{3} < \frac{1}{3}$ (e) None of these

2—Ans: e

20. Which of the following statements is *false*?

(a) $\frac{2}{3} > -\frac{1}{3}$ (b) $-\frac{2}{3} < \frac{1}{3}$ (c) $-\frac{1}{3} < -\frac{2}{3}$

(d) $\frac{2}{3} > \frac{1}{3}$ (e) None of these

2—Ans: c

21. Which of the following statements is *true*?

(a) $-2.3 > 2.1$ (b) $2.3 < 2.1$ (c) $2.1 > 2.3$

(d) $-2.3 < 2.1$ (e) None of these

1—Form: 1A—Ans: d

22. Which of the following statements is *true*?

(a) $-3.4 < -3.2$ (b) $3.4 < 3.2$ (c) $3.2 > 3.4$

(d) $-3.4 > 3.2$ (e) None of these

1—Form: 1B—Ans: a

23. Which of the following statements is *true*?

(a) $-\frac{3}{2} > -\frac{1}{2}$ (b) $-\frac{1}{2} > \frac{1}{3}$ (c) $\frac{1}{2} < -\frac{3}{2}$ (d) $\frac{1}{2} > \frac{1}{3}$ (e) None of these

1—Form: 1A—Ans: d

24. Which of the following statements is *true*?

(a) $\frac{1}{3} < \frac{1}{2}$ (b) $-\frac{3}{2} > \frac{1}{2}$ (c) $-\frac{1}{2} > \frac{1}{2}$ (d) $-\frac{1}{2} < -\frac{3}{2}$ (e) None of these

1—Form: 1B—Ans: a

25. Show each real number as a point on the real number line and place the correct inequality symbol between the two numbers.

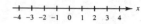

$\frac{5}{2}$ 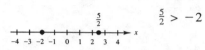 -2

1—Ans: 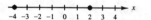 $\frac{5}{2} > -2$

26. Show each real number as a point on the real number line and place the correct inequality symbol between the two numbers.

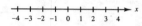

-4 ▨ 2

1—Ans: $-4 < 2$

27. Place the correct inequality symbol ($<$ or $>$) between the two numbers.

-5 ▨ -2

1—Ans: $<$

28. Place the correct inequality symbol ($<$ or $>$) between the two numbers.

-3 ▨ -1

1—Ans: $<$

29. Place the correct inequality symbol ($<$ or $>$) between the two numbers.

-4 ▨ -6

1—Ans: $>$

30. Place the correct inequality symbol ($<$ or $>$) between the two numbers.

-1 ▨ -2

1—Ans: $>$

31. Place the correct inequality symbol ($<$ or $>$) between the two numbers.

$\frac{7}{3}$ ▨ $\frac{7}{4}$

2—Ans: $>$

32. Place the correct inequality symbol ($<$ or $>$) between the two numbers.

$\frac{5}{8}$ ▨ $\frac{8}{5}$

2—Ans: $<$

33. Place the correct inequality symbol ($<$ or $>$) between the two numbers.

-0.68 ▨ -0.86

1—Form: 1C—Ans: $>$

34. Place the correct inequality symbol ($<$ or $>$) between the two numbers.

-0.57 ▨ -0.75

1—Ans: $>$

35. Place the correct inequality symbol ($<$ or $>$) between the two numbers.

$\frac{1}{5}$ ▨ $\frac{1}{4}$

1—Ans: $<$

36. Place the correct inequality symbol ($<$ or $>$) between the two numbers.

$\frac{1}{6}$ ▨ $\frac{1}{5}$

1—Ans: $<$

37. Which of the following pairs of numbers are *opposites*?

(a) -5 and $-\frac{1}{5}$

(b) -5 and $\frac{1}{5}$

(c) 5 and $|-5|$

(d) 5 and $-\frac{1}{5}$

(e) -5 and $|-5|$

1—Ans: e

38. Which of the following pairs of numbers are *opposites*?

(a) $\frac{2}{3}$ and $\frac{3}{2}$

(b) 3 and -3

(c) 5 and $\frac{1}{5}$

(d) $\frac{4}{5}$ and $\frac{8}{10}$

(e) 0.2 and $\frac{2}{10}$

1—Ans: b

39. Find the opposite of -8.

1—Ans: 8

40. Find the opposite of 7.

1—Ans: -7

41. Find the opposite of $\frac{5}{7}$.

1—Ans: $-\frac{5}{7}$

42. Find the opposite of $|-10|$.

1—Ans: -10

43. Evaluate the expression $-|-5|$.

1—Ans: -5

44. Evaluate the expression $-|-7|$.

1—Ans: -7

45. Evaluate the expression $|-16|$.

1—Ans: 16

46. Evaluate the expression $-|16|$.

1—Ans: -16

47. Which of the following statements is *false*?

  (a) $-4 < 3$ **(b)** $|-4| > 3$ **(c)** $|-4| > -3$

  (d) $|-4| < |-3|$ **(e)** $-4 < -3$

1—Ans: d

48. Which of the following statements is *false*?

  (a) $|-5| > 2$ **(b)** $|-5| > -2$ **(c)** $|-5| < |-2|$

  (d) $-5 < -2$ **(e)** $-5 < 2$

1—Ans: c

49. Which of the following statements is *false*?

  (a) $|-7| = |7|$ **(b)** $|-7| < |7|$ **(c)** $-2.4 > -3.6$

  (d) $-|7| < |-7|$ **(e)** $0 < |-10|$

1—Ans: b

50. Which of the following statements is *false*?

  (a) $-|7| < |-7|$ **(b)** $|-7| = |7|$ **(c)** $|-10| < |10|$

  (d) $-1.4 < -1.3$ **(e)** $-10 = -|10|$

1—Ans: c

51. Which of the following statements is *false*?

  (a) $-|5| = -|-5|$ **(b)** $|-5| > -|5|$ **(c)** $|-5| = |5|$

  (d) $\left|-\frac{2}{3}\right| < \left|\frac{2}{3}\right|$ **(e)** $-1 < -0.5$

1—Ans: d

52. Which of the following statements is *false*?

    (a) $-|5| < |-5|$ **(b)** $|8| = |-8|$ **(c)** $\left|\frac{3}{2}\right| = \left|-\frac{3}{2}\right|$

    (d) $-2 < -1.5$ **(e)** $|-5| < |5|$

    1—Ans: e

53. Which of the following statements is *true*?

    (a) $|-15| = -15$ **(b)** $|-7| = -|7|$ **(c)** $|3| = |-3|$

    (d) $|10| = -|10|$ **(e)** None of these

    1—Ans: c

54. Which of the following statements is *true*?

    (a) $-|5| = |-5|$ **(b)** $|7| = -|7|$ **(c)** $-|-3| = |3|$

    (d) $|15| = |-15|$ **(e)** None of these

    1—Ans: d

55. Which of the following statements is *true*?

    (a) $|-4| = |4|$ **(b)** $-|4| = |-4|$ **(c)** $|-4| = -4$

    (d) $|4| = -|-4|$ **(e)** None of these

    1—Ans: a

56. Which of the following statements is *true*?

    (a) $|-15| = -|15|$ **(b)** $|-3| = |3|$ **(c)** $-|-7| = |7|$

    (d) $|-10| = -10$ **(e)** None of these

    1—Ans: b

57. Place the correct symbol ($<$, $>$, or $=$) between the two numbers.

    $|-8|$ ▨ -8

    1—Ans: $>$

58. Place the correct symbol ($<$, $>$, or $=$) between the two numbers.

    $-|7|$ ▨ $|-7|$

    1—Ans: $<$

59. Place the correct symbol ($<$, $>$, or $=$) between the two numbers.

    $|-32|$ ▨ $|32|$

    1—Ans: $=$

60. Place the correct symbol ($<$, $>$, or $=$) between the two numbers.

$$-|16| \quad \rule{0.6cm}{0.25cm} \quad |-8|$$

1—Ans: $<$

61. Determine the *distance* between the indicated point and zero on the real number line and write an appropriate absolute value expression for the distance.

1—Ans: $2 = |-2|$

62. Determine the *distance* between the indicated point and zero on the real number line and write an appropriate absolute value expression for the distance.

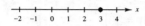

1—Ans: $3 = |3|$

63. Find all real numbers whose distance from 2.5 is 3.

1—Ans: -0.5 and 5.5

64. Find all real numbers whose distance from 3.5 is 5.

1—Ans: -1.5 and 8.5

Section 1.2   Operations with Integers

1. Which of the following statements is *false*?

(a) $|-6| - |3| = |3|$ **(b)** $-56 - (-120) = 64$ **(c)** $|10| + |-10| = 0$

(d) $-7 - (-20) = -7 + 20$ **(e)** None of these

1—Ans: c

2. Which of the following statements is *false*?

(a) $-75 - (-100) = 25$ **(b)** $-8 - |-16| = -8 + 16$ **(c)** $|-7| - |-3| = |-4|$

(d) $|8| - |-8| = 0$ **(e)** None of these

1—Ans: b

3. Which of the following statements is *false*?

(a) $6 + (-4) = 2$ **(b)** $-13 + (-8) = -21$ **(c)** $-2 + 6 = 4$

(d) $8 + (-3) = -11$ **(e)** None of these

1—Ans: d

4. Which of the following statements is *false*?

    (a) $-36 + 12 = -24$ **(b)** $-14 + 6 = 8$ **(c)** $-12 + (-6) = -18$

    (d) $43 + (-21) = 22$ **(e)** None of these

    1—Form: 1B—Ans: b

5. Which of the following statements is *true*?

    (a) The sum of 8 and -3 is 11.   **(b)** The sum of 8 and -3 is -11.

    (c) The sum of 8 and -3 is 5.   **(d)** The sum of 8 and -3 is -5.

    (e) None of these

    1—Form: 1A—Ans: c

6. Which of the following statements is *true*?

    (a) $-22 - (6 - 10) - 14 = -40$ **(b)** $-22 - (6 - 10) + 14 = -12$

    (c) $-22 - (6 - 10) + 14 = 40$ **(d)** $-22 - (6 - 10) - 14 = -32$

    (e) None of these

    1—Ans: d

7. Find the sum: $-10 + 18 + (-5)$

    1—Ans: 3

8. Find the sum: $-12 + 20 + (-4)$

    1—Ans: 4

9. Find the sum: $3 + (-1) + (-5)$

    1—Ans: -3

10. Find the sum: $2 + (-3) + (-1)$

    1—Ans: -2

11. Find the sum: $-1 + (-3) + (-7)$

    1—Ans: -11

12. Find the sum: $(-3) + (-2) + (-4)$

    1—Form: 1C—Ans: -9

13. Find the sum: $123 + (-43) + 17$

    1—Ans: 97

14. Find the sum: $239 + (-16) + (-592)$

   1—Ans: -369

15. Find the difference: $84 - (-43)$

   1—Ans: 127

16. Find the difference: $76 - (-52)$

   1—Form: 1C—Ans: 128

17. Subtract -24 from 30.

   1—Ans: 54

18. Subtract -32 from 28.

   1—Ans: 60

19. Subtract 120 from 72.

   1—Ans: -48

20. Subtract 140 from 84.

   1—Ans: -56

21. Evaluate the expression. $5 - |-3| - |-5| + |5|$

   1—Ans: 2

22. Evaluate the expression. $|-7| - |7| + |-3| - |3|$

   1—Ans: 0

23. Which of the following statements is *false*?

   (a) $7(-2) = -14$ **(b)** $(-9)5 = -45$ **(c)** $3(-4) = -12$

   (d) $(8)(-6) = 48$ **(e)** None of these

   1—Form: 1A—Ans: d

24. Which of the following statements is *false*?

   (a) $5(-7) = -35$ **(b)** $(-10)3 = -30$ **(c)** $4(-8) = 32$

   (d) $(-4)(6) = -24$ **(e)** None of these

   1—Form: 1B—Ans: c

25. Which of the following statements is *false*?

(a) $520 \div 13 = 40$ (b) $240 \div 15 = 16$ (c) $480 \div 12 = 28$

(d) $325 \div 13 = 25$ (e) None of these

1—Ans: c

26. Which of the following statements is *false*?

(a) $315 \div 15 = 21$ (b) $210 \div 70 = 4$ (c) $280 \div 14 = 20$

(d) $560 \div 14 = 40$ (e) None of these

1—Ans: b

27. Which of the following statements is *false*?

(a) $280 \div 20 = 14$ (b) $440 \div 55 = 8$ (c) $325 \div 25 = 13$

(d) $640 \div 40 = 15$ (e) None of these

1—Ans: d

28. Which of the following statements is *false*?

(a) $\dfrac{14{,}400}{24} = 600$ (b) $1089 \div 33 = 33$ (c) $552 \div 12 = 46$

(d) $\dfrac{540}{16} = 34$ (e) None of these

1—Ans: d

29. Which of the following statements is *true*?

(a) $(-7)(-8) = 56$ (b) $(-4)5 = 20$ (c) $(-7)(-8) = -56$

(d) $(-4)(-5) = -20$ (e) None of these

1—Form: 1A—Ans: a

30. Which of the following statements is *true*?

(a) $(-2)(5) = 10$ (b) $(-9)(-6) = 54$ (c) $(-2)(-5) = -10$

(d) $(-9)(-6) = -54$ (e) None of these

1—Form: 1B—Ans: b

31. Which of the following statements is *true*?

(a) $-144 \div -12 = -12$ (b) $-144 \div -8 = 18$ (c) $-144 \div 12 = 12$
(d) $-144 \div 8 = 18$ (e) None of these

1—Form: 1A—Ans: b

32. Which of the following statements is *true*?

   (a) $\left|-\dfrac{32}{4}\right| = 8$ **(b)** $\left|-\dfrac{32}{4}\right| = -2$ **(c)** $-\dfrac{32}{4} = -8$

   (d) $\left|-\dfrac{32}{8}\right| = -4$ **(e)** None of these

   1—Form: 1A—Ans: a

33. Determine which operation is undefined and state why.

   (a) $\dfrac{0}{10}$ **(b)** $0 \div 7$ **(c)** 0×8

   (d) $\dfrac{-7}{-5}$ **(e)** $7 \div 0$

   1—Form: 1B—Ans: e, Division by 0 is not defined.

34. Determine which operation is undefined and state why.

   (a) $\dfrac{4}{0}$ **(b)** $\dfrac{0}{4}$ **(c)** $5 \div -3$

   (d) 0×5 **(e)** 5×0

   1—Ans: a, Division by 0 is not defined.

35. For the quotient $-35 \div 5 = -7$, which of the following statements is true?

   (a) 5 is the numerator   **(b)** -35 is the denominator   **(c)** 5 is the denominator

   (d) -7 is the numerator   **(e)** None of these

   1—Ans: c

36. For the quotient $-35 \div 5 = -7$, which of the following statements is *true*?

   (a) -7 is the divisor   **(b)** 5 is the denominator   **(c)** -35 is the divisor

   (d) 5 is the numerator   **(e)** None of these

   1—Ans: b

37. Find the product: $0 \cdot 18$

   1—Ans: 0

38. Find the product: $|12(-4)|$

   1—Ans: 48

39. Find the product: $32 \times (-3)$

   1—Ans: -96

40. Find the product: $(-8)(5)(-2)$

   1—Ans: 80

41. Find the product: $(-8)(-3)(-5)$

1—Ans: -120

42. Find the product: $7(-2)(-3)$

1—Form: 1C—Ans: 42

43. Write the multiplication problem $4 \cdot 7$ as a repeated addition.

1—Ans: $7 + 7 + 7 + 7$

44. Write the multiplication problem $4 \cdot 6$ as a repeated addition.

1—Ans: $6 + 6 + 6 + 6$

45. Write the multiplication problem $3 \cdot (-4)$ as a repeated addition.

1—Ans: $(-4) + (-4) + (-4)$

46. Write the multiplication problem $3 \cdot (-5)$ as a repeated addition.

1—Ans: $(-5) + (-5) + (-5)$

47. Divide 360 by 12.

1—Ans: 30

48. Divide 840 by 21.

1—Ans: 40

49. Carry out the division if possible. If not possible, state why not. $12 \div 0$

1—Ans: Not defined. Cannot divide by 0.

50. Evaluate the expression: $\dfrac{10(-24)}{-16}$

1—Form: 1C—Ans: 15

51. Evaluate the expression: $\dfrac{10(-18)}{-12}$

1—Ans: 15

52. Perform the indicated division using the long division algorithm. $2016 \div 18$

2—Ans: 112

53. Perform the indicated division using the long division algorithm. $36{,}621 \div 313$

2—Ans: 117

54. Is the number 22 prime or composite?

    1—Ans: 22 is composite.

55. Is the number 13 prime or composite?

    1—Ans: 13 is prime.

56. Is the number 17 prime or composite?

    1—Ans: 17 is prime.

57. Is the number 26 prime or composite?

    1—Ans: 26 is composite.

58. Find the prime factorization of 15.

    1—Ans: $3 \cdot 5$

59. Find the prime factorization of 21.

    1—Ans: $3 \cdot 7$

60. Find the prime factorization of 95.

    1—Ans: $5 \cdot 19$

61. Find the prime factorization of 85.

    1—Ans: $5 \cdot 17$

62. Find the prime factorization of 32.

    1—Ans: $2 \cdot 2 \cdot 2 \cdot 2 \cdot 2$

63. Find the prime factorization of 48.

    1—Form: 1C—Ans: $2 \cdot 2 \cdot 2 \cdot 2 \cdot 3$

64. At the beginning of the week a bank account had a balance of $2147. During the week there were withdrawals of $345, $129, and $394. During the week there was also a deposit of $137 and an interest credit of $17. Find the balance at the end of the week.

    2—Ans: $1433

65. At the beginning of the week a bank account had a balance of $1335. During the week there were withdrawals of $714, $38, and $217. During the week there was also a deposit of $519 and an interest credit of $2. Find the balance at the end of the week.

    2—Ans: $887

66. Suppose on Monday you bought $1200 worth of stock in a company. During the rest of the week, you recorded the gains and losses as shown.

Tuesday	Wednesday	Thursday	Friday
Lost $18	Gained $25	Gained $12	Lost $3

The value of the stock at the end of the week was:

(a) $1243 **(b)** $1216 **(c)** $1237

(d) $1221 **(e)** None of these

1—Ans: b

67. Suppose on Monday you bought $1500 worth of stock in a company. During the rest of the week, you recorded the gains and losses as shown.

Tuesday	Wednesday	Thursday	Friday
Lost $18	Gained $25	Lost $16	Gained $28

Find the value of the stock at the end of the week.

2—Ans: $1519

68. A certain brand of color print film is packed 12 rolls to the carton. A store orders 8 cartons of this film and expects to make a profit of $1 per roll. If the store's wholesale cost is $288, what retail price per roll should be charged?

(a) $5.00 **(b)** $3.00 **(c)** $4.00

(d) $6.00 **(e)** $3.50

2—Ans: c

69. A certain brand of color print film is packed 12 rolls to the carton. A store orders 8 cartons of this film and expects to make a profit of $1 per roll. If the store's wholesale cost is $480, what retail price per roll should be charged?

(a) $6.00 **(b)** $5.00 **(c)** $4.50

(d) $4.00 **(e)** $7.00

2—Ans: a

70. A certain brand of color pring film retails at $4 per roll. It is packed 12 rolls to the carton. If a store orders 8 cartons of this film, find the retail value of the order.

1—Ans: $384

71. A certain brand of color print film retails at $4 per roll. It is packed 12 rolls to the carton. If a store orders 10 cartons of this film, find the retail value of the order.

1—Ans: $480

Section 1.3   Operations with Rational Numbers

1. Which of the following statements is *true*?

    (a) The least common multiple of 15 and 6 is 60.

    (b) The least common multiple of 16 and 6 is 24.

    (c) The least common multiple of 15 and 6 is 30.

    (d) The least common multiple of 16 and 6 is 96.

    (e) None of these.

    2—Form: 1A—Ans: c

2. Find the greatest common factor of 16 and 27.

    2—Ans: 1

3. Find the greatest common factor of 8 and 27.

    2—Ans: 1

4. Find the greatest common factor of 9 and 27.

    2—Ans: 9

5. Find the greatest common factor of 8 and 24.

    2—Ans: 8

6. Find the greatest common factor of 20 and 30.

    2—Ans: 10

7. Find the greatest common factor of 24 and 36.

    2—Form: 1C—Ans: 12

8. Find the least common multiple of 3 and 10.

    2—Ans: 30

9. Find the least common multiple of 12 and 15.

    2—Ans: 60

10. Find the least common multiple of 12 and 21.

    2—Form: 1C—Ans: 84

11. Find the least common multiple of 6, 14, and 18.

    2—Ans: 126

12. Which of the following fractions is in simplest form?

(a) $\frac{5}{10}$ (b) $\frac{5}{7}$ (c) $\frac{5}{15}$ (d) $\frac{5}{20}$ (e) $\frac{5}{25}$

1—Form: 1A—Ans: b

13. Which of the following fractions is in simplest form?

(a) $\frac{6}{9}$ (b) $\frac{6}{10}$ (c) $\frac{6}{11}$ (d) $\frac{6}{12}$ (e) $\frac{6}{15}$

1—Form: 1B—Ans: c

14. Which of the following fractions is *not* in simplest form?

(a) $\frac{3}{5}$ (b) $\frac{3}{8}$ (c) $\frac{3}{7}$ (d) $\frac{3}{9}$ (e) $\frac{3}{10}$

1—Ans: d

15. Which of the following fractions is *not* in simplest form?

(a) $\frac{4}{3}$ (b) $\frac{4}{5}$ (c) $\frac{4}{6}$ (d) $\frac{4}{7}$ (e) $\frac{4}{9}$

1—Ans: c

16. Which of the following fractions is *not* in simplest form?

(a) $\frac{24}{51}$ (b) $\frac{27}{8}$ (c) $2\frac{3}{4}$ (d) $\frac{17}{48}$ (e) $\frac{144}{41}$

1—Ans: a

17. Which of the following fractions is *not* in simplest form?

(a) $\frac{14}{19}$ (b) $\frac{39}{13}$ (c) $\frac{54}{11}$ (d) $2\frac{1}{8}$ (e) $\frac{23}{11}$

1—Ans: b

18. Write the fraction $\frac{30}{64}$ in simplest form.

1—Form: 1C—Ans: $\frac{15}{32}$

19. Write the fraction $\frac{38}{72}$ in simplest form.

1—Ans: $\frac{19}{36}$

20. Write the fraction $\frac{245}{210}$ in simplest form.

1—Ans: $\frac{7}{6}$

21. Write the fraction $\frac{270}{315}$ in simplest form.

1—Ans: $\frac{6}{7}$

22. Which of the following pairs of rationals are reciprocals?

(a) $8\frac{1}{3}$ and $3\frac{1}{8}$ (b) 17 and 71   (c) $\frac{7}{3}$ and $\frac{3}{7}$

(d) 2 and $-\frac{1}{2}$ (e) $\frac{1}{9}$ and $0.\overline{1}$

1—Ans: c

23. Which of the following pairs of rationals are reciprocals?

(a) 18 and 81   (b) $\frac{1}{3}$ and $0.\overline{3}$ (c) $2\frac{1}{8}$ and $8\frac{1}{2}$

(d) $-\frac{7}{8}$ and $-\frac{8}{7}$ (e) 4 and $-\frac{1}{4}$

1—Ans: d

24. Find the reciprocal of $7\frac{1}{5}$.

1—Ans: $\frac{5}{36}$

25. Find the reciprocal of $6\frac{2}{3}$.

1—Ans: $\frac{3}{20}$

26. Write the fraction in decimal form. Use the bar notation for repeating digits. $\frac{2}{33}$

1—Ans: $0.\overline{06}$

27. Which of the following statements is *true*?

(a) $\frac{1}{6} + \frac{4}{6} = \frac{5}{6}$ (b) $\frac{1}{6} + \frac{4}{6} = \frac{4}{6}$ (c) $\frac{1}{6} + \frac{4}{6} = \frac{5}{12}$

(d) $\frac{1}{6} + \frac{4}{6} = \frac{4}{36}$ (e) None of these

1—Ans: a

28. Which of the following statements is *true*?

(a) $\frac{1}{5} + \frac{3}{5} = \frac{3}{5}$ (b) $\frac{1}{5} + \frac{3}{5} = \frac{4}{10}$ (c) $\frac{1}{5} + \frac{3}{5} = \frac{3}{25}$

(d) $\frac{1}{5} + \frac{3}{5} = \frac{4}{5}$ (e) None of these

1—Ans: d

29. Which of the following statements is *true*?

(a) $\frac{1}{2} + \left(-\frac{1}{3}\right) = -\frac{1}{6}$ (b) $\frac{1}{2} + \left(-\frac{1}{3}\right) = \frac{0}{5}$ (c) $\frac{1}{2} + \left(-\frac{1}{3}\right) = \frac{1}{6}$

(d) $\frac{1}{2} + \left(-\frac{1}{3}\right) = \frac{0}{6}$ (e) None of these

1—Form: 1A–Ans: c

30. Which of the following statements is *true*?

(a) $\frac{5}{8} - \frac{1}{6} = \frac{11}{24}$ (b) $\frac{5}{8} - \frac{1}{6} = \frac{4}{2}$ (c) $\frac{5}{8} + \frac{1}{6} = -\frac{5}{48}$

(d) $\frac{5}{8} - \frac{1}{6} = \frac{4}{48}$ (e) None of these

2—Ans: a

31. Which of the following statements is *true*?

(a) $\frac{3}{8} - \frac{5}{6} = -\frac{2}{2}$ (b) $\frac{3}{8} - \frac{5}{6} = -\frac{15}{48}$ (c) $\frac{3}{8} - \frac{5}{6} = -\frac{11}{24}$

(d) $\frac{3}{8} - \frac{5}{6} = -\frac{2}{48}$ (e) None of these

2—Ans: c

32. Which of the following statements is *true*?

(a) $-2\frac{1}{3} - 4\frac{1}{4} = -6\frac{2}{7}$ (b) $-2\frac{1}{3} - 4\frac{1}{4} = -6\frac{7}{12}$ (c) $-2\frac{1}{3} - 4\frac{1}{4} = \frac{24}{12}$

(d) $-2\frac{1}{3} - 4\frac{1}{4} = -\frac{24}{12}$ (e) None of these

2—Form: 1B—Ans: b

33. Which of the following statements is *false*?

(a) $\frac{7}{8} + \frac{3}{8} = \frac{5}{4}$ (b) $\frac{1}{5} + \frac{1}{3} = \frac{3+5}{15}$ (c) $\frac{2}{5} + \frac{1}{3} = \frac{2+1}{5+3} = \frac{3}{8}$

(d) $\frac{3}{4} - \frac{1}{2} - \frac{5}{6} = -\frac{7}{12}$ (e) $5\frac{1}{4} + 2\frac{1}{8} = 7\frac{3}{8}$

2—Ans: c

34. Which of the following statements is *false*?

(a) $\frac{2}{5} - \frac{1}{3} = \frac{2-1}{5-3} = \frac{1}{2}$ (b) $\frac{3}{8} - \frac{7}{8} = -\frac{1}{2}$ (c) $\frac{1}{5} - \frac{1}{3} = \frac{3-5}{15}$

(d) $\frac{1}{2} + \frac{5}{6} - \frac{3}{4} = \frac{7}{12}$ (e) $12\frac{3}{8} - 7\frac{1}{4} = 5\frac{1}{8}$

2—Ans: a

35. Which of the following statements is *false*?

(a) $\frac{7}{8} - \frac{3}{8} = \frac{1}{2}$ (b) $\frac{1}{3} - \frac{1}{5} = \frac{5-3}{15}$ (c) $5\frac{1}{4} - 2\frac{1}{8} = 3\frac{1}{8}$

(d) $\frac{3}{4} + \frac{1}{2} - \frac{5}{6} = \frac{5}{12}$ (e) $\frac{2}{3} - \frac{1}{5} = \frac{2-1}{15} = \frac{1}{15}$

2—Ans: e

36. Evaluate the expression $\frac{1}{2} + \frac{2}{3} - \frac{4}{5}$. Write the result in simplest form.

1—Ans: $\frac{11}{30}$

37. Evaluate the expression $\frac{1}{2} + \frac{1}{4} - \frac{3}{8}$. Write the result in simplest form.

1—Ans: $\frac{3}{8}$

38. Evaluate the expression $5 + \frac{1}{3}$. Write the result in simplest form.

1—Ans: $\frac{16}{3}$

39. Evaluate the expression $8\frac{1}{6} - \frac{4}{3}$. Write the result in simplest form.

   1—Ans: $\frac{41}{6}$

40. Evaluate the expression $\frac{29}{12} - \frac{2}{3} + \frac{3}{4}$. Write the result in simplest form.

   1—Ans: $\frac{5}{2}$

41. Evaluate the expression $\frac{3}{8} - \frac{1}{12} - \frac{5}{6}$. Write the result in simplest form.

   2—Form: 1C—Ans: $-\frac{13}{24}$

42. Evaluate the expression $\frac{7}{12} - \frac{1}{6} - \frac{7}{8}$. Write the result in simplest form.

   1—Ans: $-\frac{11}{24}$

43. Which of the following statements is *true*?

   (a) $\left(-\frac{4}{5}\right)\left(-\frac{5}{8}\right) = -\frac{9}{13}$ **(b)** $\left(-\frac{4}{5}\right)\left(-\frac{5}{8}\right) = \frac{1}{2}$ **(c)** $\left(-\frac{4}{5}\right)\left(-\frac{5}{8}\right) = \frac{20}{13}$

   (d) $\left(-\frac{4}{5}\right)\left(-\frac{5}{8}\right) = -\frac{9}{40}$ **(e)** None of these

   1—Form: 1B—Ans: b

44. Which of the following statements is *true*?

   (a) $\left(-\frac{12}{7}\right)14 = -10$ **(b)** $\left(-\frac{12}{7}\right)14 = \frac{2}{7}$ **(c)** $\left(-\frac{12}{7}\right)14 = -24$

   (d) $\left(-\frac{12}{7}\right)14 = 24$ **(e)** None of these

   1—Ans: c

45. Which of the following statements is *true*?

   (a) $2\frac{3}{4} \times 5\frac{1}{3} = \frac{27}{12}$ **(b)** $2\frac{3}{4} \times 5\frac{1}{3} = \frac{44}{3}$ **(c)** $2\frac{3}{4} \times 5\frac{1}{3} = 10\frac{1}{4}$

   (d) $2\frac{3}{4} \times 5\frac{1}{3} = \frac{27}{7}$ **(e)** None of these

   2—Ans: b

46. Which of the following statements is *true*?

   (a) $-\frac{16}{5} \div 12 = -\frac{4}{15}$ **(b)** $-\frac{16}{5} \div 12 = -\frac{15}{4}$ **(c)** $-\frac{16}{5} \div 12 = -\frac{192}{5}$

   (d) $-\frac{16}{5} \div 12 = -\frac{5}{192}$ **(e)** None of these

   1—Ans: a

47. Which of the following statements is *true*?

   (a) $\frac{7}{12} \div \frac{2}{3} = \frac{8}{7}$ **(b)** $\frac{7}{12} \div \frac{2}{3} = \frac{14}{36}$ **(c)** $\frac{7}{12} \div \frac{2}{3} = \frac{7}{8}$

   (d) $\frac{7}{12} \div \frac{2}{3} = \frac{36}{14}$ **(e)** None of these

   1—Form: 1B—Ans: c

48. Which of the following statements is *true*?

(a) $2\frac{1}{6} \div 1\frac{3}{4} = \frac{24}{91}$ (b) $2\frac{1}{6} \div 1\frac{3}{4} = \frac{21}{26}$ (c) $2\frac{1}{6} \div 1\frac{3}{4} = \frac{91}{24}$

(d) $2\frac{1}{6} \div 1\frac{3}{4} = \frac{26}{21}$ (e) None of these

2—Form: 1A—Ans: d

49. Which of the following statements is *false*?

(a) $\left(\frac{2}{7}\right)\left(-\frac{3}{4}\right) = -\frac{3}{14}$ (b) $2\frac{1}{3} \div \frac{1}{2} = \frac{14}{3}$ (c) $-\frac{12/7}{-5/7} = \frac{12}{5}$

(d) $\frac{2}{3} = 0.\overline{6}$ (e) None of these

2—Ans: e

50. Evaluate the expression $\left(\frac{3}{5}\right)\left(-\frac{5}{6}\right)$. Write the result in simplest form.

1—Ans: $-\frac{1}{2}$

51. Evaluate the expression $\frac{1}{2} \cdot \frac{3}{5}$. Write the result in simplest form.

1—Ans: $\frac{3}{10}$

52. Evaluate the expression $\left(2\frac{3}{8}\right)\left(\frac{4}{9}\right)$. Write the result in simplest form.

1—Form: 1C—Ans: $\frac{19}{18}$

53. Evaluate the expression $\left(\frac{8}{25}\right)\left(-\frac{15}{4}\right)$. Write the result in simplest form.

2—Ans: $-\frac{6}{5}$

54. Evaluate the expression $\left(1\frac{1}{3}\right)\left(-\frac{3}{5}\right)\left(-\frac{9}{8}\right)$. Write the result in simplest form.

2—Ans: $\frac{9}{10}$

55. Evaluate the expression $\frac{3}{5} \div \frac{12}{5}$. Write the result in simplest form.

1—Ans: $\frac{1}{4}$

56. Evaluate the expression $\frac{3}{16} \div -\frac{7}{8}$. Write the result in simplest form.

1—Ans: $-\frac{3}{14}$

57. Evaluate the expression $\frac{25}{48} \div \frac{15}{28}$. Write the result in simplest form.

1—Ans: $\frac{35}{36}$

58. Evaluate the expression $\dfrac{-\frac{9}{20}}{-\frac{18}{35}}$. Write the result in simplest form.

1—Ans: $\frac{7}{8}$

59. Evaluate the expression $0 \div \left(-\frac{5}{6}\right)$. Write the result in simplest form.

1—Ans: 0

60. Perform the indicated operations. (Round your answer to two decimal places.)

$$7.82 - 5.23 + 3.18$$

1—Ans: 5.77

61. Perform the indicated operations. (Round your answer to two decimal places.)

$$\frac{-18.7}{-7.21}$$

1—Ans: 2.59

62. Perform the indicated operations. (Round your answer to two decimal places.)

$$(0.02)(-67.3)$$

2—Ans: -1.35

63. Perform the indicated operations. (Round your answer to two decimal places.)

$$\frac{(-16.2)(-5.3)}{-11.4}$$

2—Ans: -7.53

64. Perform the indicated operations. (Round your answer to two decimal places.)

$$103.73 \div 4.1$$

2—Ans: 25.30

65. You drive to the airport for $1\frac{1}{4}$ hours. Your flight lasts $2\frac{1}{2}$ hours and your shuttle ride lasts $\frac{1}{2}$ hour. What was the length, in hours, of the entire trip?

2—Ans: $4\frac{1}{4}$

66. On Wednesday, a stock closed at $\$63\frac{3}{4}$ per share. On Thursday, it closed at $\$61\frac{1}{8}$ per share. Determine the decrease, in dollars per share, in the price.

2—Ans: $\$2\frac{5}{8}$

67. A telephone company charges $1.15 for the first three minutes and $0.40 for each additional minute or part thereof. Determine the number of charged minutes, if the charge was $3.95.

(a) 6 minutes   **(b)** 7 minutes   **(c)** 8 minutes

(d) 9 minutes   **(e)** 10 minutes

2—Ans: e

68. A telephone company charges $1.24 for the first three minutes and $0.45 for each additional minute. Find the cost of a 33 minute call.

2—Ans: $14.74

69. A telephone company charges $1.24 for the first three minutes and $0.45 for each additional minute. Find the cost of a 25 minute call.

2—Ans: $11.14

Section 1.4 Exponents, Order of Operations, and Properties of Real Numbers

1. Which of the following statements is *true*?

(a) $5^4 = 20$ (b) $-5^4 = 625$ (c) $5^4 = 625$

(d) $(-5)^4 = -625$ (e) None of these

1—Ans: c

2. Which of the following statements is *true*?

(a) $-(-6)^2 = -36$ (b) $-(-6)^2 = 36$ (c) $-(-6)^2 = 12$

(d) $-(-6)^2 = -12$ (e) None of these

1—Form: 1B—Ans: a

3. Which of the following statements is *true*?

(a) $\dfrac{2 - 2^3}{-2} = 2$ (b) $\dfrac{2 - 2^3}{-2} = 0$ (c) $\dfrac{2 - 2^3}{-2} = 3$

(d) $\dfrac{2 - 2^3}{-2} = -3$ (e) None of these

2—Ans: c

4. Which of the following statements is *true*?

(a) $5^2 \cdot 4^3 = 10 \cdot 12$ (b) $5^2 \cdot 4^3 = 20^5$ (c) $5^2 \cdot 4^3 = 100^3$

(d) $5^2 \cdot 4^3 = 25 \cdot 64$ (e) None of these

2—Form: 1B—Ans: d

5. Which of the following statements is *false*?

(a) $\left(-\frac{1}{3}\right)^5$ is negative.   (b) $(-5)^4$ is positive.   (c) -5^4 is positive.

(d) -5^3 is negative.   (e) None of these.

1—Ans: c

6. Which of the following statements is *false*?

    (a) -2^4 is positive.   **(b)** -2^4 is negative.   **(c)** $(-2)^4$ is positive.

    (d) $-(-2)^3$ is positive.   **(e)** None of these.

    1—Ans: a

7. Which of the following statements is *false*?

    (a) $(-2)^4 = 16$ **(b)** $-2^4 = 16$ **(c)** $(-2)^3 = -8$

    (d) $(-2)^5 = -32$ **(e)** None of these.

    1—Form: 1A—Ans: b

8. Evaluate the expression. $-(-3)^3$

    (a) -27 **(b)** -9 **(c)** 27 **(d)** 9 **(e)** None of these

    1—Ans: c

9. Evaluate the expression. $-(-2)^4$

    (a) $\frac{1}{16}$ **(b)** 16 **(c)** $-\frac{1}{16}$ **(d)** -16 **(e)** None of these

    1—Ans: d

10. State whether none, one, or both of the expressions are negative.

    -5^4 and $(-5)^4$

    1—Ans: The first expression is negative.

11. State whether none, one, or both of the expressions are negative.

    $(-5)^3$ and -5^3

    1—Ans: Both expressions are negative.

12. Rewrite the expression as a product. $\left(-\frac{1}{2}\right)^3$

    1—Ans: $\left(-\frac{1}{2}\right)\left(-\frac{1}{2}\right)\left(-\frac{1}{2}\right)$

13. Rewrite the expression in exponential form. $1 \cdot 1 \cdot 1 \cdot 1 \cdot 1$

    1—Ans: 1^5

14. Rewrite the expression in exponential form. $3 \cdot 3 \cdot 3 \cdot 3 \cdot 3$

    1—Form: 1C—Ans: 3^5

15. Evaluate the expression. $\left(-\frac{1}{5}\right)^4$

    1—Ans: $\frac{1}{625}$

16. Evaluate the expression. -2^6

    1—Ans: -64

17. Evaluate the expression. 3^4

    1—Ans: 81

18. Evaluate the expression. $(-3)^4$

    1—Ans: 81

19. Which of the following statements is false?

    (a) $2 - [3 - 4] = 2 - 3 + 4 = 3$ **(b)** $-3(4 - 2^2) = -3(4) - 3(4) = -24$

    (c) $6 - [2 + 8 \div 4] = 6 - [2 + 2] = 2$ **(d)** $3[4 + (-2)^2] = 3[4] + 3[4] = 24$

    (e) $2^3 - 3^2(2 \div 3) = 8 - 9(\frac{2}{3}) = 8 - 6 = 2$

    2—Ans: b

20. Which of the following statements is false?

    (a) $-2(4 - 2^2) = -2(4) - 2(4) = -16$ **(b)** $3 - (5 - 2) = 3 - 5 + 2 = 0$

    (c) $3^2 - 2^3(3 \div 2) = 9 - 8(\frac{3}{2}) = 9 - 12 = -3$ **(d)** $6 - (3 + 6 \div 3) = 6 - (3 + 2) = 1$

    (e) $4[9 + (-3)^2] = 4(9) + 4(9) = 72$

    2—Ans: a

21. Evaluate the expression. $10 - 3[2 - (3 - 5)]$

    (a) 10   **(b)** 6   **(c)** 22   **(d)** -2 **(e)** None of these

    1—Ans: d

22. Evaluate the expression. $96 \div 4 \div 4 \cdot 2$

    (a) 48   **(b)** 12   **(c)** 192   **(d)** 3   **(e)** None of these

    1—Form: 1A—Ans: b

23. Evaluate the expression. $128 \div 4 \div 4 \cdot 2$

    (a) 256   **(b)** 4   **(c)** 64   **(d)** 16   **(e)** None of these

    1—Form: 1B—Ans: d

24. Evaluate the expression. $12 \div (2[8 - (4 - 6)^2])$

    (a) $\frac{2}{3}$ **(b)** $\frac{1}{2}$ **(c)** 1   **(d)** $\frac{3}{2}$ **(e)** None of these

    2—Ans: d

25. Evaluate the expression. $12 \div (2[(4-6)^2 - 8])$

   (a) $-\frac{2}{3}$ **(b)** $\frac{3}{2}$ **(c)** $-\frac{3}{2}$ **(d)** Not defined   **(e)** None of these

   2—Ans: c

26. Evaluate the expression. $12 \div (2[(8 - 4)^2 - 6])$

   (a) $\frac{5}{3}$ **(b)** $\frac{3}{5}$ **(c)** -3 **(d)** $\frac{6}{13}$ **(e)** None of these

   2—Ans: b

27. Evaluate the expression. $12 \div (2[6 - (8 - 4)^2])$

   (a) $-\frac{3}{5}$ **(b)** -3 **(c)** $\frac{5}{3}$ **(d)** 3 **(e)** None of these

   2—Ans: a

28. Evaluate the expression. $24 - [2(3 - 8) + 2^3]$

   2—Form: 1C—Ans: 26

29. Evaluate the expression. $7 - 3^2[2 - 2 \div 3]$

   2—Ans: -5

30. Evaluate the expression. $(-7)^2 - (2 \cdot 3^2)$

   2—Ans: 31

31. Evaluate the expression. $8 - 2[7 - (4 - 6)]$

   1—Ans: -10

32. Evaluate the expression. $8 - 2[-(7 - 4) - 6]$

   1—Ans: 26

33. Evaluate the expression. $8 - 2[6 - (7 - 4)]$

   1—Ans: 2

34. Evaluate the expression. $6 + 2^2 + \dfrac{0}{4^2 + 3^2}$

   2—Ans: 10

35. Evaluate the expression. $8 - 2[2(4 - 6) - 7]$

   1—Ans: 30

36. Use a calculator to evaluate the expression. $180 \div (7 - 2 \cdot 4)$

   2—Ans: -180

37. Use a calculator to evaluate the expression. $160 \div (9 - 5) \cdot 2$

2—Ans: 20

38. Use a calculator to evaluate the expression. $-12^2 + (-12)^2$

2—Ans: 0

39. Use a calculator to evaluate the expression. Round your answer to two decimal places.

$$200\left(1 + \frac{0.05}{12}\right)^{24}$$

2—Form: 1C—Ans: 220.99

40. Use a calculator to evaluate the expression. Round your answer to two decimal places.

$$200\left(1 + \frac{0.07}{12}\right)^{24}$$

2—Ans: 229.96

41. Place the correct symbol ($<$, $>$, or, $=$) between the given numbers.

$3 \cdot 7^2 \quad\rule{1cm}{0.3cm}\quad 21^2$

1—Ans: $<$

42. Place the correct symbol ($<$, $>$, or, $=$) between the given numbers.

$\dfrac{12 - 10}{3} \quad\rule{1cm}{0.3cm}\quad 4 - 10$

1—Ans: $>$

43. Place the correct symbol ($<$, $>$, or, $=$) between the given numbers.

$5(2^2 - 3) \quad\rule{1cm}{0.3cm}\quad 20 - 15$

1—Ans: $=$

44. Which of the following statements is *false*?

(a) $-x(2 - x) = -2x - x^2$ **(b)** $-x(2 - x) = -2x + x^2$ **(c)** $-x(2 + x) = -2x - x^2$

(d) $-x(2 - x) = x^2 - 2x$ **(e)** None of these

2—Ans: a

45. Which of the following statements is *false*?

(a) $xy^2(z) = x(y^2 z)$ **(b)** $(x - 2y) + 2z = x - 2(y - z)$ **(c)** $x^2 y(1) = x^2 y$

(d) $x^2 y + 0 = x^2 y$ **(e)** None of these

2—Ans: e

46. Which of the following statements is *false*?

   (a) $A^2(BC) = (A^2B)C$ **(b)** $2A(A - 3) = 2A^2 - 6A$ **(c)** $(A - B) + C = A - (B + C)$

   (d) $\left(\dfrac{A}{B + C}\right)\left(\dfrac{B + C}{A}\right) = 1$ **(e)** None of these

   2—Ans: c

47. Which of the following statements is *false*?

   (a) $(x + y)(x - y) = (x + y)x - y$ **(b)** $(2x - y)(2x) = (2x)^2 - y(2x)$

   (c) $2x(x - 2y) = 2x^2 - 4xy$ **(d)** $-2(x + y - 2) = -2x - 2y + 4$

   (e) None of these

   2—Ans: a

48. Which of the following statements is *false*?

   (a) $-2x(y - 3) = -2xy + 6x$ **(b)** $-2(x + y - 2) = -2x + y - 2$

   (c) $(y - 3)(-2x) = y(-2x) + 6x$ **(d)** $(x - 2)(y - 3) = x(y - 3) - 2(y - 3)$

   (e) None of these

   2—Ans: b

49. Choose the *property* of real numbers that justifies the statement $(5 \cdot 7) \cdot 1 = 5 \cdot 7$.

   (a) Distributive Property   **(b)** Commutative Property of Multiplication

   (c) Associative Property of Multiplication   **(d)** Multiplicative Identity Property

   (e) Multiplicative Inverse Property

   1—Ans: d

50. Choose the *property* of real numbers that justifies the statement $(5 \cdot 7)\dfrac{1}{5 \cdot 7} = 1$.

   (a) Distributive Property   **(b)** Commutative Property of Multiplication

   (c) Associative Property of Multiplication   **(d)** Multiplicative Identity Property

   (e) Multiplicative Inverse Property

   1—Ans: e

51. Choose the *property* of real numbers that justifies the statement $(-6 \cdot 5)4 = -6(5 \cdot 4)$

   (a) Distributive Property   **(b)** Commutative Property of Multiplication

   (c) Associative Property of Multiplication   **(d)** Multiplicative Identity Property

   (e) Multiplicative Inverse Property

   1—Form: 1A—Ans: c

52. Choose the *property* of real numbers that justifies the statement
$(3 + 2x)(x - 5) = (3 + 2x)x - (3 + 2x)5$.

  (a) Distributive Property   **(b)** Multiplicative Inverse Property

  (c) Associative Property of Multiplication   **(d)** Associative Property of Addition

  (e) Commutative Property of Multiplication

  1—Ans: a

53. Choose the *property* of real numbers that justifies the statement
$(3 + 2x)(x - 5) = (x - 5)(3 + 2x)$.

  (a) Distributive Property   **(b)** Multiplicative Inverse Property

  (c) Associative Property of Multiplication   **(d)** Associative Property of Addition

  (e) Commutative Property of Multiplication

  1—Ans: e

54. Choose the *property* of real numbers that justifies the statement
$(2x + y) - 3z = 2x + (y - 3z)$.

  (a) Additive Inverse Property   **(b)** Distributive Property

  (c) Additive Identity Property   **(d)** Associative Property of Addition

  (e) None of these

  1—Ans: d

55. Choose the *property* of real numbers that justifies the statement
$(3x + 8) + (-3x - 8) = 0$.

  (a) Additive Inverse Propery   **(b)** Additive Identity Propery

  (c) Multiplicative Inverse Property   **(d)** Multiplicative Identity Propery

  (e) Distributive Property

  1—Form: 1A—Ans: a

56. Choose the *property* of real numbers that justifies the statement $\frac{1}{3a} + 0 = \frac{1}{3a}(3a \neq 0)$.

  (a) Additive Inverse Property   **(b)** Additive Identity Property

  (c) Multiplicative Inverse Property   **(d)** Multiplicative Identity Property

  (e) Distributive Property

  1—Form: 1B—Ans: b

57. Choose the *property* of real numbers that justifies the statement
$(2x - 3y) + (x - 2y) = (x - 2y) + (2x - 3y)$.

(a) Associative Property of Multiplication

(b) Multiplicative Inverse Property

(c) Commutative Property of Addition

(d) Multiplicative Identity Property

(e) Distributive Property

1—Ans: c

58. Choose the *property(ies)* used in rewriting the expression $2x\left(2 - \dfrac{1}{2x}\right) = 2x(2) - 1$·
$x \neq 0$.

(a) Distributive Property only

(b) Multiplicative Inverse Property only

(c) Distributive Property and Multiplicative Identity Property

(d) Multiplicative Identity Property only

(e) Distributive Property and Multiplicative Inverse Property

2—Ans: e

59. Use the Commutative Property of Multiplication to rewrite $(-15 + x)4$.

1—Form: 1C—Ans: $4(-15 + x)$

60. Use the Additive Inverse Property to rewrite $(32xy) + (-32xy)$.

1—Ans: 0

61. Use the Distributive Property to rewrite $(-18 + x)5$.

1—Ans: $-18 \cdot 5 + x \cdot 5$

62. Use the Multiplicative Identity Property to rewrite $(67x)1$.

1—Ans: $67x$

63. Complete the statement satisfying the equality and *state* the property illustrated.
$(x + 2y)(\quad) = 1$

1—Ans: $\dfrac{1}{x + 2y}$, Multiplicative Inverse Property, $x + 2y \neq 0$

64. Complete the statement satisfying the equality and *state* the property illustrated.
$A + (3A + 2B) = (\quad) + 2B$

2—Ans: $A + 3A$, Associative Property of Addition

65. Complete the statement satisfying the equality and *state* the property illustrated.
$(2x)y^2 = 2(\quad)$

2—Ans: xy^2, Associative Property of Multiplication

66. Complete the statement satisfying the equality and *state* the property illustrated.
$2xy + y^2 = y^2 + (\quad)$

2—Ans: $2xy$, Commutative Property of Addition

67. Rewrite and simplify $5a(3a^2 - 2ab)$ using the appropriate properties of real numbers.

1—Ans: $15a^3 - 10a^2b$

68. Rewrite and simplify $5x^2\left(2x - \dfrac{1}{5x^2}\right)$ using the appropriate properties of real numbers.

1—Ans: $10x^3 - 1, x \neq 0$

69. When $1000 is deposited in an account earning 6% interest compounded yearly, the amount after 4 years is given by $A = 1000(1.06)^4$. Calculate the amount to the nearest cent.

(a) $1240.00   **(b)** $1262.48   **(c)** $1030.50   **(d)** $4240.00   **(e)** None of these

2—Ans: b

70. When $1000 is deposited in an account earning 8% interest compounded yearly, the amount after 4 years is given by $A = 1000(1.08)^4$. Calculate the amount to the nearest cent.

(a) $4320.00   **(b)** $1320.00   **(c)** $1042.50   **(d)** $1360.49   **(e)** None of these

2—Ans: d

71. When $5000 is deposited in an account earning 9% interest compounded yearly, the amount after 4 years is given by $A = 5000(1.09)^4$. Calculate the amount to the nearest cent.

2—Ans: $7057.91

CHAPTER 2
Fundamentals of Algebra

Section 2.1   Writing and Evaluating Algebraic Expressions

1. Which of the following is not a *term* of the algebraic expression
   $5x^2y - 7x^2 + 2xy - 3$?

   (a) $7x^2$ (b) $2xy$ (c) -3 (d) $5x^2y$ (e) $-7x^2$

   1—Ans: a

2. Which of the following is not a *term* of the algebraic expression
   $2x^2y - 5x^2 - 3xy - 5$?

   (a) $-3xy$ (b) $-5x^2$ (c) $2x^2y$ (d) $5x^2$ (e) -5

   1—Ans: d

3. Which of the following is not a *term* of the algebraic expression
   $y^4 - 3y^3 + 2y^2 - 6y + 1$?

   (a) y^4 (b) $-3y^3$ (c) $2y^2$ (d) $6y$ (e) 1

   1—Ans: d

4. Identify the coefficient of the term $-7x$.

   (a) 7 (b) -7 (c) $7x$ (d) $-7x$ (e) x

   1—Form: 2A—Ans: b

5. Identify the coefficient of the term $3y^2$.

   (a) y (b) $3y^2$ (c) 3 (d) y^2 (e) 2

   1—Form: 2B—Ans: c

6. Identify the coefficient of the term $4x^7$.

   (a) 4 (b) 7 (c) x (d) x^7 (e) $4x^7$

   1—Ans: a

7. Which of the following is *not* a coefficient of the algebraic expression
   $5x^3 - \frac{2}{3}x + \frac{1}{2}(4 - x) - 5x^2$?

   (a) -5 (b) 5 (c) $\frac{1}{2}$ (d) $-\frac{1}{2}$ (e) $-\frac{2}{3}$

   1—Ans: d, As written, the term $\frac{1}{2}(4 - x)$ has the coefficient $\frac{1}{2}$.

8. Which of the following is *not* a coefficient of the algebraic expression
$7x^3 - \frac{1}{4}x - \frac{1}{2}(4 - x) + 4x^2$?

(a) 4　　　　(b) $\frac{1}{2}$　　　　(c) $-\frac{1}{4}$　　　　(d) $-\frac{1}{2}$　　　　(e) 7

1—Ans: b, As written, the term $-\frac{1}{2}(4 - x)$ has the coefficient $-\frac{1}{2}$.

9. Identify the terms of the algebraic expression $6 - 5x + 2(x + 1)$.

1—Ans: $6, -5x, 2(x + 1)$

10. Identify the terms of the algebraic expression $7y + 3(y + 1) + 4$.

1—Form: 2C—Ans: $7y, 3(y + 1), 4$

11. Identify the terms of the algebraic expression $5x^2y^2 - 7x^2 + 2xy^2 - 3$.

1—Ans: $5x^2y^2, -7x^2, 2xy^2, -3$

12. Identify the terms of the algebraic expression $3x^2y + 2xy - 3x + 2$.

1—Ans: $3x^2y, 2xy, -3x, 2$

13. Identify any constant terms of the algebraic expression $5x^2y^2 - 7x^2 + 2xy^2 - 3$.

1—Ans: -3

14. Identify any constant terms of the algebraic expression $3x^3 - 5x^2 - 7x - 10$.

1—Ans: -10

15. Identify any constant terms of the algebraic expression $3x - 5 + x^2$.

2—Ans: -5

16. Identify the coefficient of the term $3x^4$.

1—Ans: 3

17. Identify the coefficient of the term $-8y^3$.

1—Ans: -8

18. Identify the coefficient of the term $-6(x + 3)$.

2—Ans: -6

19. Write the expression $(-x)^4$ as a product.

(a) $xxxx$　　　　　　(b) $4xxx$　　　　　　(c) $-xxxx$

(d) $(-x)(-x)(-x)(-x)$　　　　(e) None of these

1—Ans: d

20. Write the expression $(-2a)^3$ as a product.

   (a) $(-2a)(-2a)(-2a)$ **(b)** $(2a)(2a)(2a)$ **(c)** $-2aaa$
   (d) $(-2)(-2)(-2)a$ **(e)** None of these

   1—Ans: a

21. Write the expression $2(xy)^2$ as a product.

   (a) $(2)(2)xyxy$ **(b)** $2xxy$ **(c)** $2xxyy$
   (d) $2xyy$ **(e)** None of these

   1—Ans: c

22. Write the expression $2x^3y^2$ as a product.

   (a) $2xxyyy$ **(b)** $2xxxyy$ **(c)** $2xxxyyy$
   (d) $2xxyy$ **(e)** None of these

   1—Ans: b

23. Write the expression $2(3-x)^2$ as a product.

   (a) $(2)(2)(3-x)(3-x)$ **(b)** $2(3-x)(3-x)$ **(c)** $2(3-x)$
   (d) $2(x-3)(x-3)$ **(e)** None of these

   1—Ans: b

24. Write the expression a^7 as a product.

   1—Ans: $aaaaaaa$

25. Write the expression $(-y)^3$ as a product.

   1—Ans: $(-y)(-y)(-y)$

26. Write the expression $3a^2b^3$ as a product.

   1—Ans: $3aabbb$

27. Write the expression $(x+3)^2$ as a product.

   1—Ans: $(x+3)(x+3)$

28. Write the expression $(3y^3)^2$ as a product.

   1—Ans: $33yyyyyy$

29. Rewrite the product $(-a)(-a)(-a)(-a)$ in exponential form.

   (a) a^4 **(b)** $4a$ **(c)** $-4a$ **(d)** $(-a)^4$ **(e)** None of these

   1—Ans: d

30. Rewrite the product $-2xxyyy$ in exponential form.

(a) $-2x^2y^3$ (b) $(-2xy)^3$ (c) $2x^2y^3$ (d) $2x^2y$ (e) None of these

1—Ans: a

31. Rewrite the product $(4)(4)xxyy$ in exponential form.

(a) $4x^2y^2$ (b) $(4xy)^2$ (c) $8(xy)^2$ (d) $8x^2y^2$ (e) None of these

1—Ans: b

32. Rewrite the product $5\left(\dfrac{x}{y}\right)\left(\dfrac{x}{y}\right)\left(\dfrac{x}{y}\right)$ in exponential form.

(a) $\left(5\dfrac{x}{y}\right)^3$ (b) $5x^3y^3$ (c) $5\left(\dfrac{x}{y}\right)^3$ (d) $\dfrac{(5x)^3}{y^3}$ (e) None of these

1—Ans: c

33. Rewrite the product $xxxxx$ in exponential form.

1—Ans: x^5

34. Rewrite the product $(-2)(-2)(-2)aaaabbb$ in exponential form.

1—Ans: $-2^3a^4b^3$ or $(-1)^32^3a^4b^3$

35. Rewrite the product $(-3)(-3)aaaabbb$ in exponential form.

1—Ans: $3^2a^4b^3$ or $(-3)^2a^4b^3$

36. Rewrite the product $(x + 4)(x + 4)$ in exponential form.

1—Ans: $(x + 4)^2$

37. Rewrite the product $(2)(2)(2)(2)xxxx$ in exponential form.

1—Ans: $(2x)^4$

38. Evaluate $x^2 + 5$ when $x = 3$.

(a) 11   (b) 14   (c) 10   (d) 15   (e) None of these

1—Ans: b

39. Evaluate $3x - x^2$ when $x = -1$.

(a) -4 (b) 4   (c) -2 (d) 2   (e) None of these

2—Ans: a

40. Evaluate $4x - x^2$ when $x = -2$.

(a) -4 (b) -12 (c) 12 (d) 4 (e) None of these

2—Ans: b

41. Evaluate $xy - 3$ when $x = 2$ and $y = -3$.

(a) 3 (b) -3 (c) -9 (d) -4 (e) None of these

1—Ans: c

42. Evaluate $-xy + x^2$ when $x = -1$ and $y = 2$.

(a) -1 (b) 3 (c) 1 (d) -4 (e) None of these

2—Form: 2A—Ans: b

43. Evaluate $x^2 - xy$ when $x = -2$ and $y = 1$.

(a) 2 (b) -6 (c) 6 (d) -2 (e) None of these

2—Form: 2B—Ans: c

44. Evaluate $-|x - y|$ when $x = -2$ and $y = 4$.

(a) 6 (b) -6 (c) 2 (d) -2 (e) None of these

1—Ans: b

45. Evaluate $x - |y - x|$ when $x = -2$ and $y = 4$.

(a) 8 (b) 4 (c) -8 (d) -4 (e) None of these

1—Ans: c

46. Evaluate $\dfrac{2x - z}{|xy - z^2|}$ when $x = 3$, $y = 2$ and $z = -4$.

(a) -1 (b) 1 (c) $\dfrac{1}{5}$ (d) $-\dfrac{1}{5}$ (e) None of these

2—Ans: b

47. Evaluate $\dfrac{2x + z}{|z^2 - xy|}$ when $x = 3$, $y = 2$ and $z = -4$.

(a) 1 (b) $\dfrac{5}{11}$ (c) $-\dfrac{1}{10}$ (d) $\dfrac{1}{5}$ (e) None of these

2—Ans: d

48. Evaluate $-a^2 + a$ when $a = -2$.

    (a) 6   **(b)** -2 **(c)** 2   **(d)** -6 **(e)** None of these

    2—Form: 2A—Ans: d

49. Evaluate $a - a^2$ when $a = -3$.

    (a) -12 **(b)** 6   **(c)** -6 **(d)** 12   **(e)** None of these

    2—Form: 2B—Ans: a

50. Evaluate $2x^3 + x$ when $x = 2$.

    1—Ans: 18

51. Evaluate $3x - 2x^2$ when $x = 3$.

    1—Ans: -9

52. Evaluate $\dfrac{y - 3x}{x^2 - xy}$ when $x = 4$ and $y = -2$.

    1—Ans: $-\dfrac{7}{12}$

53. Evaluate $\dfrac{y - 3x}{x^2 - xy}$ when $x = -4$ and $y = 2$.

    1—Ans: $\dfrac{7}{12}$

54. Evaluate $\dfrac{y - 3x}{x^2 - xy}$ when $x = 2$ and $y = -4$.

    1—Ans: $-\dfrac{5}{6}$

55. Evaluate $\dfrac{y - 3x}{x^2 - xy}$ when $x = -2$ and $y = -4$.

    1—Ans: $-\dfrac{1}{2}$

56. Evaluate $|2x - y|$ when $x = -2$ and $y = 1$.

    2—Ans: 5

57. Evaluate $|x - 2y|$ when $x = -1$ and $y = 2$.

    2—Ans: 5

58. Evaluate $|3x - 2y|$ when $x = -1$ and $y = -2$.

    2—Ans: 1

59. Evaluate $\dfrac{2a + b}{3c - 4ab}$ when $a = 3$, $b = -2$, and $c = 2$.

2—Ans: $\dfrac{2}{15}$

60. Evaluate $\dfrac{a + 2b}{4c - 3ab}$ when $a = -2$, $b = 3$, and $c = -3$.

2—Ans: $\dfrac{2}{3}$

61. Evaluate $xyz - 2x^2z - 3xy^2$ when $x = -2$, $y = 3$, and $z = -3$.
2—Ans: 96

62. Evaluate $xyz - 2x^2z + 3xy^2$ when $x = -2$, $y = 3$, and $z = -3$.
2—Ans: -12

63. Evaluate $xyz + 2x^2z - 3xy^2$ when $x = -2$, $y = 3$, and $z = -3$.
2—Ans: 48

64. Evaluate $xyz + 2x^2z + 3xy^2$ when $x = -2$, $y = 3$, and $z = -3$.
2—Ans: -60

65. Evaluate $10x - 3[2x - (x - 4)]$ when $x = 0$, $x = 1$, and $x = -2$.
2—Ans: -12, -5, -26

66. Evaluate $8x - 4[3x - (2x - 3)]$ when $x = 0$, $x = 1$, and $x = -2$.
2—Form: 2C—Ans: -12, -8, -20

67. Use the table to find the increase in value of the expression for each one-unit increase in x.

x	-1	0	1	2	3	4
$2x + 1$						

(a) 1   **(b)** 2   **(c)** 0   **(d)** 9   **(e)** None of these

1—Ans: b

68. Use the table to find the decrease in value of the expression for each one-unit increase in x.

x	-1	0	1	2	3	4
$3 - x$						

(a) 1   (b) 0   (c) 3   (d) 4   (e) None of these

1—Ans: a

69. Complete the table and use it to find the increase in value of the expression for each one-unit increase in x.

x	-1	0	1	2	3.	4
$3 + 2x$						

1—Ans: 1, 3, 5, 7, 9, 11; increases by 2

70. Complete the table and use it to find the decrease in value of the expression for each one-unit increase in x.

x	-1	0	1	2	3	4
$4 - 3x$						

1—Ans: 7, 4, 1, -2, -5, -8; decreases by 3

Section 2.2   Simplifying Algebraic Expressions

1. Which of the following statements is *false*?

(a) $(a + 3)^4 = (a + 3)(a + 3)(a + 3)(a + 3)$ (b) $(a + 3)^4 = a^4 + 3^4$

(c) $(a + 3)^4 = (a + 3)^2(a + 3)^2$ (d) $(a + 3)^4 = (a + 3)(a + 3)^3$

(e) $(a + 3)^4 = (a + 3)^3(a + 3)$

2—Form: 2A—Ans: b

2. Which of the following statements is *false*?

(a) $(b + 3)^4 = (b + 3)(b + 3)(b + 3)(b + 3)$ (b) $(b + 3)^4 = (b + 3)^3(b + 3)$

(c) $(b + 3)^4 = (b + 3)^2(b + 3)^2$ (d) $(b + 3)^4 = (b + 3)(b + 3)^3$

(e) $(b + 3)^4 = b^4 + 3^4$

2—Form: 2B—Ans: e

3. Which of the following statements is *false*?

(a) $A^7 = A \cdot A \cdot A \cdot A \cdot A \cdot A \cdot A$

(b) $(2x)^2(2x^3) = 2 \cdot 2 \cdot 2 \cdot x \cdot x \cdot x \cdot x \cdot x$

(c) $(2xy)^2(3x^2y^2) = 12x^4y^4$

(d) $(-y)^5 = -y^5$

(e) $(2x^2)^3 = 2 \cdot 2 \cdot 2 \cdot x \cdot x \cdot x \cdot x \cdot x$

2—Ans: e, $(x^2)^3 = x^6$, not x^5

4. Which of the following statements is *false*?

(a) $2(x^2)^3 = 2 \cdot x \cdot x \cdot x \cdot x \cdot x \cdot x$

(b) $(x^3)^2 = x^6$

(c) $2x^3 = 2 \cdot 2 \cdot 2 \cdot x \cdot x \cdot x$

(d) $(2x)^3 = 2x \cdot 2x \cdot 2x$

(e) $(-x)^3 = -x^3$

1—Ans: c

5. Which of the following statements is *false*?

(a) $6a \cdot 6a \cdot 6a = (6a)^3$

(b) $6a \cdot 6a \cdot 6a = 6^3a^3$

(c) $6a \cdot 6a \cdot 6a = 6a(6a)^2$

(d) $6a \cdot 6a \cdot 6a = 6a^2(6a)$

(e) $6a \cdot 6a \cdot 6a = 216a^3$

2—Ans: d

6. Which of the following statements is *false*?

(a) $7n \cdot 7n \cdot 7n = 7^3n^3$

(b) $7n \cdot 7n \cdot 7n = 343n^3$

(c) $7n \cdot 7n \cdot 7n = 7n^2(7n)$

(d) $7n \cdot 7n \cdot 7n = (7n)^3$

(e) $7n \cdot 7n \cdot 7n = (7n)(7n)^2$

2—Ans: c

7. Simplify $(2)^2(-2)^3$.

(a) -4^5 (b) -24 (c) 32 (d) -32 (e) None of these

2—Ans: d

8. Simplify $(-8a^3)(-2a^2)$.

(a) $-16a^5$ (b) $16a^6$ (c) $16a^5$ (d) $-16a^6$ (e) None of these

2—Form: 2A—Ans: c

9. Simplify $[(x + 1)^3]^2$.

(a) $[(x^3 + 1)]^2$ (b) $(x + 1)^5$ (c) $(x + 1)^6$

(d) $(x + 1)^9$ (e) None of these

2—Form: 2A—Ans: c

10. Simplify $[(y + 2)^2]^3$.

(a) $(y + 2)^8$ (b) $(y^2 + 4)^3$ (c) $(y + 2)^5$

(d) $(y + 2)^6$ (e) None of these

2—Form: 2B—Ans: d

11. Simplify $(2a)(2b)(2a \cdot a)(2a \cdot b)(2b)$.

1—Ans: $32a^4b^3$

12. Simplify $(2ab)(2 \cdot 2a)(2 \cdot 2 \cdot a \cdot b)(b)$.

1—Ans: $32a^3b^3$

13. Simplify $-3x^2(x^4)$.

1—Ans: $-3x^6$

14. Simplify $(2x)^3y^2$.

1—Ans: $8x^3y^2$

15. Simplify $(3y)^3x^2$.

1—Ans: $27x^2y^3$

16. Simplify $x^3(2x^2)^2(3x^2)$.

2—Ans: $12x^9$

17. Simplify $(-3y^3)^4$.

1—Form: 2C—Ans: $81y^{12}$

18. Simplify $(5x^2)^3$.

1—Form: 2C—Ans: $125x^6$

19. Simplify $(-3x^2)^3(3x^2)^2$.

1—Ans: $-243x^{10}$

20. Identify the rule of algebra which justifies the statement
$(x + 3)2 + (x + 3)x = (x + 3)(2 + x)$.

(a) Commutative Property of Multiplication   (b) Multiplicative Identity Property

(c) Distributive Property   (d) Multiplicative Inverse Property

(e) Associative Property of Multiplication

1—Ans: c

21. Identify the rule of algebra which justifies the statement
$(x + 3)(x + 2) = (x + 2)(x + 3)$.

(a) Commutative Property of Multiplication

(b) Multiplicative Identity Property

(c) Distributive Property

(d) Multiplicative Inverse Property

(e) Associative Property of Multiplication

1—Ans: a

22. Identify the rule of algebra which justifies the statement
$4x + (x^2 + 4) = (x^2 + 4) + 4x$.

(a) Commutative Property of Addition

(b) Commutative Property of Multiplication

(c) Associative Property of Addition

(d) Associative Property of Multiplication

(e) Distributive Property

1—Ans: a

23. Identify the rule of algebra which justifies the statement $14\left(\frac{1}{14}\right) = 1$.

(a) Additive Identity Property

(b) Multiplicative Identity Property

(c) Additive Inverse Property

(d) Multiplicative Inverse Property

(e) Distributive Property

1—Form: 2A—Ans: d

24. Identify the rule of algebra which justifies the statement
$(12x^2 - y) - (12x^2 - y) = 0$.

(a) Additive Identity Property

(b) Multiplicative Identity Property

(c) Additive Inverse Property

(d) Multiplicative Inverse Property

(e) Distributive Property

1—Form: 2B—Ans: c

25. Which of the following statements illustrates the Associative Property of Addition?

(a) $a(xy) = (ax)y$

(b) $(a + x)y = ay + xy$

(c) $ax + 0 = ax$

(d) $(a + x) + y = (x + a) + y$

(e) $a + (x + y) = (a + x) + y$

1—Ans: e

26. Identify the rule of algebra used to justify the statement $(x^2 + 4)\left(\dfrac{1}{x^2 + 4}\right) = 1$.

1—Ans: Multiplicative Identity Property

27. What is the additive inverse of $5y$.

1—Ans: $-5y$

28. Use the Commutative Property of Multiplication to complete the statement
$6(x + 2) =$ _____.

1—Form: 2C—Ans: $(x + 2)6$

29. Use the Commutative Property of Addition to complete the statement
$7(x + 3) =$ _____.

1—Ans: $7(3 + x)$

30. Use the Associative Property of Addition to complete the statement
$7 + (x + 3) =$ _____.

1—Ans: $(7 + x) + 3$

31. Which of the following pairs of terms are *like* terms?

  (a) x^3 and y^3x **(b)** $7x^2$ and $7x$ **(c)** $3x^2$ and $3y^2$

  (d) x^2 and $-x^2$ **(e)** None of these

  1—Ans: d

32. Which of the following pairs of terms are *like* terms?

  (a) $14xy$ and $15x^2y$ **(b)** $2x^2y$ and $4xy^2$ **(c)** $5x^2$ and $7x^2$

  (d) $-3x^3$ and $4y^3$ **(e)** None of these

  1—Form: 2B—Ans: c

33. Which of the following pairs of terms are *like* terms?

  (a) $4xy$ and $5x^2y$ **(b)** $9x^2$ and $7x^2$ **(c)** $2x^2y$ and $4xy^2$

  (d) $3x^3$ and $4y^3$ **(e)** None of these

  1—Form: 2A—Ans: b

34. List all of the *like* terms of the expression $4a + 5ab + 3b - 6ab$.

  1—Ans: $5ab$ and $-6ab$

35. List all of the *like* terms of the expression $2ab^2 + a^2b - a^2 - 2ab^2 - b^2 + 3a^2b$.

  1—Ans: $2ab^2$ and $-2ab^2$; a^2b and $3a^2b$

36. For the expression $2x^2y + 3xy^2 - x^2y + x^2y^2 - xy^2 + 3x^2y$ list any *like* terms of $3x^2y$.

  1—Ans: $2x^2y$, $-x^2y$, and $3x^2y$

37. For the expression $2x^2y + 3xy^2 - x^2y + x^2y^2 - xy^2 + 3x^2y$ list any *like* terms of $3xy^2$.

  1—Ans: $3xy^2$ and $-xy^2$

38. Which of the following statements is *false*?

(a) $-(5x - 1) = -5x + 1$

(b) $-3(2x + 1) + x = -5x - 3$

(c) $4(x + 1) + 5 = 4x + 9$

(d) $4x - (5x - 1) = -x - 1$

(e) None of these

2—Ans: d

39. Which of the following statements is *false*?

(a) $3x(x - y) + y(3x - y) = 3x^2 - y^2$

(b) $3(x - y) - (x + y) = 2x$

(c) $\dfrac{5x}{3} - \dfrac{2x}{7} = \dfrac{29x}{21}$

(d) $\dfrac{5x}{7} - \dfrac{2x}{7} = \dfrac{3x}{7}$

(e) $-2x(-3x^4) + 4x^5 = 10x^5$

2—Ans: b

40. Which of the following statements is *false*?

(a) $8(-x + y) = 8y - 8x$

(b) $(-8)(-5x) = 40x$

(c) $8(-xy) = -8-xy$

(d) $-\dfrac{8}{5}x\left(-\dfrac{10x}{4}\right) = 4x^2$

(e) $4x - [(2 - x) - 7] = 5x + 5$

2—Ans: c

41. Which of the following statements is *true*?

(a) $4x(x + 3) = 4x^2 + 3$

(b) $-(x^3 + 2) = -x^3 + 2$

(c) $-4(x^3 + 6) = -4x^3 + 24$

(d) $-4(x^3 + 6) = -4x^3 - 24$

(e) None of these

2—Form: 2A—Ans: d

42. Which of the following statements is *true*?

(a) $5a(a + 3) = 5a^2 + 15a$

(b) $5a(a - 3) = 5a-15a$

(c) $5a(a + 3) = 5a^2 + 15$

(d) $5a(a - 3) = 5a^2- 15$

(e) None of these

1—Form: 2B—Ans: a

43. Which of the following statements is *true*?

(a) $5ax^3 + 2ax^3 = 10ax^3$

(b) $3x^2 + (-3x^2) = 1$

(c) $3A^2 + 4A^2 = 12A^2$

(d) $-7x^2y + 3x^2y = -4x^2y$

(e) None of these

1—Ans: d

44. Which of the following statements is *true*?

(a) $3x(x - 5) = 3x^2 - 5$ (b) $(x + 2)(x - 2) = x^2 - 4x - 4$

(c) $-(x^2 + 4x) = -x^2 + 4x$ (d) $(x^2 + 4)(-x) = -x^3 - 4x$

(e) None of these

2—Ans: d

45. Simplify $z(3x - 2y) - z[(x - y) - 2x]$.

(a) $4xz - yz$ (b) $2xz - 3yz$ (c) $4xz - 3yz$

(d) $2xz - yz$ (e) None of these

2—Ans: a

46. Simplify $2x(4y + 3) - 4(2 - xy)$.

(a) $7xy - 5$ (b) $4xy + 6x - 8$ (c) $9xy - 5$

(d) $12xy + 6x - 8$ (e) None of these

2—Form: 2B—Ans: d

47. Simplify $3y(2x + 3) - 5(3 - xy)$.

(a) $11xy + 9y - 15$ (b) $5xy + 3y + 15$ (c) $5xy - 12$

(d) $xy + 9y - 15$ (e) None of these

2—Ans: a

48. Simplify $4x - 3[x + 2(x - 1)]$.

(a) $-5x + 3$ (b) $-5x - 2$ (c) $-5x - 6$

(d) $-5x + 6$ (e) None of these

2—Form: 2A—Ans: d

49. Simplify $5y - 2[y + 3(y - 1)]$.

(a) $-3y - 3$ (b) $-3y - 6$ (c) $-3y + 6$

(d) $-3y + 2$ (e) None of these

2—Ans: c

50. Simplify $4(3x - 1) - 2(5 - x)$.

(a) $11x - 11$ (b) $14x - 14$ (c) $14x - 11$

(d) $10x - 14$ (e) None of these

2—Ans: b

51. Simplify $2x^2y(-3xy^2)^2$.

    (a) $-18x^4y^5$ **(b)** $18x^4y^4$ **(c)** $-18x^4y^4$ **(d)** $18x^4y^5$ **(e)** None of these

    2—Form: 2B—Ans: d

52. Simplify $(-3x^3y^2) + x^3(3y)^2$.

    (a) 0 **(b)** $3x^3y^2$ **(c)** $6x^3y^2$ **(d)** $9x^3y^2$ **(e)** None of these

    1—Ans: c

53. Simplify $(xy^2)^3(2x) - (x^2y^3)^2$.

    (a) 0 **(b)** x^4y^5 **(c)** $2x^2y^3 - x^4y^3$

    (d) x^4y^6 **(e)** None of these

    2—Ans: d

54. Simplify $x^4y^5 + (-2xy^2)^3$.

    (a) $-7x^4y^5$ **(b)** $x^4y^5 - 6x^3y^6$ **(c)** $-7x^8y^{10}$

    (d) $x^4y^5 - 8x^3y^6$ **(e)** None of these

    2—Ans: d

55. Simplify $(a^2b)^2(ab^2)^2$.

    (a) a^6b^6 **(b)** a^8b^8 **(c)** a^7b^7 **(d)** $a^{12}b^{12}$ **(e)** None of these

    2—Ans: a

56. Simplify $(-2x)^2(5x) + 4x^2$.

    2—Ans: $20x^3 + 4x^2$

57. Simplify $(-3y)(4y^5) + 7y^6$.

    2—Ans: $-5y^6$

58. Simplify $7x(x - 6)$.

    1—Form: 2C—Ans: $7x^2 - 42x$

59. Simplify $2x - 3(2 - 5x)$.

    1—Ans: $17x - 6$

60. Simplify $x(x - 2) - 3(3 - x)$.

    1—Ans: $x^2 + x - 9$

61. Simplify $-3A + 2[A - 4(2 - A)] + (2 - 3A)$.

    2—Ans: $4A - 14$

62. Simplify $\dfrac{5x}{12} - \dfrac{x}{8}$.

   2—Form: 2C—Ans: $\dfrac{7x}{24}$

63. Simplify $3A^2 - 5AB - A^2 + 3AB$.

   1—Ans: $2A^2 - 2AB$

64. Simplify $x^3 - x^2y + 2x + 2x^2y - x^3 - y^3$.

   2—Ans: $x^2y + 2x - y^3$

65. Simplify $15x + 8 - 4x - 9$.

   1—Form: 2C—Ans: $11x - 1$

66. Simplify $6(y - 2) - (y - 3)$.

   1—Form: 2C—Ans: $5y - 9$

67. Simplify $5x - [8 - x(3 - x)]$.

   2—Ans: $-x^2 + 8x - 8$

68. Simplify $5x(x - 2y) + 2y(5x - y)$.

   2—Ans: $5x^2 - 2y^2$

69. Simplify $-4y - 3[(x + y) - 3x] - x + 2y$.

   2—Ans: $5x - 5y$

70. Simplify $2x(x - 5y) - 5y(y - 2x)$.

   2—Ans: $2x^2 - 5y^2$

71. Simplify $x(3z - 2y) - 2x[y - (z - 2y)]$.

   2—Ans: $5xz - 8xy$

72. Simplify $(2A - 3) - 3[2(A - 3) - 4] - 2(A + 3)$.

   2—Ans: $-6A + 21$

Section 2.3   Algebra and Problem Solving

1. Which of the following algebraic expressions correctly represents the verbal expression?

   Five more than the quotient of 6 and *a*.

   (a) $5 + \dfrac{a}{6}$ **(b)** $5\left(\dfrac{6}{a}\right)$ **(c)** $5 + \dfrac{6}{a}$ **(d)** $5\left(\dfrac{a}{6}\right)$ **(e)** None of these

   1—Ans: c

2. Which of the following algebraic expressions correctly represents the verbal expression?

   Seven more than the quotient of 8 and *a*.

   (a) $7\left(\dfrac{8}{a}\right)$ **(b)** $7\left(\dfrac{a}{8}\right)$ **(c)** $7 + \dfrac{a}{8}$ **(d)** $7 + \dfrac{8}{a}$ **(e)** None of these

   1—Ans: d

3. Which of the following algebraic expressions correctly represents the verbal expression?

   Nine decreased by the product of 4 and *x*.

   (a) $9 - 4x$ **(b)** $4x - 9$ **(c)** $\left(\dfrac{9}{4}\right)x$ **(d)** $\dfrac{9}{4}x$ **(e)** None of these

   1—Ans: a

4. Which of the following algebraic expressions correctly represents the verbal expression?

   The sum of eleven and *a*, all divided by eight.

   (a) $\dfrac{11 + a}{8}$ **(b)** $11 + \dfrac{a}{8}$ **(c)** $\dfrac{11a}{8}$ **(d)** $\dfrac{11}{8} + a$ **(e)** None of these

   1—Ans: a

5. Which of the following algebraic expressions correctly represents the verbal expression?

   The sum of five and *b*, all divided by six.

   (a) $\dfrac{5b}{6}$ **(b)** $\dfrac{5 + b}{6}$ **(c)** $\dfrac{5}{6} + b$ **(d)** $5 + \dfrac{b}{6}$ **(e)** None of these

   1—Ans: b

6. Let *x* represent a number. A variable expression in *x* representing 4 added to the product of 3 and *x*, all divided by 7 is given by:

   (a) $\dfrac{3}{7}x + 4$ **(b)** $\dfrac{3x + 4}{7}$ **(c)** $3x + \dfrac{4}{7}$ **(d)** $\dfrac{3(x + 4)}{7}$ **(e)** None of these

   1—Form: 2A—Ans: b

7. Let x represent a number. A variable expression in x representing the product of 3 and x divided by seven, added to 4 is given by:

(a) $\dfrac{3}{7}x + 4$ (b) $\dfrac{3x + 4}{7}$ (c) $3x + \dfrac{4}{7}$ (d) $\dfrac{3(x + 4)}{7}$ (e) None of these

1—Ans: a

8. Let x represent a number. A variable expression in x representing the product of 3 and the sum of x and 4, all divided by 7, is given by:

(a) $\dfrac{3}{7}x + 4$ (b) $\dfrac{3x + 4}{7}$ (c) $3x + \dfrac{4}{7}$ (d) $\dfrac{3(x + 4)}{7}$ (e) None of these

1—Ans: d

9. Let x represent a number. A variable expression in x representing four-sevenths added to the product of 3 and x is given by:

(a) $\dfrac{3}{7}x + 4$ (b) $\dfrac{3x + 4}{7}$ (c) $3x + \dfrac{4}{7}$ (d) $\dfrac{3(x + 4)}{7}$ (e) None of these

1—Ans: c

10. Let x and y represent numbers. Translate the following statement into a variable expression involving x and y.

y is subtracted from 7 and the result multiplied by x.

(a) $x(7 - y)$ (b) $7x - y$ (c) $x(y - 7)$ (d) $xy - 7$ (e) None of these

2—Form: 2B—Ans: a

11. Let x and y represent numbers. Translate the following statement into a variable expression involving x and y.

Seven is subtracted from the product of x and y.

(a) $x(7 - y)$ (b) $7x - y$ (c) $x(y - 7)$ (d) $xy - 7$ (e) None of these

2—Ans: d

12. Let x and y represent numbers. Translate the following statement into a variable expression involving x and y.

y is subtracted from the product of 7 and x.

(a) $x(7 - y)$ (b) $7x - y$ (c) $x(y - 7)$ (d) $xy - 7$ (e) None of these

2—Ans: b

13. Let x and y represent numbers. Translate the following statement into a variable expression involving x and y.

Seven is subtracted from y and the result is multiplied by x.

(a) $x(7 - y)$ (b) $7x - y$ (c) $x(y - 7)$ (d) $xy - 7$ (e) None of these

2—Ans: c

14. Choose the appropriate verbal description of the following: $5x - 4$

    (a) Five times x, subtracted from four.   **(b)** Four subtracted from x, multiplied by five.

    (c) Four subtracted from the product of x and five.   **(d)** Four subtracted from five, multiplied by x.

    (e) None of these

    2—Form: 2A—Ans: c

15. Choose the appropriate verbal description of the following: $(5-4)x$

    (a) Five times x, subtracted from four.   **(b)** Four subtracted from x, multiplied by five.

    (c) Four subtracted from the product of x and five.   **(d)** Four subtracted from five, multiplied by x.

    (e) None of these

    2—Form: 2B—Ans: d

16. Translate the phrase into an algebraic expression. (Let x represent the number.)

    Ten increased by the difference of 4 and a number.

    1—Ans: $10 + (4 - x)$

17. Translate the phrase into an algebraic expression. (Let x represent the number.)

    Nine increased by the difference of 5 and a number.

    1—Form: 2C—Ans: $9 + (5 - x)$

18. Translate the phrase into an algebraic expression. (Let x represent the number.)

    Seven less than the product of a number and four.

    1—Ans: $4x - 7$

19. Let x represent a number. Translate the following statement into a variable expression involving x.

    Five added to the product of 8 and a number.

    1—Ans: $8x + 5$

20. Let x represent a number. Translate the following statement into a variable expression involving x.

    A number divided by a number ten greater than itself.

    1—Ans: $\dfrac{x}{x + 10}$

21. Translate the phrase into an algebraic expression. (Let x represent the number.)

    The difference between twice a number and twelve.

    1—Ans: $2x - 12$

22. Translate the phrase into an algebraic expression. (Let x represent the number.)

The difference between twice a number and eight.

1—Ans: $2x - 8$

23. Translate into an algebraic expression involving the indicated variables.

The product of x and y is subtracted from seven.

1—Ans: $7 - xy$

24. Translate into an algebraic expression involving the indicated variables.

The sum of x and its square is subtracted from ten.

1—Ans: $10 - (x + x^2)$

25. Write $\frac{2}{3}(2x + 1)$ in verbal form. (NOTE: Verbal descriptions are not unique.)

1—Ans: Two thirds of the sum of 1 and two times x.

26. Write $\frac{7}{3}x + 4$ in verbal form. (NOTE: Verbal descriptions are not unique.)

1—Ans: Four added to seven-thirds of x.

27. Write $\frac{1}{3}(x - 5)$ in verbal form. (NOTE: Verbal descriptions are not unique.)

1—Ans: Five subtracted from x, the result divided by three.

28. Write $\frac{2}{3}x - 4$ in verbal form. (NOTE: Verbal descriptions are not unique.)

1—Ans: Subtract four from two-thirds of x.

29. Without using a variable, write a verbal description of $3x - 7$. (NOTE: Verbal descriptions are not unique.)

2—Ans: Seven less than the product of three and a number.

30. Without using a variable, write a verbal description of $3(x - 7)$. (NOTE: Verbal descriptions are not unique.)

2—Ans: A number is diminished by seven, and the result tripled.

31. Without using a variable, write a verbal description of $\left(\dfrac{3}{x}\right) + 2$. (NOTE: Verbal descriptions are not unique.)

2—Ans: Three is divided by a number and the result is added to 2.

32. Without using a variable, write a verbal description of $\dfrac{3}{x + 2}$. (NOTE: Verbal descriptions are not unique.)

2—Ans: Three is divided by the sum of two and a number.

33. If k represents any integer, write the multiples of four in terms of k.

   2—Ans: $4k$

34. If k is an integer, write an *even* integer in terms of k.

   1—Ans: $2k$

35. If k is an integer, write an *odd* integer in terms of k.

   1—Ans: $2k + 1$ or $2k - 1$

36. Admission to a park is $4 for an adult and $2 for a child. If A and C, respectively, represent the numbers of adults and children admitted on a given day, write the expression for the total income for that day.

   1—Ans: $4A + 2C$

37. Admission to a park is $7 for an adult and $5 for a child. If A and C, respectively, represent the numbers of adults and children admitted on a given day, write the expression for the total income, in dollars, for that day.

   1—Ans: $7A + 5C$

38. Admission to a football game is $4 for an adult and $2 for a student. Let a and s, respectively, represent the numbers of adults and students admitted on a given day. Write an algabraic expression that represents, in dollars, the total revenue for that day.

   1—Ans: $4a + 2s$

39. Admission to a football game is $3 for an adult and $2 for a student. Let a and s, respectively, represent the numbers of adults and students admitted on a given day. Write an algabraic expression that represents, in dollars, the total revenue for that day.

   1—Ans: $3a + 2s$

40. The hourly wage for a factory employee is $5.25 per hour and 6 cents for each n units produced during the hour. Write an algebraic expression that represents the total hourly earnings (in dollars) for the employee.

   1—Ans: $5.25 + 0.06n$

41. The hourly wage for a factory employee is $5.35 per hour and 5 cents for each n units produced during the hour. Write an algabraic expression that represents the total hourly earnings (in dollars) for the employee.

   1—Ans: $5.35 + 0.05n$

42. A salesperson sells stoves and microwave ovens for salary plus commissions. The weekly salary is $110. The commissions are 18% on the stoves and 22% on the microwave ovens. Write and expression for the salesperson's total weekly income if x represents the sales, in dollars, of stoves and y represents the sales, in dollars, of microwave ovens.

2—Ans: $0.18x + 0.22y + 110$

43. A salesperson sells stoves and microwave ovens for salary plus commissions. The weekly salary is $125. The commissions are 21% on the stoves and 26% on the microwave ovens. Write and expression for the salesperson's total weekly income if x represents the sales, in dollars, of stoves and y represents the sales, in dollars, of microwave ovens.

2—Ans: $0.21x + 0.26y + 125$

44. A wallet contains n nickels and q quarters. Write an expression for this amount of money, in cents.

2—Form: 2C—Ans: $5n + 25q$

45. A wallet contains d dimes and q quarters. Write an expression for this amount of money, in cents.

2—Ans: $10d + 25q$

46. A wallet contains n nickels and p pennies. Write an expression for this amount of money, in cents.

2—Ans: $5n + p$

47. A cash register contains x quarters and y dimes. Write an expression for the total amount of money in dollars.

1—Ans: $0.25x + 0.10y$

48. A person rides a bicycle at a constant rate of 18 miles per hour for M miles. Write an expression for the time in hours elapsed.

1—Ans: $\dfrac{M}{18}$

49. A person adds L liters of fluid containing 65% antifreeze to a car radiator. Write an expression indicating the amount of antifreeze added.

1—Ans: $0.65L$

50. A bus travels at a constant rate of 45 miles per hour. Write an expression showing how far the bus travels in t hours.

1—Ans: $45t$

51. A bus travels at a constant rate of 48 miles per hour. Write an expression showing how far the bus travels in t hours.

1—Ans: $48t$

52. A bus travels at a constant rate of r miles per hour for 3.5 hours. Write an expression showing how far the bus travels.

1—Ans: $3.5r$

53. A bus travels at a constant rate of r miles per hour for 4.5 hours. Write an expression showing how far the bus travels.

1—Ans: $4.5r$

54. A company produces an item which costs $0.43 to produce. Write an algebraic expression, in dollars, that represents the cost of producing x items.

1—Ans: $0.43x$

55. A company produces an item which costs $0.36 to produce. Write an algebraic expression, in dollars, that represents the cost of producing x items.

1—Ans: $0.36x$

56. A company received a 2% discount for early payment of an invoice in the amount of d dollars. Write an expression, in dollars, for the discount.

1—Ans: $0.02d$

57. A company received a 3% discount for early payment of an invoice in the amount of d dollars. Write an expression, in dollars, for the discount.

1—Ans: $0.03d$

58. A company sells an item for $3.49. Write an algebraic expression, in dollars, that represents the sales revenue from selling x items.

1—Ans: $3.49x$

59. A company sells an item for $3.99. Write an algebraic expression, in dollars, that represents the sales revenue from selling x items.

1—Ans: $3.99x$

60. A company received a 2% discount for early payment of an invoice in the amount of d dollars. Write an expression, in dollars, for the amount of the discounted invoice.

2—Form: 2C—Ans: $d - 0.02d = 0.98d$

61. A company received a 3% discount for early payment of an invoice in the amount of *d* dollars. Write an expression, in dollars, for the amount of the discounted invoice.

    2—Ans: $d - 0.03d = 0.97d$

62. It costs $35 for gasoline for a trip of 600 miles. Use the guess, check, and revise strategy to estimate the cost of gasoline to travel 400 miles.

    2—Ans: Approximately $23

63. It costs $35 for gasoline for a trip of 600 miles. Use the guess, check, and revise strategy to estimate the cost of gasoline to travel 450 miles.

    2—Ans: Approximately $26

64. The property tax on a house valued at $50,000 is $600. Use the guess, check, and revise strategy to estimate the property tax on a house valued at $75,000.

    2—Ans: Approximately $900

65. The property tax on a house valued at $50,000 is $640. Use the guess, check, and revise strategy to estimate the property tax on a house valued at $75,000.

    2—Form: 2C—Ans: Approximately $960

66. Find the following products: $1 \cdot 2, 2 \cdot 4, 3 \cdot 6, 4 \cdot 8, 5 \cdot 10$

Make a table and describe a number pattern. Use your pattern to find the product of 9 and 18.

    2—Form: 2C—Ans: The pattern is a product of two and a perfect square.
              The product of 9 and 18 is $2 \cdot 9^2 = 162$.

Numbers	$1 \cdot 2$	$2 \cdot 4$	$3 \cdot 6$	$4 \cdot 8$	$5 \cdot 10$
Products	2	8	18	32	50

67. Find the following products: $1 \cdot 3, 2 \cdot 6, 3 \cdot 9, 4 \cdot 12, 5 \cdot 15$

Make a table and describe a number pattern. Use your pattern to find the product of 9 and 27.

    2—Ans: The pattern is a product of three and a perfect square.
              The product of 9 and 27 is $3 \cdot 9^2 = 243$.

Numbers	$1 \cdot 3$	$2 \cdot 6$	$3 \cdot 9$	$4 \cdot 12$	$5 \cdot 15$
Products	3	12	27	48	75

68. The dimensions of a rectangular garden are 12 feet by 16 feet. If 128 square feet are planted in vegetables, how many square feet are planted in flowers? Draw a diagram to visualize the problem.

2—Ans: 64

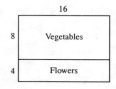

69. The dimensions of a rectangular garden are 14 feet by 16 feet. If 168 square feet are planted in vegetables, how many square feet are planted in flowers? Draw a diagram to visualize the problem.

2—Ans: 56

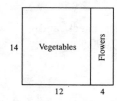

70. The annual simple interest rate on your savings account is $2\frac{1}{2}\%$. Solve a simpler problem to find the interest you will earn on a balance of $500.

2—Ans: The interest on $100 is $2.50, the interest on $200 is $5.00, the interest on $400 is $10.00, the interest on $500 is $12.50.

71. The annual simple interest rate on your savings account is $2\frac{1}{4}\%$. Solve a simpler problem to find the interest you will earn on a balance of $500.

2—Ans: The interest on $100 is $2.25, the interest on $200 is $4.50, the interest on $400 is $9.00, the interest on $500 is $11.25.

Section 2.4   Introduction to Equations

1. Determine whether the value of x is a solution to the equation $x^2 - 2x = x + 4$.

(a) $x = 0$ **(b)** $x = 1$ **(c)** $x = 4$ **(d)** $x = -2$ **(e)** $x = -4$

1—Form: 2A—Ans: c

2. Determine whether the value of x is a solution to the equation $x^2 - 2x = x + 4$.

(a) $x = 0$ **(b)** $x = -1$ **(c)** $x = 1$ **(d)** $x = -2$ **(e)** $x = -4$

1—Form: 2B—Ans: b

3. Determine whether 2, -2, both, or neither is a solution of the equation $x^2 + x = x + 4$.

2—Ans: Both 2 and -2 are solutions.

4. Determine whether 2, -2, both, or neither is a solution of the equation $x^2 + 4 = 4x + 4$.

   2—Ans: Neither 2 nor -2 are solutions.

5. Determine whether $x = -\frac{5}{3}$ is a solution of the equation $2(x - 1) = 3 - x$.

   1—Ans: $-\frac{5}{3}$ is not a solution.

6. Determine whether $x = -\frac{3}{5}$ is a solution of the equation $1 + 3x = 4 - 2x$.

   1—Ans: $-\frac{3}{5}$ is not a solution.

7. Determine whether $x = 3$ is a solution of the equation $6x + 2 = 2(x + 7)$.

   1—Ans: $x = 3$ is a solution.

8. Determine whether $x = 2$ is a solution of the equation $7x + 1 = 3(x + 3)$.

   1—Ans: $x = 2$ is a solution.

9. Decide whether $x = \frac{1}{2}$ is a solution of the equation $\frac{x}{2} + x = \frac{3}{4}$.

   1—Ans: $\frac{1}{2}$ is a solution.

10. Decide whether $x = \frac{1}{3}$ is a solution of the equation $\frac{x}{2} + x = \frac{1}{2}$.

    1—Ans: $x = \frac{1}{3}$ is a solution.

11. Decide whether $x = -3$ is a solution of the equation $\frac{1}{x} - \frac{2}{x} = -\frac{1}{3}$.

    1—Ans: $x = -3$ is not a solution.

12. Decide whether $x = -2$ is a solution of the equation $\frac{1}{x} - \frac{2}{x} = -\frac{1}{2}$.

    1—Ans: $x = -2$ is not a solution.

13. (3) is a solution of:

    (a) $x^2 = x + 3 \cdot 1$ (b) $x^2 = 2x$ (c) $x^2 = 3 + x$

    (d) $x^2 = x + 6$ (e) None of these

    1—Ans: d

14. (4) is a solution of:

   (a) $x^2 = x + 4$ **(b)** $x^2 = x + 12$ **(c)** $x^2 = 2 \cdot 2 + x$

   (d) $x^2 = 2x$ **(e)** None of these

   1—Ans: b

15. (2) is a solution of:

   (a) $2(x + 1) = x^2 + 1$ **(b)** $2x + 1 = -x^2 + 1$ **(c)** $3(x - 1) = 2x - 1$

   (d) $3x + 1 = 2x - 1$ **(e)** None of these

   1—Ans: c

16. (3) is a solution of:

   (a) $2(x - 1) = x + 1$ **(b)** $2x - 1 = -x^2 + 1$ **(c)** $2x + 1 = x - 2$

   (d) $7(x + 2) = x^2 + 3$ **(e)** None of these

   1—Ans: a

17. (4) is a solution of:

   (a) $4 - x = 0$ **(b)** $2 - x = 5$ **(c)** $x + 1 = 2$

   (d) $3 = 1 - x$ **(e)** None of these

   1—Ans: a

18. (1) is a solution of:

   (a) $4 - x = 0$ **(b)** $2 - x = 5$ **(c)** $x + 1 = 2$

   (d) $3 = 1 - x$ **(e)** None of these

   1—Ans: c

19. (-1) is a solution of:

   (a) $-x^2 = x$ **(b)** $(-x)^2 = x$ **(c)** $x = x^2$

   (d) $(-x)^2 - x = 0$ **(e)** None of these

   1—Form: 2A—Ans: a

20. (-2) is a solution of:

   (a) $x^2 = 2x$ **(b)** $(-x)^2 - 2x = 0$ **(c)** $(-x)^2 = 2x$

   (d) $-x^2 = 2x$ **(e)** None of these

   1—Form: 2B—Ans: d

21. Describe the step used in transforming the given equation into the equivalent equation.

$$3 - 7x = 2 \text{ into } -7x = -1$$

(a) Interchange the two sides of the equation.

(b) Subtract the same quantity from both sides of the equation.

(c) Divide both sides of the equation by the same *nonzero* number.

(d) Add the same quantity to both sides of the equation.

(e) Remove symbols of grouping.

1—Ans: b

22. Describe the step used in transforming the given equation into the equivalent equation.

$$3 - 7x = 2 \text{ into } 3 = 2 + 7x$$

(a) Interchange the two sides of the equation.

(b) Subtract the same quantity from both sides of the equation.

(c) Divide both sides of the equation by the same *nonzero* number.

(d) Add the same quantity to both sides of the equation.

(e) Remove symbols of grouping.

1—Ans: d

23. Describe the step used in transforming the given equation into the equivalent equation.

$$3x - 4 = 7 \text{ into } x - \frac{4}{3} = \frac{7}{3}$$

(a) Interchange the two sides of the equation.

(b) Subtract the same quantity from both sides of the equation.

(c) Divide both sides of the equation by the same *nonzero* number.

(d) Add the same quantity to both sides of the equation.

(e) Remove symbols of grouping.

1—Ans: c

24. Describe the step used in transforming the given equation into the equivalent equation.

$$3 = 2 + 7x \text{ into } 2 + 7x = 3$$

(a) Interchange the two sides of the equation.

(b) Subtract the same quantity from both sides of the equation.

(c) Divide both sides of the equation by the same *nonzero* number.

(d) Add the same quantity to both sides of the equation.

(e) Remove symbols of grouping.

1—Ans: a

25. Describe the step used in transforming the given equation into the equivalent equation.

$$6x + 2 - 2x = 5 + x + 6 \text{ into } 4x + 2 = x + 11$$

(a) Reduce fractions on one or both sides of the equation.

(b) Multiply both sides of the equation by the same nonzero quantity.

(c) Divide both sides of the equation by the same nonzero number.

(d) Combine like terms.

(e) Subtract the same quantity from both sides of the equation.

1—Ans: d

26. Describe the step used in transforming the given equation into the equivalent equation.

$$7x + 3 - 2x = 2 + x + 9 \text{ into } 5x + 3 = x + 11$$

(a) Reduce fractions on one or both sides of the equation.

(b) Multiply both sides of the equation by the same nonzero quantity.

(c) Divide both sides of the equation by the same nonzero number.

(d) Combine like terms.

(e) Subtract the same quantity from both sides of the equation.

1—Ans: d

27. Describe the step used in transforming the given equation into the equivalent equation.

$$\frac{2}{3}x - 7 = 2 - \frac{x}{2} \text{ into } 4x - 42 = 12 - 3x$$

(a) Reduce fractions on one or both sides of the equation.

(b) Multiply both sides of the equation by the same nonzero quantity.

(c) Divide both sides of the equation by the same nonzero number.

(d) Combine like terms.

(e) Subtract the same quantity from both sides of the equation.

2—Ans: b

28. Describe the step used in transforming the given equation into the equivalent equation.

$$\frac{2(x-2)}{2(3x-2)} = 2 \text{ into } \frac{x-2}{3x-2} = 2$$

(a) Reduce fractions on one or both sides of the equation.

(b) Multiply both sides of the equation by the same nonzero quantity.

(c) Divide both sides of the equation by the same nonzero number.

(d) Combine like terms.

(e) Subtract the same quantity from both sides of the equation.

2—Ans: a

29. Describe the step used in transforming the given equation into the equivalent equation.

$$\tfrac{3}{4}x + 1 = \tfrac{3}{2}x - 2 \text{ into } 3x + 4 = 6x - 8$$

(a) Reduce fractions on one or both sides of the equation.

(b) Multiply both sides of the equation by the same nonzero quantity.

(c) Divide both sides of the equation by the same nonzero number.

(d) Combine like terms.

(e) Subtract the same quantity from both sides of the equation.

1—Form: 2A—Ans: b

30. Describe the step used in transforming the given equation into the equivalent equation.

$$\tfrac{3}{4}x + 2 = \tfrac{3}{2}x - 1 \text{ into } 3x + 8 = 6x - 4$$

(a) Reduce fractions on one or both sides of the equation.

(b) Multiply both sides of the equation by the same nonzero quantity.

(c) Divide both sides of the equation by the same nonzero number.

(d) Combine like terms.

(e) Subtract the same quantity from both sides of the equation.

1—Form: 2B—Ans: b

31. Describe the step used in transforming the given equation into the equivalent equation.

    $$6x = 31 \text{ into } x = \frac{31}{6}$$

    (a) Reduce fractions on one or both sides of the equation.

    (b) Multiply both sides of the equation by the same nonzero quantity.

    (c) Divide both sides of the equation by the same nonzero number.

    (d) Combine like terms.

    (e) Subtract the same quantity from both sides of the equation.

    1—Ans: c

32. Describe the step used in transforming the given equation into the equivalent equation.

    $$5x = 23 \text{ into } x = \frac{23}{5}$$

    (a) Reduce fractions on one or both sides of the equation.

    (b) Multiply both sides of the equation by the same nonzero quantity.

    (c) Divide both sides of the equation by the same nonzero number.

    (d) Combine like terms.

    (e) Subtract the same quantity from both sides of the equation.

    1—Ans: c

33. Describe the step used in transforming the given equation into the equivalent equation.

    $$14x = 3x + 22 \text{ into } 11x = 22$$

    (a) Reduce fractions on one or both sides of the equation.

    (b) Multiply both sides of the equation by the same nonzero quantity.

    (c) Divide both sides of the equation by the same nonzero number.

    (d) Combine like terms.

    (e) Subtract the same quantity from both sides of the equation.

    1—Ans: e

34. Describe the step used in transforming the given equation into the equivalent equation.

    $$16x = 4x + 24 \text{ into } 12x = 24$$

    (a) Reduce fractions on one or both sides of the equation.

    (b) Multiply both sides of the equation by the same nonzero quantity.

    (c) Divide both sides of the equation by the same nonzero number.

    (d) Combine like terms.

    (e) Subtract the same quantity from both sides of the equation.

    1—Ans: e

35. State the step used in transforming the given equation into the equivalent equation.

$$2(x - 3) = 3(x - 7) \text{ into } 2x - 6 = 3x - 21$$

1—Ans: Remove the symbols of grouping.

36. State the step used in transforming the given equation into the equivalent equation.

$$2x - 6 = 3x - 21 \text{ into } 3x - 21 = 2x - 6$$

1—Ans: Interchange the two sides of the equation.

37. State the step used in transforming the given equation into the equivalent equation.

$$\frac{1}{2} = \frac{3x}{5} \text{ into } 5 = 6x$$

1—Ans: Multiply both sides by the same nonzero quantity.

38. State the step used in transforming the given equation into the equivalent equation.

$$\frac{18}{12} = \frac{2x}{6} \text{ into } \frac{3}{2} = \frac{x}{3}$$

1—Ans: Reduce fractions to lowest terms.

39. Match the verbal statement with the correct equation.

Three times the sum of a number and five is 75.

(a) $3(x + 5) = 75$ **(b)** $x + 5 = 3(75)$ **(c)** $x + 5(3) = 75$

(d) $3x + 5 = 75$ **(e)** None of these

1—Form: 2A—Ans: a

40. Match the verbal statement with the correct equation.

Seven times the sum of a number and 4 is 91.

(a) $7x + 4 = 91$ **(b)** $7(x + 4) = 91$ **(c)** $x + 4(7) = 91$

(d) $x + 4 = 7(91)$ **(e)** None of these

1—Form: 2B—Ans: b

41. Write an equation that states that 100 is seven more than three times a number.

1—Ans: $3m = 100 - 7$

42. Write an equation that states that when the sum of a number and 7 is divided by 3, the result is 35.

1—Ans: $\dfrac{x + 7}{3} = 35$

43. Suppose you make 36 monthly payments of $173 each to buy a used car. The total amount financed is $5000. An equation for the total interest paid is:

(a) $I = \frac{5000}{36} - 173$ (b) $I = 173 - \frac{5000}{36}$ (c) $I = 36(173) - 5000$

(d) $I = 5000 - 36(173)$ (e) None of these

1—Ans: c

44. Suppose you make 30 monthly payments of $182 each to buy a used car. The total amount financed is $4200. An equation for the total interest paid is:

(a) $I = 4200 - 30(182)$ (b) $I = 30(182) - 4200$ (c) $I = \frac{4200}{30} - 182$

(d) $I = 182 - \frac{4200}{30}$ (e) None of these

1—Ans: b

45. The price of a product one year ago was $8750. Its price increased by 9% during the past year. Its current price is given by:

(a) $P = (1 + 0.09)8750$ (b) $P = 8750 + 0.9(8750)$ (c) $P = \frac{8750}{0.91}$

(d) $P = (1 - 0.09)8750$ (e) None of these

1—Ans: a

46. The price of a product one year ago was $5740. Its price increased by 7% during the past year. Its current price is given by:

(a) $P = (1 - 0.07)5740$ (b) $P = 5740 + 0.70(5740)$ (c) $P = \frac{5740}{0.93}$

(d) $P = (1.07)5740$ (e) None of these

1—Ans: d

47. Your weekly salary is $450 and you receive a 7% raise. Your new weekly salary is given by:

(a) $S = 450 + 0.07(450)$ (b) $S = (1 - 0.07)450$ (c) $S = 450(1.7)$

(d) $S = \frac{450}{1 - 0.07}$ (e) None of these

1—Ans: a

48. Your weekly salary is $520 and you receive a 6% raise. Your new weekly salary is given by:

(a) $S = (1 - 0.06)520$ (b) $S = \frac{520}{1 - 0.06}$ (c) $S = 520(1.6)$

(d) $S = (1.06)520$ (e) None of these

1—Ans: d

49. You have set aside $3250 for the purchase of a new computer that will cost $4175. You still need $*x*. Which equation is correct?

(a) $x = 4175 + 3250$ (b) $x = 3250 - 4175$ (c) $x = 4175 - 3250$

(d) $x = 4175 \div 3250$ (e) None of these

1—Ans: c

50. You have set aside $3550 for the purchase of a new computer that will cost $4220. You still need $*x*. Which equation is correct?

(a) $x = 4220 \div 3550$ (b) $x = 4220 - 3550$ (c) $x = 4220 + 3550$

(d) $x = 3550 - 4220$ (e) None of these

1—Ans: b

51. You have set aside $4095 for the purchase of a new computer that will cost $4950. You still need $*x*. Which equation is correct?

(a) $x = 4950 - 4095$ (b) $x = 4095 - 4950$ (c) $x = 4950 + 4095$

(d) $x = 4950 \div 4095$ (e) None of these

1—Ans: a

52. You have set aside $3092 for the purchase of a new computer that will cost $3920. You still need $*x*. Which equation is correct?

(a) $x = 3920 \div 3092$ (b) $x = 3920 + 3092$ (c) $x = 3092 - 3920$

(d) $x = 3920 - 3092$ (e) None of these

1—Ans: d

53. Write an algebraic equation for the problem. Do not solve the equation.

A year ago the price of a product was $238. During the past year the price increased by 11%.

1—Ans: $P = (1.11)238$

54. Write an algebraic equation for the problem. Do not solve the equation.

A year ago the price of a product was $465. During the past year the price increased by 8.5%.

1—Ans: $P = (1.085)465$

55. Write an algebraic equation for the problem. Do not solve the equation.

A salesperson earns $300 each week, plus a year-end bonus of b dollars. If the total income for 1994 was $16,500, find the amount of the bonus.

2—Ans: $300(52) + b = 16,500$

56. Write an algebraic equation for the problem. Do not solve the equation.

> A salesperson earns $400 each week, plus a year-end bonus of *b* dollars. If the total income for 1994 was $21,300, find the amount of the bonus.

2—Form: 2C—Ans: $400(52) + b = 21,300$

57. Write an algebraic equation for the problem. Do not solve the equation.

> You make 12 monthly payments of $60 each to buy an exercise machine. If the total amount financed is $600, find the amount of interest that you pay. Let *x* represent the amount of interest, in dollars.

2—Ans: $60(12) = 600 + x$

58. Write an algebraic equation for the problem. Do not solve the equation.

> You make 12 monthly payments of $50 each to buy an exercise machine. If the total amount financed is $500, find the amount of interest that you pay. Let *x* represent the amount of interest.

2—Ans: $50(12) = 500 + x$

59. Write an algebraic equation for the problem. Do not solve the equation.

> You receive a 15% discount on an item which normally sells for $375.

1—Ans: $P = 375(1 - 0.15)$

60. Write an algebraic equation for the problem. Do not solve the equation.

> You receive a 18% discount on an item which normally sells for $283.50.

1—Ans: $P = 283.50(1 - 0.18)$

61. Write an algebraic equation for the problem. Do not solve the equation.

> The sale price of a sweater is $45.50 and the list price is $54.00. Find the amount of the discount. Let *d* represent the amount of the discount, in dollars.

1—Form: 2C—Ans: $d = 54.00 - 45.50$

62. Write an algebraic equation for the problem. Do not solve the equation.

> The sale price of a sweater is $48.50 and the list price is $57.00. Find the amount of the discount. Let *d* represent the amount of the discount, in dollars.

1—Ans: $d = 57.00 - 48.50$

63. Write an algebraic equation for the problem. Do not solve the equation.

> Your weekly salary is $475. You receive a 6.5% raise.

1—Ans: $S = 475(1 + 0.065)$

64. Write an algebraic equation for the problem. Do not solve the equation.

Your weekly salary is $630. You receive a 5.4% raise.

1—Ans: $S = 630(1 + 0.054)$

65. Write an algebraic equation for the problem. Do not solve the equation.

You have saved $125 for the purchase of a compact disc player that will cost $280. Find the additional amount that you must save. Let a represent the amount in dollars.

1—Ans: $a = 280 - 125$

66. Write an algebraic equation for the problem. Do not solve the equation.

You have saved $145 for the purchase of a compact disc player that will cost $270. Find the additional amount that you must save. Let a represent the amount in dollars.

1—Ans: $a = 270 - 145$

67. A rectangular swimming pool has a perimeter of 160 feet. Its width is two-thirds of its length. If x is the length, write an equation which expresses these facts.

2—Ans: $160 = 2\left(x + \frac{2}{3}x\right)$ or $160 = \frac{10}{3}x$

68. A rectangular swimming pool has a perimeter of 192 feet. Its width is three-fifths of its length. If x is the length, write an equation which expresses these facts.

2—Ans: $192 = 2\left(x + \frac{3}{5}x\right)$ or $192 = \frac{16}{5}x$

CHAPTER 3
Linear Equations and Problem Solving

Section 3.1   Solving Linear Equations

1. Solve the linear equation $6x + 3 + 33$.

   (a) 6   (b) 24   (c) 5   (d) -5 (e) None of these

   1—Ans: c

2. Solve the linear equation $4x + 2 + 26$.

   (a) 6   (b) 7   (c) 20   (d) -6 (e) None of these

   1—Ans: a

3. Solve the linear equation $8x - 4 + 12$.

   (a) 1   (b) 2   (c) 8   (d) -2 (e) None of these

   1—Form: 3A—Ans: b

4. Solve the linear equation $4x - 2 + 10$.

   (a) 2   (b) -3 (c) 3   (d) 8   (e) None of these

   1—Form: 3B—Ans: c

5. Solve the linear equation $7 - 4x + 5x - 11$.

   (a) 18   (b) -4 (c) $-\frac{4}{9}$ (d) -2 (e) 2

   1—Ans: e

6. Solve the linear equation $8 + 3x + -4x - 6$.

   (a) 2   (b) -14 (c) -2 (d) $\frac{2}{7}$ (e) $-\frac{2}{7}$

   1—Ans: c

7. Solve the linear equation $3x + 3 + -4x - 2$.

   (a) 1   (b) $\frac{5}{7}$ (c) $-\frac{5}{7}$ (d) -2 (e) None of these

   1—Ans: c

8. Solve the linear equation $6x + 6 + 2 - x$.

   (a) $-\frac{4}{5}$ (b) $-\frac{4}{7}$ (c) $\frac{4}{5}$ (d) $\frac{4}{7}$ (e) None of these

   1—Ans: b

9. Solve the linear equation $3 - 3x = -2 + 4x$.

   (a) $\frac{5}{7}$ **(b)** $-\frac{5}{7}$ **(c)** 1   **(d)** 2   **(e)** None of these

   1—Ans: a

10. Solve the linear equation $6 - 6x = 2 + x$.

   (a) $\frac{1}{2}$ **(b)** $-\frac{4}{7}$ **(c)** $\frac{4}{5}$ **(d)** $\frac{4}{7}$ **(e)** None of these

   1—Ans: d

11. Solve the linear equation $20 - 2x = 3x - 30$.

   (a) -10 **(b)** 5   **(c)** 0   **(d)** 10   **(e)** None of these

   1—Ans: d

12. Solve the linear equation $30 - 3x = 2x - 20$.

   (a) 5   **(b)** 0   **(c)** 10   **(d)** -10 **(e)** None of these

   1—Ans: c

13. Solve the linear equation $15 + 3x = 2x + 10$.

   (a) 0   **(b)** -5 **(c)** -10 **(d)** 5   **(e)** None of these

   1—Ans: b

14. Solve the linear equation $15 - 3x = 2x - 10$.

   (a) 5   **(b)** -10 **(c)** -5 **(d)** 0   **(e)** None of these

   1—Ans: a

15. Solve the linear equation $7 - 3x + 3 = 4 + 2x - 6$.

   (a) 2   **(b)** $\frac{1}{2}$ **(c)** $\frac{12}{5}$

   (d) There is no solution   **(e)** None of these

   1—Ans: c

16. Solve the linear equation $2 - 6 + 3x = -3x + 7$.

   (a) $\frac{11}{6}$ **(b)** $-\frac{11}{6}$ **(c)** $-\frac{1}{2}$

   (d) There is no solution   **(e)** None of these

   1—Ans: a

17. Solve the linear equation $\frac{x}{4} - 3 = 5$.

   (a) 2   **(b)** 8   **(c)** -8 **(d)** 32   **(e)** None of these

   1—Form: 3A—Ans: d

18. Solve the linear equation $\frac{x}{2} - 4 = 8$.

(a) 8   (b) -8 (c) 24   (d) 6   (e) None of these

1—Form: 3B—Ans: c

19. Solve the linear equation $-7x + 6 + 12x = 16$.

(a) $\frac{22}{5}$ (b) 2   (c) $\frac{10}{19}$ (d) $\frac{22}{19}$ (e) None of these

2—Form: 3A—Ans: b

20. Solve the linear equation $-5x + 4 + 13x = 20$.

(a) $\frac{8}{9}$ (b) $\frac{12}{9}$ (c) 3   (d) 2   (e) None of these

2—Form: 3B—Ans: d

21. Solve the linear equation $-n + \frac{1}{2} - 4n = -\frac{9}{2}$.

(a) $\frac{4}{5}$ (b) -1 (c) 1   (d) $-\frac{4}{5}$ (e) None of these

2—Ans: c

22. Solve the linear equation $-n + \frac{1}{2} - 2n = -\frac{11}{2}$.

(a) 2   (b) $\frac{5}{3}$ (c) -2 (d) $-\frac{5}{3}$ (e) None of these

2—Ans: a

23. Which linear equation is in *standard* form?

(a) $-2x = 3$ (b) $-2(x - 3) = 0$ (c) $2x - 3 = 3x - 2$

(d) $1 - 2x = 2(1 - x)$ (e) None of these

1—Ans: e

24. Which linear equation is in *standard* form?

(a) $-3x - 5 = 0$ (b) $3x = -5$ (c) $3(x + 2) = 1$

(d) $3x + 4 = 1$ (e) None of these

1—Ans: a

25. Three *consecutive even integers* add up to 138. Find the numbers.

(a) 44, 46, 48   (b) 42, 46, 50   (c) 45, 46, 47

(d) 43, 46, 49   (e) None of these

1—Ans: a

26. Three *consecutive odd integers* add up to 159. Find the numbers.

(a) 52, 53, 54   (b) 51, 53, 55   (c) 49, 53, 57

(d) 50, 53, 56   (e) None of these

1—Ans: b

27. The length of a rectangular tennis court is five feet more than twice the width. The length is 83 feet. Find the width.

(a) 171 ft   (b) 44 ft   (c) 39 ft   (d) 156 ft   (e) None of these

2—Ans: c

28. The length of a rectangular tennis court is five feet more than twice the width. The length is 97 feet. Find the width.

(a) 46 ft   (b) 199 ft   (c) 51 ft   (d) 184 ft   (e) None of these

2—Ans: a

29. A coat sells for $242.25 after being discounted 15% from its regular price. Find the regular price.

(a) $205.91   (b) $285.00   (c) $278.58

(d) $257.25   (e) None of these

2—Ans: b

30. A coat sells for $252.00 after being discounted 20% from its regular price. Find the regular price.

(a) $378.00   (b) $272.00   (c) $315.00

(d) $302.40   (e) None of these

2—Ans: c

31. The total repair bill for an automobile is $285. This includes costs of parts of $220 and labor costs of $26 per hour. How many hours of labor were used?

(a) $2\frac{1}{2}$ hours   (b) $8\frac{1}{2}$ hours   (c) 11 hours

(d) 3 hours   (e) None of these

2—Ans: a

32. The total repair bill for an automobile is $300. This includes costs of parts of $225 and labor costs of $30 per hour. How many hours of labor were used?

(a) 10 hours   (b) 2.5 hours   (c) 7.5 hours

(d) 3 hours   (e) None of these

2—Ans: b

33. Test whether or not $x = -\frac{2}{3}$ is a solution of $\frac{5}{2}x - \frac{5}{3} = 0$.

   1—Ans: It is *not* a solution.

34. Test whether or not $x = -\frac{2}{3}$ is a solution of $\frac{5}{2}x + \frac{5}{3} = 0$.

   1—Ans: It *is* a solution.

35. Find the solution of the linear equation $2 - 6x = 12 - 6x$ if there is one. If not, so state.

   1—Ans: There is no solution.

36 Find the solution of the linear equation $-6x + 2 = -6x + 12$ if there is one. If not, so state.

   1—Ans: There is no solution.

37. For what value of A does the equation $A(3 - x) = 4x + 1$ have *no solution*?

   2—Ans: $A = -4$

38. For what value of A does the equation $A(4 - x) = 2x + 3$ have *no solution*?

   2—Ans: $A = -2$

39. Solve the linear equation $14x = 0$.

   1—Ans: 0

40. Solve the linear equation $13x = 0$.

   1—Ans: 0

41. Solve the linear equation $11x = 18$.

   1—Ans: $\frac{18}{11}$

42. Solve the linear equation $7x = 16$.

   1—Form: 3C—Ans: $\frac{16}{7}$

43. Solve the equation $7x - 4 = 2x + 11$.

   1—Ans: $x = 3$

44. Solve the equation $9x - 20 = 6 - 4x$.

   1—Ans: $x = 2$

45. Solve the linear equation $3 - 8 + 4x = 5 + 9 - 6x$.

   1—Ans: $x = \frac{19}{10}$

46. Solve the linear equation $3 - 8 - 4x = 5 + 9 - 6x$.

    1—Ans: $x = \frac{19}{2}$

47. Solve the linear equation $3 - 8 + 4x = 5 + 9 + 6x$.

    1—Ans: $x = -\frac{19}{2}$

48. Solve the linear equation $3 - 4x + 8 = 5 + 9 - 6x$.

    1—Ans: $x = \frac{3}{2}$

49. Solve: $-\frac{3}{4}x = 12$.

    1—Ans: -16

50. Solve: $-\frac{4}{3}x = 12$.

    1—Ans: -9

51. Solve: $x = 3(x - 4)$.

    2—Ans: 6

52. Solve: $x = 4(x - 3)$.

    2—Ans: 4

53. Explain why the equation $2x + 1 = 2(x + 1)$ has no solution.

    1—Ans: $2x + 1 \neq 2x + 2$ for any value of x.

54. Explain why the equation $3x - 1 = 3(x - 1)$ has no solution.

    1—Form: 3C—Ans: $3x - 1 \neq 3x - 3$ for any value of x.

55. Find three consecutive integers whose sum is -24.

    2—Ans: $-9, -8, -7$

56. Find three consecutive integers whose sum is -21.

    2—Ans: $-8, -7, -6$

57. Find three consecutive odd integers whose sum is 93.

    2—Ans: $29, 31, 33$

58. Find three consecutive odd integers whose sum is 105.

    2—Ans: $33, 35, 37$

59. Find three consecutive even integers whose sum is 84.

    2—Ans: 26, 28, 30

60. Find three consecutive integers whose sum is 78.

    2—Ans: 24, 26, 28

61. Find three consecutive integers whose sum is 174.

    1—Ans: 57, 58, 59

62. Find three consecutive integers whose sum is 234.

    1—Ans: 77, 78, 79

63. An engineer's consulting fee totaled $600. This included $40 for supplies and $80 for each hour of consulting. Write an equation and solve for the number of hours of consulting.

    2—Form: 3C—Ans: $80n + 40 = 600$; $n = 7$ where n represents the number of hours

64. An engineer's consulting fee totaled $680. This included $50 for supplies and $70 for each hour of consulting. Write an equation and solve for the number of hours of consulting.

    2—Ans: $70n + 50 = 680$; $n = 9$ where n represents the number of hours

65. The purchase price of a big screen television, including finance charges, is $2641. A down payment of $400 is required, and the remainder is to be paid in 18 equal monthly payments. Write an equation and solve for the amount of the monthly payment.

    2—Ans: $18x + 400 = 2641$; $x = 124.50$ where x is the amount of the monthly payment

66. The purchase price of a big screen television, including finance charges, is $2705. A down payment of $500 is required, and the remainder is to be paid in 18 equal monthly payments. Write an equation and solve for the amount of the monthly payment.

    2—Ans: $18x + 500 = 2705$; $x = 122.50$ where x is the amount of the monthly payment

67. The length of a rectangular area is 10 feet more than twice the width of the rectangle. The length is 116 feet. Find the width.

    2—Ans: Width = 53 feet

68. The length of a rectangular area is 12 feet more than three times the width of the rectangle. The length is 156 feet. Find the width.

    2—Ans: Width = 48 feet

69. The length of a rectangle is 10 inches greater than the width and the perimeter is 120 inches. Write an equation and solve for the width of the rectangle.

   2—Ans: $2w + 2(w + 10) = 120$; $w = 25$ where w represents the width

70. The length of a rectangle is 10 inches greater than the width and the perimeter is 160 inches. Write an equation and solve for the width of the rectangle.

   2—Ans: $2w + 2(w + 10) = 160$; $w = 35$ where w represents the width

71. The total deductions from your salary amount to 34%. You take home $1623.60. What is your salary?

   1—Ans: $2460

72. The total deductions from your salary amount to 34%. You take home $2059.20. What is your salary?

   1—Ans: $3120

Section 3.2   Equations That Reduce to Linear Form

1. Solve $2 - (x - 1) = 1$.

   (a) 1   **(b)** -1 **(c)** 0   **(d)** 4   **(e)** None of these

   1—Ans: e, $x = 2$ is correct

2. Solve $1 - 3(x - 2) = 4$.

   (a) -3 **(b)** -1 **(c)** 3   **(d)** 1   **(e)** None of these

   1—Ans: d

3. Solve $-2(y + 5) + y = 2$.

   (a) 8   **(b)** -8 **(c)** -12 **(d)** 12   **(e)** None of these

   2—Form: 3A—Ans: c

4. Solve $-4(y + 3) + 3y = 4$.

   (a) -1 **(b)** -8 **(c)** -16 **(d)** 8   **(e)** None of these

   2—Ans: c

5. Solve $2(3 + x) = 3(x - 4)$.

   (a) 18   **(b)** -18 **(c)** 5   **(d)** -5 **(e)** None of these

   2—Ans: a

6. Solve $3(x + 1) = 2(9 - x)$.

   (a) -3 **(b)** 3 **(c)** $\frac{4}{17}$ **(d)** $\frac{17}{4}$ **(e)** None of these

   2—Ans: b

7. Solve $2(x - 3) + 4 = 5 - (x + 1)$.

   (a) 2 **(b)** -1 **(c)** -2 **(d)** 1 **(e)** None of these

   1—Ans: a

8. Solve $2(x + 2) = -(x + 5)$.

   (a) 3 **(b)** 0 **(c)** -1 **(d)** -3 **(e)** None of these

   1—Ans: d

9. Solve $2(x - 5) - 2 = 2(2 - x)$.

   (a) 2 **(b)** 4 **(c)** -1 **(d)** 0 **(e)** None of these

   1—Ans: b

10. Solve $8 - (12 - x) = 1 - 3(x + 3)$.

   (a) -4 **(b)** 1 **(c)** -1 **(d)** 0 **(e)** None of these

   1—Ans: c

11. Solve $[5(x + 2) - 2(2x + 1)] = 5$.

   (a) -3 **(b)** 0 **(c)** -1 **(d)** 3 **(e)** None of these

   1—Ans: a

12. Solve $[9 + 6(x + 3)] = (2x - 1)$.

   (a) -1 **(b)** -7 **(c)** -5 **(d)** -3 **(e)** None of these

   1—Ans: b

13. Solve $2x - 3[x - (4 - 2x)] = 3 - 5x$.

   (a) $\frac{2}{9}$ **(b)** $-\frac{9}{2}$ **(c)** $-\frac{2}{9}$ **(d)** $\frac{9}{2}$ **(e)** None of these

   2—Ans: d

14. Solve $2 - 3[7 - 2(4 - x)] = 2x - 1$.

   (a) $-\frac{3}{4}$ **(b)** $\frac{4}{3}$ **(c)** $\frac{3}{4}$ **(d)** $-\frac{4}{3}$ **(e)** None of these

   2—Ans: c

15. Solve $3x - [x - 2(3 - 2x)] = -5$.

   (a) $\frac{2}{11}$ **(b)** $\frac{11}{2}$ **(c)** $-\frac{2}{11}$ **(d)** $-\frac{11}{2}$ **(e)** None of these

   2—Ans: b

16. Solve $3x - [2(3 - 2x) - x] = 4$.

    (a) $\frac{5}{4}$ **(b)** $-\frac{4}{5}$ **(c)** $-\frac{5}{4}$ **(d)** $\frac{4}{5}$ **(e)** None of these

    2—Ans: a

17. Solve $\frac{1}{4} - \frac{1}{8}x = -\frac{1}{2}$.

    (a) $\frac{8}{3}$ **(b)** -6 **(c)** 6 **(d)** -2 **(e)** None of these

    2—Ans: c

18. Solve $\frac{1}{4} - \frac{1}{2}x = \frac{1}{8}$.

    (a) $-\frac{1}{2}$ **(b)** $-\frac{1}{4}$ **(c)** -1 **(d)** $\frac{1}{4}$ **(e)** None of these

    2—Form: 3B—Ans: d

19. Solve $\frac{x}{5} - \frac{1}{4} = \frac{x}{3}$.

    (a) $-\frac{15}{2}$ **(b)** $-\frac{15}{8}$ **(c)** $-\frac{1}{2}$ **(d)** $\frac{15}{2}$ **(e)** None of these

    1—Ans: b

20. Solve $\frac{x}{5} - \frac{3}{10} = \frac{x}{4}$.

    (a) -6 **(b)** $-\frac{1}{6}$ **(c)** 6 **(d)** $\frac{1}{6}$ **(e)** None of these

    1—Ans: a

21. Solve $\frac{x}{3} + \frac{x - 2}{4} = -\frac{1}{6}$.

    (a) $-\frac{4}{7}$ **(b)** $\frac{4}{7}$ **(c)** $\frac{7}{4}$ **(d)** 0 **(e)** None of these

    2—Ans: b

22. Solve $\frac{x}{3} - \frac{2 - x}{4} = \frac{1}{6}$.

    (a) $\frac{8}{7}$ **(b)** 8 **(c)** $-\frac{4}{7}$ **(d)** $-\frac{8}{7}$ **(e)** None of these

    2—Ans: a

23. Solve $\dfrac{x + 5}{2} = \dfrac{3}{2} - x$.

(a) $-\dfrac{2}{3}$ (b) -1 (c) $\dfrac{2}{3}$ (d) $-\dfrac{7}{4}$ (e) None of these

2—Ans: a

24. Solve $\dfrac{x + 7}{3} = \dfrac{4}{3} - x$.

(a) $-\dfrac{3}{4}$ (b) $-\dfrac{3}{2}$ (c) $\dfrac{3}{4}$ (d) $-\dfrac{17}{6}$ (e) None of these

2—Ans: a

25. Solve $\dfrac{3 - x}{4} = \dfrac{x + 7}{5}$.

(a) $\dfrac{8}{9}$ (b) $\dfrac{13}{9}$ (c) 13 (d) $-\dfrac{13}{9}$ (e) None of these

1—Ans: d

26. Solve $\dfrac{x - 3}{4} = \dfrac{7 + x}{5}$.

(a) 43 (b) 13 (c) $\dfrac{43}{9}$ (d) $\dfrac{13}{9}$ (e) None of these

1—Ans: a

27. Solve $\dfrac{y - 2}{3} - y = \dfrac{2y + 1}{3}$.

(a) $-\dfrac{3}{2}$ (b) $-\dfrac{4}{3}$ (c) $-\dfrac{3}{4}$ (d) $-\dfrac{2}{3}$ (e) None of these

2—Form: 3A—Ans: c

28. Solve $\dfrac{y + 2}{3} - y = \dfrac{3y + 1}{3}$.

(a) $\dfrac{1}{5}$ (b) $-\dfrac{1}{5}$ (c) $\dfrac{1}{3}$ (d) 3 (e) None of these

2—Form: 3B—Ans: a

29. Use cross-multiplication to solve $\dfrac{5 - 2x}{4} = \dfrac{2x + 1}{3}$.

(a) $\dfrac{5}{7}$ (b) $\dfrac{14}{11}$ (c) $\dfrac{11}{14}$ (d) $\dfrac{7}{5}$ (e) None of these

2—Form: 3A—Ans: c

30. Use cross-multiplication to solve $\dfrac{3 + 2x}{3} = \dfrac{2x - 5}{4}$.

(a) $-\dfrac{2}{27}$ (b) $\dfrac{17}{4}$ (c) $\dfrac{4}{17}$ (d) $-\dfrac{27}{2}$ (e) None of these

2—Form: 3B—Ans: d

31. Solve $2(x - 3) - 1 = 1$.

1—Ans: 4

32. Solve $3 - (2 - 4x) = -3$.

1—Ans: -1

33. Solve $5(x - 4) = -5$.

2—Ans: 3

34. Solve $3(x - 4) = -6$.

2—Ans: 2

35. Solve $2(2 - x) = 3(x + 8)$.

1—Ans: -4

36. Solve $3(x + 3) = 2 - (1 - 2x)$.

1—Ans: -8

37. Solve $5(3x - 2) - (12x - 10) = 2(x + 2)$.

2—Ans: 4

38. Solve $3(5 - x) + 5(2x - 3) = 3(2x - 1)$.

2—Form: 3C—Ans: -3

39. Solve $2[3(4 - 3x) - 2x] - 4x = -(x + 1)$.

2—Ans: 1

40. Solve $3[2(4 + 3x) - 3x] - 5x = -(x + 1)$.

2—Ans: -5

41. Solve $[2(x - 3) - 3(1 - 2x)] = -25$.

1—Ans: -2

42. Solve $[3(1 - 2x) - 4(3 - x)] = 7$.

1—Ans: -8

43. Solve $3x + [2(1 - 2x) + 5] = 5 - 7x$.

2—Ans: $-\frac{1}{3}$

44. Solve $3x - [2(1 - 2x) - 5] = 5 - 7x$.

2—Ans: $\frac{1}{7}$

45. Solve $\frac{1}{3}x + \frac{1}{4} = \frac{1}{2}x$.

2—Ans: $\frac{3}{2}$

46. Solve $\frac{1}{3}x + \frac{3}{4} = \frac{2}{3}x$.

1—Ans: $\frac{9}{4}$

47. Solve $\frac{x}{5} - \frac{x}{6} = \frac{1}{8}$.

1—Ans: $\frac{15}{4}$

48. Solve $\frac{x}{4} - \frac{x}{5} = \frac{1}{6}$.

2—Ans: $\frac{10}{3}$

49. Solve $\frac{x}{3} - \frac{(x - 2)}{4} = \frac{1}{5}$.

2—Ans: $-\frac{18}{5}$

50. Solve $\frac{x}{3} + \frac{(x - 2)}{4} = \frac{1}{5}$.

2—Ans: $\frac{6}{5}$

51. Solve $\frac{x}{3} - \frac{(x - 2)}{4} = -\frac{1}{5}$.

2—Ans: $-\frac{42}{5}$

52. Solve $\dfrac{x}{3} + \dfrac{(x-2)}{4} = -\dfrac{1}{5}$.

    2—Ans: $\dfrac{18}{35}$

53. Solve $\dfrac{x-3}{6} + \dfrac{3x+2}{4} = \dfrac{33}{12}$.

    2—Ans: 3

54. Solve $\dfrac{x-3}{4} + \dfrac{5x+1}{6} = \dfrac{19}{12}$.

    2—Form: 3C—Ans: 2

55. Solve $\dfrac{2x-3}{5} = \dfrac{x+3}{4}$.

    2—Ans: 9

56. Solve $\dfrac{2x+3}{5} = \dfrac{3-x}{4}$.

    2—Ans: $\dfrac{3}{13}$

57. Solve $1.4x - 0.6(8 - x) = 35(0.24)$.

    2—Ans: 6.6

58. Solve $1.2x - 0.8(7 - x) = 30(0.24)$.

    2—Ans: 6.4

59. Solve $1.7x - 8.2 = 2.5x + 3.8$.

    2—Ans: -15

60. Solve $12.7x + 15.0 = 6.4x + 2.4$.

    2—Ans: -2

61. Use cross-multiplication to solve $\dfrac{x-3}{4} = \dfrac{x}{8}$.

    2—Ans: 6

62. Use cross-multiplication to solve $\dfrac{x-4}{3} = \dfrac{x}{6}$.

    2—Ans: 8

63. Two people can complete 75% of a task in t hours and t must satisfy the equation
$\dfrac{t}{8} + \dfrac{t}{12} = 0.75$. Solve for t.

   1—Ans: 3.6 hours

64. Two people can complete 75% of a task in t hours and t must satisfy the equation
$\dfrac{t}{6} + \dfrac{t}{9} = 0.75$. Solve for t.

   1—Ans: 2.7 hours

65. Two people can complete 90% of a task in t hours and t must satisfy the equation
$\dfrac{t}{9} + \dfrac{t}{18} = 0.90$. Solve for t.

   1—Ans: 5.4 hours

66. Two people can complete 80% of a task in t hours and t must satisfy the equation
$\dfrac{t}{15} + \dfrac{t}{5} = 0.80$. Solve for t.

   1—Ans: 3 hours

67. Two people can complete 70% of a task in t hours where t must satisfy the
equation $\dfrac{t}{10} + \dfrac{t}{5} = 0.70$. Solve for t.

   2—Ans: $\dfrac{7}{3}$ hours

68. Two people can complete 60% of a task in t hours where t must satisfy the
equation $\dfrac{t}{12} + \dfrac{t}{6} = 0.60$. Solve for t.

   2—Ans: $\dfrac{12}{5}$ hours

69. If a number is decreased by 10, and the result is divided by 2, the answer is 15.
Find the number.

   2—Form: 3C—Ans: 40

70. If a number is increased by 10, and the result is divided by 2, the answer is 15.
Find the number.

   2—Ans: 20

Section 3.3   Problem Solving with Percents

1. Convert 1.415 to percent form.

(a) 141.5%   (b) 14.15%   (c) 1415%   (d) 0.01415%   (e) None of these

1—Ans: a

2. Convert .0745 to percent form.

(a) 0.00745%   (b) 74.5%   (c) 745%   (d) 7.45%   (e) None of these

1—Ans: d

3. Convert 27.5% to decimal form.

(a) 2.75   (b) 0.0275   (c) 2,750   (d) 0.275   (e) None of these

1—Ans: d

4. Convert 138% to decimal form.

(a) 13,800   (b) 13.8   (c) 1.38   (d) 0.138   (e) None of these

1—Ans: c

5. Change 24% to a fraction in simplest form.

(a) $\frac{12}{5}$ (b) $\frac{24}{1}$ (c) $\frac{240}{1}$ (d) $\frac{6}{25}$ (e) None of these

2—Form: 3A—Ans: d

6. Change 32% to a fraction in simplest form.

(a) $\frac{8}{25}$ (b) $\frac{32}{1}$ (c) $\frac{320}{1}$ (d) $\frac{16}{5}$ (e) None of these

2—Form: 3B—Ans: a

7. Change the decimal 0.086 to a percent.

(a) 8.6%   (b) 0.86%   (c) 86%   (d) 0.086%   (e) None of these

1—Form: 3A—Ans: a

8. Change the decimal 0.074 to a percent.

(a) 74%   (b) 0.74%   (c) 7.4%   (d) 0.074%   (e) None of these

1—Ans: c

9. Change the fraction $\frac{5}{4}$ to a percent.

(a) 1.25%   (b) 12.5%   (c) 125%   (d) 0.125%   (e) None of these

1—Ans: c

10. Change the fraction $\frac{6}{5}$ to a percent.

   (a) 1.20%   **(b)** 12.0%   **(c)** 0.120%   **(d)** 120%   **(e)** None of these

   1—Form: 3B—Ans: d

11. What is 40% of 70?

   (a) 0.571   **(b)** 28   **(c)** 57.1%   **(d)** 0.28   **(e)** None of these

   1—Ans: b

12. What is 20% of 85?

   (a) 17   **(b)** 0.235   **(c)** 0.17%   **(d)** 23.5%   **(e)** None of these

   1—Ans: a

13. 17 is what percent of 136?

   (a) 0.125   **(b)** 8   **(c)** 800   **(d)** 12.5   **(e)** None of these

   1—Ans: d

14. 23 is what percent of 460?

   (a) 5   **(b)** 20   **(c)** 0.05   **(d)** 200   **(e)** None of these

   1—Ans: a

15. 181 is what percent of 905?

   (a) 0.20   **(b)** 20   **(c)** 5   **(d)** 500   **(e)** None of these

   1—Ans: b

16. 28 is what percent of 175?

   (a) 0.16   **(b)** 625   **(c)** 16   **(d)** 6.25   **(e)** None of these

   1—Ans: c

17. 6370 is 18.2% of what number?

   (a) 35,000   **(b)** 1159. 34   **(c)** 115,935   **(d)** 350   **(e)** None of these

   1—Form: 3A—Ans: a

18. 6764 is 17.8% of what number?

   (a) 380   **(b)** 1203. 99   **(c)** 120,399   **(d)** 38,000   **(e)** None of these

   1—Form: 3B—Ans: d

19. In your Philosophy course you made 445 points but missed a B (80%) by 3 points. How many points were possible?

(a) 560   (b) 448   (c) 553   (d) 557   (e) None of these

2—Ans: a

20. In your History course you made 410 points which was five points more than needed for and A (90%). How many points were possible?

(a) 365   (b) 460   (c) 500   (d) 450   (e) None of these

2—Ans: d

21. The revenue generating capacity of a football stadium was increased from $68,200 to $75,800. What was the percent increase?

(a) 11.1%   (b) 10.0%   (c) 7600   (d) 90.0%   (e) None of these

1—Ans: a

22. The revenue generating capacity of a football stadium was increased from $68,200 to $75,800. The old capacity was what percent of the new capacity?

(a) 11.1%   (b) 10.0%   (c) 7600   (d) 90.0%   (e) None of these

1—Ans: d

23. Two years ago your rent was $100 per week. In each year since, it was raised by 10%. What is your weekly rent now?

(a) $121   (b) $120   (c) $125   (d) $123   (e) None of these

2—Ans: a

24. Two years ago your annual rent was $3600. In each year since, it was raised by 10%. What is your annual rent now?

(a) $4320   (b) $4500   (c) $4444   (d) $4356   (e) None of these

2—Ans: d

25. Convert $\frac{5}{8}$ to percent form.

1—Ans: 62.5%

26. Convert $\frac{19}{40}$ to percent form.

1—Ans: 47.5%

27. Change 62.5% to a fraction in simplest form.

1—Ans: $\frac{5}{8}$

28. Change 12% to a fraction in simplest form.

1—Ans: $\frac{3}{25}$

29. Change 7.5% to a fraction in simplest form.

    1—Ans: $\frac{3}{40}$

30. Change 15% to a fraction in simplest form.

    1—Ans: $\frac{3}{20}$

31. Change $1\frac{1}{2}$% to a decimal.

    1—Ans: 0.015

32. Change $2\frac{1}{2}$% to a decimal.

    1—Ans: 0.025

33. 72 is 18% of what number?

    2—Ans: 400

34. 33 is 11% of what number?

    2—Ans: 300

35. Find 25.4% of $484.50 to the nearest cent.

    1—Ans: $123.06

36. Find 21.3% of $389.75 to the nearest cent.

    1—Ans: $83.02

37. What is 150% of 70?

    1—Ans: 105

38. What is 150% of 80?

    1—Ans: 120

39. Forty-five is what percent of 125?

    1—Ans: 36%

40. Forty-eight is what percent of 160?

    1—Ans: 30%

41. What is $\frac{1}{2}$% of 70?

    1—Ans: 0.35

42. What is $\frac{1}{2}$% of 50?

   1—Ans: 0.25

43. Twenty-two is 20% of what number?

   1—Form: 3C—Ans: 110

44. Twenty-four is 20% of what number?

   1—Ans: 120

45. Two hundred twenty-five is what percent of 180?

   1—Ans: 125%

46. Two hundred forty is what percent of 200?

   1—Form: C—Ans: 120%

47. In your Accounting course, 600 points were possible. You missed an A (90%) by 3 points. Find your point total.

   1—Ans: 537

48. In your Chemistry course, 480 points were possible. You missed an A (90%) by 2 points. Find your point total.

   1—Ans: 430

49. To earn a grade of B-, you must answer 72 questions correctly on an exam of 90 questions. To earn a B-, what percent must you answer correctly?

   1—Ans: 80%

50. To earn a grade of A-, you must answer 81 questions correctly on an exam of 90 questions. To earn an A-, what percent must you answer correctly?

   1—Ans: 90%

51. A hockey arena increased its seating capacity of 18,500 by 8 percent. How many seats were added to the arena?

   1—Ans: 1480

52. A hockey arena increased its seating capacity of 17,800 by 7 percent. How many seats were added to the arena?

   1—Ans: 1246

53. The capacity of a stadium which seated 10,200 is increased by 12%. Find the new capacity.

   1—Ans: 11,424

54. The capacity of a stadium which seated 10,200 is increased to 12,100. Find the percent increase.

   1—Ans: 18.6%

55. The capacity of a stadium which seated 10,200 is increased to 12,100. What percent of the new capacity is the old capacity?

   1—Ans: 84.3%

56. The capacity of a stadium which seated 10,200 is increased 14%. Find the new capacity.

   1—Ans: 11,628

57. Your rent is currently $460 per month, which is a 15% increase since you moved in. What was your original rent?

   1—Ans: $400

58. Your rent is currently $392 per month, which is a 12% increase since you moved in. What was your original rent?

   1—Ans: $350

59. Last year's snowfall was 22% higher than this year's total of 74.2 inches. Find last year's total snowfall.

   1—Ans: 90.5 inches

60. This year's snowfall was 18% lower than last year's total of 90.5 inches. What was this year's total snowfall?

   1—Ans: 74.2 inches

61. A labor contract increased all employees' hourly wage by $5\frac{1}{2}$%. Find the amount of the raise for an employee whose wage is $12.00 per hour.

   1—Ans: $0.66

62. A labor contract increased all employees' hourly wage by $5\frac{1}{2}$%. Find the amount of the raise for an employee whose wage is $14.00 per hour.

   1—Ans: $0.77

63. A discount store sold 450 gallons of paint one week. The next week the store sold 135 fewer gallons. Find the percent decrease.

   1—Ans: 30%

64. A discount store sold 480 gallons of paint one week. The next week the store sold 168 fewer gallons. Find the percent decrease.

1—Ans: 35%

65. Approximately 21% of air is oxygen. Find the approximate number of liters of oxygen in a room containing 16,200 liters of air.

1—Ans: 3402 liters

66. Approximately 21% of air is oxygen. Find the approximate number of liters of oxygen in a room containing 18,200 liters of air.

1—Form: 3C—Ans: 3822 liters

67. The female enrollment at a small college is 780. This represents 52% of the total student enrollment. Find the total student enrollment.

1—Ans: 1500

68. The male enrollment at a small college is 864. This represents 54% of the total student enrollment. Find the total student enrollment.

1—Ans: 1600

Section 3.4   Ratios and Proportions

1. The ratio of 5 to 8 is given by:

  (a) $\frac{13}{8}$ **(b)** $\frac{5}{8}$ **(c)** $\frac{5}{3}$ **(d)** $\frac{8}{5}$ **(e)** None of these

  1—Ans: b

2. The ratio of 8 to 5 is given by:

  (a) $\frac{13}{8}$ **(b)** $\frac{5}{8}$ **(c)** $\frac{5}{3}$ **(d)** $\frac{8}{5}$ **(e)** None of these

  1—Ans: d

3. Find the ratio of $4\frac{1}{2}$ to $3\frac{1}{4}$.

  (a) $\frac{18}{13}$ **(b)** $\frac{36}{26}$ **(c)** $\frac{26}{36}$ **(d)** $\frac{13}{18}$ **(e)** None of these

  1—Form: 3A—Ans: a

4. Find the ratio of $4\frac{1}{4}$ to $3\frac{1}{2}$.

  (a) $\frac{34}{28}$ **(b)** $\frac{14}{17}$ **(c)** $\frac{17}{14}$ **(d)** $\frac{28}{34}$ **(e)** None of these

  1—Ans: c

5. The ratio of 3 gallons to 6 quarts is:

  (a) $\frac{3}{6}$ **(b)** $\frac{2}{1}$ **(c)** $\frac{9}{6}$ **(d)** $\frac{1}{2}$ **(e)** None of these

  1—Ans: b

6. The ratio of $7\frac{1}{2}$ dollars to 75 cents is:

   (a) $\frac{1}{10}$ **(b)** $\frac{825}{75}$ **(c)** $\frac{10}{1}$ **(d)** $\frac{11}{1}$ **(e)** None of these

   1—Ans: c

7. Find a ratio to compare the relative sizes of 36 seconds to 4 minutes.

   (a) $\frac{9}{1}$ **(b)** $\frac{1}{9}$ **(c)** $\frac{3}{20}$ **(d)** $\frac{20}{3}$ **(e)** None of these

   1—Ans: c

8. Find a ratio to compare the relative sizes of 40 seconds to 5 minutes.

   (a) $\frac{8}{1}$ **(b)** $\frac{1}{8}$ **(c)** $\frac{15}{2}$ **(d)** $\frac{2}{15}$ **(e)** None of these

   1—Form: 3B—Ans: d

9. Find a ratio to compare the relative sizes of 3 kilometers to 200 meters.

   (a) $\frac{15}{1}$ **(b)** $\frac{1}{15}$ **(c)** $\frac{3}{200}$ **(d)** $\frac{200}{3}$ **(e)** None of these

   1—Ans: a

10. Find a ratio to compare the relative sizes of 4 kilometers to 250 meters.

   (a) $\frac{1}{16}$ **(b)** $\frac{16}{1}$ **(c)** $\frac{4}{250}$ **(d)** $\frac{250}{4}$ **(e)** None of these

   1—Ans: b

11. An 11 ounce jar of peanut butter costs $1.76. The *unit price* in dollars per ounce is:

   (a) 16   **(b)** 0.11   **(c)** 0.16   **(d)** 6.25   **(e)** None of these

   1—Ans: c

12. A 13 ounce can of coffee costs $2.99. The *unit price* in dollars per ounce is:

   (a) 0.23   **(b)** 4.35   **(c)** 3.68   **(d)** 23   **(e)** None of these

   1—Ans: a

13. A 12 ounce package of candy costs $3. Which of the following has a smaller unit price?

   (a) 10 ounces at $2.30   **(b)** 8 ounces at $2.06   **(c)** 5 ounces at $1.50

   (d) 6 ounces at $1.74   **(e)** None of these

   2—Ans: a

14. A 1 pound package of candy costs $3.20. Which of the following has a smaller unit price?

   (a) 12 ounces at $3.00   **(b)** 10 ounces at $2.30   **(c)** 8 ounces at $2.08

   (d) 6 ounces at $1.74   **(e)** None of these

   2—Ans: e

15. A 10 ounce package of candy costs $2.30. Which of the following has a smaller unit price?

    (a) 12 ounces at $3.00   **(b)** 1 pound at $3.20   **(c)** 8 ounces at $2.08

    (d) 6 ounces at $1.74   **(e)** None of these

    2—Ans: b

16. A 8 ounce box of candy costs $2.08. Which of the following has a smaller unit price?

    (a) 4 ounces at $1.40   **(b)** 5 ounces at $1.50   **(c)** 12 ounces at $3.00

    (d) 6 ounces at $1.74   **(e)** None of these

    2—Ans: c

17. Solve the proportion for x: $\dfrac{16}{9} = \dfrac{64}{x}$

    (a) $\dfrac{73}{16}$ **(b)** $\dfrac{1}{36}$ **(c)** 36   **(d)** $\dfrac{16}{73}$ **(e)** None of these

    2—Form: 3A—Ans: c

18. Solve the proportion for x: $\dfrac{4}{9} = \dfrac{x}{54}$

    (a) $\dfrac{58}{9}$ **(b)** $\dfrac{9}{58}$ **(c)** $\dfrac{1}{24}$ **(d)** 24   **(e)** None of these

    2—Form: 3B—Ans: d

19. Solve the proportion for x: $\dfrac{20}{x} = \dfrac{27}{12}$

    (a) $x = \dfrac{1}{45}$ **(b)** $x = \dfrac{9}{80}$ **(c)** $x = \dfrac{80}{9}$ **(d)** $x = 45$ **(e)** None of these

    1—Ans: c

20. Solve the proportion for x: $\dfrac{12}{x} = \dfrac{20}{27}$

    (a) $x = \dfrac{80}{9}$ **(b)** $x = \dfrac{81}{5}$ **(c)** $x = \dfrac{9}{80}$ **(d)** $x = \dfrac{5}{81}$ **(e)** None of these

    1—Ans: b

21. Solve the proportion for x: $\dfrac{x + 14}{x + 7} = -\dfrac{4}{3}$

    (a) -1 **(b)** -10 **(c)** -2 **(d)** 2   **(e)** None of these

    2—Form: 3A—Ans: b

22. Solve the proportion for x: $\dfrac{x + 14}{x - 2} = -\dfrac{3}{5}$

    (a) 3   **(b)** -3 **(c)** -2 **(d)** -8 **(e)** None of these

    2—Form: 3B—Ans: d

23. The ratio of a certain number to 9 is the same as the ratio of 7 to 3. The number is:

    (a) $\frac{27}{7}$ **(b)** 21   **(c)** $\frac{7}{21}$ **(d)** $\frac{3}{7}$ **(e)** None of these

    1—Ans: b

24. The ratio of a certain number to 9 is the same as the ratio of 3 to 7. The number is:

    (a) $\frac{7}{21}$ **(b)** $\frac{7}{3}$ **(c)** 21   **(d)** $\frac{27}{7}$ **(e)** None of these

    1—Ans: d

25. A car used 9.3 gallons of gasoline while traveling 255 miles. A trip of 1573 miles will use (to the nearest $\frac{1}{10}$ gallon):

    (a) 169.1 gallons   **(b)** 27.4 gallons   **(c)** 57.4 gallons

    (d) 6.2 gallons   **(e)** None of these

    1—Ans: c

26. A car used 12.4 gallons of gasoline while traveling 346 miles. A trip of 945 miles will use (to the nearest $\frac{1}{10}$ gallon):

    (a) 27.9 gallons   **(b)** 33.9 gallons   **(c)** 76.2 gallons

    (d) 2.7 gallons   **(e)** None of these

    1—Ans: b

27. If one can feed 307 birds for a month for $10.50, how many birds could one feed for a month for $45?

    (a) 72   **(b)** 1381   **(c)** 1316   **(d)** 3223   **(e)** None of these

    1—Ans: c

28. If one can feed 189 birds for a month for $9.20, how many birds could one feed for a month for $100?

    (a) 2054   **(b)** 205   **(c)** 18,900   **(d)** 21   **(e)** None of these

    1—Ans: a

29. Find the ratio of $4\frac{3}{4}$ to $3\frac{1}{6}$.

    1—Ans: $\frac{3}{2}$

30. Find the ratio of $4\frac{3}{5}$ to $11\frac{1}{2}$.

    1—Ans: $\frac{2}{5}$

31. Find the ratio of 45 to 18.

   1—Ans: $\frac{5}{2}$

32. Find the ratio of 35 to 21.

   1—Ans: $\frac{5}{3}$

33. Find the ratio of $10\frac{4}{7}$ weeks to 60 days.

   2—Ans: $\frac{37}{30}$

34. Find the ratio of $6\frac{3}{4}$ gallons to 17 quarts.

   2—Ans: $\frac{27}{17}$

35. Find the ratio of $5\frac{5}{8}$ gallons to 18 pints.

   2—Ans: $\frac{5}{2}$

36. Find the ratio of $4\frac{3}{8}$ pounds to 50 ounces.

   2—Ans: $\frac{7}{5}$

37. Find a ratio to compare the relative sizes of 10 inches to 3 feet.

   1—Ans: $\frac{5}{18}$

38. Find a ratio to compare the relative sizes of 14 inches to 2 feet.

   1—Ans: $\frac{7}{12}$

39. Find a ratio to compare the relative sizes of 50 grams to 2 kilograms.

   1—Ans: $\frac{1}{40}$

40. Find a ratio to compare the relative sizes of 60 grams to 3 kilograms.

   1—Form: 3C—Ans: $\frac{1}{50}$

41. Find the *unit price* (in dollars per ounce) for a 24-ounce jar of salsa that sells for $3.36.

   1—Ans: $0.14 per ounce

42. Find the unit price (in dollars per ounce) for a 28-ounce jar of spaghetti sauce that sells for $1.68.

   1—Ans: $0.06 per ounce

43. Find the unit price (in dollars per ounce) for a 15-ounce jar of peanut butter that sells for $2.70.

1—Ans: $0.18 per ounce

44. Find the unit price (in dollars per ounce) for a 13-ounce can of coffee that sells for $3.38.

1—Ans: $0.26 per ounce

45. Which has the smaller unit price: a 12-ounce box of cereal for $2.87 or a 10-ounce box of cereal for $2.51?

1—Ans: The larger box

46. Which has the smaller unit price: a 14-ounce box of cereal for $3.55 or a 10-ounce box of cereal for $2.51?

1—Ans: The smaller box, slightly

47. Which product has the lower unit price: a 12.3-ounce box of cereal that sells for $3.28 or a 13-ounce box of cereal that sells for $3.36? Explain.

1—Form: 3C—Ans:

The 13-ounce box of cereal has the lower unit price of $0.258 per ounce. The 12.3-ounce box has the higher unit price of $0.2\overline{6}$ per ounce.

48. Which product has the lower unit price: 16-ounce box of rigatoni that sells for $1.24 or a 24-ounce box of fettucini that sells for $1.89? Explain.

1—Ans:

The 16-ounce box of rigatoni has the lower unit price of $0.0775 per ounce. The 24-ounce box of fettucini has the higher unit price of 0.07875.

49. Identify the means of the proportion $\dfrac{x}{12} = \dfrac{3}{16}$.

1—Ans: 12 and 3

50. Identify the extremes of the proportion $\dfrac{x}{12} = \dfrac{3}{16}$.

1—Ans: x and 16

51. Can $\dfrac{5}{x} = \dfrac{7}{3}$ be obtained from $\dfrac{x}{3} = \dfrac{5}{7}$?

1—Ans: Yes, they are equivalent.

52. Can $\dfrac{5}{x} = \dfrac{7}{3}$ be obtained from $\dfrac{x}{5} = \dfrac{3}{7}$?

    1—Ans: Yes, they are equivalent.

53. Solve the proportion for x: $\dfrac{2}{x-1} = \dfrac{6}{2x+1}$

    2—Ans: 4

54. Solve the proportion for x: $\dfrac{9}{x+2} = \dfrac{3}{x-2}$

    2—Ans: 4

55. The ratio of a certain number to 18 is the same as the ratio of 2 to 15. Find the number.

    1—Ans: $\frac{12}{5}$

56. The ratio of a certain number to 25 is the same as the ratio of 3 to 35. Find the number.

    1—Ans: $\frac{15}{7}$

57. The ratio of a certain number to 30 is the same as the ratio of 7 to 24. Find the number.

    1—Ans: $\frac{35}{4}$

58. The ratio of a certain number to 24 is the same as the ratio of 7 to 30. Find the number.

    1—Ans: $\frac{28}{5}$

59. If $\frac{1}{2}$ inch represents 15 miles on a map, how many miles does $5\frac{1}{2}$ inches represent?

    2—Form: 3C—Ans: 165 miles

60. If $\frac{1}{2}$ inch represents 12 miles on a map, how many miles does $5\frac{1}{2}$ inches represent?

    2—Ans: 132 miles

61. If a car uses 5.9 gallons of gasoline while traveling 154 miles, how many gallons (to the nearest $\frac{1}{10}$ gallon) will be used during an 846 mile trip?

    1—Ans: 32.4 gallons

62. If a car uses 7.8 gallons of gasoline while traveling 209 miles, how many gallons (to the nearest $\frac{1}{10}$ gallon) will be used during a 758 mile trip?

    1—Ans: 28.3 gallons

63. You use 4 gallons of gasoline to travel 104 miles. Find the number of gallons you would need to travel 338 miles.

    2—Ans: 13 gallons

64. You use 4 gallons of gasoline to travel 112 miles. Find the number of gallons you would need to travel 392 miles.

    2—Ans: 14 gallons

65. 75 pounds of bird feed costs $19.50. How much will 352 pounds of bird feed cost?

    2—Ans: $91.52

66. 47 pounds of bird feed costs $12.85. How much will 650 pounds of bird feed cost?

    2—Ans: $177.71

67. 89 pounds of bird feed costs $21.00. How much will 1,305 pounds of bird feed cost?

    2—Ans: $307.92

68. 66 pounds of bird feed costs $15.45. How much will 975 pounds of bird feed cost?

    2—Ans: $228.24

69. The tax on a property valued at $92,000 is $1288. Find the tax on a property valued at $63,000.

    2—Ans: $882

70. The tax on a property valued at $84,000 is $1260. Find the tax on a property valued at $57,000.

    2—Ans: $855

71. The consumer price index was 113.6 in 1987 and 140.3 in 1992. You purchased a set of coins in 1987 for $240. What was the expected replacement value in 1992?

    2—Ans: about $296

72. The consumer price index was 113.6 in 1987 and 140.3 in 1992. You purchased a set of coins in 1987 for $280. What was the expected replacement value in 1992?

    2—Ans: about $346

Section 3.5   Geometric and Scientific Applications

1. Which of the following is *not* a properly derived variation of the formula for the area of a triangle, $A = \frac{1}{2}bh$?

   (a) $h = \dfrac{2A}{b}$ **(b)** $b = \dfrac{2A}{h}$ **(c)** $2Ab = h$ **(d)** $2 = \dfrac{bh}{A}$ **(e)** None of these

   1—Ans: c

2. Which of the following is *not* a properly derived variation of the formula for the volume of a rectangular solid, $V = lwh$?

   (a) $l = \dfrac{V}{wh}$ **(b)** $w = \dfrac{V}{lh}$ **(c)** $h = \dfrac{V}{wl}$ **(d)** $\dfrac{V}{l + w} = h$.   **(e)** None of these

   1—Ans: d

3. If a principal of P dollars is invested in an account paying an annual interest rate of r (in decimal form) for t years, then the interest in dollars is given by $I = Prt$. Which of the following is *not* a properly derived variation of this formula?

   (a) $P = \dfrac{I}{rt}$ **(b)** $I - rt = P$ **(c)** $\dfrac{I}{Pr} = t$ **(d)** $r = \dfrac{I}{Pt}$ **(e)** None of these

   1—Ans: b

4. If a principal of P dollars is invested in an account paying an annual interest rate of r (in decimal form) for t years, then the interest in dollars is given by $I = Prt$. Which of the following is *not* a properly derived variation of this formula?

   (a) $r = I - Pt$ **(b)** $P = \dfrac{I}{rt}$ **(c)** $t = \dfrac{I}{Pr}$ **(d)** $r = \dfrac{I}{Pt}$ **(e)** None of these

   1—Ans: a

5. The area of a triangle is 30 square inches. If the base is 1 foot, find the height (in inches).

   (a) 5 feet   **(b)** 60 inches   **(c)** $\frac{15}{6}$ inches   **(d)** 5 inches   **(e)** None of these

   1—Form: 3A—Ans: d

6. The area of a triangle is 42 square inches. If the base is 1 foot, find the height (in inches).

   (a) 7 inches   **(b)** $\frac{7}{2}$ inches   **(c)** 84 inches   **(d)** 7 feet   **(e)** None of these

   1—Ans: a

7. The radius of an orange is 1.5 inches. Find the volume, in cubic inches. (to two decimal places)

   (a) 42.39   **(b)** 14.14   **(c)** 4.5   **(d)** 9.42   **(e)** None of these

   1—Ans: b

8. The radius of an orange is 1.6 inches. Find the volume, in cubic inches. (to two decimal places)

    (a) 51.47   **(b)** 5.46   **(c)** 17.16   **(d)** 10.72   **(e)** None of these

    1—Ans: c

9. The formula for the area of a rectangle is $A = lw$. A rectangular plot has an area of 20,000 square feet. The plot is 50 feet wide. How long is it?

    (a) 40 feet   **(b)** 400 feet   **(c)** 50 feet   **(d)** 200 feet   **(e)** None of these

    1—Ans: b

10. The formula for the area of a rectangle is $A = lw$. A rectangular plot has an area of 20,000 square feet. The plot is 400 feet long. How wide is it?

    (a) 40 feet   **(b)** 400 feet   **(c)** 50 feet   **(d)** 200 feet   **(e)** None of these

    1—Ans: c

11. The formula for the area of a rectangle is $A = lw$. A rectangular plot has a length of 400 feet and a width of 50 feet. What is its area?

    (a) 20,000 square feet   **(b)** 900 square feet   **(c)** 10,000 square feet

    (d) 80,000 square feet   **(e)** None of these

    1—Ans: a

12. The formula for the area of a rectangle is $A = lw$. A rectangular plot has an area of 15,000 square feet. The plot is 300 feet long. How wide is it?

    (a) 100 feet   **(b)** 500 feet   **(c)** 30 feet   **(d)** 50 feet   **(e)** None of these

    1—Ans: d

13. The formula for the area of a rectangle is $A = lw$. If the area is 255 square inches and the width is 15 inches, find the length.

    (a) 112.5 inches   **(b)** 3825 inches   **(c)** 25 inches   **(d)** 17 inches   **(e)** None of these

    1—Ans: d

14. The formula for the area of a rectangle is $A = lw$. If the length is 81 inches and the width is 27 inches, what is the area?

    (a) 3 inches   **(b)** 2187 square inches   **(c)** 243 square inches

    (d) 9 inches   **(e)** None of these

    1—Ans: b

15. The volume of a box is given by $V = lwh$. One foot is equal to 12 inches. Use these facts to find the volume of a box in cubic inches if $l = 3.5$ feet, $w = 1.75$ feet, $h = 13$ inches.

  (a) 79,625   **(b)** 11,466   **(c)** 137,592   **(d)** 955.5   **(e)** None of these

  1—Ans: b

16. The volume of a box is given by $V = lwh$. One foot is equal to 12 inches. Use these facts to find the volume of a box in cubic inches if $l = 4.25$ feet, $w = 2.50$ feet, $h = 15$ inches.

  (a) 22,950   **(b)** 159,375   **(c)** 275,400   **(d)** 1912.5   **(e)** None of these

  1—Ans: a

17. The volume of a box is given by $V = lwh$. One foot is equal to 12 inches. Use these facts to find the volume of a box in cubic inches if $l = 3.75$ feet, $w = 2.25$ feet, $h = 19$ inches.

  (a) 1923.75   **(b)** 160.3125   **(c)** 23,085   **(d)** 277,020   **(e)** None of these

  1—Ans: c

18. The volume of a box is given by $V = lwh$. One foot is equal to 12 inches. Use these facts to find the volume of a box in cubic inches if $l = 4.50$ feet, $w = 1.25$ feet, $h = 11$ inches.

  (a) 61.875   **(b)** 742.5   **(c)** 106,920   **(d)** 8910   **(e)** None of these

  1—Ans: d

19. If a principal of P dollars is invested in an account paying an annual interest rate of r (in decimal form) for t years, then the interest in dollars is given by $I = Prt$. What interest is earned when $2000 is invested for six months at an annual rate of $7\frac{1}{2}\%$?

  (a) $150   **(b)** $75   **(c)** $2075   **(d)** $2150   **(e)** None of these

  1—Ans: b

20. If a principal of P dollars is invested in an account paying an annual interest rate of r (in decimal form) for t years, then the interest in dollars is given by $I = Prt$. What interest is earned when $2000 is invested for six months at an annual rate of 6%?

  (a) $60   **(b)** $2060   **(c)** $120   **(d)** $2120   **(e)** None of these

  1—Ans: a

21. If a principal of P dollars is invested in an account paying an annual interest rate of r (in decimal form) for t years, then the interest in dollars is given by $I = Prt$. What interest is earned when $2000 is invested for eight months at an annual rate of $7\frac{1}{2}\%$?

  (a) $2100   **(b)** $225   **(c)** $2225   **(d)** $100   **(e)** None of these

  1—Ans: d

22. If a principal of P dollars is invested in an account paying an annual interest rate of r (in decimal form) for t years, then the interest in dollars is given by $I = Prt$. What interest is earned when $2000 is invested for nine months at an annual rate of 6%?

(a) $160   (b) $2090   (c) $90   (d) $2160   (e) None of these

1—Ans: c

23. Assume that interest is computed using the formula for *simple* interest, $I = Prt$. Find the principal, P, required to earn $105 interest in six months at an annual rate of 8.4%.

(a) $1250   (b) $2605   (c) $1355   (d) $2500   (e) None of these

1—Ans: d

24. Assume that interest is computed using the formula for *simple* interest, $I = Prt$. Find the principal, P, required to earn $138 interest in nine months at an annual rate of 8%.

(a) $2300   (b) $1725   (c) $1863   (d) $2438   (e) None of these

1—Ans: a

25. Use the simple interest formula, $I = Prt$. What annual interest rate will produce $161 interest in one year on a principal of $2875?

(a) 0.056%   (b) 5.6%   (c) 56%   (d) 0.56%   (e) None of these

1—Ans: b

26. Use the simple interest formula, $I = Prt$. What annual interest rate will produce $256 interest in one year on a principal of $4000?

(a) 6.4%   (b) 0.064%   (c) 0.64%   (d) 64%   (e) None of these

1—Ans: a

27. Use the simple interest formula, $I = Prt$. What annual interest rate will produce $243 interest in one year on a principal of $3000?

(a) 81%   (b) 0.081%   (c) 0.81%   (d) 8.1%   (e) None of these

1—Ans: d

28. Use the simple interest formula, $I = Prt$. What annual interest rate will produce $343 interest in one year on a principal of $7000?

(a) 0.049%   (b) 49%   (c) 4.9%   (d) 0.49%   (e) None of these

1—Ans: c

29. Suppose you jog at an average rate of 6 kilometers per hour. How long will it take to jog 14 kilometers?

    (a) 100 minutes   **(b)** 120 minutes   **(c)** 140 minutes   **(d)** 160 minutes   **(e)** None of these

    1—Ans: c

30. Suppose you jog at an average rate of 6 kilometers per hour. How long will it take to jog 10 kilometers?

    (a) 100 minutes   **(b)** 120 minutes   **(c)** 140 minutes   **(d)** 160 minutes   **(e)** None of these

    1—Ans: a

31. You ran a 10 kilometer race in 43.5 minutes. What was your average rate, in kilometers per hour?

    (a) 4.35   **(b)** 435   **(c)** ≈ 13.8 **(d)** ≈ 23 **(e)** None of these

    1—Ans: c

32. You ran a 10 kilometer race in 41.5 minutes. What was your average rate, in kilometers per hour?

    (a) 415   **(b)** ≈ 0.24 **(c)** 4.15   **(d)** ≈ 14.5 **(e)** None of these

    1—Ans: d

33. You can cycle at a rate of 12 miles per hour. How many miles can you travel in 2 hours and 20 minutes?

    (a) 28   **(b)** 5.14   **(c)** 0.086   **(d)** $11.\overline{6}$ **(e)** None of these

    1—Form: 3A—Ans: a

34. You can cycle at a rate of 14 miles per hour. How many miles can you travel in 2 hours and 20 minutes?

    (a) 10   **(b)** 6   **(c)** $32.\overline{6}$ **(d)** 0.1   **(e)** None of these

    1—Form: 3B—Ans: c

35. Find the selling price per pound of a blended coffee made from 8 pounds of coffee worth $9.20 per pound and 12 pounds of coffee worth $5.50 per pound.

    (a) $7.35   **(b)** $1.61   **(c)** $6.98   **(d)** $32.20   **(e)** None of these

    1—Ans: c

36. Find the selling price per pound of a blended coffee made from 8 pounds of coffee worth $8.50 per pound and 12 pounds of coffee worth $5.95 per pound.

    (a) $1.56   **(b)** $31.17   **(c)** $6.97   **(d)** $7.23   **(e)** None of these

    1—Form: 3B—Ans: c

37. If you can complete a job in $4\frac{1}{2}$ hours, what percent of the job should be completed in 1 hour and 45 minutes?

 (a) 40%   **(b)** $33\frac{1}{3}\%$ **(c)** 35%   **(d)** 38.9%   **(e)** None of these

 1—Ans: d

38. If you can complete a job in $3\frac{1}{2}$ hours, what percent of the job should be completed in 1 hour and 45 minutes?

 (a) 50%   **(b)** 45%   **(c)** 55%   **(d)** 40%   **(e)** None of these

 1—Ans: a

39. An experienced painter can paint a room in 10 hours working alone. An apprentice can do the same job in 15 hours working alone. How many hours will it take them to paint the room if they work together?

 (a) 6   **(b)** 12.5   **(c)** 12   **(d)** 25   **(e)** None of these

 2—Ans: a

40. An experienced painter can paint a room in 15 hours working alone. An apprentice can do the same job in 30 hours working alone. How many hours will it take them to paint the room if they work together?

 (a) 20   **(b)** 22.5   **(c)** 10   **(d)** 45   **(e)** None of these

 2—Ans: c

41. If you can complete a job in $6\frac{1}{2}$ hours, what percent of the job should be completed in 4 hours and 24 minutes?

 (a) $66\frac{2}{3}\%$ **(b)** 67.7%   **(c)** 60%   **(d)** 70%   **(e)** None of these

 1—Ans: b

42. If you can complete a job in $6\frac{1}{2}$ hours, what percent of the job should be completed in 3 hours and 12 minutes?

 (a) 50%   **(b)** 55%   **(c)** 49.2%   **(d)** 47.3%   **(e)** None of these

 1—Ans: c

43. A drain pipe can empty a pool in $9\frac{2}{3}$ hours. The pool holds 38,280 gallons. At what rate (in gallons per minute) does the water flow through the drain pipe?

 (a) 638   **(b)** 66   **(c)** 580   **(d)** 3960   **(e)** None of these

 1—Ans: b

44. A drain pipe can empty a pool in $5\frac{3}{4}$ hours. The pool holds 16,560 gallons. At what rate (in gallons per minute) does the water flow through the drain pipe?

 (a) 276   **(b)** 345   **(c)** 2880   **(d)** 48   **(e)** None of these

 1—Ans: d

45. Solve the formula for the area of triangle, $A = \frac{1}{2}bh$ for the height, h.

1—Ans: $h = \dfrac{2A}{b}$

46. Solve the formula for the perimeter of a rectangle, $P = 2l + 2w$, for the width, w.

1—Ans: $w = \dfrac{P - 2l}{2}$

47. Solve the formula for the volume of a circular cylinder, $V = \pi r^2 h$, for the height, h.

1—Ans: $h = \dfrac{V}{\pi r^2}$

48. Solve the formula for the volume of rectangular box, $V = l \cdot w \cdot h$, for h.

1—Ans: $h = \dfrac{V}{lw}$

49. If a principal of P dollars is invested in an account paying an annual interest rate of r (in decimal form) for t years, then the balance A of the account is given by $A = P + Prt$. Solve this equation for t.

1—Ans: $t = \dfrac{A - P}{Pr}$

50. If a principal of P dollars is invested in an account paying an annual interest rate of r (in decimal form) for t years, then the balance A of the account is given by $A = P + Prt$. Solve this equation for r.

1—Ans: $r = \dfrac{A - P}{Pt}$

51. If a principal of P dollars is invested in an account paying an annual interest rate of r (in decimal form) for t years, then the balance A of the account is given by $A = P + Prt$. Solve this equation for P.

1—Ans: $P = \dfrac{A}{1 + rt}$

52. If a principal of P dollars is invested in an account paying an annual interest rate of r (in decimal form) for t years, then the balance A of the account is given by $A = P + Prt$. Solve this equation for rt.

1—Ans: $rt = \dfrac{A - P}{P}$

53. The perimeter of a rectangular patio is 54 feet. If the patio is 10 feet wide, what is its length?

1—Ans: 17 feet

54. The perimeter of a rectangular patio is 56 feet. If the patio is 10 feet wide, what is its length?

1—Ans: 18 feet

55. The volume of a rectangular room is 1536 cubic feet. If the height is one-half the length and the width is 12 feet, find the height and the length of the room.

1—Form: 3C—Ans: height = 8 feet, length = 16 feet

56. The volume of a rectangular room is 2304 cubic feet. If the height is one-half the width and the length is 18 feet, find the height and the width of the room.

1—Ans: height = 8 feet, width = 16 feet

57. The formula for the perimeter of a rectangle is $P = 2l + 2w$. A rectangle is 90 feet wide and twice as long as it is wide. Find its perimeter.

1—Ans: 540 feet

58. The formula for the perimeter of a rectangle is $P = 2l + 2w$. A rectangle's length is three times its width. Find the perimeter if the width is 30 feet.

1—Ans: 240 feet

59. Given the formulas: Area of a rectangle, $A = lw$; Perimeter of a rectangle, $P = 2l + 2w$; Volume of a rectangular box, $V = lwh$. A rectangular box has a base that is 27 inches by 18 inches and its height is 15 inches. Find the area of the base.

1—Ans: 486 square inches

60. Given the formulas: Area of a rectangle, $A = lw$; Perimeter of a rectangle, $P = 2l + 2w$; Volume of a rectangular box, $V = lwh$. A rectangular box has a base that is 27 inches by 18 inches and its height is 15 inches. Find the perimeter of the base of the box.

1—Ans: 90 inches

61. Given the formulas: Area of a rectangle, $A = lw$; Perimeter of a rectangle, $P = 2l + 2w$; Volume of a rectangular box, $V = lwh$. A rectangular box has a base that is 27 inches by 18 inches and its height is 15 inches. Find the volume of the box.

1—Ans: 7290 cubic inches

62. Given the formulas: Area of a rectangle, $A = lw$; Perimeter of a rectangle, $P = 2l + 2w$; Volume of a rectangular box, $V = lwh$. A rectangular box has a base that is 27 inches by 18 inches and its height is 15 inches. Find the area of the longer side of the box.

1—Ans: 405 square inches

63. The area of a rectangle is given by $A = lw$. Find the area of a rectangle in square inches if $l = 5.25$ feet and $w = 7.75$ feet. (Recall that 1 foot = 12 inches.)

1—Ans: 5859 square inches

64. The perimeter of a rectangle is given by $P = 2l + 2w$. Find the perimeter in inches given that $l = 29.25$ feet and $w = 17.50$ feet. (Recall that 1 foot = 12 inches.)

1—Ans: 1122 inches

65. A business borrowed x dollars at 8% simple interest for one year. If the business paid $920 in interest, find the principal, x.

1—Ans: $11,500

66. A business borrowed x dollars at 8% simple interest for one year. If the business paid $992 in interest, find the principal, x.

1—Ans: $12,400

67. A homeowner borrowed $8000 for one year on a simple interest home equity loan. If the homeowner paid $760 in interest, what was the annual interest rate?

1—Ans: 9.5%

68. A homeowner borrowed $8500 for one year on a simple interest home equity loan. If the homeowner paid $765 in interest, what was the annual interest rate?

1—Ans: 9%

69. If a principal of P dollars is invested in an account paying an annual interest rate of r (in decimal form) for t years, then the interest in dollars is given by $I = Prt$. Calculate the interest earned when $3000 is invested for six months at an annual rate of 6.5%.

1—Ans: $97.50

70. If a principal of P dollars is invested in an account paying an annual interest rate of r (in decimal form) for t years, then the interest in dollars is given by $I = Prt$. Calculate the interest earned when $2000 is invested for eight months at an annual rate of 6.6%.

1—Ans: $88

71. How much money was invested for 60 days (2 months) at an annual rate of 12% interest to earn $300? The simple interest formula is $I = Prt$.

1—Ans: $15,000

72. Use the simple interest formula, $I = Prt$, to find how much money was invested for three months at an annual rate of 8.4% to earn $357.

1—Ans: $17,000

73. Use the simple interest formula, $I = Prt$, to find how much money was invested for eight months at an annual rate of 7.2% to earn $744.

1—Ans: $15,500

74. Use the simple interest formula, $I = Prt$, to find how much money was invested for nine months at an annual rate of 8.4% to earn $189.

1—Ans: $3000

75. Use the formula for simple interest, $I = Prt$. Find the annual interest rate which will produce $61.62 interest in six months on a principal of $1580.

2—Ans: 7.8%

76. Use the formula for simple interest, $I = Prt$. Find the annual interest rate which will produce $33.58 interest in four months on a principal of $1460.

2—Ans: 6.9%

77. Two persons start a race together. One runs at a rate of 8.6 kilometers per hour and the second runs at a rate of 8.3 kilometers per hour. How far will the first runner be ahead of the second after 50 minutes?

1—Ans: $\frac{1}{4}$ kilometer or 250 meters

78. Two persons start a race together. One runs at a rate of 8.6 kilometers per hour and the second runs at a rate of 8.3 kilometers per hour. How far will the first runner be ahead of the second after 75 minutes?

1—Ans: $\frac{3}{8}$ kilometer or 375 meters

79. Two persons start a race together. One runs at a rate of 8.6 kilometers per hour and the second runs at a rate of 8.3 kilometers per hour. How far will the first runner be ahead of the second after 90 minutes?

1—Ans: $\frac{9}{20}$ kilometer or 450 meters

80. Two persons start a race together. One runs at a rate of 8.6 kilometers per hour and the second runs at a rate of 8.3 kilometers per hour. How far will the first runner be ahead of the second after 40 minutes?

1—Ans: $\frac{1}{5}$ kilometer or 200 meters

81. A grocer wants to mix cashew nuts worth $8 per pound with peanuts worth $3 per pound. She wants to obtain a mixture to sell for $4 per pound. If ten pounds of peanuts are used, what is the total weight of the mixture?

2—Ans: 12.5 pounds

82. A grocer wants to mix cashew nuts worth $8 per pound with peanuts worth $3 per pound. She wants to obtain a mixture to sell for $4 per pound. If ten pounds of peanuts are used, what is the total value in dollars of the mixture?

   2—Ans: $50

83. The owner of a gift shop mixes almonds worth $4.60 per pound with 10 pounds of raisins worth $2.50 per pound. If the mixture sells for $3.20 per pound, how many pounds of almonds are needed?

   2—Form: 3C—Ans: 5

84. The owner of a gift shop mixes almonds worth $4.80 per pound with 10 pounds of raisins worth $2.20 per pound. If the mixture sells for $3.50 per pound, how many pounds of almonds are needed?

   2—Ans: 10

85. How many ounces of pure antifreeze must be added to 100 ounces of 40% antifreeze solution to obtain a 50% solution?

   1—Ans: 20 ounces

86. How many ounces of pure antifreeze must be added to 100 ounces of 40% antifreeze solution to obtain a 60% solution?

   1—Ans: 50 ounces

87. Thirty ounces of pure gold are added to 50 ounces of a gold alloy that is 20% gold. What is the percent concentration of gold in the mixture?

   2—Ans: 50%

88. Ten ounces of pure gold are added to 40 ounces of a gold alloy that is 25% gold. What is the percent concentration of gold in the mixture?

   2—Ans: 40%

89. How many ounces of water must be added to 100 ounces of 40% antifreeze solution to obtain a 25% solution?

   1—Ans: 60 ounces

90. How many ounces of water must be added to 100 ounces of 40% antifreeze solution to obtain a 16% solution?

   1—Ans: 150 ounces

91. A man can complete a job in three hours which a second person can complete in four hours. Working together how long will it take them to complete the job?

   1—Ans: $\frac{12}{7} = 1\frac{5}{7}$ hours

92. One person completes $\frac{1}{3}$ of a job in an hour and another person completes $\frac{1}{5}$ of the job in an hour. Working together how long will it take them to complete the job?

1—Ans: $\frac{15}{8} = 1\frac{7}{8}$ hours

93. A tank holds 19,800 gallons and has two drains. One drain allows water to flow out at 25 gallons per minute and the other drains at 30 gallons per minute. If both drains are open how long (in hours) does it take to drain the tank?

1—Ans: 6 hours

94. A tank holds 23,100 gallons and has two drains. One drain allows water to flow out at 25 gallons per minute and the other drains at 30 gallons per minute. If both drains are open how long (in hours) does it take to drain the tank?

1—Ans: 7 hours

95. A drain can empty a large washing machine in 15 minutes. If the water flows through the drain at a rate of 5 gallons per minute, what is the capacity, in gallons, of the washing machine?

1—Ans: 75

96. A drain can empty a large washing machine in 18 minutes. If the water flows through the drain at a rate of 4 gallons per minute, what is the capacity, in gallons, of the washing machine?

1—Ans: 72

97. A tank holds 26,400 gallons and has two drains. One drain allows water to flow out at 25 gallons per minute and the other drains at 30 gallons per minute. If both drains are open how long (in hours) does it take to drain the tank?

1—Ans: 8 hours

98. A tank holds 16,500 gallons and has two drains. One drain allows water to flow out at 25 gallons per minute and the other drains at 30 gallons per minute. If both drains are open how long (in hours) does it take to drain the tank?

1—Ans: 5 hours

Section 3.6   Linear Inequalities

1. Match the graph with the inequality.

    (a) $x \leq -2$ **(b)** $x < -2$ **(c)** $x \geq -2$ **(d)** $x > -2$ **(e)** None of these

1—Ans: d

2. Match the graph with the inequality.

(a) $x \leq -2$ **(b)** $x < -2$ **(c)** $x \geq -2$ **(d)** $x > -2$ **(e)** None of these

1—Form: 3B—Ans: b

3. Match the graph with the inequality.

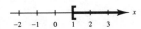

(a) $x > 1$ **(b)** $x \geq 1$ **(c)** $x < 1$ **(d)** $x \leq 1$ **(e)** None of these

1—Ans: b

4. Match the graph with the inequality.

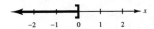

(a) $x \geq 0$ **(b)** $x > 2$ **(c)** $x < 0$ **(d)** $x \leq 0$ **(e)** None of these

1—Ans: d

5. Match the graph with the inequality.

(a) $-2 \leq x \leq 2$ **(b)** $-2 \leq x < 2$ **(c)** $-2 < x \leq 2$ **(d)** $-2 < x < 2$ **(e)** None of these

1—Form: 3A—Ans: c

6. Match the graph with the inequality.

(a) $-1 \leq x \leq 1$ **(b)** $-1 \leq x < 1$ **(c)** $-1 < x \leq 1$ **(d)** $-1 < x < 1$ **(e)** None of these

1—Ans: b

7. Which of the following is the graph of the inequality $-\frac{1}{2} < x \leq 2$?

(a)

(b)

(c)

(d)

(e)

1—Ans: a

8. Which of the following is the graph of the inequality $-\frac{1}{2} \le x \le 2$?

(a)

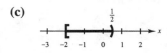

(b)

(c)

(d)

(e)

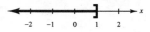

1—Ans: e

9. Which of the following verbal descriptions is graphed as shown?

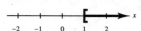

(a) x is less than 1

(b) x is less than or equal to 1

(c) x is greater than 1

(d) x is greater than or equal to 1

(e) None of these

1—Ans: b

10. Which of the following verbal descriptions is graphed as shown?

(a) x is less than 1.

(b) x is less than or equal to 1.

(c) x is greater than 1.

(d) x is greater than or equal to 1.

(e) None of these

1—Ans: d

11. Choose the verbal statement equivalent to $2 \le x < 3$.

(a) x is between 2 and 3.

(b) x is greater than or equal to 2.

(c) x is no greater than 3.

(d) x is less than 3 but not less than 2.

(e) x is greater than 3 and no greater than 2.

1—Ans: d

12. Choose the verbal statement equivalent to $2 < x \le 3$.

(a) x lies between 2 and 3.

(b) x is less than 3 or equal to 3.

(c) x is no smaller than 2.

(d) x is less than 2 but not less than 3.

(e) x is greater than 2 but no greater than 3.

1—Ans: e

13. Match the graph with the inequality.

(a) $1 - 3x \leq 4$ **(b)** $3x - 1 \leq -2$ **(c)** $1 - 3x > 4$

(d) $3x - 1 > -2$ **(e)** None of these

2—Ans: a

14. Match the graph with the inequality.

(a) $1 - 2x \leq 3$ **(b)** $1 - 2x < 3$ **(c)** $3 \leq 1 - 2x$

(d) $3 < 1 - 2x$ **(e)** None of these

2—Ans: d

15. Which of the values of x satisfies the linear inequality $3 - 2x > 4$?

(a) 0   **(b)** -1 **(c)** 1   **(d)** $-\frac{1}{2}$ **(e)** None of these

1—Ans: b

16. Which of the values of x satisfies the linear inequality $5 < 1 - 3x$?

(a) 0   **(b)** -1 **(c)** -2 **(d)** $-\frac{4}{3}$ **(e)** None of these

1—Ans: c

17. Which of the values of x satisfies the linear inequality $3 - 2x \geq 4$?

(a) 0   **(b)** 4   **(c)** 1   **(d)** $-\frac{1}{2}$ **(e)** None of these

1—Ans: d

18. Which of the values of x satisfies the linear inequality $5 \leq 1 - 3x$?

(a) $-\frac{4}{3}$ **(b)** 0   **(c)** $\frac{1}{3}$ **(d)** 1   **(e)** None of these

1—Ans: a

20. Which of these can be produced from the inequality $2(7 - 2x) \leq 5$?

(a) $9 \leq 4x$ **(b)** $4x - 14 > 5$ **(c)** $4x > 9$

(d) $-4x \leq 5 + 14$ **(e)** None of these

1—Ans: a

21. Solve the inequality $-\dfrac{x}{3} - 18 \leq 3$.

(a) $x \leq -63$ **(b)** $x \leq 45$ **(c)** $x \geq 45$ **(d)** $x \geq -63$ **(e)** None of these

2—Ans: d

22. Solve the inequality $-\dfrac{x}{4} - 16 \le 4$.

    (a) $x \le -80$ **(b)** $x \ge -80$ **(c)** $x \ge 48$ **(d)** $x \le 48$ **(e)** None of these

    2—Ans: b

23. Solve the inequality $3x + 2 > 5x - 8$.

    (a) $x < -5$ **(b)** $x > -5$ **(c)** $x < 5$ **(d)** $x > 5$ **(e)** None of these

    2—Form: 3A—Ans: c

24. Solve the inequality $3x - 2 > 5x + 4$.

    (a) $x > -3$ **(b)** $x < -3$ **(c)** $x > 3$ **(d)** $x < 3$ **(e)** None of these

    2—Form: 3B—Ans: b

25. Solve the inequality $15 - 5(3 - 2x) \le 4(x - 3)$.

    (a) $x \ge -2$ **(b)** $x \ge \dfrac{7}{4}$ **(c)** $x \le \dfrac{7}{4}$ **(d)** $x \le -2$ **(e)** None of these

    2—Form: 3A—Ans: d

26. Solve the inequality $8 - 4(3x + 5) \le 6(x - 8)$.

    (a) $x \ge -\dfrac{34}{3}$ **(b)** $x \le -\dfrac{34}{3}$ **(c)** $x \ge 2$ **(d)** $x \le 2$ **(e)** None of these

    2—Form: 3B—Ans: c

27. Solve the inequality $-4 \le 4 - 2x < 4$.

    (a) $0 < x \le 4$ **(b)** $0 \le x < 4$ **(c)** $-4 \le x < 0$

    (d) $-4 < x \le 0$ **(e)** None of these

    2—Ans: a

28. Solve the inequality $-4 < 4 - 2x \le 4$.

    (a) $0 < x \le 4$ **(b)** $0 \le x < 4$ **(c)** $-4 \le x < 0$

    (d) $-4 < x \le 0$ **(e)** None of these

    2—Ans: b

29. Graph the inequality $-3 < x < 3$.

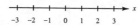

    1—Ans: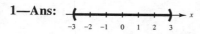

30. Graph the inequality $-1 \leq x \leq 1$.

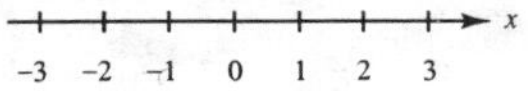

1—Ans:

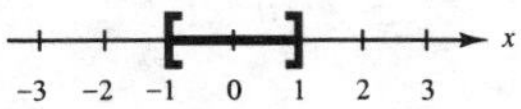

31. Graph the inequality $-\frac{3}{2} < x \leq \frac{5}{2}$.

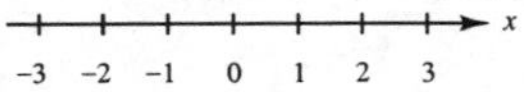

1—Ans:

32. Graph the inequality $-\frac{3}{2} \leq x \leq \frac{5}{2}$.

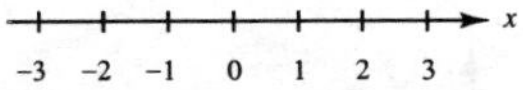

1—Ans:

33. Graph the inequality $-\frac{3}{2} \leq x < \frac{5}{2}$.

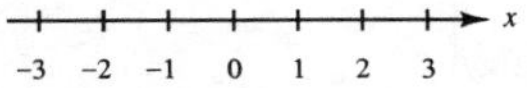

1—Ans:

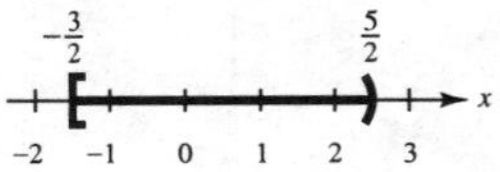

34. Graph the inequality $-\frac{3}{2} < x < \frac{5}{2}$.

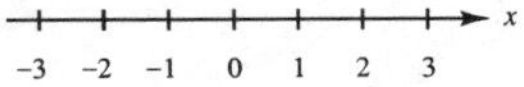

1—Ans:

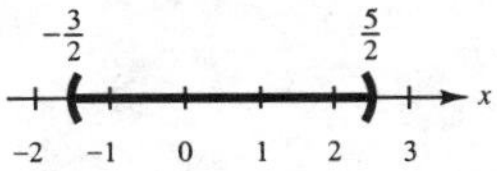

35. Write the inequality whose graph is shown below.

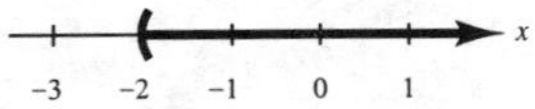

1—Ans: $x > -2$

36. Write the inequality whose graph is shown below.

1—Ans: $x \geq -1$

37. Write the inequality whose graph is shown below.

1—Ans: $\frac{1}{2} < x \leq 4$

38. Write the inequality whose graph is shown below.

1—Ans: $\frac{1}{2} < x < 4$

39. Use inequality notation to denote the statement:

x is greater than -1 but not greater than 5.

1—Ans: $-1 < x \leq 5$

40. Use inequality notation to denote the statement:

x is less than 10 but not less than 2.

1—Ans: $2 \leq x < 10$

41. Use inequality notation to denote the statement:
n is at least seven.

1—Ans: $n \geq 7$

42. Use inequality notation to denote the statement:
n is at most eight.

1—Ans: $n \leq 8$

43. Use inequality notation to denote the statement:
n is more than negative five.

1—Ans: $n > -5$

44. Use inequality notation to denote the statement:
n is less than negative three.

1—Ans: $n < -3$

45. Does $x = -3$ satisfy the linear inequality $3 - \frac{1}{3}x \leq 4$?

    1—Ans: It does satisfy it.

46. Does $x = -6$ satisfy the linear inequality $3 - \frac{1}{3}x \leq 4$?

    1—Ans: It does *not* satisfy it.

47. Solve the inequality $16 - 5x \geq 1$.

    1—Ans: $x \leq 3$

48. Solve the inequality $18 - 4x \geq 2$.

    1—Form: 3C—Ans: $x \leq 4$

49. Solve the inequality $3x - 1 < 11$.

    1—Ans: $x < 4$

50. Solve the inequality $2x - 1 < 9$.

    1—Ans: $x < 5$

51. Solve the inequality $2(3 - 2x) < 1 + x$.

    1—Ans: $1 < x$ or $x > 1$

52. Solve the inequality $5(1 - 2x) \geq 2 - x$.

    1—Ans: $\frac{1}{3} \geq x$ or $x \leq \frac{1}{3}$

53. Solve the inequality $2 - x \geq 5(1 - 2x)$.

    1—Ans: $x \geq \frac{1}{3}$ or $\frac{1}{3} \leq x$

54. Solve the inequality $5(2 - x) > 1 - 3x$.

    1—Ans: $\frac{9}{2} > x$ or $x < \frac{9}{2}$

55. Solve the inequality $-3 < 5x - 6 < 3$.

    2—Form: 3C—Ans: $\frac{3}{5} < x < \frac{9}{5}$

56. Solve the inequality $-2 < 6x - 3 < 2$.

    2—Ans: $\frac{1}{6} < x < \frac{5}{6}$

57. Solve the inequality $4 > \dfrac{x + 4}{-3} > 1$.

    2—Ans: $-16 < x < -7$

58. Solve the inequality $5 > \dfrac{x+5}{-4} > 2$.

   2—Ans: $-25 < x < -13$

59. Solve the inequality $-1 \le 2x + 3 < 7$.

   1—Ans: $-2 \le x < 2$

60. Solve the inequality $-3 < 2x + 2 < 6$.

   1—Ans: $-\frac{5}{2} < x < 2$

61. A telephone call costs $1.20 for the first 3 minutes and $0.35 for each additional minute. If one can spend no more than $5.00 for the call, write an inequality expressing the restriction on the time, t, in minutes.

   1—Ans: $1.20 + (t - 3)(0.35) < 5$

62. A telephone call costs $1.20 for the first 3 minutes and $0.35 for each additional minute. If one can spend no more than $7.00 for the call, write an inequality expressing the restriction on the time, t, in minutes.

   1—Ans: $1.20 + (t - 3)(0.35) < 7$

63. A baseball player is offered an annual salary of $500,000 or a base salary of $350,000 plus a bonus of $1000 for each hit. How many hits must the player make to earn more than $500,000? Write an inequality and solve for the number of hits.

   2—Ans: $350,000 + 1000x > 500,000$; $x > 150$

64. A baseball player is offered an annual salary of $600,000 or a base salary of $420,000 plus a bonus of $1000 for each hit. How many hits must the player make to earn more than $600,000? Write an inequality and solve for the number of hits.

   2—Ans: $420,000 + 1000x > 600,000$; $x > 180$

65. A sales agent is offered a monthly salary of $2800 or a base salary of $1000 plus a 12% commission on the agent's monthly sales. If the agent chooses $2800, then the agent expects sales to be less than what amount? Write an inequality and solve for the monthly sales.

   2—Ans: $2800 > 1000 + 0.12x$; $x < 15,000$

66. A sales agent is offered a monthly salary of $3200 or a base salary of $1200 plus a 10% commission on the agent's monthly sales. If the agent chooses $3200, then the agent expects sales to be less than what amount? Write an inequality and solve for the monthly sales.

   2—Ans: $3200 > 1200 + 0.10x$; $x < 20,000$

67. A telephone call costs $1.20 for the first 3 minutes and $0.35 for each additional minute. If one can spend no more than $6.00 for the call, write an inequality expressing the restriction on the time, t, in minutes.

1—Ans: $1.20 + (t - 3)(0.35) < 6$

68. A telephone call costs $1.20 for the first 3 minutes and $0.35 for each additional minute. If one can spend no more than $10.00 for the call, write an inequality expressing the restriction on the time, t, in minutes.

1—Ans: $1.20 + (t - 3)(0.35) < 10$

69. To earn a grade of B, a student must have an average of at least 80 points on five tests. A student's grades on the first four tests were 76, 82, 87, and 77. How many points must the student score on the fifth test to earn a grade of B? Write an inequality and solve for the score on the fifth test.

2—Ans: $\dfrac{76 + 82 + 87 + 77 + x}{5} \geq 80; x \geq 78$

70. To earn a grade of B, a student must have an average of at least 80 points on five tests. A student's grades on the first four tests were 79, 83, 89, and 75. How many points must the student score on the fifth test to earn a grade of B? Write an inequality and solve for the score on the fifth test.

2—Form: 3C—Ans: $\dfrac{79 + 83 + 89 + 75 + x}{5} \geq 80; x \geq 74$

Section 3.7   Absolute Value Equations and Inequalities

1. Solve $|x| = 8$.

   (a) 8   **(b)** -8 **(c)** 8 and -8 **(d)** $|8|$ **(e)** None of these

   1—Ans: c

2. Solve $|x| = -4$.

   (a) 4   **(b)** -4 **(c)** 4 and -4 **(d)** No solution   **(e)** None of these

   1—Ans: d

3. Solve $|x + 3| = 5$.

   (a) 2   **(b)** -2 and 2   **(c)** -8 and 2   **(d)** -2 and 8   **(e)** None of these

   1—Ans: c

4. Solve $|3x + 1| = 2$.

   (a) $\frac{1}{3}$ **(b)** -1 and $\frac{1}{3}$ **(c)** -1 **(d)** $-\frac{1}{3}$ and 1   **(e)** None of these

   1—Form: 3A—Ans: b

5. Solve $\left|2 - \frac{1}{2}x\right| = 6$.

  (a) -8 and 16 (b) -16 and 8 (c) -8 (d) 8 (e) None of these

  2—Form: 3B—Ans: a

6. Solve $\left|\frac{1}{3}x + 2\right| = 1$.

  (a) -3 (b) -3 and -1 (c) -9 and -3 (d) $-\frac{1}{3}$ and -1 (e) None of these

  2—Ans: c

7. Solve $|1.25 - 2.5x| = 1$.

  (a) -0.1 (b) 0.1 and 0.9 (c) -0.1 and 0.9

  (d) 0.1 and -0.9 (e) None of these

  2—Ans: b

8. Which of the following absolute value equations has *no* solution?

  (a) $|y - 3| = 0$ (b) $|y - 3| = 1$ (c) $|3 - x| = 1$

  (d) $|3 - x| = -1$ (e) None of these

  1—Ans: d

9. Which of the following absolute value equations has *only one* solution?

  (a) $|x + 1| = 4$ (b) $|x + 1| = 0$ (c) $|x + 1| = -4$

  (d) $|x + 1| = 1$ (e) None of these

  1—Ans: b

10. Which of the following absolute value equations has *two* solutions?

  (a) $|y - 2| = 0$ (b) $|x - 2| = -3$ (c) $|x + 2| = 0$

  (d) $|x - 2| = 3$ (e) None of these

  1—Ans: d

11. Write $x + 1 = 4$ and $x + 1 = -4$ as an equivalent single equation.

  (a) $x + 1 = 0$ (b) $|x| = 3$ (c) $|x + 1| = -4$

  (d) $|x + 1| = 4$ (e) None of these

  1—Ans: d

12. Write a single equation that is equivalent to the following statement. The distance between *t* and 2 is 9.

  (a) $|t - 2| = 9$ (b) $|t + 2| = 9$ (c) $|t - 9| = 2$

  (d) $|t + 9| = 2$ (e) None of these

  1—Form: 3A—Ans: a

13. Write a single equation that is equivalent to the following statement. The distance between x and -3 is 8.

(a) $|x - 3| = 8$ (b) $|x - 8| = 3$ (c) $|x + 3| = 8$

(d) $|x + 8| = 3$ (e) None of these

1—Form: 3B—Ans: c

14. Write an absolute value inequality that represents the following verbal statement. The set of all real numbers x whose distance from 0 is less than 5.

(a) $|x| < -5$ (b) $|x - 5| < 0$ (c) $|x| < 5$

(d) $|x - 5| > 0$ (e) $|x| > 5$

1—Ans: c

15. Write an absolute value inequality that represents the following verbal statement. The set of all real numbers x whose distance from 2 is no more than 6.

(a) $|x - 6| < 2$ (b) $|x - 2| < 6$ (c) $|x - 2| \le 2$

(d) $|x - 2| \le 6$ (e) $|x - 2| \ge 6$

1—Ans: d

16. Which of the following values is *not* a solution of the inequality $|x| > 4$?

(a) 5   (b) -6 (c) 4   (d) -4.1 (e) -10

1—Ans: c

17. Which of the following values is *not* a solution of the inequality $|x + 2| < 3$?

(a) -4 (b) 3   (c) -3 (d) 0   (e) -1

1—Ans: b

18. Which of the following values is *not* a solution of the inequality $|3x - 4| \ge 2$?

(a) -5 (b) -2 (c) 1   (d) 2   (e) 7

1—Ans: c

19. Sketch the solution to $|x| \le 2$.

1—Ans: b

20. Sketch the solution to $|5 - x| > 3$.

(a)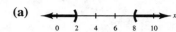

(b)

(c)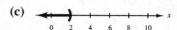

(d)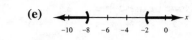

(e)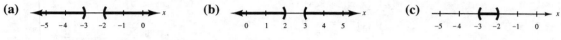

1—Ans: a

21. Sketch the solution to $|2x + 5| < 1$.

(a)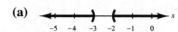

(b)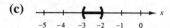

(c)

(d)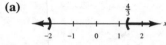

(e)

1—Ans: c

22. Sketch the solution to $|3x - 1| \geq 5$.

(a)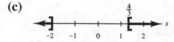

(b)

(c)

(d)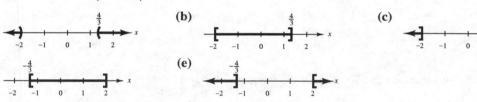

(e)

1—Ans: e

23. Solve $|x| > 1$.

(a) $\{x \mid x < -1 \text{ or } x > 1\}$
(b) $\{x \mid x < 1 \text{ or } x > -1\}$
(c) $\{x \mid -1 < x < 1\}$
(d) $\{x \mid 1 < x < -1\}$
(e) None of these

1—Ans: a

24. Solve $|2 + m| < 3$.

(a) $\{m \mid m < -5 \text{ or } m > 1\}$
(b) $\{m \mid m < 1 \text{ or } m > -5\}$
(c) $\{m \mid -5 < m < 1\}$
(d) $\{m \mid 1 < m < -5\}$
(e) None of these

1—Form: 3A—Ans: c

25. Solve $|3x| \geq 12$.

(a) $\{x \mid x \geq 4 \text{ or } x \geq -4\}$
(b) $\{x \mid x \leq -4 \text{ or } x \geq 4\}$
(c) $\{x \mid x \geq -4 \text{ or } x \leq 4\}$
(d) $\{x \mid -4 \leq x \leq 4\}$
(e) None of these

1—Form: 3B—Ans: b

26. Solve $|-x| \leq 3$.

    (a) $\{x | x \leq -3 \text{ or } x \geq 3\}$ **(b)** $\{x | x \leq 3 \text{ or } x \geq -3\}$ **(c)** $\{x | 3 \leq x \leq -3\}$

    (d) $\{x | -3 \leq x \leq 3\}$ **(e)** None of these

    1—Ans: d

27. Write an absolute value inequality that matches the following graph.

    (a) $|x| > 6$ **(b)** $|x| < 6$ **(c)** $|x| \leq 6$

    (d) $|x| \geq 6$ **(e)** $|x - 6| < 0$

    1—Ans: b

28. Write an absolute value inequality that matches the following graph.

    (a) $|x - 1| < 3$ **(b)** $|x + 1| < 3$ **(c)** $|x - 3| < 1$

    (d) $|x + 3| < 1$ **(e)** $|x - 1| > 3$

    1—Ans: a

29. Write an absolute value inequality that matches the following graph.

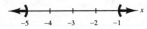

    (a) $|x - 2| > 3$ **(b)** $|x + 2| < 3$ **(c)** $|x - 3| < 2$

    (d) $|x + 3| > 2$ **(e)** $|x + 3| < 2$

    1—Ans: d

30. Solve $|x| = 4$.

    1—Ans: 4 and -4

31. Solve $|x| = -7$.

    1—Ans: There is no solution because it is not possible for the absolute value of a real number to be negative.

32. Solve $|x| = 0$.

    1—Ans: 0

33. Solve $|y - 4| = 12$.

    1—Ans: -8 and 16

34. Solve $|2x + 1| = 5$.

   1—Ans: -3 and 2

35. Solve $|3x - 2| = 7$.

   1—Form: 3C—Ans: $-\frac{5}{3}$ and 3

36. Solve $|4x + 1| - 5 = -2$.

   1—Ans: -1 and $\frac{1}{2}$

37. Solve $\left|4 + \frac{2}{3}x\right| = 4$.

   2—Ans: -12 and 0

38. Solve $\left|\frac{1}{4}x - 2\right| = 0$.

   2—Ans: 8

39. Solve $|1.5x - 3| = 2$.

   2—Ans: $0.\overline{6}$ and $3.\overline{3}$

40. How many solutions are there to the absolute value equation $|3x - 5| = 0$?

   1—Ans: 1

41. How many solutions are there to the absolute value equation $|2x + 17| = -3$?

   1—Ans: No solutions

42. How many solutions are there to the absolute value equation $|3 - 2x| = 0$?

   1—Ans: 1

43. Sketch the solution to $|v| > 3$.

   1—Ans:

44. Sketch the solution to $|x - 1| \leq 7$.

   1—Ans:

45. Sketch the solution to $|3x + 2| > 14$.

   1—Ans:

46. Solve the inequality $|x| < 10$.

    1—Ans: $\{x \,|\, -10 < x < 10\}$

47. Solve the inequality $|x| > 1$.

    1—Ans: $\{x \,|\, x < -1 \text{ or } x > 1\}$

48. Solve the inequality $|y| \leq 5$.

    1—Ans: $\{y \,|\, -5 \leq y \leq 5\}$

49. Solve the inequality $|a + 2| < 4$.

    1—Ans: $\{a \,|\, -6 < a < 2\}$

50. Solve the inequality $|5t| > 25$.

    1—Ans: $\{t \,|\, t < -5 \text{ or } t > 5\}$

51. Solve the inequality $|2u| \leq 7$.

    1—Ans: $\left\{u \,\middle|\, -\frac{7}{2} \leq u \leq \frac{7}{2}\right\}$

52. Solve the inequality $|y - 7| \leq 3$.

    1—Ans: $\{y \,|\, 4 \leq y \leq 10\}$

53. Solve the inequality $|3 - x| \geq 8$.

    1—Ans: $\{x \,|\, x \leq -5 \text{ or } x \geq 11\}$

54. Solve the inequality $|2x - 4| > 4$.

    2—Ans: $\{x \,|\, x < 0 \text{ or } x > 4\}$

55. Solve the inequality $|1 + 3x| < 2$.

    2—Form: 3C—Ans: $\left\{x \,\middle|\, -1 < x < \frac{1}{3}\right\}$

56. Solve the inequality $\left|\frac{x}{2} + 1\right| \geq 1$.

    2—Ans: $\{x \,|\, x \leq -4 \text{ or } x \geq 0\}$

57. Write an absolute value inequality that matches the following graph.

    1—Ans: $|x + 1| \leq 2$

58. Write an absolute value inequality that matches the following graph.

1—Ans: $|x - 2| \geq 3$

59. Write an absolute value inequality that matches the following graph.

1—Ans: $|x - 3| < 5$

60. Write $2 - 3t = 6$ and $2 - 3t = -6$ as an equivalent single equation.

1—Ans: $|2 - 3t| = 6$

61. Write a single equation that is equivalent to the following statement. The distance between x and 7 is 5.

1—Ans: $|x - 7| = 5$

62. Write a single equation that is equivalent to the following statement. The distance between x and -6 is 1.

2—Ans: $|x + 6| = 1$

63. Write an absolute value inequality that represents the following verbal statement. The set of all real numbers x whose distance from 8 is at least 3.

2—Ans: $|x - 8| \geq 3$

64. Write an absolute value inequality that represents the following verbal statement. The set of all real numbers x whose distance from -2 is more than 9.

2—Ans: $|x + 2| > 9$

65. Write an absolute value inequality that represents the following verbal statement. The set of all real numbers x whose distance from 0 is at most 5.

2—Ans: $|x| \leq 5$

66. A scale is advertised to be accurate to within 0.05 ounces. If you need to weigh 12 ounces of a material, describe how much of the material you may have if you use the given scale.

2—Ans: You will have somewhere between 11.95 ounces and 12.05 ounces of material.

67. An odometer on a bicycle is accurate to within 0.10 miles. If the odometer reads that you have traveled 2.37 miles, describe how far you may have actually traveled.

2—Form: 3C—Ans: You have traveled somewhere between 2.27 and 2.47 miles.

68. A meat thermometer is advertised to be accurate to 5°F. In order to thoroughly cook a turkey, the manufacturer suggests that it cooks to a temperature of 185°F. When the thermometer reads 185°F, describe the possible temperature of the turkey.

   2—Ans: The turkey's temperature is actually between 180°F and 190°F.

69. A given tape measure is accurate to $\frac{1}{16}$ of an inch. If you measure the length of a room to be 13 feet and $4\frac{3}{16}$ inches (i.e. $160\frac{3}{16}$ inches), describe the actual length of the room.

   2—Ans: The length of the room is actually between 13 feet $4\frac{1}{8}$ inches and 13 feet $4\frac{1}{4}$ inches.

70. The volume of a certain cereal box is accurate to $\frac{1}{5}$ of an ounce. The label of the box indicates that it contains 11 ounces of cereal. Describe the actual volume of cereal in the box.

   2—Ans: The box actually contains between $10\frac{4}{5}$ ounces and $11\frac{1}{5}$ ounces of cereal.

CHAPTER 4
Graphs and Functions

Section 4.1   Ordered Pairs and Graphs

1.

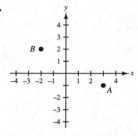

The coordinates of point *A* are:

(a) $(4, 2)$ **(b)** $(3, -1)$ **(c)** $(-3, -2)$ **(d)** $(-2, 2)$ **(e)** None of these

1—Ans: b

2.

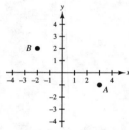

The coordinates of point *B* are:

(a) $(4, 2)$ **(b)** $(3, -1)$ **(c)** $(-3, -2)$ **(d)** $(-2, 2)$ **(e)** None of these

1—Ans: d

3.

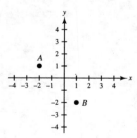

The coordinates of point *A* are:

(a) $(2, -1)$ **(b)** $(-2, 1)$ **(c)** $(1, -2)$ **(d)** $(-1, 2)$ **(e)** None of these

1—Form: 4A—Ans: b

4.

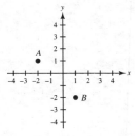

The coordinates of point *B* are:

(a) $(2, -1)$ **(b)** $(-2, 1)$ **(c)** $(1, -2)$ **(d)** $(-1, 2)$ **(e)** None of these

1—Form: 4B—Ans: c

5. Which of the points are *not* plotted on the accompanying graph?

(a) $(0, -2)$ **(b)** $(3, 1)$ **(c)** $(-2, -3)$ **(d)** $(-1, 0)$ **(e)** None of these

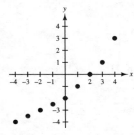

1—Ans: d

6. Which of the points are *not* plotted on the accompanying graph?

(a) $(-4, -4)$ **(b)** $(0, -4)$ **(c)** $(1, -1)$ **(d)** $(-2, -3)$ **(e)** None of these

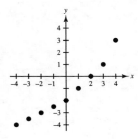

1—Ans: b

7. Estimate the coordinates of point *A*.

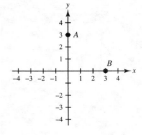

1—Ans: $(0, 3)$

8. Estimate the coordinates of point *B*.

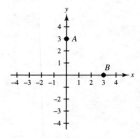

1—Ans: $(3, 0)$

9. Determine the quadrant in which the point $(4, -2)$ is located.

(a) Quadrant I   (b) Quadrant II   (c) Quadrant III

(d) Quadrant IV   (e) None of these

1—Ans: d

10. Determine the quadrant in which the point $(-4, 2)$ is located.

(a) Quadrant I   (b) Quadrant II   (c) Quadrant III

(d) Quadrant IV   (e) None of these

1—Ans: b

11. Determine the quadrant in which the point $\left(-5, \frac{3}{2}\right)$ is located.

1—Ans: Quadrant II

12. Determine the quadrant in which the point $(-2.4, -3.01)$ is located.

1—Ans: Quadrant III

13. Determine the quadrant in which the point $(3.5, -7.2)$ is located.

1—Ans: Quadrant IV

14. Determine the quadrant in which the point $\left(\frac{4}{13}, \frac{7}{5}\right)$ is located.

1—Ans: Quadrant I

15. Choose the quadrant (or quadrants) in which the point $(-3, y)$ must be located if *y* is a real number.

(a) Quadrant I or Quadrant IV   (b) Quadrant II

(c) Quadrant III   (d) Quadrant II or Quadrant III

(e) None of these

1—Ans: d

16. Choose the quadrant (or quadrants) in which the point $(x, -2)$ must be located if $x < 0$.

   (a) Quadrant I or Quadrant IV   **(b)** Quadrant II

   (c) Quadrant III   **(d)** Quadrant II or Quadrant III

   (e) None of these

   1—Ans: c

17. Determine the quadrant (or quadrants) in which the point $(x, -3)$ must be located if x is a real number.

   1—Ans: Quadrants III or IV

18. Determine the quadrant (or quadrants) in which the point $(x, 3)$ must be located if x is a real number.

   1—Ans: Quadrants I or II

19. Plot the points $(2, 3)$, $(2, 5)$, and $(6, 3)$. Connect the points with line segments to form a triangle.

   2—Form: 4C—Ans:

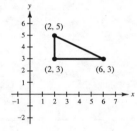 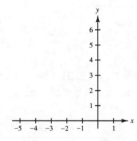

20. Plot the points $(-1, 2)$, $(-1, 4)$, and $(-5, 2)$. Connect the points with line segments to form a triangle.

   2—Ans:

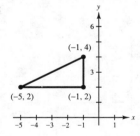

21. Plot the points $(3, -2)$, $(4, 1)$, and $(-1, 3)$. Connect the points with line segments to form a triangle.

    1—Ans:

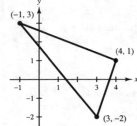

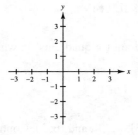

22. Plot the points $(2, 1)$, $(-1, 2)$, $(-2, -1)$ and $(1, -2)$. Connect the points with line segments to form a square.

    1—Ans:

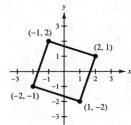

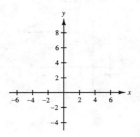

23. Plot the points $(-4, 5)$, $(-2, 2)$, $(6, 2)$ and $(4, 5)$. Connect the points with line segments to form a parallelogram.

    2—Ans:

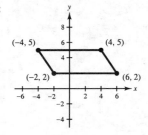

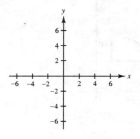

24. Plot the points $(-5, -2)$, $(-2, 2)$, $(1, -2)$ and $(4, 2)$. Connect the points with line segments to form a parallelogram.

    2—Ans:

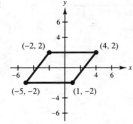

25. Plot the points in the table on the coordinate system.

x	0	−2	−3	−4	4	2	3	5	1
y	2	1	0	−2	3	1	1.5	4.5	1.5

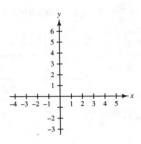

2—Ans:

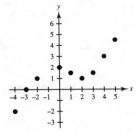

26. Plot the points in the table on the coordinate system.

x	0	2	−2	−3	4	−4	5	−5	6
y	3	4	2	2.5	3	3	0	4	−4

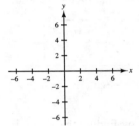

2—Ans:

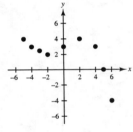

27. Plot the points in the table on the coordinate system.

x	0	2	−2	−3	3	5	−4	−6	6
y	4	3	4.5	5	2	1	4.5	4	0

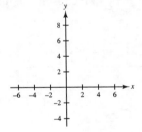

2—Ans:

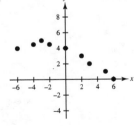

28. Plot the points in the table on the coordinate system.

x	0	2	−2	4	−3	−4	5	6	−5
y	−2	−1	−3	−1	−3.5	−3	0	2	0

2—Ans:

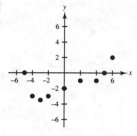

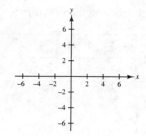

29. Complete the table by finding the *y* coordinates of the solution points.

x	−4	−2	0	2	4
y = 3x − 6					

1—Ans: −18, −12, −6, 0, 6

30. Complete the table by finding the *y* coordinates of the solution points.

x	−4	−2	0	2	4
$y = \frac{3}{2}x - 3$					

1—Ans: −9, −6, −3, 0, 3

31. Complete the table and plot the results on the rectangular coordinate system.

x	−2	−1	0	1	2
y = 4x − 3					

2—Ans: −11, −7, −3, 1, 5

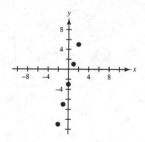

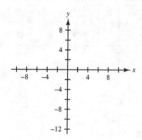

32. Complete the table and plot the results on the rectangular coordinate system.

x	-2	-1	0	1	2
$y = 4x - 2$					

2—Form: 4C—Ans: $-10, -6, -2, 2, 6$

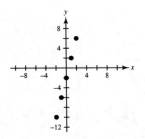

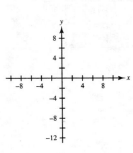

33. Complete the table and plot the results on the rectangular coordinate system.

x	-2	-1	0	1	2
$y = -3x + 4$					

2—Ans: $10, 7, 4, 1, -2$

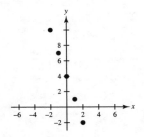

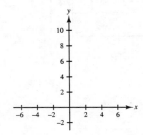

34. Complete the table and plot the results on the rectangular coordinate system.

x	-4	-2	0	2	4
$y = 4 + 3x$					

2—Ans: $-8, -2, 4, 10, 16$

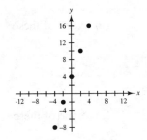

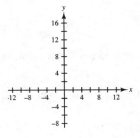

35. Complete the table and plot the results on the rectangular coordinate system.

x	-4	-2	0	2	4
$y = 3x - 4$					

2—Ans: $-16, -10, -4, 2, 8$

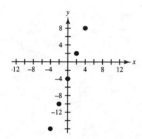

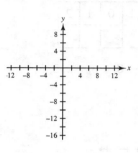

36. Complete the table and plot the results on the rectangular coordinate system.

x	-4	-2	0	2	4
$y = -3x - 4$					

2—Ans: $8, 2, -4, -10, -16$

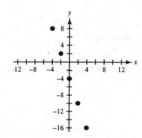

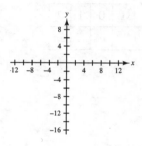

37. Which of the following ordered pairs is a solution of the equation $3y = 2x + 5$?

    (a) $(4, -1)$ **(b)** $(3, 2)$ **(c)** $(1, 1)$ **(d)** $(2, 3)$ **(e)** None of these

    1—Ans: d

38. Which of the following ordered pairs is a solution of the equation
$2y + 3x + 5 = 0$?

    (a) $(-1, 1)$ **(b)** $(-3, 2)$ **(c)** $(-2, 3)$ **(d)** $(1, 4)$ **(e)** None of these

    1—Ans: b

39. Which of the following ordered pairs is a solution of the equation $y = -\frac{3}{4}x$?

    (a) $(-8, 6)$ **(b)** $(-8, -6)$ **(c)** $(6, -8)$ **(d)** $(-6, 8)$ **(e)** None of these

    1—Ans: a

40. Which of the following ordered pairs is a solution of the equation $y = -\frac{2}{5}x$?

(a) $(15, -6)$ (b) $(15, 6)$ (c) $(6, -15)$ (d) $(-6, 15)$ (e) None of these

1—Ans: a

41. Which of the following ordered pairs is *not* a solution of the equation $3x - 4y = 12$?

(a) $(-4, 0)$ (b) $(-4, -6)$ (c) $(0, -3)$ (d) $(8, 3)$ (e) None of these

1—Form: 4A—Ans: a

42. Which of the following ordered pairs is *not* a solution of the equation $4x - 3y = 12$?

(a) $(0, -4)$ (b) $(-6, -12)$ (c) $(6, 4)$ (d) $(-3, 0)$ (e) None of these

1—Form: 4B—Ans: d

43. Which of the following ordered pairs is *not* a solution of the equation $3y = 4x - 6$?

(a) $(3, 2)$ (b) $\left(1, -\frac{2}{3}\right)$ (c) $(3, 4)$ (d) $(-3, -6)$ (e) None of these

1—Ans: c

44. Which of the following ordered pairs is *not* a solution of the equation $3y + 4x + 6 = 0$?

(a) $(-3, 4)$ (b) $\left(-1, -\frac{2}{3}\right)$ (c) $(-3, 2)$ (d) $(3, -6)$ (e) None of these

1—Ans: a

45. Explain why the ordered pair $\left(0, \frac{7}{4}\right)$ is *not* a solution of the equation $x - 4y = 7$.

1—Ans: $\left(0, \frac{7}{4}\right)$ is not a solution because $0 - 4\left(\frac{7}{4}\right) = -7$.

46. Explain why the ordered pair $\left(0, \frac{8}{5}\right)$ is *not* a solution of the equation $x - 5y = 8$.

1—Ans: $\left(0, \frac{8}{5}\right)$ is not a solution because $0 - 5\left(\frac{8}{5}\right) = -8$.

47. For the equation $4y - 2x = 7$, find y when $x = 7$.

(a) $-\frac{7}{4}$ (b) $\frac{21}{4}$ (c) $\frac{4}{21}$ (d) $-\frac{21}{4}$ (e) None of these

1—Ans: b

48. For the equation $5x - 3y = 20$, find y when $x = -10$.

(a) 10 (b) 2 (c) $-\frac{70}{3}$ (d) -10 (e) None of these

1—Ans: c

49. For the equation $7x + 5y = 4$, find y when $x = -\frac{1}{4}$.

1—Ans: $y = \frac{23}{20}$

50. For the equation $7x + 5y = 4$, find y when $x = -\frac{3}{2}$.

1—Ans: $y = \frac{29}{10}$

51. For the equation $7y + 4x = -21$ find y when $x = -7$.

(a) 1   **(b)** -1 **(c)** 7   **(d)** -7 **(e)** None of these

1—Ans: a

52. For the equation $6y - 13x = 5$, find y when $x = -5$.

(a) 10   **(b)** $\frac{35}{3}$ **(c)** $-\frac{1}{10}$ **(d)** -10 **(e)** None of these

1—Ans: d

53. Complete the table and plot the results on the rectangular coordinate system.

y	-6	-3	0	3	6
$x = -\frac{1}{3}y + 1$					

2—Ans: $3, 2, 1, 0, -1$

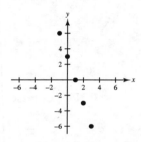
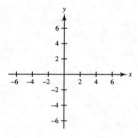

54. Complete the table and plot the results on the rectangular coordinate system.

y	-4	-2	0	2	4
$x = -\frac{1}{2}y + 2$					

2—Ans: $4, 3, 2, 1, 0$

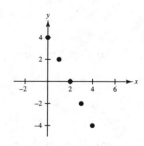
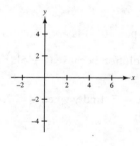

55.

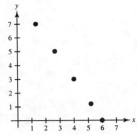

The points plotted on the graph as shown are consistent with the solution points of:

(a) $3x + 2y = 18$ **(b)** $4x + 3y = 24$ **(c)** $6x + 5y = 30$

(d) $7x + 3y = 21$ **(e)** None of these

1—Ans: a

56.

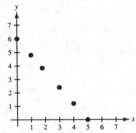

The points plotted on the graph as shown are consistent with the solution points of:

(a) $3x + 2y = 18$ **(b)** $4x + 3y = 24$ **(c)** $6x + 5y = 30$

(d) $7x + 3y = 21$ **(e)** None of these

1—Ans: c

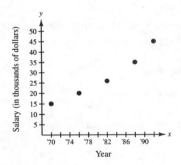

GRAPH FOR 57–58

57. A person's salaries for selected years are shown on the graph. Choose the best estimated value for the person's salary for 1984.

(a) $28,000   **(b)** $25,000   **(c)** $21,000

(d) $35,000   **(e)** None of these

1—Form: 4A—Ans: a

58. A person's salaries for selected years are shown on the graph. Choose the best estimated value for the person's salary for 1990.

(a) $35,000   **(b)** $45,000   **(c)** $34,000

(d) $40,000   **(e)** None of these

1—Form: 4B—Ans: d

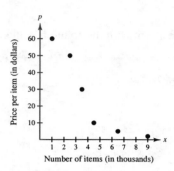

GRAPH FOR 59–60

59. The demand for a product at selected prices is shown on the graph. x is the number (in thousands) which can be sold at the price, P, in dollars. Estimate the sales expected if the price is set at $40.

1—Ans: 3000 Estimate may vary a little.

60. The demand for a product at selected prices is shown on the graph. x is the number (in thousands) which can be sold at the price, P, in dollars. Estimate the sales expected if the price is set at $55.

1—Ans: 1800 Estimate may vary a little.

61. The cost of producing x units of product is given by $y = 0.80x + 4000$. Complete the table to determine the cost, y, for producing x units. Plot the ordered pairs.

x	100	200	300	400
$y = 0.80x + 4000$				

1—Ans: 4080, 4160, 4240, 4320

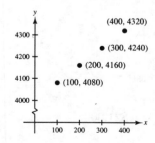

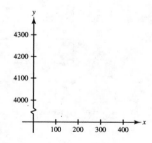

62. The cost of producing x units of product is given by $y = 0.70x + 5000$. Complete the table to determine the cost, y, for producing x units. Plot the ordered pairs.

x	100	200	300	400
$y = 0.70x + 5000$				

1—Ans: 5070, 5140, 5210, 5280

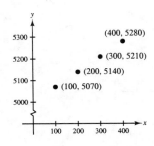

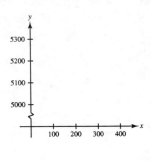

63. You park your vehicle in a parking garage which charges \$3.00 for the first hour and \$1.00 for each additional hour of parking. Write an equation that relates the total charge to the number of hours parked. Let C represent the total charge and let h represent the number of hours parked. Complete the table and plot the ordered pairs.

h	1	2	3	4
$C =$				

2—Form: 4C—Ans: $C = 3 + 1(h - 1)$; 3, 4, 5, 6

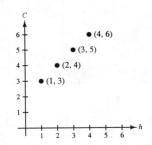

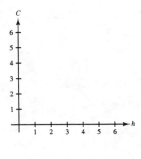

64. You park your vehicle in a parking garage which charges $4.00 for the first hour and $1.00 for each additional hour of parking. Write an equation that relates the total charge to the number of hours parked. Let C represent the total charge and let h represent the number of hours parked. Complete the table and plot the ordered pairs.

h	1	2	3	4
C =				

2—Ans: $C = 4 + 1(h - 1)$; 4, 5, 6, 7

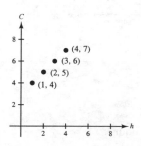

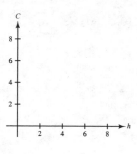

Section 4.2   Graphs of Equations in Two Variables

1.

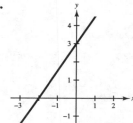

Match the graph with its equation.

(a) $y = \frac{3}{2}x + 3$ **(b)** $y = \frac{2}{3}x + 3$ **(c)** $y = -\frac{3}{2}x + 3$

(d) $y = -\frac{2}{3}x + 3$ **(e)** None of these

1—Form: 4A—Ans: a

2.

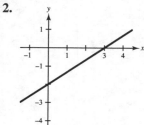

Match the graph with its equation.

(a) $y = \frac{3}{2}x - 2$ **(b)** $y = -\frac{2}{3}x - 2$ **(c)** $y = -\frac{3}{2}x - 2$

(d) $y = \frac{2}{3} - 2$ **(e)** None of these

1—Ans: d

3.

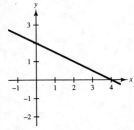

Match the graph with its equation.

(a) $y = -\frac{1}{2}x + 2$ **(b)** $y = \frac{1}{2}x + 2$ **(c)** $y = -2x + 2$

(d) $y = 2x + 2$ **(e)** None of these

1—Ans: a

4.

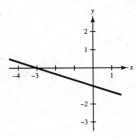

Match the graph with its equation.

(a) $y = 3x - 1$ **(b)** $y = -3x - 1$ **(c)** $y = \frac{1}{3}x - 1$

(d) $y = -\frac{1}{3}x - 1$ **(e)** None of these

1—Ans: d

5.

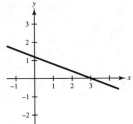

Match the graph with its equation.

(a) $y = \frac{5}{2}x + 3$ **(b)** $x + y + 2 = 0$ **(c)** $y = \frac{3}{4}x - 1$

(d) $y = -\frac{2}{5}(x - 3)$ **(e)** None of these

1—Ans: d

6.

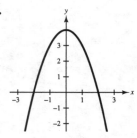

Match the graph with its equation.

(a) $y^2 - x = 4$ **(b)** $x^2 + y = 4$ **(c)** $y^2 + x = 4$

(d) $x^2 - y = 4$ **(e)** None of these

1—Ans: b

7.

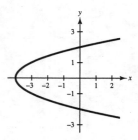

Match the graph with its equation.

(a) $y^2 - x = 4$ **(b)** $x^2 + y = 4$ **(c)** $y^2 + x = 4$

(d) $x^2 - y = 4$ **(e)** None of these

1—Ans: a

8.

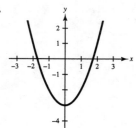

Match the graph with its equation.

(a) $x^2 + y = 3$ **(b)** $x^2 - y = 3$ **(c)** $y^2 + x = 3$

(d) $y^2 - x = 3$ **(e)** None of these

1—Ans: b

9.

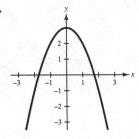

Match the graph with its equation.

(a) $y - x^2 = 3$

(b) $y + x^2 = 3$

(c) $x - y^2 = 3$

(d) $x + y^2 = 3$

(e) None of these

1—Form: 4A—Ans: b

10.

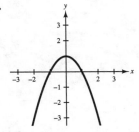

Match the graph with its equation.

(a) $x + y^2 = 1$

(b) $x - y^2 = 1$

(c) $y + x^2 = 1$

(d) $y - x^2 = 1$

(e) None of these

1—Form: 4B—Ans: c

11.

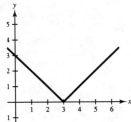

Match the graph with its equation.

(a) $y = |x - 3|$

(b) $y = |x + 3|$

(c) $|y - 2| = x$

(d) $|y + 3| = x$

(e) None of these

1—Ans: a

12.

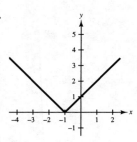

Match the graph with its equation.

(a) $y = |x| - 1$ **(b)** $y = |x| + 1$ **(c)** $y = |x + 1|$

(d) $y = |x - 1|$ **(e)** None of these

1—Ans: c

13.

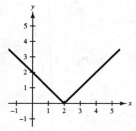

Match the graph with its equation.

(a) $y = |x| + 2$ **(b)** $y = |x - 2|$ **(c)** $y = |x| - 2$

(d) $y = |x + 2|$ **(e)** None of these

1—Form: 4B—Ans: b

14.

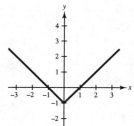

Match the graph with its equation.

(a) $y = |x| - 1$ **(b)** $y = |x| + 1$ **(c)** $y = |x + 1|$

(d) $y = |x - 1|$ **(e)** None of these

1—Ans: a

15.

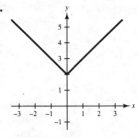

Match the graph with its equation.

(a) $y = |x| + 2$ **(b)** $y = |x - 2|$ **(c)** $y = |x| - 2$

(d) $y = |x + 2|$ **(e)** None of these

1—Ans: a

16. Complete the table and use the results to sketch the graph of the equation $y = \frac{2}{3}x + 1$.

x	-6	-3	0	3	6
$y =$					

1—Ans: $-3, -1, 1, 3, 5$

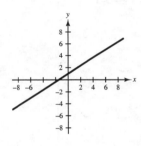

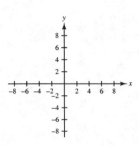

17. Complete the table and use the results to sketch the graph of the equation $y = -\frac{1}{2}x - 1$.

x	-8	-6	0	4	8
$y =$					

1—Ans: $3, 2, -1, -3, -5$

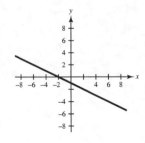

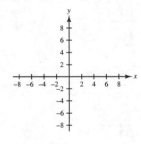

18. Complete the table and use the results to sketch the graph of the equation $x - 6 = 2y$.

x	-4	-2	0	2	4
$y =$					

2—Ans: $y = \frac{1}{2}x - 3$; $-5, -4, -3, -2, -1$

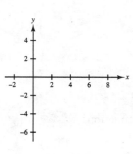

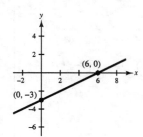

19. Complete the table and use the results to sketch the graph of the equation $x - 9 = 3y$.

x	-6	-3	0	3	6
$y =$					

2—Form: 4C—Ans: $y = \frac{1}{3}x - 3$; $-5, -4, -3, -2, -1$

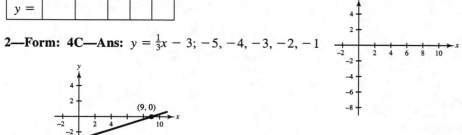

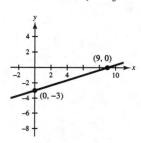

20. Complete the table and use the results to sketch the graph of the equation $x^2 + y = -1$.

x	-2	-1	0	1	2
$y =$					

2—Ans: $y = -x^2 - 1$; $-5, -2, -1, -2, -5$

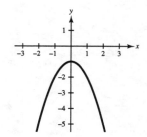

21. Complete the table and use the results to sketch the graph of the equation $x^2 + y = -4$.

x	-2	-1	0	1	2
$y =$					

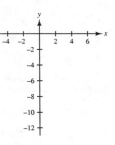

2—Form: 4C—Ans: $y = -x^2 - 4$; $-8, -5, -4, -5, -8$

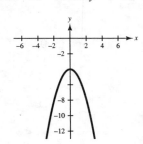

22. Find the intercepts of the graph of the equation $5x + 3y = 15$.

(a) $(5, 0)$ and $(0, 3)$ (b) $(-5, 0)$ and $(-3, 0)$ (c) $(3, 0)$ and $(0, 5)$

(d) $(-3, 0)$ and $(0, -5)$ (e) None of these

1—Ans: c

23. Find the intercepts of the graph of the equation $5x - 4y = 20$.

(a) $(0, 5)$ and $(4, 0)$ (b) $(0, -5)$ and $(-4, 0)$ (c) $(0, -5)$ and $(4, 0)$

(d) $(0, 5)$ and $(-4, 0)$ (e) None of these

1—Ans: c

24. Find the intercepts of the graph of the equation $4x - 5y = 20$.

(a) $(0, 4)$ and $(5, 0)$ (b) $(0, -4)$ and $(5, 0)$ (c) $(0, -4)$ and $(-5, 0)$

(d) $(0, 4)$ and $(-5, 0)$ (e) None of these

1—Ans: b

25. Find the intercepts of the graph of the equation $3x - 5y = 15$.

(a) $(-5, 0)$ and $(0, 3)$ (b) $(3, 0)$ and $(0, -5)$ (c) $(5, 0)$ and $(0, 3)$

(d) $(5, 0)$ and $(0, -3)$ (e) None of these

1—Ans: d

26. Find the intercepts of the graph of the equation $2x - 3y = 6$.

(a) $(3, 0)$ and $(0, -2)$ (b) $(2, 0)$ and $(0, 3)$ (c) $(3, 0)$ and $(0, 2)$

(d) $(2, 0)$ and $(0, -3)$ (e) None of these

1—Ans: a

27. Find the intercepts of the graph of the equation $y = |x| - 3$.

  (a) $(0, -3)$ **(b)** $(-3, 0)$ and $(0, -3)$ **(c)** $(-3, 0)$ and $(3, 0)$

  (d) $(0, -3)$; $(3, 0)$ and $(-3, 0)$ **(e)** $(0, -3)$ and $(3, 0)$

  1—Ans: d

28. Find the intercepts of the graph of the equation $y = |x| - 5$.

  (a) $(0, -5)$ **(b)** $(-5, 0)$ and $(0, -5)$ **(c)** $(-5, 0)$ and $(5, 0)$

  (d) $(0, -5)$ and $(5, 0)$ **(e)** $(0, -5)$; $(5, 0)$ and $(-5, 0)$

  1—Ans: e

29. Find the intercepts of the graph of the equation $y = 4 - x^2$.

  (a) $(2, 0)$ and $(-2, 0)$; $(0, 4)$ **(b)** $(0, 4)$ **(c)** $(2, 0)$ and $(-2, 0)$

  (d) $(0, 4)$ and $(2, 0)$ **(e)** None of these

  2—Ans: a

30. Find the intercepts of the graph of the equation $y = 9 - x^2$.

  (a) $(0, 9)$ **(b)** $(3, 0)$ and $(-3, 0)$ **(c)** $(3, 0)$ and $(-3, 0)$; $(0, 9)$

  (d) $(0, 9)$ and $(3, 0)$ **(e)** None of these

  2—Ans: c

31. Find all x- and y- intercepts of the graph of the equation $y = |x| - 4$.

  1—Ans: $(4, 0)$ and $(-4, 0)$; $(0, -4)$

32. Find all x- and y- intercepts of the graph of the equation $y = 3 - |x|$.

  1—Ans: $(3, 0)$ and $(-3, 0)$; $(0, 3)$

33. Find all x- and y- intercepts of the graph of the equation $y = x^2 - 4$.

  2—Ans: $(2, 0)$ and $(-2, 0)$; $(0, -4)$

34. Find all x- and y- intercepts of the graph of the equation $y = x^2 - 9$.

  2—Form: 4C—Ans: $(3, 0)$ and $(-3, 0)$; $(0, -9)$

35. Sketch the graph of the equation $x^2 + 12y = 36$. List at least five points used.

x				
y				

2—Ans: Points listed will vary.

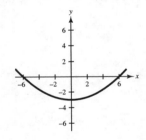

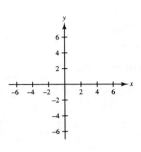

36. Sketch the graph of the equation $x^2 - 12y = 36$. List at least five points used.

x				
y				

2—Ans: Points listed will vary.

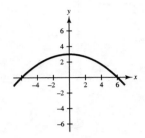

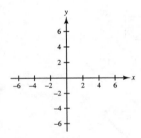

37. Sketch the graph of the equation $y^2 + 12x = 36$. List at least five points used.

x				
y				

2—Ans: Points listed will vary.

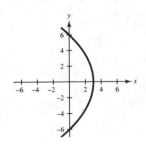

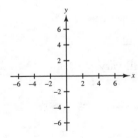

38. Sketch the graph of the equation $y^2 - 12x = 36$. List at least five points used.

x				
y				

2—Ans: Points listed will vary.

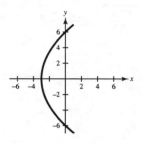

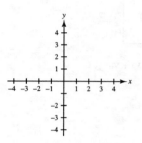

39. Sketch the graph of the equation $y = |x| - 2$. List at least five points used.

x				
y				

2—Ans: Points listed will vary.

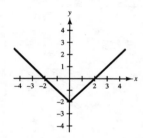

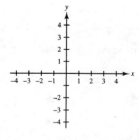

40. Sketch the graph of the equation $y = 2 - |x|$. List at least five points used.

x				
y				

2—Ans: Points listed will vary.

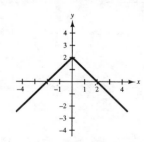

41. Use a graphing calculator to graph $y = 3x + 8$, in a standard setting. The result resembles which of the following?

(a)

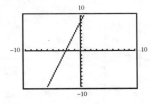

(b)

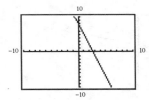

(c)

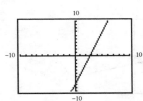

(d)

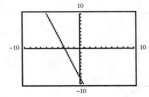

(e) None of these

1—T—Ans: a

42. Use a graphing calculator to graph $3y - x = 6$, in a standard setting. The result resembles which of the following?

(a)

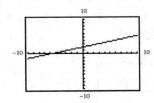

(b)

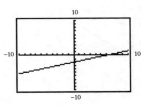

(c)

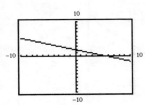

(d)

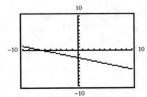

(e) None of these

1—T—Ans: a

43. Use a graphing calculator to graph $3y - x = -6$, in a standard setting. The result resembles which of the following?

(a)

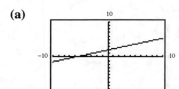

(b)

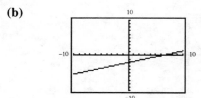

(c)

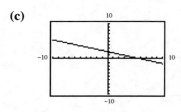

(d)

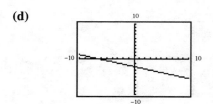

(e) None of these

1—T—Form: 4B—Ans: b

44. Use a graphing calculator to graph $y = |x + 2| + 1$, in a standard setting. The result resembles which of the following?

(a)

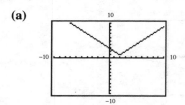

(b)

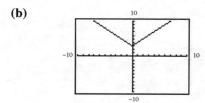

(c)

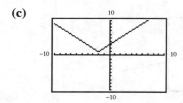

(d)

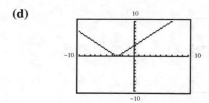

(e) None of these

1—T—Form: 4A—Ans: c

45. Use a graphing calculator to graph $y = |x + 1| + 2$, in a standard setting. The result resembles which of the following?

(a)

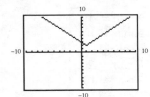

(b)

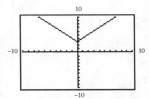

(c)

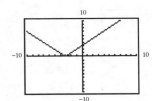

(d)

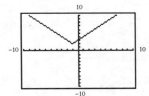

(e)   None of these

1—T—Ans: d

46. Use a graphing calculator to graph $y = -\frac{2}{7}x + 3$. Use a standard setting and sketch the result on the coordinate axes.

1—T—Ans:

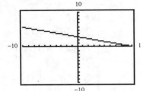

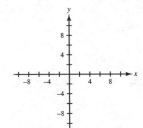

47. Use a graphing calculator to graph $y = |2x + 1|$. Use a standard setting and sketch the result on the coordinate axes.

1—T—Ans:

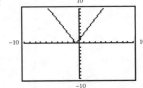

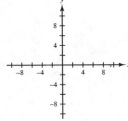

48. Use a graphing calculator on a standard setting to graph $y = 4 - \frac{1}{2}x^2$ and sketch the result on the coordinate axes.

1—T—Ans:

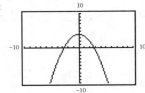

49. Choose a viewing window that shows the important characteristics of the graph of $y = x^2 - 15$.

(a)
```
RANGE
Xmin = -10
Xmax = 10
Xscl = 1
Ymin = -10
Ymax = 10
Yscl = 1
```

(b)
```
RANGE
Xmin = -20
Xmax = 20
Xscl = 5
Ymin = -10
Ymax = 10
Yscl = 1
```

(c)
```
RANGE
Xmin = -10
Xmax = 10
Xscl = 1
Ymin = -20
Ymax = 10
Yscl = 5
```

(d)
```
RANGE
Xmin = -10
Xmax = 10
Xscl = 1
Ymin = -10
Ymax = 20
Yscl = 5
```

(e) None of these

1—T—Ans: c

50. Choose a viewing window that shows the important characteristics of the graph of $y = x^2 - 18$.

(a)
```
RANGE
Xmin = -10
Xmax = 10
Xscl = 1
Ymin = -10
Ymax = 10
Yscl = 1
```

(b)
```
RANGE
Xmin = -20
Xmax = 20
Xscl = 5
Ymin = -10
Ymax = 10
Yscl = 1
```

(c)
```
RANGE
Xmin = -10
Xmax = 10
Xscl = 1
Ymin = -20
Ymax = 10
Yscl = 5
```

(d)
```
RANGE
Xmin = -10
Xmax = 10
Xscl = 1
Ymin = -10
Ymax = 20
Yscl = 5
```

(e) None of these

1—T—Ans: c

51. You are depreciating a computer worth $2400 over five years. At the end of five years, the salvage value is $600. Write an equation that relates the value of the computer to the number of years. Let y represent the value of the computer after t years. Sketch the graph of the equation.

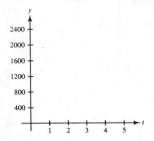

2—Ans: $y = 2400 - 360t$

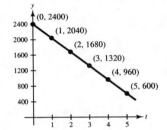

52. You are depreciating a computer worth $2400 over five years. At the end of five years, the salvage value is $800. Write an equation that relates the value of the computer to the number of years. Let y represent the value of the computer after t years. Sketch the graph of the equation.

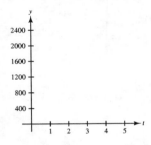

2—Ans: $y = 2400 - 320t$

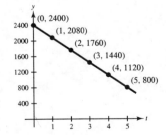

Section 4.3   Relations, Functions, and Graphs

1. Determine the domain of the relation $\{(-3, 4), (-2, 1), (-1, 0), (0, 1), (1, 4)\}$.

   1—Ans: $D = \{-3, -2, -1, 0, 1\}$

2. Determine the domain of the relation $\{(-1, 4), (0, 1), (1, 0), (2, 1), (3, 4)\}$.

   1—Ans: $D = \{-1, 0, 1, 2, 3\}$

3. Determine the range of the relation $\{(-3, 4), (-2, 1), (-1, 0), (0, 1), (1, 4)\}$.

   1—Ans: $R = \{0, 1, 4\}$

4. Determine the range of the relation $\{(-1, 4), (0, 1), (1, 0), (2, 1), (3, 4)\}$.

   1—Ans: $R = \{0, 1, 4\}$

5. Find the domain and the range of the relation
   $\{(1980, \$300), (1985, \$325), (1990, \$330), (1995, \$300)\}$.

   1—Ans: $D = \{1980, 1985, 1990, 1995\}$ and $R = \{\$300, \$325, \$330\}$

6. Find the domain and the range of the relation
   $\{(1975, \$420), (1980, \$450), (1985, \$420), (1990, \$425)\}$.

   1—Form: 4C—Ans: $D = \{1975, 1980, 1985, 1990\}$ and $R = \{\$420, \$425, \$450\}$

7. Determine the range of the function $h(x) = |x| + 1$ for the domain $D = \{-2, -1, 0, 1, 2\}$.
   Sketch a graphical representation of the function.

   2—Ans: $R = \{1, 2, 3\}$

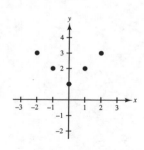

8. Determine the range of the function $h(x) = |x| - 1$ for the domain $D = \{-2, -1, 0, 1, 2\}$. Sketch a graphical representation of the function.

   2—Ans: $R = \{-1, 0, 1\}$

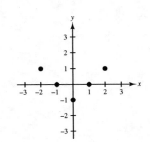
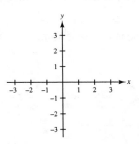

9. Which of the following relations is a function?

   (a) $\{(1, 3), (2, 5), (3, 7), (4, 5)\}$ **(b)** $\{(1, 3), (2, 5), (3, 7), (1, 5)\}$ **(c)** $\{(1, 3), (2, 5), (3, 7), (2, 3)\}$
   (d) $\{(1, 3), (2, 5), (3, 7), (3, 5)\}$ **(e)** None of these

   1—Form: 4A—Ans: a

10. Which of the following relations is a function?

    (a) $\{(2, 5), (3, 7), (4, 9), (3, 9)\}$ **(b)** $\{(2, 5), (3, 7), (4, 9), (5, 11)\}$ **(c)** $\{(2, 5), (3, 7), (4, 9), (2, 7)\}$
    (d) $\{(2, 5), (3, 7), (4, 9), (2, 9)\}$ **(e)** None of these

    1—Form: 4B—Ans: b

11. Explain why the relation is *not* a function.

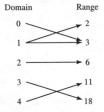

    1—Ans: 1 is paired with two different second components, 2 and 3.

12. Explain why the relation is *not* a function.

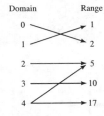

    1—Form: 4C—Ans: 4 is paired with two different second components, 5 and 17.

13. Explain why the relation $\{(x, 4), (y, 4), (z, 4)\}$ is a function.

    1—Ans: No first component has two different second components, therefore the relation is a function.

14. Explain why the relation $\{(x, 3), (y, 3), (z, 3)\}$ is a function.

1—Ans: No first component has two different second components, therefore the relation is a function.

15. Use the vertical line test to determine which of the graphs represents a function of x.

(a)

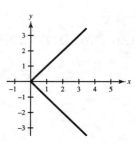

(b)

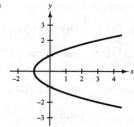

(c)

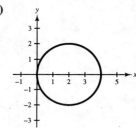

(d)

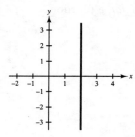

(e) None of these

1—Form: 4A—Ans: b

16. Use the vertical line test to determine which of the graphs represents a function of x.

(a)

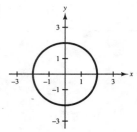

(b)

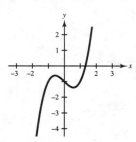

(c)

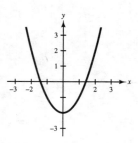

(d)

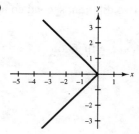

(e) None of these

1—Form: 4B—Ans: c

17. Use the vertical line test to determine which of the graphs represents a function of *x*.

(a)

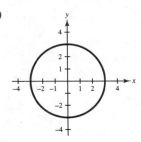

(b)

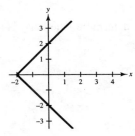

(c)

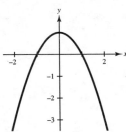

(d)

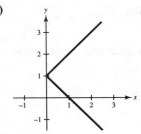

(e) None of these

1—Ans: c

18. Use the vertical line test to determine which of the graphs represents a function of *x*.

(a)

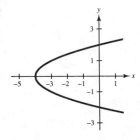

(b)

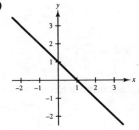

(c)

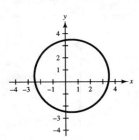

(d)

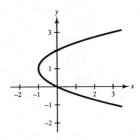

(e) None of these

1—Ans: d

19. Use the vertical line test to determine whether *y* is a function of *x*.

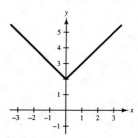

    1—Ans: Yes, *y* is a function of *x*.

20. Use the vertical line test to determine whether *y* is a function of *x*.

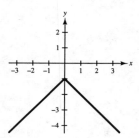

    1—Ans: Yes, *y* is a function of *x*.

21. Use the vertical line test to determine whether *y* is a function of *x*.

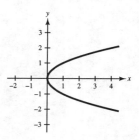

    1—Form: 4C—Ans: No, *y* is not a function of *x*.

22. Use the vertical line test to determine whether *y* is a function of *x*.

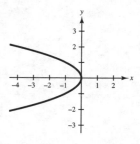

    1—Ans: No, *y* is not a function of *x*.

23. Sketch the graph of the equation, $|x| + y = 2$, and use the vertical line test to determine whether y is a function of x.

   2—Ans: y is a function of x.

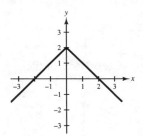

24. Sketch the graph of the equation, $|x| - y = 2$, and use the vertical line test to determine whether y is a function of x.

   2—Ans: y is a function of x.

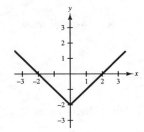

25. Use a graphing utility to graph the equation $y = x^3 + 2x^2$ in a standard setting. Sketch the graph and use the vertical line test to determine whether y is a function of x.

   2—T—Ans: Yes, the equation is a function.

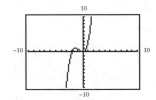

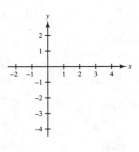

26. Use a graphing utility to graph the equation $y = x^3 - 2x^2$ in a standard setting. Sketch the graph and use the vertical line test to determine whether y is a function of x.

   2—T—Ans: Yes, the equation is a function.

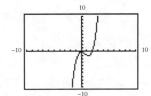

27. Given $f(x) = x^3 + x$, evaluate $f(-1)$.

   (a) -2 **(b)** 0 **(c)** -4 **(d)** 2 **(e)** None of these

   1—Ans: a

28. Given $f(x) = x^3 - x$, evaluate $f(-1)$.

   (a) -4 **(b)** 0 **(c)** -2 **(d)** 2 **(e)** None of these

   1—Ans: b

29. Given $f(x) = -x^2 + 2$, evaluate $f(3)$.

   (a) 11 **(b)** -7 **(c)** -4 **(d)** 8 **(e)** None of these

   2—Form: 4A—Ans: b

30. Given $f(x) = -x^2 + 1$, evaluate $f(3)$.

   (a) 10 **(b)** -5 **(c)** 7 **(d)** -8 **(e)** None of these

   2—Form: 4B—Ans: d

31. Given $f(x) = 3 - 2x$, evaluate $f(-4)$.

   (a) -5 **(b)** 11 **(c)** -4 **(d)** 4 **(e)** None of these

   1—Ans: b

32. Given $f(x) = 4 - \frac{1}{3}x$, evaluate $f(-3)$.

   (a) 5 **(b)** 3 **(c)** 7 **(d)** 1 **(e)** None of these

   1—Ans: a

33. Given $f(x) = |x| - 4$, evaluate $f(-2)$.

   (a) -6 **(b)** 2 **(c)** 6 **(d)** -2 **(e)** None of these

   1—Ans: d

34. Given $f(x) = 10 - |x|$, evaluate $f(-5)$.

   (a) 5 **(b)** 15 **(c)** -5 **(d)** -15 **(e)** None of these

   1—Ans: a

35. Given $f(x) = 3x + 4$, evaluate $f(2)$.

   1—Ans: 10

36. Given $f(x) = 6x - 5$, evaluate $f(-3)$.

   1—Ans: -23

37. Given $g(s) = \frac{1}{2}s^2$, evaluate $g(6)$.

   1—Ans: 18

38. Given $g(s) = \frac{1}{2}s^2$, evaluate $g(8)$.

   1—Ans: 32

39. Given $h(t) = |t + 4|$, evaluate $h(-6)$.

   1—Ans: 2

40. Given $h(t) = |t| - 5$, evaluate $h(-2)$.

   1—Ans: -3

41. Given $f(x) = x^3 - 3$, evaluate $f(0)$.

   1—Ans: -3

42. Given $f(x) = x^3 + 3$, evaluate $f(-1)$.

   1—Ans: 2

43. Given $h(t) = -16t^2 + 100$, evaluate $h(1.5)$.

   2—Ans: 64

44. Given $h(t) = -16t^2 + 100$, evaluate $h(2.5)$.

   2—Ans: 0

45. Write the formula for the circumference C of a circle with radius r. Explain why the formula is a function.

   1—Ans: $C = 2\pi r$. The formula is a function because no first component r has two different second components C.

46. Write the formula for the area A of a circle with radius r. Explain why the formula is a function.

   1—Ans: $A = \pi r^2$. The formula is a function because no first component r has two different second components A.

47. The function $d(t) = 55t$ gives the distance (in miles) that a car will travel in t hours at an average speed of 55 miles per hour. Find the distance traveled for $t = 3$.

   1—Ans: 165 miles

48. The function $d(t) = 55t$ gives the distance (in miles) that a car will travel in t hours at an average speed of 55 miles per hour. Find the distance traveled for $t = 4$.

   1—Ans: 220 miles

49. The demand for a product is a function of its price. Given the demand function $f(p) = 25 - 2p$, where p is the price in dollars, find $f(5)$.

1—Ans: 15

50. The demand for a product is a function of its price. Given the demand function $f(p) = 25 - 2p$, where p is the price in dollars, find $f(10)$.

1—Ans: 5

51. The function $I(t) = 3t$ gives the simple interest earned on \$100 invested at an annual rate of 3%. Find the interest earned after 4 years.

1—Ans: \$12

52. The function $I(t) = 5.25t$ gives the simple interest earned on \$150 invested at an annual rate of 3.5%. Find the interest earned after 6 years.

1—Ans: \$31.50

53. The function $V(r) = \frac{4}{3}\pi r^3$ gives the volume of a sphere of radius r. Find the volume of a sphere of radius 1 in.

2—Ans: $\frac{4}{3}\pi$ cubic inches

54. The function $V(r) = \frac{4}{3}\pi r^3$ gives the volume of a sphere of radius r. Find the volume of a sphere of radius 2 ft.

2—Ans: $\frac{32}{2}\pi$ cubic feet

Section 4.4   Slope and Graphs of Linear Equations

1. Estimate the slope of the line from its graph.

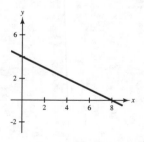

1—Ans: $-\frac{1}{2}$

2. Estimate the slope of the line from its graph.

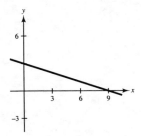

1—Ans: $-\frac{1}{3}$

3. A line with positive slope ($m > 0$).

(a) Rises from left to right   (b) Falls from left to right   (c) Is horizontal

(d) Is vertical   (e) None of these

2—Ans: a

4. A line with negative slope ($m < 0$).

(a) Rises from left to right   (b) Falls from left to right   (c) Is horizontal

(d) Is vertical   (e) None of these

2—Ans: b

5. Choose the correct description of the line through the points $(-2, 3)$ and $(-2, 1)$.

(a) The line is vertical   (b) The line is horizontal

(c) The line rises from the left to right   (d) The line falls from left to right

(e) None of these

1—Ans: a

6. Choose the correct description of the line through the points $(-2, 3)$ and $(1, 3)$.

(a) The line is vertical   (b) The line is horizontal

(c) The line rises from the left to right   (d) The line falls from left to right

(e) None of these

1—Ans: b

7. Choose the correct description of the line through the points $(-2, 3)$ and $(1, -3)$.

(a) The line is vertical   (b) The line is horizontal

(c) The line rises from the left to right   (d) The line falls from left to right

(e) None of these

1—Ans: d

8. Choose the correct description of the line through the points $(-2, 3)$ and $(1, 5)$.

   (a) The line is vertical   **(b)** The line is horizontal

   (c) The line rises from the left to right   **(d)** The line falls from left to right

   (e) None of these

   1—Ans: c

9. Which two points are on a horizontal line?

   (a) $(2, 4), (2, -6)$ **(b)** $(-3, -2), (4, 0)$ **(c)** $(2, 4), (-7, 4)$

   (d) $(-2, 5), (3, 1)$ **(e)** None of these

   1—Ans: c

10. Which two points are on a line with a positive slope?

   (a) $(2, 4), (2, -6)$ **(b)** $(-3, -2), (4, 0)$ **(c)** $(2, 4), (-7, 4)$

   (d) $(-2, 5), (3, 1)$ **(e)** None of these

   1—Ans: b

11. Which two points are on a line with a negative slope?

   (a) $(2, 4), (2, -6)$ **(b)** $(-3, -2), (4, 0)$ **(c)** $(2, 4), (-7, 4)$

   (d) $(-2, 5), (3, 1)$ **(e)** None of these

   1—Ans: d

12. Which two points are on a vertical line?

   (a) $(2, 4), (2, -6)$ **(b)** $(-3, -2), (4, 0)$ **(c)** $(2, 4), (-7, 4)$

   (d) $(-2, 5), (3, 1)$ **(e)** None of these

   1—Ans: a

13. A line is vertical. Describe its slope.

   1—Ans: Undefined

14. A line is horizontal. Describe its slope.

   1—Ans: Zero, 0

15. The slope of a line is positive. Describe the behavior of the line.

   1—Ans: It rises from left to right.

16. The slope of a line is negative. Describe the behavior of the line.

   1—Ans: It falls from left to right.

17. Find x so that the line joining $(x, -4)$ and $(2, 6)$ rises from left to right. If not possible, so state.

   2—Ans: Any $x < 2$

18. Find x so that the line joining $(x, -4)$ and $(2, 6)$ falls from left to right. If not possible, so state.

   2—Ans: Any $x > 2$

19. Find the slope of the line passing through the points $(-2, 4)$ and $(3, 2)$.

   (a) $-\frac{5}{2}$ **(b)** 6   **(c)** $-\frac{2}{5}$ **(d)** $\frac{2}{5}$ **(e)** None of these

   1—Ans: c

20. Find the slope of the line passing through the points $(2, -4)$ and $(3, 2)$.

   (a) $-\frac{5}{2}$ **(b)** 6   **(c)** $-\frac{2}{5}$ **(d)** $\frac{2}{5}$ **(e)** None of these

   1—Ans: b

21. Find the slope of the line passing through the points $(4, -2)$ and $(2, 3)$.

   (a) $-\frac{5}{2}$ **(b)** $\frac{1}{6}$ **(c)** $-\frac{2}{5}$ **(d)** $\frac{5}{2}$ **(e)** None of these

   1—Ans: a

22. Find the slope of the line passing through the points $(-2, 2)$ and $(3, 4)$.

   (a) $-\frac{5}{2}$ **(b)** 6   **(c)** $-\frac{2}{5}$ **(d)** $\frac{2}{5}$ **(e)** None of these

   1—Ans: d

23. Find the slope of the line passing through the points $(-3, -2)$ and $(1, 3)$.

   (a) $\frac{4}{5}$ **(b)** 2   **(c)** $\frac{5}{4}$ **(d)** -2 **(e)** None of these

   1—Form: 4A—Ans: c

24. Find the slope of the line passing through the points $(-4, -1)$ and $(3, 4)$.

   (a) $\frac{5}{7}$ **(b)** 2   **(c)** $\frac{7}{5}$ **(d)** -2 **(e)** None of these

   1—Form: 4B—Ans: a

25. Find the slope of the line passing through the points $(-3, -5)$ and $(2, 4)$.

   1—Form: 4C—Ans: $\frac{9}{5}$

26. Find the slope of the line passing through the points $(-5, 2)$ and $(1, 6)$.

   1—Ans: $\frac{2}{3}$

27. Find the slope of the line passing through the points $(6, 8)$ and $(-1, 8)$.

   1—Ans: 0

28. Find the slope of the line passing through the points $(1, 7)$ and $(-3, 7)$.

1—Ans: 0

29. Which of the following equations of a line is in *slope-intercept form?*

(a) $3y + 2x = 7$ $\qquad$ **(b)** $x = -\dfrac{3}{2}y + \dfrac{7}{2}$ $\qquad$ **(c)** $y = -\dfrac{2}{3}x + \dfrac{7}{3}$

(d) $\dfrac{x}{3} + \dfrac{y}{2} = \dfrac{7}{6}$ $\qquad$ **(e)** None of these

1—Ans: c

30. Which of the following equations of a line is in *slope-intercept form?*

(a) $2x - 5y = 4$ $\qquad$ **(b)** $y = \dfrac{2}{5}x - \dfrac{4}{5}$ $\qquad$ **(c)** $x = \dfrac{5}{2}y + 2$

(d) $\dfrac{x}{5} - \dfrac{y}{2} = \dfrac{2}{5}$ $\qquad$ **(e)** None of these

1—Ans: b

31. Which of the following equations of a line is in *slope-intercept form?*

(a) $y = -\dfrac{1}{2}x + 7$ $\qquad$ **(b)** $x = -2y + 7$ $\qquad$ **(c)** $\dfrac{x}{2} + \dfrac{y}{1} = \dfrac{7}{2}$

(d) $2y + x = 7$ $\qquad$ **(e)** None of these

1—Ans: a

32. Which of the following equations of a line is in *slope-intercept form?*

(a) $x = \dfrac{1}{7}y + \dfrac{2}{7}$ $\qquad$ **(b)** $\dfrac{x}{1} - \dfrac{y}{7} = \dfrac{2}{7}$ $\qquad$ **(c)** $7x - y = 2$

(d) $y = 7x - 2$ $\qquad$ **(e)** None of these

1—Ans: d

33. The slope of the line $3x - 5y = 4$ is:

(a) $-\dfrac{5}{3}$ $\qquad$ **(b)** $\dfrac{5}{3}$ $\qquad$ **(c)** $-\dfrac{3}{5}$ $\qquad$ **(d)** $\dfrac{3}{5}$ $\qquad$ **(e)** None of these

1—Form: 4A—Ans: d

34. The slope of the line $3x + 5y = 4$ is:

(a) $-\dfrac{5}{3}$ $\qquad$ **(b)** $\dfrac{5}{3}$ $\qquad$ **(c)** $-\dfrac{3}{5}$ $\qquad$ **(d)** $\dfrac{3}{5}$ $\qquad$ **(e)** None of these

1—Form: 4B—Ans: c

35. The slope of the line $5x - 3y = 4$ is:

(a) $-\dfrac{5}{3}$ $\qquad$ **(b)** $\dfrac{5}{3}$ $\qquad$ **(c)** $-\dfrac{3}{5}$ $\qquad$ **(d)** $\dfrac{3}{5}$ $\qquad$ **(e)** None of these

1—Ans: b

36. The slope of the line $5x + 3y = 4$ is:

(a) $-\frac{5}{3}$ (b) $\frac{5}{3}$ (c) $-\frac{3}{5}$ (d) $\frac{3}{5}$ (e) None of these

1—Ans: a

37. Find the slope of the line $5x - 2y = 9$.

1—Ans: $m = \frac{5}{2}$

38. Find the slope of the line $9x - 3y = 5$.

1—Ans: $m = 3$

39. The graph of the equation $y = \frac{1}{2}x + 2$ is:

(a)

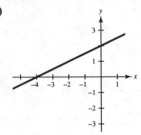

(b)

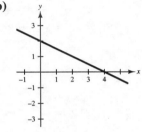

(c)

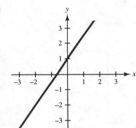

(d)

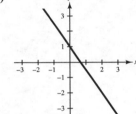

1—Ans: a

40. The graph of the equation $y = \frac{3}{2}x + 1$ is:

(a)

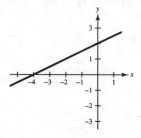

(b)

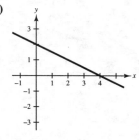

(c)

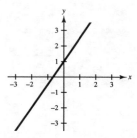

(d)

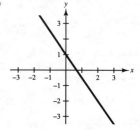

1—Ans: c

41. The graph of the equation $y = -\frac{1}{2}x + 2$ is:

(a)

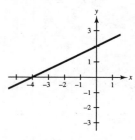

(b)

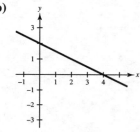

(c)

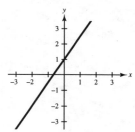

(d)

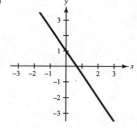

1—Form: 4A—Ans: b

42. The graph of the equation $y = -\frac{3}{2}x + 1$ is:

(a)

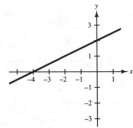

(b)

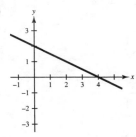

(c)

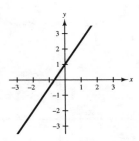

(d)

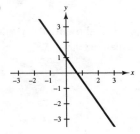

1—Form: 4B—Ans: d

43. Write the equation $3x + 2y - 10 = 0$ in *slope-intercept form*. Use the slope and y-intercept to graph the line.

2—Ans: $y = -\frac{3}{2}x + 5$

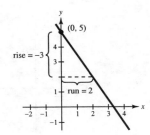

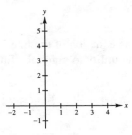

44. Write the equation $5x + 2y - 8 = 0$ in *slope-intercept form*. Use the slope and y-intercept to graph the line.

2—Form: 4C—Ans: $y = -\frac{5}{2}x + 4$

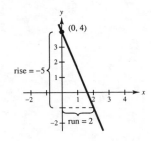

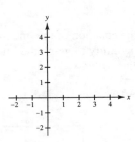

45. Graph the equation $y = -\frac{4}{3}x - 2$ showing the *y*-intercept and one additional point, by coordinates, on the coordinate axes.

1—Ans:

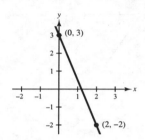

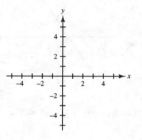

46. Graph the equation $y = -\frac{5}{2}x + 3$ showing the *y*-intercept and one additional point, by coordinates, on the coordinate axes.

1—Ans:

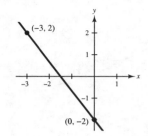

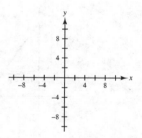

47. Write the equation of the line $3x + 4y - 12 = 0$ in *slope-intercept form.* Use a graphing utility to graph the line in a standard setting. Determine any intercepts of the line.

2—T—Ans: $y = -\frac{3}{4}x + 3$; $(4, 0)$ and $(0, 3)$

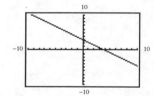

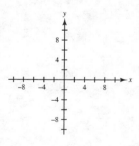

48. Write the equation of the line $3x - 4y + 12 = 0$ in *slope-intercept form.* Use a graphing utility to graph the line in a standard setting. Determine any intercepts of the line.

2—T—Ans: $y = \frac{3}{4}x + 3$; $(-4, 0)$ and $(0, 3)$

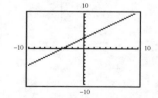

49. Write the equation in *slope-intercept form* for the line shown graphically.

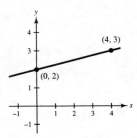

1—Ans: $y = \frac{1}{4}x + 2$

50. Write the equation in *slope-intercept form* for the line shown graphically.

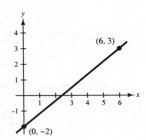

1—Ans: $y = \frac{5}{6}x - 2$

51. Choose the line which is *parallel* to $y = -3x + 7$.

   (a) $x - 3y = 7$ **(b)** $6x + 2y = 7$ **(c)** $2x + 6y = 7$

   (d) $3x - y = 7$ **(e)** None of these

   1—Ans: b

52. Choose the line which is *parallel* to $y = \frac{1}{3}x + 5$.

   (a) $2x - 6y = 5$ **(b)** $6x + 2y = 5$ **(c)** $2x + 6y = 5$

   (d) $3x - y = 5$ **(e)** None of these

   1—Ans: a

53. Choose the line which is *perpendicular* to $y = \frac{1}{3}x + 5$.

   (a) $2x - 6y = 5$ **(b)** $6x + 2y = 5$ **(c)** $2x + 6y = 5$

   (d) $3x - y = 5$ **(e)** None of these

   1—Ans: b

54. Choose the line which is *perpendicular* to $y = -\frac{1}{3}x + 4$.

   (a) $x - 3y = 4$ **(b)** $3x + y = 4$ **(c)** $x + 3y = 4$

   (d) $3x - y = 4$ **(e)** None of these

   1—Ans: d

55. Determine whether the pair of lines $y = \frac{1}{2}x - 5$; $y = \frac{1}{2}x + 7$ are perpendicular, parallel, or neither.

    1—Ans: Parallel

56. Determine whether the pair of lines $y = \frac{5}{3}x - 4$; $y = \frac{3}{5}x - 2$ are perpendicular, parallel, or neither.

    1—Ans: Neither

57. Determine whether the pair of lines $y = \frac{3}{7}x + 3$; $y = -\frac{7}{3}x + 3$ are perpendicular, parallel, or neither.

    1—Ans: Perpendicular

58. Determine whether the pair of lines $y = -\frac{3}{8}x - 2$; $y = \frac{8}{3}x + 2$ are perpendicular, parallel, or neither.

    1—Ans: Perpendicular

59. Determine whether the pair of lines $4x + 5y = 6$; $4x - 5y = 6$ are perpendicular, parallel, or neither.

    2—Ans: Neither

60. Determine whether the pair of lines $4x - 5y = 6$; $5x + 4y = 6$ are perpendicular, parallel, or neither.

    2—Ans: Perpendicular

61. Determine whether the pair of lines $4x + 3y = 4$; $8x + 6y = 3$ are perpendicular, parallel, or neither.

    2—Ans: Parallel

62. Determine whether the pair of lines $4x - 5y = 6$; $5x - 4y = 6$ are perpendicular, parallel, or neither.

    2—Ans: Neither

63. Determine whether the pair of lines $2x + y + 3 = 0$ and $x - 2y + 2 = 0$ are perpendicular, parallel, or neither.

    2—Form: 4C—Ans: Perpendicular

64. Determine whether the pair of lines $3x + y - 4 = 0$ and $x - 3y + 1 = 0$ are perpendicular, parallel, or neither.

    2—Ans: Perpendicular

65. Determine whether the pair of lines $2x + y - 1 = 0$ and $2x + y + 2 = 0$ are perpendicular, parallel, or neither.

2—Ans: Parallel

66. Determine whether the pair of lines $4x + y - 3 = 0$ and $4x + y + 2 = 0$ are perpendicular, parallel, or neither.

2—Ans: Parallel

Section 4.5   **Equations of Lines**

1. Find the slope of the line $y + 2 = 0$. If it is not possible, explain why.

1—Ans: $m = 0$

2. Find the slope of the line $x + 2 = 0$. If it is not possible, explain why.

1—Ans: The slope of a vertical line is undefined.

3. Find an equation of the line with slope 5 and passing through the point $(3, -2)$.
Write your answer in *point-slope form*.

   (a) $(x - 3) = 5(y + 2)$ (b) $y + 2 = 5(x - 3)$ (c) $y - 2 = 5(x + 3)$

   (d) $y - 3 = 5(x + 2)$ (e) None of these

1—Ans: b

4. Find an equation of the line with slope $-\frac{3}{2}$ and passing through the point $(4, -1)$.
Write your answer in *point-slope form*.

   (a) $y - 1 = -\frac{3}{2}(x + 4)$ (b) $x - 4 = \frac{2}{3}(y + 1)$ (c) $y - 4 = -\frac{3}{2}(x + 1)$

   (d) $y + 1 = -\frac{3}{2}(x - 4)$ (e) None of these

1—Ans: d

5. Find an equation of the line with slope $\frac{1}{2}$ and passing through the point $(2, -1)$.
Write your answer in *general form*.

   (a) $y = \frac{1}{2}x - 2$ (b) $x - 2y - 4 = 0$ (c) $x - 2y + 4 = 0$

   (d) $y = \frac{1}{2}x + 2$ (e) None of these

2—Ans: b

6. Find an equation of the line with slope $\frac{1}{3}$ and passing through the point $(2, -1)$.
Write your answer in *general form*.

   (a) $y = \frac{1}{3}x - \frac{5}{3}$ (b) $x - 3y + 5 = 0$ (c) $x - 3y - 5 = 0$

   (d) $y = \frac{1}{3}x + \frac{5}{3}$ (e) None of these

2—Ans: c

7. Write the *point-slope form* of the equation of the line passing through the point $(-7, 2)$ with the slope of -4.

   1—Ans: $(y - 2) = -4(x + 7)$

8. Write the *point-slope form* of the equation of the line passing through the point $(5, -7)$ with the slope of $-\frac{2}{5}$.

   1—Ans: $(y + 7) = -\frac{2}{5}(x - 5)$

9. Write the *point-slope form* of the equation of the line passing through the point $(8, -4)$ with the slope of $\frac{5}{12}$.

   1—Ans: $(y + 4) = \frac{5}{12}(x - 8)$

10. Write the *point-slope form* of the equation of the line passing through the point $(-4, 7)$ with the slope of $\frac{2}{9}$.

    1—Ans: $(y - 7) = \frac{2}{9}(x + 4)$

11. Write an equation of the line passing through the points $(2, 4)$ and $(-7, 2)$. Write your answer in *slope-intercept form.*

    (a) $y = -\frac{9}{2}x + 13$ **(b)** $y = \frac{9}{2}x - 5$ **(c)** $y = -\frac{2}{9}x + \frac{40}{9}$

    (d) $y = \frac{2}{9}x + \frac{32}{9}$ **(e)** None of these

    1—Ans: d

12. Write an equation of the line passing through the points $(4, 2)$ and $(2, -7)$. Write your answer in *slope-intercept form.*

    (a) $y = -\frac{9}{2}x + 20$ **(b)** $y = \frac{9}{2}x - 16$ **(c)** $y = -\frac{2}{9}x + \frac{18}{9}$

    (d) $y = \frac{2}{9}x + \frac{10}{9}$ **(e)** None of these

    1—Ans: b

13. Write an equation of the line passing through the points $(1, -5)$ and $(3, 2)$. Write your answer in *general form.*

    (a) $7x - 2y - 17 = 0$ **(b)** $7x + 2y - 25 = 0$ **(c)** $2x - 7y + 8 = 0$

    (d) $2x + 7y - 20 = 0$ **(e)** None of these

    2—Form: 4A—Ans: a

14. Write an equation of the line passing through the points $(2, -5)$ and $(5, 2)$. Write your answer in *general form.*

    (a) $7x + 3y - 41 = 0$ **(b)** $7x - 3y - 29 = 0$ **(c)** $3x - 7y - 1 = 0$

    (d) $3x + 7y - 29 = 0$ **(e)** None of these

    2—Form: 4B—Ans: b

15. A line passes through points $(-2, 4)$ and $(7, 2)$. Write its equation in *slope-intercept form*.

2—Ans: $y = -\frac{2}{9}x + \frac{32}{9}$

16. A line passes through points $(2, 4)$ and $(7, -2)$. Write its equation in *slope-intercept form*.

2—Ans: $y = -\frac{6}{5}x + \frac{32}{5}$

17. A line passes through points $(4, -2)$ and $(2, 7)$. Write its equation in *slope-intercept form*.

2—Ans: $y = -\frac{9}{2}x + 16$

18. A line passes through points $(4, 2)$ and $(-2, 7)$. Write its equation in *slope-intercept form*.

2—Form: 4C—Ans: $y = -\frac{5}{6}x + \frac{16}{3}$

19. Which of the following equations represents a horizontal line?

(a) $2x + 3y - 2 = 0$ (b) $5x - 12 = 0$ (c) $4y + 9 = 0$

(d) $3x - 4y - 12 = 0$ (e) None of these

1—Ans: c

20. Which of the following equations represents a horizontal line?

(a) $5y - 12 = 0$ (b) $7x - 4 = 0$ (c) $3x + 7y - 4 = 0$

(d) $2x + 2y - 5 = 0$ (e) None of these

1—Ans: a

21. Which of the following equations represents a vertical line?

(a) $5x + 4 = 0$ (b) $5x + 4y - 9 = 0$ (c) $4x - 5y + 9 = 0$

(d) $4y + 5 = 0$ (e) None of these

1—Ans: a

22. Which of the following equations represents a vertical line?

(a) $4x + 7y - 3 = 0$ (b) $4y - 7 = 0$ (c) $7x - 4y - 3 = 0$

(d) $7x - 4 = 0$ (e) None of these

1—Ans: d

23. Write an equation for a vertical line through $(4, -2)$.

(a) $x = -2$ (b) $y = -2$ (c) $y = 4$ (d) $x = 4$ (e) None of these

1—Form: 4A—Ans: d

24. Write an equation for a horizontal line through $(4, -2)$.

(a) $x = -2$ (b) $y = -2$ (c) $y = 4$ (d) $x = 4$ (e) None of these

1—Form: 4B—Ans: b

25. A horizontal line has a y-intercept of $(0, -2)$. Write its equation.

1—Ans: $y = -2$

26. A horizontal line passes through the point $(3, 2)$. Write its equation.

1—Ans: $y = 2$

27. A horizontal line passes through the point $(-5, 3)$. Write its equation.

1—Ans: $y = 3$

28. A horizontal line passes through the origin. Write its equation.

1—Ans: $y = 0$

29. A vertical line passes through the point $(3, 2)$. Write its equation.

1—Ans: $x = 3$

30. A vertical line passes through the point $(-5, 3)$. Write its equation.

1—Ans: $x = -5$

31. A vertical line passes through the origin. Write its equation.

1—Ans: $x = 0$

32. A vertical line has an x-intercept of $(3, 0)$. Write its equation.

1—Ans: $x = 3$

33. A line is parallel to $3x + 2y = 8$ and passes through the point $(5, 2)$. Its equation is:

(a) $y - 5 = -\frac{3}{2}(x - 2)$ (b) $y - 2 = \frac{2}{3}(x - 5)$ (c) $y - 2 = \frac{3}{2}(x - 5)$

(d) $y - 2 = -\frac{3}{2}(x - 5)$ (e) None of these

2—Ans: d

34. A line is parallel to $3x - 2y = 8$ and passes through the point $(5, 2)$. Its equation is:

(a) $y - 5 = -\frac{3}{2}(x - 2)$ (b) $y - 2 = \frac{2}{3}(x - 5)$ (c) $y - 2 = \frac{3}{2}(x - 5)$

(d) $y - 2 = -\frac{3}{2}(x - 5)$ (e) None of these

2—Ans: c

35. A line is parallel to $3x + 2y = 8$ and passes through the point $(2, 5)$. Its equation is:

   (a) $y - 5 = -\frac{3}{2}(x - 2)$ **(b)** $y - 2 = \frac{2}{3}(x - 5)$ **(c)** $y - 2 = \frac{3}{2}(x - 5)$

   (d) $y - 2 = -\frac{3}{2}(x - 5)$ **(e)** None of these

   2—Ans: a

36. A line is parallel to $2x - 3y = 10$ and passes through the point $(5, 2)$. Its equation is:

   (a) $y - 5 = -\frac{3}{2}(x - 2)$ **(b)** $y - 2 = \frac{2}{3}(x - 5)$ **(c)** $y - 2 = \frac{3}{2}(x - 5)$

   (d) $y - 2 = -\frac{3}{2}(x - 5)$ **(e)** None of these

   2—Ans: b

37. A line is perpendicular to $3x + 2y = 8$ and passes through the point $(5, 2)$. Its equation is:

   (a) $y - 2 = -\frac{3}{2}(x - 5)$ **(b)** $y - 2 = \frac{2}{3}(x - 5)$ **(c)** $y - 2 = -\frac{2}{3}(x - 5)$

   (d) $y - 5 = \frac{2}{3}(x - 2)$ **(e)** None of these

   2—Form: 4A—Ans: b

38. A line is perpendicular to $3x - 2y = 8$ and passes through the point $(5, 2)$. Its equation is:

   (a) $y - 2 = -\frac{3}{2}(x - 5)$ **(b)** $y - 2 = \frac{2}{3}(x - 5)$ **(c)** $y - 2 = -\frac{2}{3}(x - 5)$

   (d) $y - 5 = \frac{2}{3}(x - 2)$ **(e)** None of these

   2—Form: 4B—Ans: c

39. A line is perpendicular to $2x - 3y = 8$ and passes through the point $(5, 2)$. Its equation is:

   (a) $y - 2 = -\frac{3}{2}(x - 5)$ **(b)** $y - 2 = \frac{2}{3}(x - 5)$ **(c)** $y - 2 = -\frac{2}{3}(x - 5)$

   (d) $y - 5 = -\frac{3}{2}(x - 2)$ **(e)** None of these

   2—Ans: a

40. A line is perpendicular to $2x - 3y = 8$ and passes through the point $(2, 5)$. Its equation is:

   (a) $y - 2 = -\frac{3}{2}(x - 5)$ **(b)** $y - 5 = \frac{2}{3}(x - 2)$ **(c)** $y - 5 = -\frac{2}{3}(x - 2)$

   (d) $y - 5 = -\frac{3}{2}(x - 2)$ **(e)** None of these

   2—Ans: d

41. Find an equation of the line that passes through the point $(3, 1)$ and is parallel to the line $x + 4y - 8 = 0$.

   2—Form: 4C—Ans: $y = -\frac{1}{4}x + \frac{7}{4}$

42. Find an equation of the line that passes through the point $(4, 2)$ and is parallel to the line $x + 3y - 6 = 0$.

     2—Ans: $y = -\frac{1}{3}x + \frac{10}{3}$

43. Write in *general form* the equation of a line which is parallel to $7x - 12y - 4 = 0$ and passes through point $(2, -1)$.

     2—Ans: $7x - 12y - 26 = 0$

44. Write in *general form* the equation of a line which is parallel to $7x + 12y - 4 = 0$ and passes through point $(2, -1)$.

     2—Ans: $7x + 12y - 2 = 0$

45. Find an equation of the line that passes through the point $(3, 1)$ and is perpendicular to the line $x + 4y - 8 = 0$.

     2—Ans: $y = 4x - 11$

46. Find an equation of the line that passes through the point $(4, 2)$ and is perpendicular to the line $x + 3y - 6 = 0$.

     2—Ans: $y = 3x - 10$

47. Write in *general form* the equation of a line which is perpendicular to $12x - 7y - 4 = 0$ and passes through point $(2, -1)$.

     2—Ans: $7x + 12y - 2 = 0$

48. Write in *general form* the equation of a line which is perpendicular to $12x + 7y - 4 = 0$ and passes through point $(2, -1)$.

     2—Ans: $7x - 12y - 26 = 0$

49. A person is paying $20 per week to repay a $200 loan. Match this with the appropriate graph.

(a)
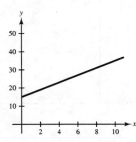

(b)
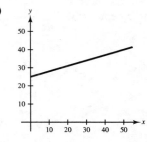

(c)
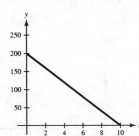

(d)
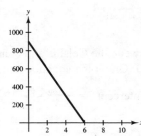

(e) None of these

1—Ans: c

50. An employee is paid $15 per hour plus $2 for each unit produced per hour. Match this with the appropriate graph.

(a)
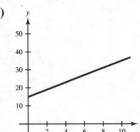

(b)
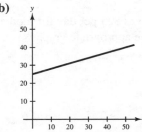

(c)
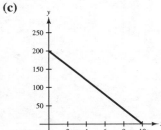

(d)
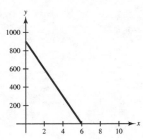

(e) None of these

1—Ans: a

51. The linear relationship between the Fahrenheit and Celsius temperature scales is given by $F = \frac{9}{5}C + 32$. Graph the equation and list the slope and F-intercept.

   2—Ans: Slope $= \frac{9}{5}$ F-intercept $= 32$

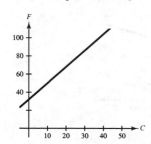

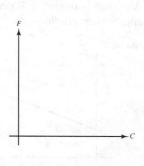

52. The linear relationship between the Celsius and Fahrenheit temperature scales is given by $C = \frac{5}{9}(F - 32)$. Graph the equation and list the slope and C-intercept.

   2—Ans: Slope $= \frac{5}{9}$ C-intercept $= -\frac{160}{9} \approx -17.8$

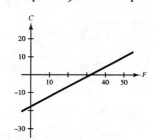

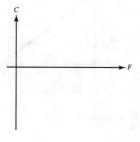

53. A sales representative receives \$25 per day for food and \$0.30 for each mile traveled. Match this with the appropriate graph.

(a)

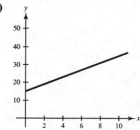

(b)

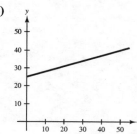

(c)

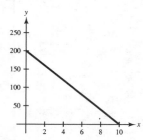

(d)

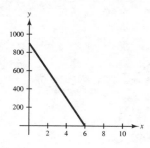

(e) None of these

   1—Ans: b

54. A word processor that was purchased for $900 depreciates $150 per year. Match this with the appropriate graph.

(a)

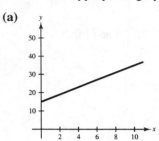

(b)

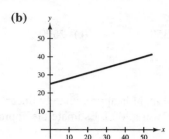

(c)

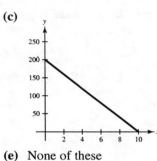

(d)

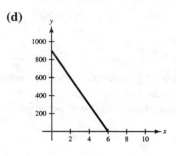

(e) None of these

1—Ans: d

55. A car travels for t hours at an average speed of 55 miles per hour. Write the distance d (in miles) as a linear function of t and evaluate the function for $t = 6$.

1—Ans: $d = 55t$; 330

56. A car travels for t hours at an average speed of 65 miles per hour. Write the distance d (in miles) as a linear function of t and evaluate the function for $t = 5$.

1—Form: 4C—Ans: $d = 65t$; 325

57. A school's growth in enrollment is approximately linear. In 1970 it had 2000 students and in 1990 there were 3000. Estimate the approximate number of students in 1976.

(a) 2250   **(b)** 2350   **(c)** 2300   **(d)** 2500   **(e)** None of these

1—Ans: c

58. A school's growth in enrollment is approximately linear. In 1970 it had 2000 students and in 1990 there were 3000. Estimate the approximate number of students in 1982.

(a) 2500   **(b)** 2600   **(c)** 2650   **(d)** 2550   **(e)** None of these

1—Ans: b

59. A school's growth in enrollment is approximately linear. In 1970 it had 2000 students and in 1990 there were 3000. Estimate the approximate number of students in 1978.

   (a) 2400   **(b)** 2350   **(c)** 2500   **(d)** 2450   **(e)** None of these

   1—Ans: a

60. A school's growth in enrollment is approximately linear. In 1970 it had 2000 students and in 1990 there were 3000. Estimate the approximate number of students in 1983.

   (a) 2700   **(b)** 2550   **(c)** 2600   **(d)** 2650   **(e)** None of these

   1—Ans: d

61. The growth of the number of employees hired by a company has been linear for the past ten years, starting at 323 ten years ago and currently standing at 393. Estimate the number of employees that will be employed three years from now (by linear extrapolation).

   1—Ans: 414

62. The growth of the number of employees hired by a company has been linear for the past ten years, starting at 415 ten years ago and currently standing at 495. Estimate the number of employees that will be employed two years from now (by linear extrapolation).

   1—Ans: 511

63. A real estate agent receives a weekly salary of $600 plus a commission of 3% of the total monthly sales. Write a linear equation giving the wages W in terms of sales s. Identify the slope and y-intercept of the graph of the equation.

   1—Ans: $W = 0.03s + 600$; slope is 0.03; y-intercept is $(0, 600)$

64. A real estate agent receives a weekly salary of $800 plus a commission of 3% of the total monthly sales. Write a linear equation giving the wages W in terms of sales s. Identify the slope and y-intercept of the graph of the equation.

   1—Ans: $W = 0.03s + 800$; slope is 0.03; y-intercept is $(0, 800)$

Section 4.6   Graphs of Linear Inequalities

1. Determine which of the following points is a solution of the linear inequality $2x - 5y < 6$.

   (a) $(0, -2)$ **(b)** $(4, 0)$ **(c)** $(2, 1)$ **(d)** $(2, -1)$ **(e)** None of these

   1—Form: 4A—Ans: c

2. Determine which of the following points is a solution of the linear inequality $2x - 3y < 5$.

   (a) $(0, -3)$ **(b)** $(3, 0)$ **(c)** $(2, -1)$ **(d)** $(2, 1)$ **(e)** None of these

   1—Form: 4B—Ans: d

3. Determine which of the following points is a solution of the linear inequality $2x + y > 0$.

   (a) $(-5, 9)$ **(b)** $(1, -1)$ **(c)** $(-1, 1)$ **(d)** $(0, 0)$ **(e)** None of these

   1—Ans: b

4. Determine which of the following points is a solution of the linear inequality $2x + y < 0$.

   (a) $(5, -9)$ **(b)** $(1, -1)$ **(c)** $(-1, 1)$ **(d)** $(0, 0)$ **(e)** None of these

   1—Ans: c

5. Determine which of the following points is a solution of the linear inequality $2x - y > 0$.

   (a) $(5, 9)$ **(b)** $(-1, -1)$ **(c)** $(-1, 1)$ **(d)** $(0, 0)$ **(e)** None of these

   1—Ans: a

6. Determine which of the following points is a solution of the linear inequality $2x - y < 0$.

   (a) $(0, 0)$ **(b)** $(1, -1)$ **(c)** $(1, 1)$ **(d)** $(-5, -9)$ **(e)** None of these

   1—Ans: d

7. Determine which of the following points is *not* a solution of the linear inequality $3x - 8y \geq 0$.

   (a) $(3, 2)$ **(b)** $(8, 3)$ **(c)** $(2, -3)$ **(d)** $(0, -1)$ **(e)** None of these

   1—Ans: a

8. Determine which of the following points is *not* a solution of the linear inequality $-5x - 9y \leq 7$.

   (a) $(4, 2)$ **(b)** $(-1, -2)$ **(c)** $(0, 1)$ **(d)** $(-5, 2)$ **(e)** None of these

   1—Ans: b

9. Determine which of the following points is *not* a solution of the linear inequality $3x - 6y > 4$.

   (a) $(3, -1)$ **(b)** $(2, 0)$ **(c)** $(-1, -1)$ **(d)** $(5, 1)$ **(e)** None of these

   1—Ans: c

10. Determine which of the following points is *not* a solution of the linear inequality $4x + 5y \leq 1$.

    (a) $(-1, 1)$ **(b)** $(2, -3)$ **(c)** $(3, -3)$ **(d)** $(1, 0)$ **(e)** None of these

    1—Ans: d

11. Determine whether or not the point $(-5, 4)$ satisfies the linear inequality $4x + y < 12$.

    1—Form: 4C—Ans: It does.

12. Determine whether or not the point $(3, 2)$ satisfies the linear inequality $y - 2x < -10$.

    1—Ans: It does not.

13. Determine whether or not the point $(3, 2)$ satisfies the linear inequality $3x - 2y \leq 0$.

    1—Ans: It does not.

14. Determine whether or not the point $(3, 2)$ satisfies the linear inequality $3x - 2y \geq 0$.

    1—Ans: It does.

15. Match the correct graph with the linear inequality $x > -2$.

    (a)

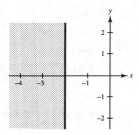

    (b)

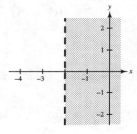

    (c)

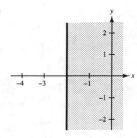

    (d)

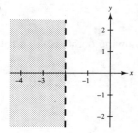

    (e) None of these

    1—Ans: b

16. Match the correct graph with the linear inequality $x \geq -2$.

(a)

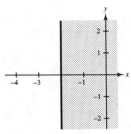

(b)

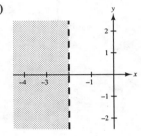

(c)

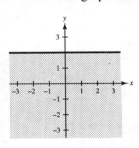

(d)

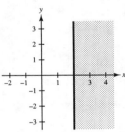

(e) None of these

1—Ans: c

17. Match the correct graph with the linear inequality $y \geq 2$.

(a)

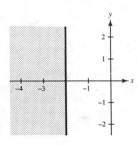

(b)

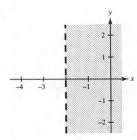

(c)

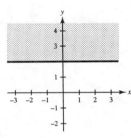

(d)

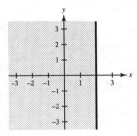

(e) None of these

1—Form: 4A—Ans: b

18. Match the correct graph with the linear inequality $x \geq 2$.

(a)

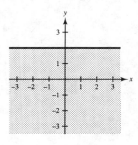

(b)

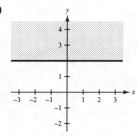

(c)

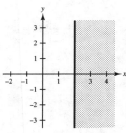

(d)

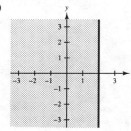

(e) None of these

1—Form: 4B—Ans: c

19. Match the correct graph with the linear inequality $x < -2$.

(a)

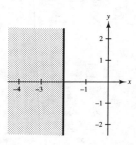

(b)

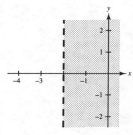

(c)

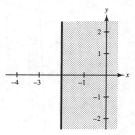

(d)

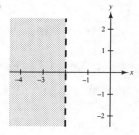

(e) None of these

1—Ans: d

20. Match the correct graph with the linear inequality $x \leq -2$.

(a)

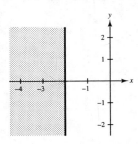

(b)

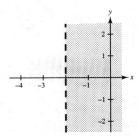

(c)

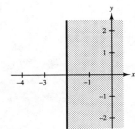

(d)

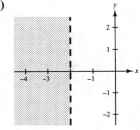

(e) None of these

1—Ans: a

21. Match the correct graph with the linear inequality $x + 3y \leq 0$.

(a)

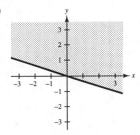

(b)

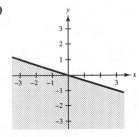

(c)

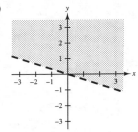

(d)

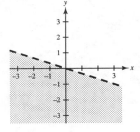

(e) None of these

1—Ans: b

22. Match the correct graph with the linear inequality $x + 3y \geq 0$.

(a)
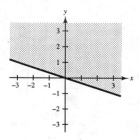

(b)
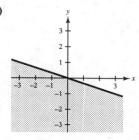

(c)
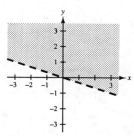

(d)
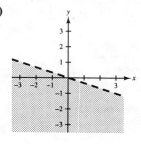

(e) None of these

1—Ans: a

23. Match the correct graph with the linear inequality $2x + 3y < 6$.

(a)
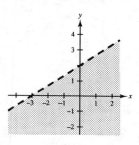

(b)
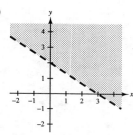

(c)
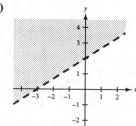

(d)
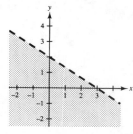

(e) None of these

1—Form: 4A—Ans: d

24. Match the correct graph with the linear inequality $3x + 4y < 8$.

(a)

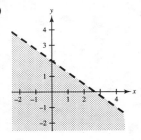

(b)

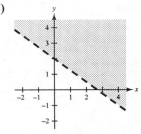

(c)

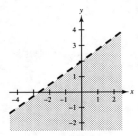

(d)

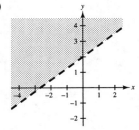

(e) None of these

1—Form: 4B—Ans: a

25. Match the correct graph with the linear inequality $2x + y < 4$.

(a)

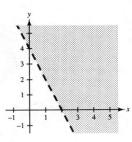

(b)

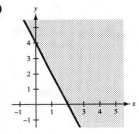

(c)

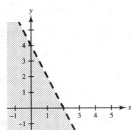

(d)

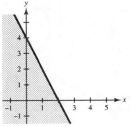

(e) None of these

2—Ans: c

26. Match the correct graph with the linear inequality $2x + y \leq 4$.

(a)

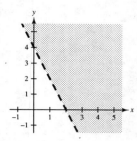

(b)

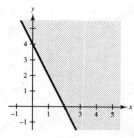

(c)

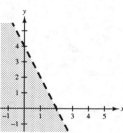

(d)

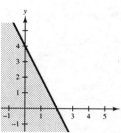

(e) None of these

2—Ans: d

27. Match the correct graph with the linear inequality $2x + y > 4$.

(a)

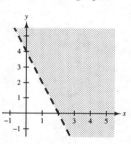

(b)

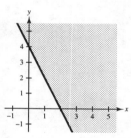

(c)

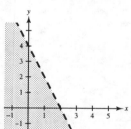

(d)

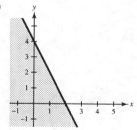

(e) None of these

2—Ans: a

28. Match the correct graph with the linear inequality $2x + y \geq 4$.

(a)

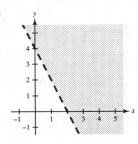

(b)

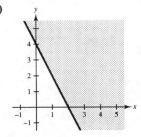

(c)

(d)

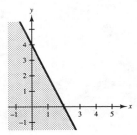

(e) None of these

2—Ans: b

29. Match the correct graph with the linear inequality $\dfrac{x}{2} + \dfrac{y}{4} + 1 > 0$.

(a)

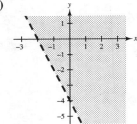

(b)

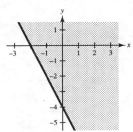

(c)

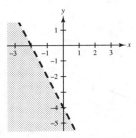

(d)

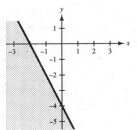

(e) None of these

2—Ans: a

30. Match the correct graph with the linear inequality $\frac{x}{2} + \frac{y}{4} + 1 \geq 0$.

(a)

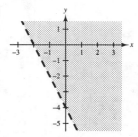

(b)

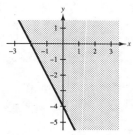

(c)

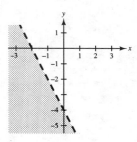

(d)

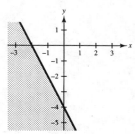

(e)   None of these

2—Ans: b

31. Match the correct graph with the linear inequality $\frac{x}{2} + \frac{y}{4} + 1 < 0$.

(a)

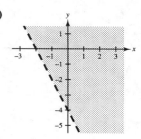

(b)

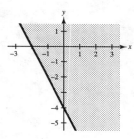

(c)

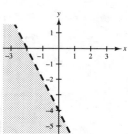

(d)

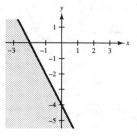

(e)   None of these

2—Ans: c

32. Match the correct graph with the linear inequality $\frac{x}{2} + \frac{y}{4} + 1 \leq 0$.

(a)

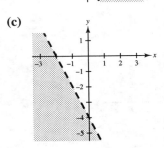

(b)

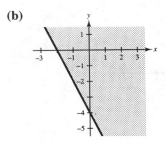

(c)

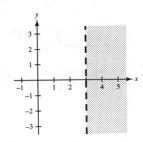

(d)

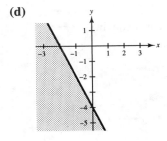

(e) None of these

2—Ans: d

33. Sketch the graph of the linear inequality $x > 3$.

1—Ans:

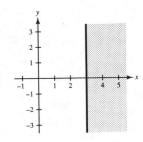

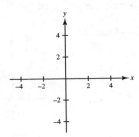

34. Sketch the graph of the linear inequality $x \geq 3$.

1—Form: 4C —Ans:

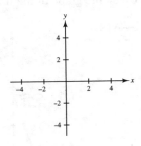

35. Sketch the graph of the linear inequality $3x - y < 0$.

    1—Ans:

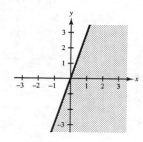

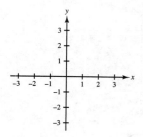

36. Sketch the graph of the linear inequality $3x - y > 0$.

    1—Ans:

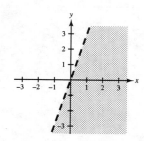

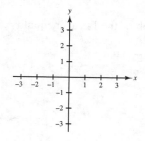

37. Sketch the graph of the linear inequality $3x - y \geq 0$.

    1—Ans:

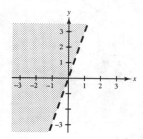

38. Sketch the graph of the linear inequality $3x - y \leq 0$.

    1—Ans:

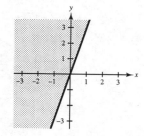

39. Sketch the graph of the linear inequality $x + y > 4$.

1—Ans:

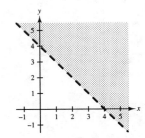

40. Sketch the graph of the linear inequality $x + y > 5$.

1—Ans:

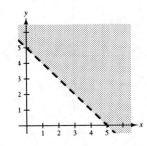

41. Sketch the graph of the linear inequality $-5x + 3y > 3$.

2—Ans: $y > \frac{5}{3}x + 1$

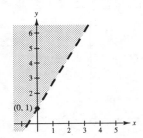

42. Sketch the graph of the linear inequality $-5x + 4y > 4$.

2—Ans: $y > \frac{5}{4}x + 1$

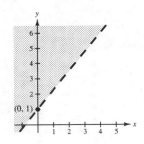

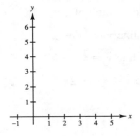

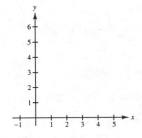

43. Sketch the graph of the linear inequality $y + 1 \leq \frac{1}{3}(x - 1)$.

2—Ans:

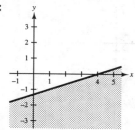

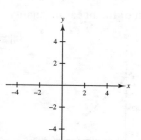

44. Sketch the graph of the linear inequality $y + 1 < \frac{1}{3}(x - 1)$.

2—Ans:

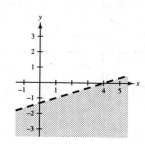

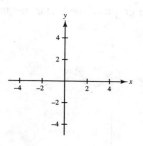

45. The points on the graph of $2x - 3y > 6$ lie:

    (a) above the line $y = \frac{2}{3}x - 2$ **(b)** on or above the line $y = \frac{2}{3}x - 2$

    (c) below the line $y = \frac{2}{3}x - 2$ **(d)** on or below the line $y = \frac{2}{3}x - 2$

    (e) on the line $y = \frac{2}{3}x - 2$

    1—Ans: c

46. The points on the graph of $2x - 3y \geq 6$ lie:

    (a) above the line $y = \frac{2}{3}x - 2$ **(b)** on or above the line $y = \frac{2}{3}x - 2$

    (c) below the line $y = \frac{2}{3}x - 2$ **(d)** on or below the line $y = \frac{2}{3}x - 2$

    (e) on the line $y = \frac{2}{3}x - 2$

    1—Ans: d

47. The points on the graph of $2x - 3y \leq 6$ lie:

    (a) above the line $y = \frac{2}{3}x - 2$ **(b)** on or above the line $y = \frac{2}{3}x - 2$

    (c) below the line $y = \frac{2}{3}x - 2$ **(d)** on or below the line $y = \frac{2}{3}x - 2$

    (e) on the line $y = \frac{2}{3}x - 2$

    1—Ans: b

48. The points on the graph of $2x - 3y < 6$ lie:

    (a) above the line $y = \frac{2}{3}x - 2$ **(b)** on or above the line $y = \frac{2}{3}x - 2$

    (c) below the line $y = \frac{2}{3}x - 2$ **(d)** on or below the line $y = \frac{2}{3}x - 2$

    (e) on the line $y = \frac{2}{3}x - 2$

    1—Ans: a

49. Write a linear inequality satisfied by all the points on a graph *above* the line $y = -\frac{1}{2}x$.

    2—Ans: $y > -\frac{1}{2}x$ or $x + 2y > 0$

50. Write a linear inequality satisfied by all the points on a graph *on* or *below* the line $y = -\frac{1}{2}x$.

    2—Ans: $y \leq -\frac{1}{2}x$ or $x + 2y \leq 0$

51. Write the inequality whose graph consists of all points below the *x*-axis.

    1—Form: 4C—Ans: $y < 0$

52. Write the inequality whose graph consists of all points on or below the *x*-axis.

    1—Ans: $y \leq 0$

53. Write the linear inequality whose graph lies *above* or *on* the line $4x - 5y = 3$.

    2—Ans: $y \geq \frac{4}{5}x - \frac{3}{5}$ or $4x - 5y - 3 \leq 0$

54. Write the linear inequality whose graph lies *below* the line $4x - 5y = 3$.

    2—Ans: $y < \frac{4}{5}x - \frac{3}{5}$ or $4x - 5y - 3 > 0$

55. Using a graphing calculator with the shade function to graph $y \leq -x + 2$, the display screen, in a standard setting, looks like:

    (a) 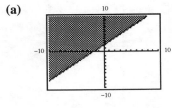   **(b)**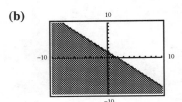

    (c) 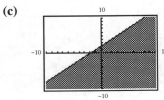   **(d)**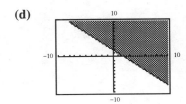

    (e) None of these

    2—T—Ans: b

56. Using a graphing calculator with the shade function to graph $y \leq x + 2$, the display screen, in a standard setting, looks like:

(a)

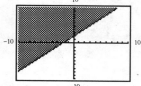

(b)

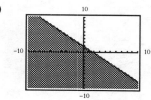

(c)

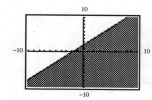

(d)

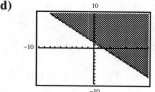

(e) None of these

2—T—Ans: c

57. Using a graphing calculator with the shade function to graph $y \geq -x + 2$, the display screen, in a standard setting, looks like:

(a)

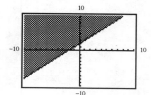

(b)

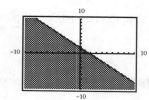

(c)

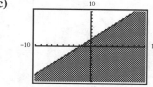

(d)

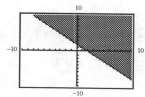

(e) None of these

2—T—Ans: d

58. Using a graphing calculator with the shade function to graph $y \geq x + 2$, the display screen, in a standard setting, looks like:

(a)

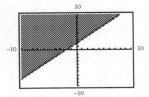

(b)

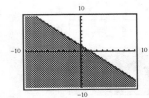

(c)

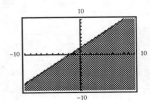

(d)

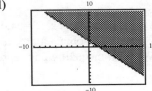

(e) None of these

2—T—Ans: a

59. Use a graphing calculator with the shade function to graph $y \leq -\frac{1}{2}x - 1$. Show on the coordinate axes what the display screen, in a standard setting, looks like.

2—T—Ans:

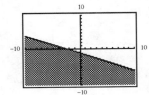

60. Use a graphing calculator with the shade function to graph $y \geq -\frac{1}{2}x - 1$. Show on the coordinate axes what the display screen, in a standard setting, looks like.

2—T—Ans:

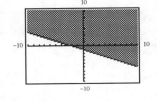

61. Use a graphing utility, in standard setting, to graph the inequality $4x + 6y - 9 \leq 0$.

1—T—Ans:

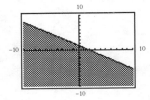

62. Use a graphing utility, in standard setting, to graph the inequality $6x + 4y - 9 \le 0$.

1—T—Ans: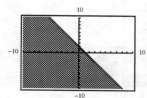

63. The revenue for selling x units of product is $R = 4.4x$. The cost of producing x units is $C = x + 17$. To obtain a profit, the revenue must be greater than the cost. Write an inequality that represents profit and graph the inequality.

2—Ans: $4.4x > x + 17$

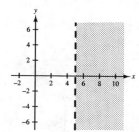

64. The revenue for selling x units of product is $R = 3.5x$. The cost of producing x units is $C = x + 10$. To obtain a profit, the revenue must be greater than the cost. Write an inequality that represents profit and graph the inequality.

2—Ans: $3.5x > x + 10$

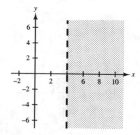

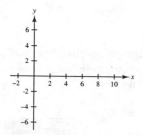

CHAPTER 5
Exponents and Polynomials

Section 5.1 Adding and Subtracting Polynomials

1. The degree of the polynomial $3x^2 - 5x^6 + x^3 - 2x + 4$ is:

   (a) 3   (b) 2   (c) 6   (d) 1   (e) None of these

   1—Ans: c

2. The degree of the polynomial $2 + 3x - x^3 - 5x^2$ is:

   (a) 3   (b) 0   (c) 1   (d) 2   (e) None of these

   1—Ans: a

3. Identify the degree of the polynomial $-5x^4 + 5x^2 + 7$.

   1—Ans: 4

4. Identify the degree of the polynomial $-4x^5 + 6x^3 + 3$.

   1—Form: 5C—Ans: 5

5. The leading coefficient of the polynomial $3x^2 - 5x^6 + x^3 - 2x + 4$ is:

   (a) 3   (b) -5 (c) -2 (d) 4   (e) None of these

   1—Ans: b

6. The leading coefficient of the polynomial $2 + 3x - x^3 - 5x^2$ is:

   (a) 2   (b) -5 (c) 3   (d) -1 (e) None of these

   1—Ans: d

7. Find the degree and leading coefficient of the polynomial $-6x + 8$.

   1—Ans: Degree 1, leading coefficient -6

8. Find the degree and leading coefficient of the polynomial 10.

   1—Ans: Degree 0, leading coefficient 10

9. Identify the leading coefficient of the polynomial $12y - 5y^3 + 7y^2 + 2$.

   1—Ans: -5

10. Identify the leading coefficient of the polynomial $9y - 6y^2 + 4y^3 + 8$.

    1—Ans: 4

11. Which most specifically describes $2 - 7x$?

    (a) Monomial   **(b)** Binomial   **(c)** Trinomial

    (d) Polynomial   **(e)** Not a polynomial

    1—Ans: b

12. Which most specifically describes $7x^2 - 5 + 2x$?

    (a) Monomial   **(b)** Binomial   **(c)** Trinomial

    (d) Polynomial   **(e)** Not a polynomial

    1—Ans: c

13. Which most specifically describes $5x - 3x + \dfrac{1}{x}$?

    (a) Monomial   **(b)** Binomial   **(c)** Trinomial

    (d) Polynomial   **(e)** Not a polynomial

    1—Ans: e

14. Which most specifically describes $5 - 3x + 4x^2 + x^3 - 2x^4$?

    (a) Monomial   **(b)** Binomial   **(c)** Trinomial

    (d) Polynomial   **(e)** Not a polynomial

    1—Ans: d

15. Classify the polynomial as a monomial, binomial, or trinomial: $11x^2$

    1—Ans: monomial

16. Classify the polynomial as a monomial, binomial, or trinomial: $11 + x^2$

    1—Form: 5C—Ans: binomial

17. Write a monomial of degree 3 and leading coefficient -2.

    1—Ans: $-2x^3$, Answers vary

18. Write a monomial of degree 0 and leading coefficient 7.

    1—Ans: 7

19. Which of the following polynomials is in standard form?

(a) $3x^2 - 7 + 2x$ (b) $8 - 3x$ (c) $2x + 3x^2 - 4x^3$

(d) $2x^2 + 3x - 2 - x^3$ (e) None of these

1—Ans: e

20. Which of the following polynomials is in standard form?

(a) $2x^2 + x^4 - x^3 - 3$ (b) $x^4 - x^3 + 2x^2 - 3$ (c) $3 - 2x^2 + x^3 - x^4$

(d) $x^2 + x^3 + 2x^4$ (e) None of these

1—Ans: b

21. Which of the following polynomials is in standard form?

(a) $x^3 - x^4 + x - x^2$ (b) $x + x^3 - x^2 - x^4$ (c) $-2x^4 - x^2 + 3$

(d) $3 - x^2 - 2x^4$ (e) None of these

1—Ans: c

22. Which of the following polynomials is in standard form?

(a) $-5x + 7$ (b) $x^4 - x^3 + 2x - x^2$ (c) $x^4 + 2x - x^3 - x^2$

(d) $7 - 5x$ (e) None of these

1—Ans: a

23. Write the polynomial $2x + x^3 - 2x^2 - x^4$ in standard form.

1—Form: 5C—Ans: $-x^4 + x^3 - 2x^2 + 2x$

24. Write the polynomial $4 - 3x + 2x^2 - x^4$ in standard form.

1—Ans: $-x^4 + 2x^2 - 3x + 4$

25. Write the polynomial $6 + x^2 - 2x - x^3$ in standard form.

1—Ans: $-x^3 + x^2 - 2x + 6$

26. Write the polynomial $8 - 4x^2 + 5x - x^3$ in standard form.

1—Ans: $-x^3 - 4x^2 + 5x + 8$

27. The expression $\frac{1}{2}x^2 - 2x^{-2}$ is *not* a polynomial because:

(a) There are not enough terms.   (b) An exponent is *not* non-negative.

(c) An exponent is *not* an integer.   (d) A coefficient is not an integer.

(e) It has no constant term.

1—Ans: b

28. The expression $\frac{3}{2}x - 3x^{-1}$ is *not* a polynomial because:

(a) There is no constant term.

(b) An exponent is *not* an integer.

(c) A coefficient is negative.

(d) An exponent is *not* a non-negative.

(e) A coefficient is not an integer.

1—Ans: d

29. The expression $5x^{1/2} - \frac{2}{3}x^2$ is *not* a polynomial because:

(a) It has no constant term.

(b) A coefficient is not an integer.

(c) There are not enough terms.

(d) A coefficient is negative.

(e) An exponent is *not* an integer..

1—Ans: e

30. The expression $\frac{5}{3}x - 2x^{1/2}$ is *not* a polynomial because:

(a) A coefficient is not an integer.

(b) It has no constant term.

(c) An exponent is *not* an integer.

(d) A coefficient is negative.

(e) There are not enough terms.

1—Ans: c

31. State why $8x^{1/2}$ is not a polynomial.

1—Ans: An exponent is *not* an integer.

32. State why $\dfrac{5}{3} - \dfrac{3}{x}$ is not a polynomial.

1—Ans: $-\dfrac{3}{x}$ is not of the form ax^n, where n is a positive integer.

33. Find the sum of the polynomials $(x^2 - 3x + 2)$ and $(-2x^2 - 2x + 1)$.

(a) $-x^2 - x + 1$

(b) $3x^2 - x + 1$

(c) $3x^2 - 5x + 3$

(d) $-x^2 - 5x + 3$

(e) None of these

1—Ans: d

34. Find the sum of the polynomials $(-3x^2 + 2x - 3)$ and $(2x^2 - 2x + 1)$.

(a) $-x^2 - 2$

(b) $-5x^2 - 2$

(c) $-5x^2 + 4x - 4$

(d) $-x^2 + 4x - 4$

(e) None of these

1—Ans: a

35. Find the sum of the polynomials and write the result in standard form:

$$(2n^2 - 8n + 5) + (-3n^2 - n - 2)$$

(a) $-n^2 - 5$ **(b)** $3 - 9n - n^2$ **(c)** $-n^2 - 9n + 3$

(d) $-9n - n^2 + 3$ **(e)** None of these

1—Form: 5A—Ans: c

36. Find the sum of the polynomials and write the result in standard form:

$$(-4n^2 + 11n + 1) + (n^2 - n - 7)$$

(a) $10n - 3n^2 - 6$ **(b)** $-3n^2 + 10n - 6$ **(c)** $-3n^2 + 5$

(d) $-6 + 10n - 3n^2$ **(e)** None of these

1—Form: 5B—Ans: b

37. Find the sum of the polynomials $(-2x^3 + x - 3)$ and $(x^4 + 2x^3 - 3x^2 + 5)$.

(a) $x^4 + 4x^3 - 3x^2 - x + 8$ **(b)** $x^4 - 4x^3 + 3x^2 - 8$ **(c)** $x^4 - 3x^2 + x + 2$

(d) $x^4 - 2x^2 + 2$ **(e)** None of these

1—Ans: c

38. Find the sum of the polynomials $(2x^4 - 3x^2 - 5)$ and $(x^3 + 3x^2 + 5x + 5)$.

(a) $3x^2 + 5x$ **(b)** $2x^4 - x^3 - 6x^2 - 5x - 10$ **(c)** $x^4 - 6x^2 - 5x$

(d) $2x^4 + x^3 + 5x$ **(e)** None of these

1—Ans: d

39. Find the sum of the polynomials $(2x^5 - x^3 + 3x - 2)$ and $(x^5 + x^3 - 3x + 2)$.

(a) $3x^5$ **(b)** $x^5 - 2x^3 + 3x - 4$ **(c)** $3x^5 - 2x^3 + 6x - 4$

(d) x^5 **(e)** None of these

1—Ans: a

40. Find the sum of the polynomials $(3x^6 - x^4 + 3x^2)$ and $(x^6 + x^4 - 3x^2 - 1)$.

(a) $2x^6 - 2x^4 + 6x^2 - 1$ **(b)** $4x^6 - 1$ **(c)** $2x^6 - 1$

(d) $4x^6 - 2x^4 + 6x^2 + 1$ **(e)** None of these

1—Ans: b

41. Find the sum of $(1 + 2x - 3x^2)$ and $(2x^2 - x - 2)$.

1—Ans: $-x^2 + x - 1$

42. Find the sum of $(3 + x - 2x^2)$ and $(x^2 + 2x - 2)$.

1—Ans: $-x^2 + 3x + 1$

43. Find the sum of $(4 + 3x - 2x^2)$ and $(3x^2 - 2x + 1)$.

   1—Ans: $(x^2 + x + 5)$

44. Find the sum of $(2 - 3x + 4x^2)$ and $(-2x^2 + 2x - 3)$.

   1—Ans: $2x^2 - x - 1$

45. Find the sum of $(3x^4 + 2x^3 - 7x + 1)$ and $(-2x^4 - 2x^3 + x^2 + x - 1)$.

   1—Ans: $x^4 + x^2 - 6x$

46. Find the sum of $(5x^4 + x^3 + 7x^2 + 3x)$ and $(-x^4 + x^3 - 7x^2 - 3)$.

   1—Ans: $4x^4 + 2x^3 + 3x - 3$

47. Subtract $(-2x^3 + x^2 - 2x + 3)$ from $(2x^3 - x^2 - 3x - 2)$.

   (a) $4x^3 - 2x^2 - x - 5$ **(b)** $4x^3 - 5x + 1$ **(c)** $-2x^2 - x - 5$

   (d) $-4x^3 + 2x^2 + x + 5$ **(e)** None of these

   1—Ans: a

48. Subtract $(x^5 - 3x^3 - 2x + 1)$ from $(3x^5 + x^3 + 2x - 3)$.

   (a) $-2x^5 - 4x^3 - 4x + 4$ **(b)** $2x^5 - 2x^3 - 2$ **(c)** $-2x^5 - 2x^3 - 2$

   (d) $2x^5 + 4x^3 + 4x - 4$ **(e)** None of these

   1—Ans: d

49. Subtract $(3x^3 + 4x^2 - 5)$ from $(x^3 - 3x + 5)$.

   (a) $-2x^3 - 4x^2 + 3x - 10$ **(b)** $-2x^3 - 4x^2 - 3x + 10$ **(c)** $2x^3 + 4x^2 + 3x - 10$

   (d) $2x^3 - 4x^2 + 3x - 10$ **(e)** None of these

   1—Form: 5A—Ans: b

50. Subtract $(-x^6 + 2x^4 - 2x^2 - 1)$ from $(2x^6 - 2x^4 - 2x^2 + 1)$.

   (a) $3x^6 - 4x^2$ **(b)** $-3x^6 + 4x^2$ **(c)** $3x^6 - 4x^4 + 2$

   (d) $-3x^6 + 4x^4 - 2$ **(e)** None of these

   1—Form: 5B—Ans: c

51. Subtract $(4x^3 - 7x^2 + 3)$ from $(2x^3 + 8x - 5)$.

   (a) $-2 + 8x + 7x^2 - 2x^3$ **(b)** $-2x^3 + 15x - 8$ **(c)** $-2x^3 + 15x^2 - 8$

   (d) $-2x^3 + 7x^2 + 8x - 8$ **(e)** None of these

   1—Form: 5A—Ans: d

52. Subtract $(5x^3 - 9x + 1)$ from $(x^3 + 10x^2 - 6)$.

   (a) $-4x^3 + 10x^2 + 9x - 7$ (b) $7 + 9x + 10x^2 - 4x^3$ (c) $-4x^3 + 19x^2 - 7$

   (d) $-4x^3 + 19x - 7$ (e) None of these

   1—Form: 5B—Ans: a

53. Subtract $(-2x^3 + x^2 - 3x + 2)$ from $(x^3 - 2x^2 - 5x - 7)$.

   1—Ans: $3x^3 - 3x^2 - 2x - 9$

54. Subtract $(3x^3 - 5x^2 + 7x - 4)$ from $(x^3 + x^2 - 3x + 2)$.

   1—Ans: $-2x^3 + 6x^2 - 10x + 6$

55. Perform the operations: $2(x^2 - x - 2) - 3(x^2 - 2x + 1) + (-x^2 + x - 2)$.

   (a) $-2x^2 - 2x - 3$ (b) $-2x^2 - 7x - 3$ (c) $5x - 9$

   (d) $-2x^2 + 5x - 9$ (e) None of these

   2—Form: 5A—Ans: d

56. Perform the operations: $3(2 - x - 2x^2) - 2(x^2 - 3x + 1) + 3(2x + 1)$.

   (a) $-4x^2 + 2x + 8$ (b) $-8x^2 - 3x + 5$ (c) $-8x^2 + 9x + 7$

   (d) $4x^2 + 9x + 11$ (e) None of these

   2—Form: 5B—Ans: c

57. Perform the operations: $3(x^2 + x) - 2(x^2 - x) + 4(x - x^2)$.

   2—Ans: $-3x^2 + 9x$

58. Perform the operations: $4(x^2 + x) - 3(x^2 - x) + 2(x - x^2)$.

   2—Ans: $-x^2 + 9x$

59. Perform the operations: $2(1 - x - 2x^2) - (3 - 2x - 3x^2) - (2x^2 + 3)$.

   2—Ans: $-3x^4 - 4$

60. Perform the operations: $3(2 - 3x - x^2) - 2(2 - 3x - 2x^2) - 3(1 - 3x)$.

   2—Ans: $x^2 + 6x - 1$

61. Perform the operations: $(-14x^3 + 9x^2 - 6x) - (x^3 + 9x^2 + 8) + (6x^3 - x)$.

   2—Form: 5C—Ans: $-9x^3 - 7x - 8$

62. Perform the operations: $(-12x^3 + 10x^2 - 7x) - (x^3 + 10x^2 + 9) + (7x^3 - x)$.

   2—Ans: $-6x^3 - 8x - 9$

63. Perform the operations: $2(3x^2 - 4x - 2) - 4(1 - 3x + x^2) - 2(2 - 2x)$.

2—Ans: $2x^2 + 8x - 12$

64. Perform the operations: $3(3x^2 - 3x - 9) - 4(2 - 2x - 2x^2) - 2(1 - 2x^2)$.

2—Ans: $21x^2 - x - 37$

Section 5.2   Multiplying Polynomials: Special Products

1. Multiply and simplify $(2x - 7)(-3x)$.

   (a) $-6x^2 - 21x$ **(b)** $-6x^2 + 21x$ **(c)** $6x^2 - 21x$

   (d) $21x + 6x^2$ **(e)** None of these

   1—Form: 5A—Ans: b

2. Multiply and simplify $(5x + 3)(-4x)$.

   (a) $-20x^2 + 12x$ **(b)** $-20x^2 + 3$ **(c)** $20x^2 - 12x$

   (d) $-20x^2 - 12x$ **(e)** None of these

   1—Form: 5B—Ans: d

3. Multiply and simplify $5x^2(2x - x^3 + 5)$.

   (a) $10x^3 - x^3 + 5$ **(b)** $-5x^5 + 2x + 5$ **(c)** $5x^2 - 10x^3 - 25x^2$

   (d) $-5x^5 + 10x^3 + 25x^2$ **(e)** None of these

   1—Ans: d

4. Multiply and simplify $7x^2(2 + x^2 - x^3)$.

   (a) $-7x^5 + 7x^4 + 14x^2$ **(b)** $-7x^5 + x^2 + 2$ **(c)** $7x^5 - 7x^4 - 14x^2$

   (d) $14x^2 + x^2 - x^3$ **(e)** None of these

   1—Ans: a

5. Multiply and simplify $3x(x^3 + 2x^2 - x^4)$.

   (a) $3x^4 + 2x^2 - x^4$ **(b)** $-3x^5 + x^3 + 2x^2$ **(c)** $-3x^5 + 3x^4 + 6x^3$

   (d) $3x^5 - 3x^4 - 6x^3$ **(e)** None of these

   1—Ans: c

6. Multiply and simplify $2x^2(3 - 2x^3 - x^2)$.

   (a) $4x^5 + 2x^4 - 6x^2$ **(b)** $-4x^5 - 2x^4 + 6x^2$ **(c)** $6x^2 - 2x^3 - x^2$

   (d) $-4x^5 - x^2 + 3$ **(e)** None of these

   1—Ans: b

7. Multiply and simplify $-2x^2(3 - 2x^2)$.

    1—Ans: $4x^4 - 6x^2$

8. Multiply and simplify $-3x^3(2x - 4)$.

    1—Ans: $-6x^4 + 12x^3$

9. Multiply and simplify $(3x^2 - 2x)(-7x)$.

    1—Ans: $-21x^3 + 14x^2$

10. Multiply and simplify $(3x - 2x^2)(-3x^2)$.

    1—Ans: $6x^4 - 9x^3$

11. Multiply and simplify $x(4x)^2$.

    1—Ans: $16x^3$

12. Multiply and simplify $x(3x)^2$.

    1—Ans: $9x^3$

13. Multiply and simplify $(3 - x^2 + 2x^3)(-2x^2)$.

    1—Ans: $-4x^5 + 2x^4 - 6x^2$

14. Multiply and simplify $(2x^2 - 3x + 2x^3)(3x)$.

    1—Ans: $6x^4 + 6x^3 - 9x^2$

15. The FOIL Method is illustrated for $(5x - 2)(3x + 4)$ by:

    (a) $20x - 6x + 15x^2 - 8$ **(b)** $15x^2 + 20x - 6x - 8$ **(c)** $15x^2 - 6x + 20x - 8$

    (d) $15x^2 + 14x - 8$ **(e)** None of these

    1—Ans: b

16. The FOIL Method is illustrated for $(3x - 5)(2x + 7)$ by:

    (a) $6x^2 + 21x - 10x - 35$ **(b)** $6x^2 + 11x - 35$ **(c)** $21x - 10x + 6x^2 - 35$

    (d) $6x^2 - 10x + 21x - 35$ **(e)** None of these

    1—Ans: a

17. The FOIL Method is illustrated for $(2x + 3)(4x - 5)$ by:

    (a) $8x^2 + 2x - 15$ **(b)** $12x - 10x + 8x^2 - 15$ **(c)** $8x^2 - 10x + 12x - 15$

    (d) $8x^2 + 12x - 10x - 15$ **(e)** None of these

    1—Ans: c

18. The FOIL Method is illustrated for $(7x - 1)(4x + 1)$ by:

(a) $28x^2 - 4x + 7x - 1$

(b) $7x - 4x + 28x^2 - 1$

(c) $28x^2 + 3x - 1$

(d) $28x^2 + 7x - 4x - 1$

(e) None of these

1—Ans: d

19. Use the FOIL Method to multiply $(7x + 9)(x - 3)$. Show the steps.

1—Ans: $7x^2 - 21x + 9x - 27 = 7x^2 - 12x - 27$

20. Use the FOIL Method to multiply $(5x - 9)(2x + 3)$. Show the steps.

1—Ans: $10x^2 + 15x - 18x - 27 = 10x^2 - 3x - 27$

21. Multiply and simplify $(2x - 1)(x + 4)$.

(a) $2x^2 - 4$

(b) $2x^2 + 10x + 4$

(c) $2x^2 + 7x - 4$

(d) $2x^2 - 7x - 4$

(e) None of these

1—Ans: c

22. Multiply and simplify $(3x - 2)(2x + 3)$.

(a) $6x^2 - 5x - 6$

(b) $6x^2 - 6$

(c) $6x^2 + 13x - 6$

(d) $6x^2 + 5x - 6$

(e) None of these

1—Ans: d

23. Multiply and simplify $(4x - 3)(2x + 1)$.

(a) $8x^2 - 3$

(b) $8x^2 + 4x - 6x - 3$

(c) $8x^2 + 2x - 3$

(d) $8x^2 - 2x - 3$

(e) None of these

1—Form: 5A—Ans: d

24. Multiply and simplify $(5x + 1)(2x - 3)$.

(a) $10x^2 - 3$

(b) $10x^2 + 13x - 3$

(c) $10x^2 - 13x - 3$

(d) $10x^2 - 15x + 2x - 3$

(e) None of these

1—Form: 5B—Ans: c

25. Multiply and simplify $(5x - 6)(3x + 2)$.

1—Ans: $15x^2 - 8x - 12$

26. Multiply and simplify $(7x - 3)(2x + 4)$.

1—Ans: $14x^2 + 22x - 12$

27. Multiply and simplify $(5x + 6)(3x - 4)$.

1—Ans: $15x^2 - 2x - 24$

28. Multiply and simplify $(3x - 7)(8x - 3)$

    1—Ans: $24x^2 - 65x + 21$

29. Multiply and simplify $(4 + 3x - 2x^2)(4 - 3x + 2x^2)$.

    (a) $-4x^4 + 12x^3 - 9x^2 + 16$ **(b)** $4x^4 + 12x^3 - 9x^2 + 16$

    (c) $-4x^4 - 9x^2 + 16$ **(d)** $-4x^4 + 12x^3 + 7x^2 - 24x + 16$

    (e) None of these

    2—Ans: a

30. Multiply and simplify $(5 - 4x - 3x^2)(5 + 4x - 3x^2)$.

    (a) $9x^4 - 16x^2 + 25$ **(b)** $9x^4 - 30x^2 + 25$

    (c) $9x^4 + 12x^3 - 30x^2 + 25$ **(d)** $9x^4 - 46x^2 + 25$

    (e) None of these

    2—Ans: d

31. Multiply and simplify $(4x^2 + 5x - 3)(x^2 - 1)$.

    2—Ans: $4x^4 + 5x^3 - 7x^2 - 5x + 3$

32. Multiply and simplify $(5x^2 - 4x - 6)(x^2 - 1)$.

    2—Form: 5C—Ans: $5x^4 - 4x^3 - 11x^2 + 4x + 6$

33. Simplify the expression $-4t(t^2 - t + 2) - t(t - 1)$.

    (a) $-4t^3 + 3t^2 - 7t$ **(b)** $-4t^3 - 5t^2 - 7t$ **(c)** $-4t^3 - 5t^2 + 7t$

    (d) $-4t^3 + 3t^2 + 7t$ **(e)** None of these

    2—Form: 5A—Ans: a

34. Simplify the expression $-6s(s^2 + s - 1) - s(s - 1)$.

    (a) $-6s^3 + 5s^2 + 7s$ **(b)** $-6s^2 - 7s^2 + 7s$ **(c)** $-6s^3 + 5s^2 - 7s$

    (d) $-6s^3 - 7s^2 - 7s$ **(e)** None of these

    2—Form: 5B—Ans: b

35. Simplify the expression $2x(3 - 5x - 2x^2) - (10x - 5x^3)$.

    (a) $x^3 - 15x + 3$ **(b)** $-7x^2 - 9x$ **(c)** $-9x^3 - 10x^2 - 4x$

    (d) $x^3 - 10x^2 - 4x$ **(e)** None of these

    2—Ans: d

36. Simplify the expression $3x^2(5 - 2x) - 2(7 - 2x^2 - 3x^3)$.

(a) $12x^3 + 11x^2 - 14$ (b) $19x^2 - 14$ (c) $-12x^3 + 4x^2 - 2x + 5$

(d) $-12x^3 + 19x - 14$ (e) None of these

2—Ans: b

37. Simplify the expression $2x(5 - 2x^2) - 3(1 - 2x - 3x^2)$.

(a) $-13x^3 + 16x - 3$ (b) $-4x^3 - 9x^2 - 6x$ (c) $-4x^3 + 9x^2 + 16x - 3$

(d) $-2x^3 + 9x^2 + 6x - 3$ (e) None of these

2—Ans: c

38. Simplify the expression $4x^2(2 - x) - x(3 - 2x - 6x^2)$.

(a) $2x^3 + 10x^2 - 3x$ (b) $-4x^3 + 2x^2 - 3x$ (c) $10x^3 + 10x^2 - 3x$

(d) $-2x^3 + 6x^2 - 3x$ (e) None of these

2—Ans: a

39. Simplify the expression $-3x^2(1 - 4x) - 3x(x^2 - 3x - 4)$.

2—Ans: $9x^3 + 6x^2 + 12x$

40. Simplify the expression $-5x(3 + 4x - 2x^2) + 2x^2(1 - 4x)$.

2—Ans: $2x^3 - 18x^2 - 15x$

41. Simplify the expression $(2 - 3x^2)(x - 4) - (2x)^2$.

2—Ans: $-3x^3 + 8x^2 + 2x - 8$

42. Simplify the expression $(5 - 3x^2)(2x + 1) - (3x)^2$.

2—Ans: $-6x^3 - 12x^2 + 10x + 5$

43. Which of the following leads to the *difference* of squares?

(a) $(3x - 5)(3x - 5)$ (b) $(3x + 5)(3x + 5)$ (c) $(3x + 5)(3x - 5)$

(d) $(3x - 5)(5 - 3x)$ (e) None of these

1—Ans: c

44. Which of the following leads to the *difference* of squares?

(a) $(7 - 2x)(7 - 2x)$ (b) $(7 - 2x)(7 + 2x)$ (c) $(7 - 2x)(2x - 7)$

(d) $(7 + 2x)(2x + 7)$ (e) None of these

1—Ans: b

45. Which of the following leads to the *difference* of squares?

    (a) $(4 - 2x)(2x + 4)$ **(b)** $(4 - 2x)(4 - 2x)$ **(c)** $(4 - 2x)(2x - 4)$

    (d) $(4 + 2x)(2x + 4)$ **(e)** None of these

    1—Ans: a

46. Which of the following leads to the *difference* of squares?

    (a) $(7x - 3)(3 - 7x)$ **(b)** $(7x + 3)(3 + 7x)$ **(c)** $(7x + 3)(7x + 3)$

    (d) $(7x - 3)(7x - 3)$ **(e)** None of these

    1—Ans: e, $(7x - 3)(7x + 3)$ would give $(7x)^2 - (3)^2$

47. Use the square of a binomial to find the product $(5x - 3)^2$.

    1—Ans: $(5x)^2 - 2(5x)(3) + (-3)^2 = 25x^2 - 30x + 9$

48. Use the square of a binomial to find the product $(3x + 5)^2$.

    1—Form: 5C—Ans: $(3x)^2 + 2(3x)(5) + (5)^2 = 9x^2 + 30x + 25$

49. Use the sum and difference of two terms to find the product $(6x + 5)(6x - 5)$.

    1—Ans: $(6x)^2 - (5)^2 = 36x^2 - 25$

50. Use the sum and difference of two terms to find the product $(4x - 7)(4x + 7)$.

    1—Ans: $(4x)^2 - (7)^2 = 16x^2 - 49$

51. Multiply and simplify $(3x - 7)^2$.

    (a) $9x^2 + 49$ **(b)** $9x^2 + 42x + 49$ **(c)** $9x^2 - 42x + 49$

    (d) $9x^2 - 21x + 49$ **(e)** None of these

    1—Form: 5A—Ans: c

52. Multiply and simplify $(5x + 4)^2$.

    (a) $25x^2 + 20x + 16$ **(b)** $25x^2 + 16$ **(c)** $25x^2 + 20x + 4$

    (d) $25x^2 + 40x + 16$ **(e)** None of these

    1—Form: 5B—Ans: d

53. Multiply and simplify $(7x - 3)^2$.

    (a) $49x^2 - 42x + 9$ **(b)** $49x^2 + 9$ **(c)** $49x^2 - 9$

    (d) $49x^2 - 21x + 9$ **(e)** None of these

    1—Ans: a

54. Multiply and simplify $(6x - 5)^2$.

  (a) $36x^2 - 25$ **(b)** $36x^2 - 60x + 25$ **(c)** $36x^2 + 25$

  (d) $36x^2 - 30x + 25$ **(e)** None of these

  1—Ans: b

55. Multiply and simplify $(2x - 1)^3$.

  1—Ans: $8x^3 - 12x^2 + 6x - 1$

56. Multiply and simplify $(3x - 2)^3$.

  1—Ans: $27x^3 - 54x^2 + 36x - 8$

57. Multiply and simplify $(2x - 3)^3$.

  1—Ans: $8x^3 - 36x^2 + 54x - 27$

58. Multiply and simplify $(4x - 3)^3$.

  1—Ans: $64x^3 - 144x^2 + 108x - 27$

59. Multiply and simplify $(x - 1)^3$.

  1—Ans: $x^3 - 3x^2 + 3x - 1$

60. Multiply and simplify $(x + 1)^3$.

  1—Form: 5C—Ans: $x^3 + 3x^2 + 3x + 1$

61. Perform the indicated multiplications and simplify.

  $(3x + 2)^2 - (3x - 2)^2$

  1—Ans: $24x$

62. Perform the indicated multiplications and simplify.

  $(2x - 3)^2 - (2x + 3)^2$

  1—Ans: $-24x$

63. The length of a rectangle is $2x + 5$ and the width is $x + 2$. Find an expression for the area of the rectangle.

  1—Ans: $(2x + 5)(x + 2)$ or $2x^2 + 9x + 10$

64. The length of a rectangle is $3x + 2$ and the width is $x + 3$. Find an expression for the area of the rectangle.

  1—Form: 5C—Ans: $(3x + 2)(x + 3)$ or $3x^2 + 11x + 6$

Section 5.3   Negative Exponents and Scientific Notation

1. Which of the following statements is *false*?

(a) $3^{-2} = \dfrac{1}{9}$ 　　　(b) $\dfrac{1}{3^2} = 3^{-2}$ 　　　(c) $5^{-2} = -10$

(d) $5x^{-3} = \dfrac{5}{x^3}$ 　　　(e) All of the statements are true.

1—Ans: c

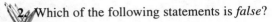

2. Which of the following statements is *false*?

(a) $4^{-2} = \dfrac{1}{16}$ 　　　(b) $5x^{-3} = \dfrac{1}{5x^3}$ 　　　(c) $\dfrac{3}{x^2} = 3x^{-2}$

(d) $(2x)^{-1} = \dfrac{1}{2x}$ 　　　(e) All of the statements are true.

1—Ans: b

3. Which of the following statements is *false*?

(a) $3x^{-1} = \dfrac{1}{3x}$ 　　　(b) $\dfrac{4}{x^2} = 4x^{-2}$ 　　　(c) $(2x)^{-1} = \dfrac{1}{2x}$

(d) $5^{-2} = \dfrac{1}{25}$ 　　　(e) All of the statements are true.

1—Ans: a

4. Which of the following statements is *false*?

(a) $3x^{-1} = \dfrac{3}{x}$ 　　　(b) $6^{-2} = \dfrac{1}{36}$ 　　　(c) $4x^{-2} = \dfrac{4}{x^2}$

(d) $(4x)^{-1} = \dfrac{4}{x}$ 　　　(e) All of the statements are true.

1—Ans: d

5. Rewrite $\dfrac{x^{-9}}{x^{-3}}$ with positive exponents.

(a) x^6 　　　(b) $\dfrac{1}{x^6}$ 　　　(c) x^3 　　　(d) $\dfrac{1}{x^3}$ 　　　(e) None of these

1—Form: 5B—Ans: b

6. Rewrite $\dfrac{x^{-10}}{x^{-2}}$ with positive exponents.

(a) $\dfrac{1}{x^8}$ 　　　(b) x^8 　　　(c) $\dfrac{1}{x^5}$ 　　　(d) x^5 　　　(e) None of these

1—Form: 5A—Ans: a

7. Simplify $\dfrac{3}{5^{-2}}$.

   1—Ans: 75

8. Simplify $\dfrac{3}{4^{-2}}$.

   1—Ans: 48

9. Rewrite $\dfrac{1}{4x^{-3}}$ with positive exponents.

   1—Ans: $\dfrac{x^3}{4}$

10. Rewrite $2x^{-3}y^2$ with positive exponents.

    1—Ans: $\dfrac{2y^2}{x^3}$

11. Choose the expression which is *not* a valid rule of exponents.

    (a) $a^m \cdot a^n = a^{n+m}$ **(b)** $a^0 = 1$ **(c)** $(a^m)^n = a^{n+m}$

    (d) $(ab)^n = a^n b^n$ **(e)** $\dfrac{a^m}{a^n} = a^{m-n}$

    1—Form: 5A—Ans: c

12. Choose the expression which is *not* a valid rule of exponents.

    (a) $a^m \cdot a^n = a^{n+m}$ **(b)** $(ab)^n = a^n b^n$ **(c)** $(a^n)^m = a^{nm}$

    (d) $a^1 = 0$ **(e)** $\dfrac{a^m}{a^n} = a^{m-n}$

    1—Form: 5B—Ans: d

13. Choose the expression which is *not* a valid rule of exponents.

    (a) $a^m \cdot a^n = a^{m \cdot n}$ **(b)** $(ab)^n = a^n b^n$ **(c)** $(a^n)^m = a^{nm}$

    (d) $a^0 = 1$ **(e)** $\dfrac{a^n}{b^n} = a^{n-m}$

    1—Ans: a

14. Choose the expression which is *not* a valid rule of exponents.

    (a) $a^m \cdot a^n = a^{m+n}$ **(b)** $(ab)^n = a^n b^n$ **(c)** $(a^n)^m = a^{nm}$

    (d) $a^0 = 1$ **(e)** $\dfrac{a^n}{b^n} = (a-b)^n$

    1—Ans: e

15. Complete $(a^m)^n = \rule{1cm}{0.3cm}$ to state a rule of exponents.

    1—Ans: a^{nm}

16. Complete $a^n a^m = \rule{1cm}{0.3cm}$ to state a rule of exponents.

    1—Ans: a^{n+m}

17. Which of the statements is *true*?

    (a) $-x^2 = (-x)^2$ **(b)** $(2a^2)^0 = 0$ **(c)** $3x^{-1} = \dfrac{1}{3x}$

    (d) $(a^2)^3 = a^6$ **(e)** None of these

    1—Ans: d

18. Which of the statements is *true*?

    (a) $(-x)^2 = -x^2$ **(b)** $(2a^2)^0 = 0$ **(c)** $3x^{-1} = \dfrac{3}{x}$

    (d) $(a^2)^3 = a^5$ **(e)** None of these

    1—Ans: c

19. Which of the statements is *true*?

    (a) $-(x)^2 = -x^2$ **(b)** $(2a^2)^0 = 0$ **(c)** $3x^{-1} = \dfrac{1}{3x}$

    (d) $(a^2)^3 = a^5$ **(e)** None of these

    1—Ans: a

20. Which of the statements is *true*?

    (a) $-x^2 = (-x)^2$ **(b)** $(2a^2)^0 = 1$ **(c)** $3x^{-1} = \dfrac{1}{3x}$

    (d) $(a^2)^3 = a^5$ **(e)** None of these

    1—Ans: b

21. Use the rules of exponents to simplify the expression. Write your answer with only positive exponents. (Assume that no variable is zero.)

$$(-35x^5y^{-1})^0(2x^{-4}y^3)^{-2}$$

    (a) $\dfrac{x^8}{4y^6}$ **(b)** $-\dfrac{4x^8}{y^6}$ **(c)** $4x^8y^{-6}$ **(d)** $-\dfrac{35x^{13}}{4y^7}$ **(e)** None of these

    2—Form: 5A—Ans: a

22. Use the rules of exponents to simplify the expression. Write your answer with only positive exponents. (Assume that no variable is zero.)

$$(-36x^{-1}y^6)^0(3x^{-3}y^4)^{-2}$$

(a) $-\dfrac{4x^5}{y^2}$ **(b)** $-6x^6y^{-8}$ **(c)** $\dfrac{x^6}{9y^8}$ **(d)** $-\dfrac{6x^6}{y^8}$ **(e)** None of these

2—Form: 5B—Ans: c

23. Use the rules of exponents to simplify the expression. Write your answer with only positive exponents. (Assume that no variable is zero.)

$$(-2a^2b^3)(-3ab)^3$$

1—Ans: $54a^5b^6$

24. Use the rules of exponents to simplify the expression. Write your answer with only positive exponents. (Assume that no variable is zero.)

$$\dfrac{-3y^{-2}}{(2y)^{-3}}$$

1—Ans: $-24y$

25. Use the rules of exponents to simplify the expression. Write your answer with only positive exponents. (Assume that no variable is zero.)

$$2x^{-2}(2x^2y)^0$$

1—Ans: $\dfrac{2}{x^2}$

26. Use the rules of exponents to simplify the expression. Write your answer with only positive exponents. (Assume that no variable is zero.)

$$\left(\dfrac{3x^2}{y^{-2}}\right)^{-1}$$

1—Ans: $\dfrac{1}{3x^2y^2}$

27. Use the rules of exponents to simplify the expression. Write your answer with only positive exponents. (Assume that no variable is zero.)

$$\left(\dfrac{b^2}{3a}\right)^{-2}$$

1—Ans: $\dfrac{9a^2}{b^4}$

28. Use the rules of exponents to simplify the expression. Write your answer with only positive exponents. (Assume that no variable is zero.)

$$\left(\frac{x^{-2}y^3}{4}\right)^{-2}$$

1—Ans: $\dfrac{16x^4}{y^6}$

29. Use the rules of exponents to simplify the expression. Write your answer with only positive exponents. (Assume that no variable is zero.)

$$(3x^{-4}y^3)^{-4}$$

2—Form: 5C—Ans: $\dfrac{x^{16}}{81y^{12}}$

30. Use the rules of exponents to simplify the expression. Write your answer with only positive exponents. (Assume that no variable is zero.)

$$(2x^{-5}y^3)^{-4}$$

2—Ans: $\dfrac{x^{20}}{16y^{12}}$

31. Use the rules of exponents to simplify the expression. Write your answer with only positive exponents. (Assume that no variable is zero.)

$$(-8x^{-1}y^2)(9x^4y^{-3})$$

2—Ans: $\dfrac{-72x^3}{y}$

32. Use the rules of exponents to simplify the expression. Write your answer with only positive exponents. (Assume that no variable is zero.)

$$(-7x^{-2}y^4)(6xy^{-1})$$

2—Form: 5C—Ans: $\dfrac{-42y^3}{x}$

33. Which of the following is *not* equal to 1?

  (a) a^3a^{-3} **(b)** $-(2xy)^0$ **(c)** $b^n \div b^n$ **(d)** $(2+3)^0$ **(e)** $(-x+y)^0$

1—Ans: b

34. Which of the following is *not* equal to 1?

  (a) a^3a^{-3} **(b)** $(-2xy)^0$ **(c)** $\dfrac{b^n}{b^n}$ **(d)** $b^n \div b^{-n}$ **(e)** $(2+3)^0$

1—Ans: d

35. The number 0.000475 in scientific notation is:

(a) 4.75×10^4 (b) 475×10^{-6} (c) 4.75×10^{-4}

(d) 47.5×10^{-5} (e) None of these

1—Ans: c

36. The number 9,830,000 in scientific notation is:

(a) 9.83×10^5 (b) 9.83×10^6 (c) 98.3×10^5

(d) 9.83×10^{-6} (e) None of these

1—Ans: b

37. The number 73.4 in scientific notation is:

(a) 734×10^1 (b) 7.34×10^{-1} (c) 734×10^{-1}

(d) 7.34×10^1 (e) None of these

1—Ans: d

38. The number 0.00408 in scientific notation is:

(a) 4.08×10^3 (b) 40.8×10^4 (c) 40.8×10^{-4}

(d) 4.08×10^{-4} (e) None of these

1—Ans: e, 4.08×10^{-3} is correct.

39. Write 8.7514 in scientific notation.

1—Ans: 8.7514×10^0

40. Write 0.00000018742 in scientific notation.

1—Ans: 1.8742×10^{-7}

41. Write 0.0000063 in scientific notation.

1—Ans: 6.3×10^{-6}

42. Write 0.000051 in scientific notation.

1—Form: 5C—Ans: 5.1×10^{-5}

43. Write 95,600,000 in scientific notation.

1—Ans: 9.56×10^7

44. Write 780,400,000 in scientific notation.

1—Ans: 7.804×10^8

45. The number 2.73×10^{-5} converted to decimal form is:

   (a) 0.0000273   **(b)** 273,000   **(c)** 0.00000273

   (d) 27,300,000   **(e)** None of these

   1—Ans: a

46. The number 3.71×10^7 converted to decimal form is:

   (a) 0.000000371   **(b)** 37,100,000   **(c)** 0.0000000371

   (d) 3,710,000,000   **(e)** None of these

   1—Ans: b

47. The number 2.14×10^2 converted to decimal form is:

   (a) 0.0214   **(b)** 21,400   **(c)** 0.214

   (d) 0.00214   **(e)** None of these

   1—Ans: e, 214 is correct.

48. The number 5.74×10^{-8} converted to decimal form is:

   (a) 574,000,000   **(b)** 57,400,000   **(c)** 0.0000000574

   (d) 0.00000000574   **(e)** None of these

   1—Ans: c

49. Write 1.8121×10^{12} in decimal form.

   1—Ans: 1,812,100,000,000

50. Write 1×10^9 in decimal form.

   1—Ans: 1,000,000,000

51. Write 2.638×10^{-4} in decimal form.

   1—Ans: 0.0002638

52. Write 3.725×10^{-3} in decimal form.

   1—Ans: 0.003725

53. Write 6.214×10^5 in decimal form.

   1—Ans: 621,400

54. Write 5.663×10^6 in decimal form.

   1—Form: 5C—Ans: 5,663,000

55. The quotient $6.4 \times 10^8 \div 1.6 \times 10^5$ is equal to:

(a) 4.0×10^3 (b) 4.0×10^{13} (c) 2.5×10^{-3}

(d) 4.0×10^{-3} (e) None of these

1—Form: 5A—Ans: a

56. The product $(2.5 \times 10^7) \times (3.0 \times 10^{-3})$ is equal to:

(a) 7.5×10^{-4} (b) 7.5×10^4 (c) 75×10^5

(d) 7.5×10^{-21} (e) None of these

1—Form: 5B—Ans: b

57. The number 2.0×10^5 when raised to the 3rd power, $(2.0 \times 10^5)^3$, is equal to:

(a) 6.0×10^{15} (b) 8.0×10^8 (c) 8.0×10^{15}

(d) 8.0×10^{125} (e) None of these

1—Ans: c

58. The product $(5.0 \times 10^7) \times (7.0 \times 10^5)$ is equal to:

(a) 35×10^{35} (b) 3.5×10^{12} (c) 35×10^2

(d) 3.5×10^{13} (e) None of these

1—Ans: d

59. Calculate the power $(3.0 \times 10^4)^3$ and express the answer in standard scientific notation.

1—Ans: 2.7×10^{13}

60. Calculate the product $(7.0 \times 10^8) \times (2.0 \times 10^{-6})$ and express the answer in standard scientific notation.

1—Ans: 1.4×10^3

61. Carry out the calculation using a scientific calculator and express the answer in standard scientific notation.

$$(1.6 \times 10^{-4})^3$$

(a) 409.6×10^{-10} (b) 4.096×10^{-12} (c) 4.096×10^{-7}

(d) 0.4096×10^{-11} (e) None of these

2—Ans: b

62. Carry out the calculation using a scientific calculator and express the answer in standard scientific notation.

$$(5.6 \times 10^{-8}) \times (3.5 \times 10^{12})$$

(a) 1.96×10^5 **(b)** 1.96×10^{-5} **(c)** 19.6×10^4

(d) 196,000   **(e)** None of these

2—Ans: a

63. Carry out the calculation using a scientific calculator and express the answer in standard scientific notation.

$$(2.6 \times 10^{-27}) \times (3.5 \times 10^{15})$$

2—Ans: 9.1×10^{-12}

64. Carry out the calculation using a scientific calculator and express the answer in standard scientific notation.

$$27,000,000,000 \div 0.0000015$$

2—Ans: 1.8×10^{16}

65. Carry out the calculation using a scientific calculator and express the answer in standard scientific notation.

$$(1.25 \times 10^{-5})^{-3}$$

2—Ans: 5.12×10^{14}

66. Carry out the calculation using a scientific calculator and express the answer in standard scientific notation.

$$(8.4 \times 10^{14}) \times (5.0 \times 10^6)^2$$

2—Ans: 2.1×10^{28}

Section 5.4   Dividing Polynomials

1. If $x \neq 0$, dividing $27x^6$ by $3x^2$ gives:

(a) $9x^3$ **(b)** $9x^8$ **(c)** $9x^4$ **(d)** $81x^8$ **(e)** None of these

1—Ans: c

2. If $x \neq 0$, dividing $81x^8$ by $27x^2$ gives:

(a) $3x^4$ **(b)** $3x^6$ **(c)** $3x^{10}$ **(d)** $9x^6$ **(e)** None of these

1—Ans: b

3. If $x \neq 0$, dividing $64x^9$ by $12x^3$ gives:

(a) $\frac{16}{3}x^6$ **(b)** $\frac{16}{3}x^3$ **(c)** $4x^6$ **(d)** $\frac{4}{3}x^{12}$ **(e)** None of these

1—Form: 5A—Ans: a

4. If $x \neq 0$, dividing $48x^{10}$ by $18x^2$ gives:

   (a) $\frac{8}{3}x^5$ **(b)** $\frac{8}{3}x^{12}$ **(c)** $3x^8$ **(d)** $\frac{8}{3}x^8$ **(e)** None of these

   1—Form: 5B—Ans: d

5. Assuming $x \neq 0$, perform the division $76x^9 \div 4x^3$.

   1—Ans: $19x^6$

6. Assuming $x \neq 0$, perform the division $72x^{12} \div 27x^3$

   1—Ans: $\frac{8}{3}x^9$

7. If $x \neq 0$, dividing $(27x^4 + 18x^3)$ by $9x^2$ gives:

   (a) $5x^5$ **(b)** $3x^2 + 2x$ **(c)** $3x^7 + 2x^5$

   (d) $3x^2 + 2x^{3/2}$ **(e)** None of these

   1—Ans: b

8. If $x \neq 0$, dividing $(16x^6 - 32x^4)$ by $4x^2$ gives:

   (a) $4x^4 - 8x^2$ **(b)** -4 **(c)** $12x^4 - 28x^2$

   (d) $4x^3 - 8x^2$ **(e)** None of these

   1—Ans: a

9. If $x \neq 0$, dividing $(24x^8 - 12x^6)$ by $6x$ gives:

   (a) $2x$ **(b)** $4x^8 - 12x^6$ **(c)** $4x^7 - 2x^5$

   (d) $18x^7 - 6x^5$ **(e)** None of these

   1—Ans: c

10. If $x \neq 0$, dividing $(81x^{10} - 27x^8)$ by $9x^2$ gives:

   (a) $9x^5 - 3x^4$ **(b)** $6(x^5 - x^4)$ **(c)** $9x^{12} - 3x^{10}$

   (d) $9x^8 - 3x^6$ **(e)** None of these

   1—Ans: d

11. Assuming $x \neq 0$, perform the division $(18x^5 - 27x^3) \div 3x^2$.

   1—Ans: $6x^3 - 9x$

12. Assuming $x \neq 0$, perform the division $(42x^8 - 24x^{12}) \div 6x^4$.

   1—Ans: $7x^4 - 4x^8$

13. Assuming $x \neq 0$, divide $(27x^3 - 18x^2 + 12x^4)$ by $(12x^3)$.

   1—Ans: $\dfrac{9}{4} - \dfrac{3}{2x} + x$

14. Assuming $x \neq 0$, divide $(24x^4 - 21x^5 - 28x^3)$ by $8x^2$.

   1—Ans: $3x^2 - \frac{21}{8}x^3 - \frac{7}{2}x$

15. Assuming $x \neq 0$, divide $(30x^6 - 24x^5 - 16x^4)$ by $12x^5$.

   1—Ans: $\left(\frac{5}{2}x - 2 - \frac{4}{3x}\right)$

16. Assuming $x \neq 0$, divide $(25x^7 - 35x^5 - 15x^3)$ by $15x^5$.

   1—Ans: $\frac{5}{3}x^2 - \frac{7}{3} - \frac{1}{x^2}$

17. Perform the division by cancellation and by subtracting exponents (Assume the denominator is not zero): $\frac{6^3x}{6^2x^3}$

   (a) $6x^2$ **(b)** $\frac{x^2}{6}$ **(c)** $\frac{6}{x^2}$ **(d)** $\frac{1}{6x^2}$ **(e)** None of these

   1—Form: 5A—Ans: c

18. Perform the division by cancellation and by subtracting exponents (Assume the denominator is not zero): $\frac{7^3x}{7^2x^4}$

   (a) $\frac{7}{x^3}$ **(b)** $7x^3$ **(c)** $\frac{1}{7x^3}$ **(d)** $\frac{x^3}{7}$ **(e)** None of these

   1—Form: 5B—Ans: a

19. Simplify the expression $\frac{36(xy^2)^2}{-8(x^2y)^2}$. (Assume the denoniminator is not zero.)

   2—Ans: $\frac{-9y^2}{2x^2}$

20. Simplify the expression $\frac{-24(x^2y)^2}{16(xy^2)^2}$. (Assume the denoniminator is not zero.)

   2—Form: 5C—Ans: $\frac{-3x^2}{2y^2}$

21. Perform the division and simplify. (Assume the denominator is not zero.)

   $$\frac{n^3 + 4n - 8}{n}$$

   1—Ans: $n^2 + 4 - \frac{8}{n}$

22. Perform the division and simplify. (Assume the denominator is not zero.)

$$\frac{m^4 + 5m - 9}{m}$$

1—Form: 5C—Ans: $m^3 + 5 - \dfrac{9}{m}$

23. Assuming $x \neq 3$, $(2x^2 - 3x + 2) \div (x - 3)$ gives:

(a) $2x - 9 + \dfrac{29}{x - 3}$ (b) $2x + 9 - \dfrac{25}{x - 3}$ (c) $2x - \dfrac{2}{3}$

(d) $2x + 3 + \dfrac{11}{x - 3}$ (e) None of these

1—Ans: d

24. Assuming $x \neq -2$, $(3x^2 - 7x - 4) \div (x + 2)$ gives:

(a) $3x - 1 + \dfrac{6}{x + 2}$ (b) $3x - 13 + \dfrac{22}{x + 2}$ (c) $(3x - 2)$

(d) $3x + 1 - \dfrac{2}{x + 2}$ (e) None of these

1—Ans: b

25. Assuming $x \neq 2$, $(4x^2 - x - 8) \div (x - 2)$ gives:

(a) $4x + 7 + \dfrac{6}{x - 2}$ (b) $4x - 9 + \dfrac{10}{x - 2}$ (c) $4x + 9 + \dfrac{26}{x - 2}$

(d) $(4x + 4)$ (e) None of these

1—Form: 5A—Ans: a

26. Assuming $x \neq -3$, $(6x^2 + 5x - 9) \div (x + 3)$ gives:

(a) $6x + 23 - \dfrac{78}{x + 3}$ (b) $(6x - 3)$ (c) $6x - 13 + \dfrac{30}{x + 3}$

(d) $6x - 23 - \dfrac{78}{x + 3}$ (e) None of these

1—Form: 5B—Ans: c

27. Assuming $x \neq 2$, $(2x^3 - x^2 - 4x - 4) \div (x - 2)$ gives:

(a) $(2x^2 + 3x + 2)$ (b) $(2x^2 + 3x - 2)$ (c) $(2x^2 - 3x + 2)$

(d) $(2x^2 - 3x - 2)$ (e) None of these

2—Ans: a

28. Assuming $x \neq 2$, $(2x^3 - x^2 - 8x + 4) \div (x - 2)$ gives:

   (a) $(2x^2 + 3x + 2)$ **(b)** $(2x^2 + 3x - 2)$ **(c)** $(2x^2 - 3x + 2)$

   (d) $(2x^2 - 3x - 2)$ **(e)** None of these

   2—Ans: b

29. Assuming $x \neq 2$, $(2x^3 - 7x^2 + 8x - 4) \div (x - 2)$ gives:

   (a) $(2x^2 + 3x + 2)$ **(b)** $(2x^2 + 3x - 2)$ **(c)** $(2x^2 - 3x + 2)$

   (d) $(2x^2 - 3x - 2)$ **(e)** None of these

   2—Ans: c

30. Assuming $x \neq 2$, $(2x^3 - 7x^2 + 4x + 4) \div (x - 2)$ gives:

   (a) $(2x^2 + 3x + 2)$ **(b)** $(2x^2 + 3x - 2)$ **(c)** $(2x^2 - 3x + 2)$

   (d) $(2x^2 - 3x - 2)$ **(e)** None of these

   2—Ans: d

31. Assuming $x \neq \frac{3}{2}$, $(4x^4 - 9x^2 - 2x + 3) \div (2x - 3)$ gives:

   (a) $(2x^3 + 3x^2 - 1)$ **(b)** $(2x^3 - 3x^2 - 1)$ **(c)** $(2x^3 + 3x^2 + 1)$

   (d) $(2x^3 - 3x^2 + 1)$ **(e)** None of these

   2—Ans: a

32. Assuming $x \neq -\frac{3}{2}$, $(4x^4 - 9x^2 - 2x - 3) \div (2x + 3)$ gives:

   (a) $(2x^3 + 3x^2 - 1)$ **(b)** $(2x^3 - 3x^2 - 1)$ **(c)** $(2x^3 + 3x^2 + 1)$

   (d) $(2x^3 - 3x^2 + 1)$ **(e)** None of these

   2—Ans: b

33. Assuming $x \neq \frac{3}{2}$, $(4x^4 - 9x^2 + 2x - 3) \div (2x - 3)$ gives:

   (a) $(2x^3 + 3x^2 - 1)$ **(b)** $(2x^3 - 3x^2 - 1)$ **(c)** $(2x^3 + 3x^2 + 1)$

   (d) $(2x^3 - 3x^2 + 1)$ **(e)** None of these

   2—Ans: c

34. Assuming $x \neq -\frac{3}{2}$, $(4x^4 - 9x^2 + 2x + 3) \div (2x + 3)$ gives:

   (a) $(2x^3 + 3x^2 - 1)$ **(b)** $(2x^3 - 3x^2 - 1)$ **(c)** $(2x^3 + 3x^2 + 1)$

   (d) $(2x^3 - 3x^2 + 1)$ **(e)** None of these

   2—Ans: d

35. Assuming $x \neq -2$, divide $(6x^3 + 16x^2 + 7x - 2)$ by $(x + 2)$.

    (a) $6x^2 - 4x - 1$ **(b)** $6x^2 + 4x + 1$ **(c)** $6x^2 - 4x + 1$

    (d) $6x^2 + 4x - 1$ **(e)** None of these

    1—Form: 5A—Ans: d

36. Assuming $x \neq -3$, divide $(5x^3 + 18x^2 + 8x - 3)$ by $(x + 3)$.

    (a) $5x^2 - 3x - 1$ **(b)** $5x^2 + 3x - 1$ **(c)** $5x^2 - 3x + 1$

    (d) $5x^2 + 3x + 1$ **(e)** None of these

    1—Form: 5B—Ans: b

37. Assuming $x \neq 2$, divide $(2x^2 + 7x - 4)$ by $(x - 2)$.

    1—Ans: $2x + 11 + \dfrac{18}{x - 2}$

38. Assuming $x \neq -2$, divide $(4x^2 + x - 4)$ by $(x + 2)$.

    1—Ans: $4x - 7 + \dfrac{10}{x + 2}$

39. Perform the division and simplify. (Assume the denominator is not zero.)

$$\frac{7x^4 - 8x^3 + 4x - 1}{2x}$$

    1—Ans: $\dfrac{7x^3}{2} - 4x^2 + 2 - \dfrac{1}{2x}$

40. Perform the division and simplify. (Assume the denominator is not zero.)

$$\frac{6x^4 - 9x^2 + 8x - 3}{2x}$$

    1—Ans: $3x^3 - \dfrac{9x}{2} + 4 - \dfrac{3}{2x}$

41. Assuming $x \neq -3$, divide $(3x^3 + 5x^2 - 11x + 3)$ by $(x + 3)$.

    2—Ans: $3x^2 - 4x + 1$

42. Assuming $x \neq -3$, divide $(3x^3 + 5x^2 - 13x - 3)$ by $(x + 3)$.

    2—Ans: $3x^2 - 4x - 1$

43. Assuming $x \neq 2$, divide $(x^4 - 16)$ by $(x - 2)$.

    2—Ans: $x^3 + 2x^2 + 4x + 8$

44. Assuming $x \neq -2$, divide $(x^4 - 16)$ by $(x + 2)$.

   2—Ans: $x^3 - 2x^2 + 4x - 8$

45. Assuming $x \neq -\frac{3}{4}$, divide $(16x^2 - 9)$ by $(4x + 3)$.

   1—Ans: $4x - 3$

46. Assuming $x \neq -\frac{4}{3}$, divide $(9x^2 - 16)$ by $(3x + 4)$.

   1—Form: 5C—Ans: $3x - 4$

47. The expression $\left(\dfrac{5x^3}{x^2} - 3x\right)$ when simplified becomes:

   (a) $2x$ **(b)** $8x$ **(c)** $-8x$ **(d)** $-2x$ **(e)** None of these

   1—Ans: a

48. The expression $\left(\dfrac{5x^3}{x^2} + 3x\right)$ when simplified becomes:

   (a) $2x$ **(b)** $8x$ **(c)** $-8x$ **(d)** $-2x$ **(e)** None of these

   1—Ans: b

49. The expression $\left(\dfrac{-5x^3}{x^2} + 3x\right)$ when simplified becomes:

   (a) $2x$ **(b)** $8x$ **(c)** $-8x$ **(d)** $-2x$ **(e)** None of these

   1—Ans: d

50. The expression $\left(\dfrac{-5x^3}{x^2} - 3x\right)$ when simplified becomes:

   (a) $2x$ **(b)** $8x$ **(c)** $-8x$ **(d)** $-2x$ **(e)** None of these

   1—Ans: c

51. Simplify the expression $\dfrac{x^2 - 2x + 1}{x - 1} - (4x - 3); x \neq 1$.

   1—Ans: $-3x + 2$

52. Simplify the expression $\dfrac{x^2 - 2x + 1}{x - 1} - (3x - 4); x \neq 1$.

   1—Ans: $-2x + 3$

53. Correct the *cancellation* indicated. If correct as shown, so state.

$$\frac{9 + 13}{5 + 9} = \frac{\cancel{9} + 13}{5 + \cancel{9}} = \frac{13}{5}$$

1—Ans: Invalid, $\dfrac{9 + 13}{5 + 9} = \dfrac{22}{14} = \dfrac{11}{7}$

54. Correct the *cancellation* indicated. If correct as shown, so state.

$$\frac{87}{28} = \frac{8\cancel{7}}{2\cancel{8}} = \frac{7}{2}$$

1—Ans: Invalid, $\dfrac{87}{28}$ is in lowest terms.

55. Use the long division algorithm to find: $(4x^2 + 4x - 2) \div (2x - 1)$

2—Ans: $(2x + 3) + \dfrac{1}{2x - 1}$

56. Use the long division algorithm to find: $(4x^2 + 4x - 1) \div (2x + 1)$

2—Form: 5C—Ans: $(2x + 1) - \dfrac{2}{2x + 1}$

57. Use the long division algorithm to find: $(x^3 - 27) \div (x - 3)$

2—Ans: $x^2 + 3x + 9$

58. Use the long division algorithm to find: $(x^3 + 8) \div (x + 2)$

2—Ans: $x^2 - 2x + 4$

C H A P T E R   6
Factoring and Solving Equations

Section 6.1   Factoring Polynomials with Common Factors

1. Find the greatest common factor of 72 and 54.

    (a) 24   **(b)** 18   **(c)** 9   **(d)** 3   **(e)** None of these

    1—Ans: b

2. Find the greatest common factor of 96 and 68.

    (a) 4   **(b)** 2   **(c)** 8   **(d)** 24   **(e)** None of these

    1—Ans: a

3. Find the greatest common factor of $48n^2m^3$ and $80nm^2$.

    (a) $24nm^2$ **(b)** $16nm^2$ **(c)** $16n^2m$ **(d)** $24n^2m$ **(e)** None of these

    1—Form: 6A—Ans: b

4. Find the greatest common factor of $54c^3d^2$ and $90c^2d$.

    (a) $18cd^2$ **(b)** $27cd^2$ **(c)** $27c^2d$ **(d)** $18c^2d$ **(e)** None of these

    1—Form: 6B—Ans: d

5. Find the greatest common factor of $4x^3y^2$, $8x^2y^3$, and $12xy^3$.

    (a) 4   **(b)** $4xy^2$ **(c)** xy^3 **(d)** xy^2 **(e)** None of these

    1—Ans: b

6. Find the greatest common factor of $12x^3y^2$, $6x^2y^3$, and $15x^2y^2$.

    (a) $6x^2y^2$ **(b)** $60x^3y^3$ **(c)** $3x^2y^2$ **(d)** $3xy$ **(e)** None of these

    1—Ans: c

7. Find the greatest common factor of $20x^3y^2$, $16xy^3$, and $12x^2y^2$.

    (a) $4xy^2$ **(b)** $240x^3y^3$ **(c)** $4x^2y^2$ **(d)** $4x^2y^{-2}$ **(e)** None of these

    1—Ans: a

8. Find the greatest common factor of $15x^4y^2$, $10x^2y^3$, and $20x^3y^3$.

    (a) $60x^4y^3$ **(b)** $30x^2y^2$ **(c)** $5xy$ **(d)** $5x^2y^2$ **(e)** None of these

    1—Ans: d

9. Find the greatest monomial factor of $25xy^2 - 35x^2y^3$.

    (a) 4   **(b)** $5x$ **(c)** $5y^2$ **(d)** $5xy^2$ **(e)** None of these

    1—Ans: d

10. Find the greatest monomial factor of $21x^3y^2 - 35xy^3$.

    (a) 7   **(b)** $7y^2$ **(c)** $7xy^2$ **(d)** $7xy$ **(e)** None of these

    1—Ans: c

11. Find the greatest monomial factor of $28x^3y^4 - 42x^2y^3$.

    (a) $7x^2y^2$ **(b)** $14x^2y^3$ **(c)** $7x^3$ **(d)** 14   **(e)** None of these

    1—Ans: b

12. Find the greatest monomial factor of $18x^2y^4 - 42x^2y^5$.

    (a) $6x^2y^4$ **(b)** x^2 **(c)** $18x^2y^4$ **(d)** $6x^2$ **(e)** None of these

    1—Ans: a

13. Find the greatest common factor of 112 and 128.

    1—Ans: 16

14. Find the greatest common factor of 132 and 99.

    1—Ans: 33

15. Find the greatest common factor of 144 and 126.

    1—Ans: 18

16. Find the greatest common factor of 120 and 168.

    1—Ans: 24

17. Find the greatest common factor of $24a^6$, $36a^3$, and $54a^2$.

    1—Ans: $6a^2$

18. Find the greatest common factor of $32b^4$, $48b^5$, and $24b^3$.

    1—Ans: $8b^3$

19. Find the greatest common factor of $20x^3y^3$, $30x^4y^2$, and $50x^4y^3$.

    1—Ans: $10x^3y^2$

20. Find the greatest common factor of $30x^4y^2$, $45x^2y^3$, and $60xy^4$.

    1—Ans: $15xy^2$

21. After factoring out the greatest common monomial factor, the remaining factor of $24y^4 - 20y^2 - 28y$ is:

  (a) $6y^3 - 5y - 7$ **(b)** $12y^2 - 10y - 14$ **(c)** $4y$

  (d) $6y^2 - 5y - 7$ **(e)** None of these

  1—Ans: a

22. After factoring out the greatest common monomial factor, the remaining factor of $42y^4 - 21y^2 - 35y^3$ is:

  (a) $7y^2$ **(b)** $6y^3 - 3y - 5y^2$ **(c)** $6y^2 - 3 - 5y$

  (d) $6y^2 - 3y - 5$ **(e)** None of these

  1—Ans: c

23. Factor out the greatest common monomial factor of the polynomial $28x + 56x^3$.

  (a) $7x(4 + 8x^2)$ **(b)** $4x(7 + 14x^2)$ **(c)** $14x(2 + 4x^2)$

  (d) $28x(1 + 2x^2)$ **(e)** None of these

  1—Form: 6A—Ans: d

24. Factor out the greatest common monomial factor of the polynomial $32x + 64x^3$.

  (a) $8x(4 + 8x^2)$ **(b)** $32x(1 + 2x^2)$ **(c)** $16x(2x + 4x^2)$

  (d) $4x(8x + 16x^2)$ **(e)** None of these

  1—Form: 6B—Ans: b

25. Factoring out the greatest common *negative* monomial factor of $-3y^3 + 7y^2 - y$, one obtains:

  (a) $-(3y^3 - 7y^2 + y)$ **(b)** $-y(3y^2 + 7y - 1)$ **(c)** $-3y(y^2 - 7y + 1)$

  (d) $-y(3y^2 - 7y + 1)$ **(e)** None of these

  1—Ans: d

26. Factoring out the greatest common *negative* monomial factor of $-2y^4 - 6y^3 + 4y^2$, one obtains:

  (a) $-(2y^4 + 6y^3 - 4y^2)$ **(b)** $-2y^2(y^2 + 3y - 2)$ **(c)** $-2y^2(y^2 - 3y + 2)$

  (d) $-y^2(2y^2 + 6y - 4)$ **(e)** None of these

  1—Ans: b

27. Factoring out the greatest common *negative* monomial factor of $-4y^4 - 16y^3 + 12y^2$, one obtains:

  (a) $-4y^2(y^2 + 4y - 3)$ **(b)** $-4y^2(y^2 - 4y + 3)$ **(c)** $-4(y^4 + 4y^3 - 3y^2)$

  (d) $-y^2(4y^2 - 16y + 12)$ **(e)** None of these

  1—Ans: a

28. Factoring out the greatest common *negative* monomial factor of $-12y^4 - 18y^3 + 6y^2$, one obtains:

    (a) $-6y^2(2y^2 - 3y + 1)$ **(b)** $-6(2y^2 - 3y + 1)$ **(c)** $-6y^2(2y^2 + 3y - 1)$

    (d) $-6(2y^4 + 3y^3 - y^2)$ **(e)** None of these

    1—Ans: c

29. Factor out the greatest monomial factor of $45x^2y^3 - 35x^3y^2$.

    1—Ans: $5x^2y^2(9y - 7x)$

30. Factor out the greatest monomial factor of $30x^4y^2 - 42x^3y^4$.

    1—Ans: $6x^3y^3(5x - 7y)$

31. Factor the polynomial $27x^7 + 45x^2 - 54x$.

    1—Form: 6C—Ans: $9x(3x^6 + 5x - 6)$

32. Factor the polynomial $49x^6 + 35x^3 - 63x$.

    1—Ans: $7x(7x^5 + 5x^2 - 9)$

33. Factor the polynomial $18y^4 + 27y^3 - 36y^2$.

    1—Ans: $9y^2(2y^2 + 3y - 4)$

34. Factor the polynomial $24y^5 - 12y^3 - 60y^2$.

    1—Ans: $12y^2(2y^3 - y - 5)$

35. Factor the polynomial $56y - 14y^3 - 42y^4$.

    1—Ans: $14y(4 - y^2 - 3y^3)$

36. Factor the polynomial $12y^5 - 42y^4 - 18y^3$.

    1—Ans: $6y^3(2y^2 - 7y - 3)$

37. Factor out a negative common monomial factor: $-40y^3 + 15y^2 + 5y$

    1—Ans: $-5y(8y^2 - 3y - 1)$

38. Factor out a negative common monomial factor: $-10y^3 + 25y^2 + 5y$

    1—Form: 6C—Ans: $-5y(2y^2 - 5y - 1)$

39. Factor out the greatest common *negative* monomial factor.

    $-24y^4 - 16y^3 + 8y^2$

    1—Ans: $-8y^2(3y^2 + 2y - 1)$

40. Factor out the greatest common *negative* monomial factor.

$$-24y^4 - 12y^3 + 8y^2$$

   1—Ans: $-4y^2(6y^2 + 3y - 2)$

41. The polynomial $x^2(x + 3) - 2(x + 3)$ factors into:

   (a) $(x + 3)(x^2 + 2)$ **(b)** $(x + 3)(x^2 - 2)$ **(c)** $(x^2 - 2)(x - 3)$

   (d) $(x - 3)(x^2 + 2)$ **(e)** None of these

   1—Ans: b

42. The polynomial $x^2(x - 4) - 3(x - 4)$ factors into:

   (a) $(x + 4)(x^2 - 3)$ **(b)** $(x - 4)(x^2 + 3)$ **(c)** $(x - 4)(x^2 - 3)$

   (d) $(x + 4)(x^2 + 3)$ **(e)** None of these

   1—Ans: c

43. The polynomial $x^2(x + 2) - 2(x + 2)$ factors into:

   (a) $(x + 2)(x^2 - 2)$ **(b)** $(x - 2)(x^2 + 2)$ **(c)** $(x - 2)(x^2 - 2)$

   (d) $(x + 2)(x^2 + 2)$ **(e)** None of these

   1—Ans: a

44. The polynomial $x^2(x - 3) + 4(x - 3)$ factors into:

   (a) $(x + 3)(x^2 - 4)$ **(b)** $(x + 3)(x^2 + 4)$ **(c)** $(x - 3)(x^2 - 4)$

   (d) $(x - 3)(x^2 + 4)$ **(e)** None of these

   1—Ans: d

45. Identify the common binomial factor of the polynomial
$13a(3a + 1) + 2(3a + 1)$.

   1—Ans: $3a + 1$

46. Identify the common binomial factor of the polynomial
$11a(4a - 1) + 3(4a - 1)$.

   1—Ans: $4a - 1$

47. Factor $5x(x^2 + 3) - 4(x^2 + 3)$.

   1—Ans: $(x^2 + 3)(5x - 4)$

48. Factor $3x^2(2x - 5) + 4(2x - 5)$.

   1—Ans: $(2x - 5)(3x^2 + 4)$

49. Factor $2x^3 - x^2 - 6x + 3$ by grouping.

  (a) $(2x + 1)(x^2 - 3)$ **(b)** $(2x - 1)(x^2 - 3)$ **(c)** $(2x - 1)(x^2 + 3)$

  (d) $(2x + 1)(x^2 + 2)$ **(e)** None of these

  2—Ans: b

50. Factor $x^3 - 2x^2 - 3x + 6$ by grouping.

  (a) $(x - 2)(x^2 + 3)$ **(b)** $(x + 2)(x^2 + 3)$ **(c)** $(x + 2)(x^2 - 3)$

  (d) $(x - 2)(x^2 - 3)$ **(e)** None of these

  2—Ans: d

51. Factor $2x^2 - x - 10x + 5$ by grouping.

  (a) $(x - 5)(2x - 1)^2$ **(b)** $(x + 5)(2x - 1)$ **(c)** $(x - 5)(2x - 1)$

  (d) $(x - 5)^2(2x - 1)$ **(e)** None of these

  2—Form: 6A—Ans: c

52. Factor $3x^2 - x - 12x + 4$ by grouping.

  (a) $(x - 4)(3x - 1)^2$ **(b)** $(x - 4)^2(3x - 1)$ **(c)** $(x + 4)(3x - 1)$

  (d) $(x - 4)(3x - 1)$ **(e)** None of these

  2—Form: 6B—Ans: d

53. Factor $x^2y^2 + 2xy^2 - 3x^2 - 6x$ by grouping.

  (a) $(x^2 - 2x)(y^2 + 3)$ **(b)** $(x^2 - 2x)(y^2 - 3)$ **(c)** $(x^2 + 2x)(y^2 - 3)$

  (d) $(x^2 + 3x)(y^2 - 2)$ **(e)** None of these

  2—Ans: c

54. Factor $x^2y^2 + 3xy^2 - 2x^2 - 6x$ by grouping.

  (a) $(x^2 - 3x)(y^2 - 2)$ **(b)** $(x^2 - 3x)(y^2 + 2)$ **(c)** $(x^2 + 2x)(y^2 - 3)$

  (d) $(x^2 + 3x)(y^2 - 2)$ **(e)** None of these

  2—Ans: d

55. Factor $x^3 + 3x^2 - 5x - 15$ by grouping.

  2—Ans: $(x + 3)(x^2 - 5)$

56. Factor $x^3 - 3x^2 - 5x + 15$ by grouping.

  2—Ans: $(x - 3)(x^2 - 5)$

57. Factor $x^3 - 3x^2 + 5x - 15$ by grouping.

  2—Ans: $(x + 3)(x^2 + 5)$

58. Factor $x^3 + 5x^2 - 3x - 15$ by grouping.

2—Ans: $(x + 5)(x^2 - 3)$

59. Factor $x^3 + 4xy - 2x^2y - 8y^2$ by grouping.

2—Ans: $(x^2 + 4y)(x - 2y)$

60. Factor $x^3 - 4xy + 2x^2y - 8y^2$ by grouping.

2—Ans: $(x^2 - 4y)(x + 2y)$

61. Factor $x^3 - 2xy + 4x^2y - 8y^2$ by grouping.

2—Ans: $(x^2 - 2y)(x + 4y)$

62. Factor $x^3 + 2xy - 4x^2y - 8y^2$ by grouping.

2—Ans: $(x^2 + 2y)(x - 4y)$

63. Complete the factorization: $8y(y^2 + 1) - (y^2 + 1) = (y^2 + 1)($ $)$.

1—Form: 6C—Ans: $(8y - 1)$

64. Complete the factorization: $6y(y^2 + 2) - (y^2 + 2) = (y^2 + 2)($ $)$.

1—Ans: $(6y - 1)$

Section 6.2   Factoring Trinomials

1. Find the missing factor: $x^2 + 10x - 24 = (x + 12)($ $)$.

   (a) $x - 2$ **(b)** $x + 12$ **(c)** $x - 12$ **(d)** $x + 2$ **(e)** None of these

1—Form: 6A—Ans: a

2. Find the missing factor: $x^2 + 9x - 36 = (x + 12)($ $)$.

   (a) $x - 24$ **(b)** $x + 24$ **(c)** $x + 3$ **(d)** $x - 3$ **(e)** None of these

1—Form: 6B—Ans: d

3. Factor $x^2 + 8x + 12$.

   (a) $(x + 6)(x + 2)$ **(b)** $(x + 12)(x + 1)$ **(c)** $(x + 3)(x + 4)$

   (d) $(x + 5)(x + 3)$ **(e)** It does not factor.

1—Ans: a

4. Factor $x^2 - x - 12$.

   (a) $(x + 6)(x - 2)$ **(b)** $(x - 4)(x + 3)$ **(c)** $(x + 4)(x - 3)$

   (d) $(x - 6)(x + 2)$ **(e)** It does not factor.

   1—Ans: b

5. Factor $x^2 + 5x - 6$.

   (a) $(x + 2)(x + 3)$ **(b)** $(x + 6)(x - 1)$ **(c)** $(x - 6)(x + 1)$

   (d) $(x - 2)(x - 3)$ **(e)** It does not factor.

   1—Form: 6A—Ans: b

6. Factor $x^2 - 5x - 6$.

   (a) $(x + 6)(x - 1)$ **(b)** $(x + 2)(x + 3)$ **(c)** $(x - 2)(x - 3)$

   (d) $(x - 6)(x + 1)$ **(e)** It does not factor.

   1—Form: 6B—Ans: d

7. Factor $x^2 + 9x + 20$.

   (a) $(x + 10)(x + 2)$ **(b)** $(x + 20)(x + 1)$ **(c)** $(x + 4)(x + 5)$

   (d) $(x + 6)(x + 3)$ **(e)** It does not factor.

   1—Ans: c

8. Factor $x^2 + 8x + 20$.

   (a) $(x + 10)(x + 2)$ **(b)** $(x + 3)(x + 5)$ **(c)** $(x + 4)(x + 5)$

   (d) $(x + 10)(x - 2)$ **(e)** It does not factor.

   1—Ans: e

9. Factor $x^2 + 8x - 20$.

   (a) $(x + 10)(x + 2)$ **(b)** $(x + 5)(x - 4)$ **(c)** $(x - 5)(x + 4)$

   (d) $(x + 10)(x - 2)$ **(e)** It does not factor.

   1—Ans: d

10. Factor $x^2 - 8x - 20$.

   (a) $(x - 10)(x + 2)$ **(b)** $(x - 12)(x + 4)$ **(c)** $(x - 5)(x - 3)$

   (d) $(x + 10)(x - 2)$ **(e)** It does not factor.

   1—Ans: a

11. Factor $x^2 - 3x - 54$.
    (a) $(x + 9)(x - 6)$ (b) $(x - 27)(x + 2)$ (c) $(x - 8)(x + 5)$
    (d) $(x - 9)(x + 6)$ (e) It does not factor.
    1—**Ans:** d

12. Factor $x^2 + 3x - 54$.
    (a) $(x + 9)(x - 6)$ (b) $(x - 27)(x + 2)$ (c) $(x - 8)(x + 5)$
    (d) $(x - 9)(x + 6)$ (e) It does not factor.
    1—**Ans:** a

13. Factor $x^2 + 15x + 54$.
    (a) $(x + 9)(x - 6)$ (b) $(x - 9)(x - 6)$ (c) $(x + 9)(x + 6)$
    (d) $(x - 9)(x + 6)$ (e) It does not factor.
    1—**Ans:** c

14. Factor $x^2 - 15x + 54$.
    (a) $(x + 9)(x - 6)$ (b) $(x - 9)(x - 6)$ (c) $(x + 9)(x + 6)$
    (d) $(x - 9)(x + 6)$ (e) It does not factor.
    1—**Ans:** b

15. Factor $x^2 - 2x - 35$.
    1—**Ans:** $(x - 7)(x + 5)$

16. Factor $x^2 + 2x - 35$.
    1—**Ans:** $(x + 7)(x - 5)$

17. Factor $x^2 + 3x - 40$.
    1—**Ans:** $(x + 8)(x - 5)$

18. Factor $x^2 - 3x - 40$.
    1—**Ans:** $(x - 8)(x + 5)$

19. Factor $x^2 + 12x + 27$.
    1—**Ans:** $(x + 3)(x + 9)$

20. Factor $x^2 - 12x + 27$.
    1—**Ans:** $(x - 3)(x - 9)$

21. Factor $x^2 - 8x + 12$.

    1—Ans: $(x - 6)(x - 2)$

22. Factor $x^2 - 7x + 12$.

    1—Form: 6C—Ans: $(x - 3)(x - 4)$

23. Factor $x^2 - x - 110$.

    1—Ans: $(x - 11)(x + 10)$

24. Factor $x^2 - 4x - 117$.

    1—Ans: $(x - 13)(x + 9)$

25. Factor $x^2 - 8xy + 16y^2$.

    (a) $(x + 4y)(x + 4y)$ **(b)** $(x - 4y)(x - 4y)$ **(c)** $(4x - y)(4x - y)$

    (d) $(x - 2y)(x - 8y)$ **(e)** None of these

    1—Ans: b

26. Factor $x^2 + 8xy + 16y^2$.

    (a) $(x + 4y)(x + 4y)$ **(b)** $(x - 4y)(x - 4y)$ **(c)** $(4x + y)(4x + y)$

    (d) $(x + 2y)(x + 8y)$ **(e)** None of these

    1—Ans: a

27. Factor $x^2 + 10xy + 16y^2$.

    (a) $(x + 4y)(x + 4y)$ **(b)** $(x - 4y)(x - 4y)$ **(c)** $(4x + y)(x + 4y)$

    (d) $(x + 2y)(x + 8y)$ **(e)** None of these

    1—Ans: d

28. Factor $x^2 - 10xy + 16y^2$.

    (a) $(x + 4y)(x + 4y)$ **(b)** $(x - 12y)(x + 2y)$ **(c)** $(x - 2y)(x - 8y)$

    (d) $(x - 4y)(x - 4y)$ **(e)** None of these

    1—Ans: c

29. Factor $x^2 - 20xy + 96y^2$.

    (a) $(x + 8y)(x + 12y)$ **(b)** $(x + 24y)(x - 4y)$ **(c)** $(x - 24y)(x + 4y)$

    (d) $(x - 12y)(x - 8y)$ **(e)** None of these

    1—Ans: d

30. Factor $x^2 + 20xy + 96y^2$.

    (a) $(x + 8y)(x + 12y)$ **(b)** $(x + 24y)(x - 4y)$ **(c)** $(x - 24y)(x + 4y)$

    (d) $(x - 12y)(x - 8y)$ **(e)** None of these

    1—Ans: a

31. Factor $x^2 + 20xy - 96y^2$.

    (a) $(x + 8y)(x + 12y)$ **(b)** $(x + 24y)(x - 4y)$ **(c)** $(x - 24y)(x + 4y)$

    (d) $(x - 12y)(x - 8y)$ **(e)** None of these

    1—Ans: b

32. Factor $x^2 - 20xy - 96y^2$.

    (a) $(x + 8y)(x + 12y)$ **(b)** $(x + 24y)(x - 4y)$ **(c)** $(x - 24y)(x + 4y)$

    (d) $(x - 12y)(x - 8y)$ **(e)** None of these

    1—Ans: c

33. Factor $x^2 + 10xy - 24y^2$.

    (a) $(x + 6y)(x + 4y)$ **(b)** $(x + 12y)(x - 2y)$ **(c)** $(x - 12y)(x + 2y)$

    (d) $(x - 6y)(x - 4y)$ **(e)** None of these

    1—Ans: b

34. Factor $x^2 - 10xy - 24y^2$.

    (a) $(x + 6y)(x + 4y)$ **(b)** $(x + 12y)(x - 2y)$ **(c)** $(x - 12y)(x + 2y)$

    (d) $(x - 6y)(x - 4y)$ **(e)** None of these

    1—Ans: c

35. Factor $x^2 + 10xy + 24y^2$.

    (a) $(x + 6y)(x + 4y)$ **(b)** $(x + 12y)(x - 2y)$ **(c)** $(x - 12y)(x + 2y)$

    (d) $(x - 6y)(x - 4y)$ **(e)** None of these

    1—Ans: a

36. Factor $x^2 - 10xy + 24y^2$.

    (a) $(x + 6y)(x + 8y)$ **(b)** $(x + 12y)(x - 2y)$ **(c)** $(x - 12y)(x + 2y)$

    (d) $(x - 6y)(x - 4y)$ **(e)** None of these

    1—Ans: d

37. Factor $x^2 - 6xy - 91y^2$.

    1—Ans: $(x - 13y)(x + 7y)$

38. Factor $x^2 - 12xy - 28y^2$.

    1—Ans: $(x - 14y)(x + 2y)$

39. Factor $n^2 - nm - 20m^2$.

    1—Ans: $(n - 5m)(n + 4m)$

40. Factor $n^2 - nm - 30m^2$.

    1—Form: 6C—Ans: $(n - 6m)(n + 5m)$

41. Factor $x^2 + 11xy - 80y^2$.

    1—Ans: $(x + 16y)(x - 5y)$

42. Factor $x^2 + 16xy - 80y^2$.

    1—Ans: $(x + 20y)(x - 4y)$

43. Factor $a^2 + 12ab + 35b^2$.

    1—Ans: $(a + 5b)(a + 7b)$

44. Factor $a^2 + 10ab + 21b^2$.

    1—Ans: $(a + 3b)(a + 7b)$

45. Factor $x^2 - 4xy - 60y^2$.

    1—Ans: $(x - 10y)(x + 6y)$

46. Factor $x^2 + 7xy - 60y^2$.

    1—Ans: $(x + 12y)(x - 5y)$

47. Factor the trinomial $5x^2 - 5x - 10$ *completely*.

    (a) $(x - 2)(5x + 5)$ **(b)** $5(x + 2)(x - 1)$ **(c)** $5(x - 2)(x + 1)$

    (d) $(5x - 10)(x + 1)$ **(e)** None of these

    1—Ans: c

48. Factor the trinomial $3x^2 - 3x - 18$ *completely*.

    (a) $3(x + 3)(x - 2)$ **(b)** $(x - 3)(3x + 6)$ **(c)** $(3x - 9)(x + 2)$

    (d) $3(x - 3)(x + 2)$ **(e)** None of these

    1—Ans: d

49. Factor the trinomial $2x^3 - 14x^2 + 20x$ *completely*.

   (a) $2x(x - 5)(x - 2)$ **(b)** $x(2x - 10)(x - 2)$ **(c)** $2(x^2 - 5x)(x - 2)$

   (d) $x(2x - 4)(x - 5)$ **(e)** None of these

   2—Form: 6A—Ans: a

50. Factor the trinomial $2x^3 - 14x^2 + 24x$ *completely*.

   (a) $2(x^2 - 4x)(x - 3)$ **(b)** $x(2x - 6)(x - 4)$ **(c)** $2x(x - 4)(x - 3)$

   (d) $x(2x - 4)(x - 3)$ **(e)** None of these

   2—Form: 6B—Ans: c

51. Factor the trinomial $6y^4 - 18y^3 - 24y^2$ *completely*.

   (a) $(6y - 6)(y^3 + 4y^2)$ **(b)** $(6y + 6)(y^3 - 4y^2)$ **(c)** $6y^2(y - 1)(y + 4)$

   (d) $6y^2(y + 1)(y - 4)$ **(e)** None of these

   2—Ans: d

52. Factor the trinomial $6y^4 + 18y^3 - 24y^2$ *completely*.

   (a) $(6y - 6)(y^3 + 4y^2)$ **(b)** $(6y + 6)(y^3 - 4y^2)$ **(c)** $6y^2(y - 1)(y + 4)$

   (d) $6y^2(y + 1)(y - 4)$ **(e)** None of these

   2—Ans: c

53. Factor the trinomial $5y^4 - 15y^3 - 50y^2$ *completely*.

   (a) $5y^2(y + 2)(y - 5)$ **(b)** $(5y - 10)(y^3 + 5y^2)$ **(c)** $(5y + 10)(y^3 - 5y^2)$

   (d) $5y^2(y - 2)(y + 5)$ **(e)** None of these

   2—Ans: a

54. Factor the trinomial $5y^4 + 15y^3 - 50y^2$ *completely*.

   (a) $5y^2(y + 2)(y - 5)$ **(b)** $5y^2(y - 2)(y + 5)$ **(c)** $(5y + 10)(y^3 - 5y)$

   (d) $(5y - 10)(y^3 + 5y^2)$ **(e)** None of these

   2—Ans: b

55. Factor the trinomial $7x^2 - 14x - 56$ *completely*.

   1—Ans: $7(x + 2)(x - 4)$

56. Factor the trinomial $7x^2 + 14x - 56$ *completely*.

   1—Ans: $7(x - 2)(x + 4)$

57. Factor the trinomial $7x^2 + 42x + 56$ *completely*.

   1—Ans: $7(x + 2)(x + 4)$

58. Factor the trinomial $7x^2 - 42x + 56$ *completely*.

   1—Ans: $7(x - 2)(x - 4)$

59. Factor the trinomial $4x^4 - 36x^3 + 72x^2$ *completely*.

   2—Ans: $4x^2(x - 6)(x - 3)$

60. Factor the trinomial $4x^4 + 36x^3 + 72x^2$ *completely*.

   2—Ans: $4x^2(x + 6)(x + 3)$

61. Find the missing factor: $3x^2 + 33x - 36 = 3(x - 1)($ $)$

   2—Form: 6C—Ans: $x + 12$

62. Find the missing factor: $3x^2 - 33x - 36 = 3(x + 1)($ $)$

   2—Ans: $x - 12$

63. Factor the trinomial $x^2 + 7x + 6$ and draw a geometric model of the result.

   2—Ans: $(x + 1)(x + 6)$

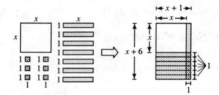

64. Factor the trinomial $x^2 + 8x + 7$ and draw a geometric model of the result.

   2—Ans: $(x + 1)(x + 7)$

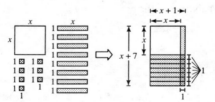

Section 6.3   More about Factoring Trinomials

1. Find the missing factor: $5x^2 + 9x - 2 = (x + 2)($ $)$

   1—Ans: $5x - 1$

2. Find the missing factor: $5x^2 - 9x - 2 = (x - 2)($ $)$

   1—Ans: $5x + 1$

3. Find the missing factor: $20x^2 - 13x - 21 = (4x + 3)($ $)$

   1—Ans: $5x - 7$

4. Find the missing factor: $20x^2 - 13x - 21 = (5x - 7)($ $)$

   1—Ans: $4x + 3$

5. Find the missing factor: $20x^2 + 13x - 21 = (4x - 3)($ $)$

   1—Ans: $5x + 7$

6. Find the missing factor: $20x^2 + 13x - 21 = (5x + 7)($ $)$

   1—Ans: $4x - 3$

7. Factor $5x^2 - 8x - 4$.

   (a) $(5x + 2)(x - 2)$ **(b)** $(5x - 1)(x + 4)$ **(c)** $(5x + 1)(x - 4)$

   (d) $(5x - 2)(x + 2)$ **(e)** None of these

   1—Ans: a

8. Factor $5x^2 + 19x - 4$.

   (a) $(5x + 2)(x - 2)$ **(b)** $(5x - 1)(x + 4)$ **(c)** $(5x + 1)(x - 4)$

   (d) $(5x - 2)(x + 2)$ **(e)** None of these

   1—Ans: b

9. Factor $5x^2 - 19x - 4$.

   (a) $(5x + 2)(x - 2)$ **(b)** $(5x - 1)(x + 4)$ **(c)** $(5x + 1)(x - 4)$

   (d) $(5x - 2)(x + 2)$ **(e)** None of these

   1—Ans: c

10. Factor $5x^2 + 8x - 4$.

   (a) $(5x + 2)(x - 2)$ **(b)** $(5x - 1)(x + 4)$ **(c)** $(5x + 1)(x - 4)$

   (d) $(5x - 2)(x + 2)$ **(e)** None of these

   1—Ans: d

11. Factor $8x^2 - 14x + 3$.

   (a) $(2x - 3)(4x - 1)$ **(b)** $(4x - 3)(2x - 1)$ **(c)** $(8x - 3)(x - 1)$

   (d) $(8x - 1)(x - 3)$ **(e)** None of these

   1—Form: 6A—Ans: a

12. Factor $8x^2 - 14x + 5$.

   (a) $(8x - 5)(x - 1)$ **(b)** $(4x - 1)(2x - 5)$ **(c)** $(2x - 1)(4x - 5)$

   (d) $(8x - 1)(x - 5)$ **(e)** None of these

   1—Form: 6B—Ans: c

13. Factor $7x^2 + 43x + 6$.

   (a) $(7x + 6)(x + 1)$ **(b)** $(7x - 6)(x - 1)$ **(c)** $(7x + 1)(x + 6)$

   (d) $(7x - 1)(x - 6)$ **(e)** None of these

   1—Ans: c

14. Factor $7x^2 + 13x + 6$.

   (a) $(7x + 6)(x + 1)$ **(b)** $(7x - 6)(x - 1)$ **(c)** $(7x + 1)(x + 6)$

   (d) $(7x - 1)(x - 6)$ **(e)** None of these

   1—Ans: a

15. Factor $7x^2 - 13x + 6$.

   (a) $(7x + 6)(x + 1)$ **(b)** $(7x - 6)(x - 1)$ **(c)** $(7x + 1)(x + 6)$

   (d) $(7x - 1)(x - 6)$ **(e)** None of these

   1—Ans: b

16. Factor $7x^2 - 43x + 6$.

   (a) $(7x + 6)(x + 1)$ **(b)** $(7x - 6)(x - 1)$ **(c)** $(7x + 1)(x + 6)$

   (d) $(7x - 1)(x - 6)$ **(e)** None of these

   1—Ans: d

17. Factor $6x^2 - 7x - 5$.

   (a) $(3x + 5)(2x - 1)$ **(b)** $(2x + 5)(3x - 1)$ **(c)** $(3x - 5)(2x + 1)$

   (d) $(2x - 5)(3x + 1)$ **(e)** None of these

   1—Ans: c

18. Factor $6x^2 + 7x - 5$.

   (a) $(3x + 5)(2x - 1)$ **(b)** $(2x + 5)(3x - 1)$ **(c)** $(3x - 5)(2x + 1)$

   (d) $(2x - 5)(3x + 1)$ **(e)** None of these

   1—Ans: a

19. Factor $5x^2 - 12x + 4$.

   1—Ans: $(5x - 2)(x - 2)$

20. Factor $5x^2 + 12x + 4$.

   1—Ans: $(5x + 2)(x + 2)$

21. Factor $9x^2 + 15x + 4$.

   1—Ans: $(3x + 4)(3x + 1)$

22. Factor $9x^2 + 18x + 5$.

    1—Form: 6C—Ans: $(3x + 5)(3x + 1)$

23. Factor $7x^2 + 41x - 6$.

    1—Ans: $(7x - 1)(x + 6)$

24. Factor $7x^2 - 41x - 6$.

    1—Ans: $(7x + 1)(x - 6)$

25. Factor $6x^2 + 13x + 5$.

    1—Ans: $(3x + 5)(2x + 1)$

26. Factor $6x^2 - 13x + 5$.

    1—Ans: $(3x - 5)(2x - 1)$

27. Factor $6x^2 + 17x + 5$.

    1—Ans: $(2x + 5)(3x + 1)$

28. Factor $6x^2 - 17x + 5$.

    1—Ans: $(2x - 5)(3x - 1)$

29. Find the missing factor: $-4x^2 - 8x - 3 = -(2x + 1)(\quad)$

    1—Ans: $2x + 3$

30. Find the missing factor: $-4x^2 - 13x - 3 = -(4x + 1)(\quad)$

    1—Form: 6C—Ans: $x + 3$

31. Factor $-6x^2 + 7x - 2$.

    (a) $-(2x + 1)(3x + 2)$ **(b)** $-(2x + 2)(3x + 1)$ **(c)** $-(2x - 1)(3x - 2)$

    (d) $-(2x - 2)(3x - 1)$ **(e)** None of these

    1—Form: 6A—Ans: c

32. Factor $-6x^2 + 11x - 3$.

    (a) $-(3x + 3)(2x + 1)$ **(b)** $-(3x - 1)(2x - 3)$ **(c)** $-(3x + 1)(2x + 3)$

    (d) $-(3x - 3)(2x - 1)$ **(e)** None of these

    1—Form: 6B—Ans: b

33. For $3y^2 + By - 2$, the trinomial does *not* factor if $B =$

    (a) -1 **(b)** 5 **(c)** 6 **(d)** -5 **(e)** None of these

    2—Ans: c

34. For $3y^2 + By - 2$, the trinomial does *not* factor if $B =$

    (a) -1 **(b)** -6 **(c)** 1 **(d)** -5 **(e)** None of these

    2—Ans: b

35. For $5x^2 + Bx + 3$, the trinomial does *not* factor if $B =$

    (a) 8 **(b)** 15 **(c)** -8 **(d)** -16 **(e)** None of these

    2—Ans: b

36. For $5x^2 + Bx + 3$, the trinomial does *not* factor if $B =$

    (a) -15 **(b)** 16 **(c)** -8 **(d)** -16 **(e)** None of these

    2—Ans: a

37. Find *two positive integers*, b, for which $7z^2 + bz + 3$ is factorable.

    2—Ans: 22 and 10

38. Find *two negative integers*, b, for which $7z^2 + bz + 3$ is factorable.

    2—Ans: -22 and -10

39. Find *two positive integers*, b, for which $7z^2 + bz - 3$ is factorable.

    2—Ans: 4 and 20

40. Find *two negative integers*, b, for which $7z^2 + bz - 3$ is factorable.

    2—Ans: -4 and -20

41. A factored form of $-4x^2 + 2x + 6$ is:

    (a) $2(-2x - 3)(x + 1)$ **(b)** $2(-2x + 3)(x - 1)$ **(c)** $2(-2x + 3)(x + 1)$

    (d) $2(-2x - 3)(x - 1)$ **(e)** None of these

    1—Ans: c

42. A factored form of $-4x^2 - 2x + 6$ is:

    (a) $2(-2x - 3)(x + 1)$ **(b)** $2(-2x + 3)(x - 1)$ **(c)** $2(-2x + 3)(x + 1)$

    (d) $2(-2x - 3)(x - 1)$ **(e)** None of these

    1—Ans: d

43. A factored form of $-4x^2 - 10x - 6$ is:

(a) $2(-2x - 3)(x + 1)$ (b) $2(-2x + 3)(x - 1)$ (c) $2(-2x + 3)(x + 1)$

(d) $2(-2x - 3)(x - 1)$ (e) None of these

1—Ans: a

44. A factored form of $-4x^2 + 10x - 6$ is:

(a) $2(-2x - 3)(x + 1)$ (b) $2(-2x + 3)(x - 1)$ (c) $2(-2x + 3)(x + 1)$

(d) $2(-2x - 3)(x - 1)$ (e) None of these

1—Ans: b

45. Factor $6x^2 - 3x - 18$ *completely*.

(a) $(6x + 9)(x - 2)$ (b) $3(2x - 3)(x + 2)$ (c) $3(2x + 3)(x - 2)$

(d) $(3x - 6)(2x + 3)$ (e) None of these

1—Ans: c

46. Factor $6x^2 + 3x - 18$ *completely*.

(a) $3(2x - 3)(x + 2)$ (b) $(6x - 9)(x + 2)$ (c) $3(2x + 3)(x - 2)$

(d) $(2x - 3)(3x + 6)$ (e) None of these

1—Ans: a

47. Factor $6x^2 + 15x - 9$ *completely*.

(a) $3(2x + 3)(x - 1)$ (b) $3(2x - 1)(x + 3)$ (c) $3(2x - 3)(x + 1)$

(d) $3(2x + 1)(x - 3)$ (e) None of these

1—Form: 6A—Ans: b

48. Factor $6x^2 + 10x - 4$ *completely*.

(a) $2(3x + 1)(x - 2)$ (b) $2(3x - 2)(x + 1)$ (c) $2(3x + 2)(x - 1)$

(d) $2(3x - 1)(x + 2)$ (e) None of these

1—Form: 6B—Ans: d

49. Factor $18x^2 - 3x - 6$ *completely*.

(a) $(3x - 2)(6x + 3)$ (b) $3(2x - 1)(3x + 2)$ (c) $(9x - 6)(2x + 1)$

(d) $3(2x + 1)(3x - 2)$ (e) None of these

1—Ans: d

50. Factor $18x^2 + 3x - 6$ *completely.*

    (a) $(6x - 3)(3x + 2)$ **(b)** $3(2x - 1)(3x + 2)$ **(c)** $(2x - 1)(9x + 6)$

    (d) $3(2x + 1)(3x - 2)$ **(e)** None of these

    1—Ans: b

51. Factor $-4x^2 + 14x - 6$ *completely.*

    1—Ans: $-2(x - 3)(2x - 1)$

52. Factor $-4x^2 - 14x - 6$ *completely.*

    1—Ans: $-2(x + 3)(2x + 1)$

53. Factor $6u^2v^2 + 11uv^2 - 7v^2$ *completely.*

    1—Ans: $v^2(3u + 7)(2u - 1)$

54. Factor $6u^2v^2 - 11uv^2 - 7v^2$ *completely.*

    1—Ans: $v^2(3u - 7)(2u + 1)$

55. Which of the listed factored forms is correct for $2x^2 + x - 6$?

    (a) $2x(x + 2) - 3(x + 2) = (x + 2)(2x - 3)$ **(b)** $2x(x + 2) + 3(x + 2) = (x + 2)(2x + 3)$

    (c) $2x(x - 2) + 3(x - 2) = (x - 2)(2x + 3)$ **(d)** $2x(x - 2) - 3(x - 2) = (x - 2)(2x - 3)$

    (e) None of these

    1—Ans: a

56. Which of the listed factored forms is correct for $2x^2 + 7x + 6$?

    (a) $2x(x + 2) - 3(x + 2) = (x + 2)(2x - 3)$ **(b)** $2x(x + 2) + 3(x + 2) = (x + 2)(2x + 3)$

    (c) $2x(x - 2) + 3(x - 2) = (x - 2)(2x + 3)$ **(d)** $2x(x - 2) - 3(x - 2) = (x - 2)(2x - 3)$

    (e) None of these

    1—Ans: b

57. Rewrite the middle term of the trinomial $6x^2 + 29x + 20$ so that the trinomial can be factored by grouping.

    1—Ans: $29x = 24x + 5x$

58. Rewrite the middle term of the trinomial $6x^2 + 23x + 15$ so that the trinomial can be factored by grouping.

    1—Form: 6C—Ans: $23x = 18x + 5x$

59. Factor $2x^2 - 11x - 6$ by grouping. Show steps.

    2—Ans: $2x^2 - 12x + x - 6 = 2x(x - 6) + (x - 6) = (x - 6)(2x + 1)$

60. Factor $2x^2 + 11x - 6$ by grouping. Show steps.

2—Ans: $2x^2 + 12x - x - 6 = 2x(x + 6) - (x + 6) = (x + 6)(2x - 1)$

61. Factor $2x^2 - 13x + 6$ by grouping. Show steps.

2—Ans: $2x^2 - 12x - x + 6 = 2x(x - 6) - (x - 6) = (x - 6)(2x - 1)$

62. Factor $2x^2 + 13x + 6$ by grouping. Show steps.

2—Ans: $2x^2 + 12x + x + 6 = 2x(x + 6) + (x + 6) = (x + 6)(2x + 1)$

63. Supply the missing step in the factorization by grouping: $7x^2 + 13x - 2 = ?$
$$= (7x^2 + 14x) - (x + 2)$$
$$= 7x(x + 2) - (x + 2)$$
$$= (x + 2)(7x - 1)$$

1—Ans: $7x^2 + 14x - x - 2$

64. Supply the missing step in the factorization by grouping: $5x^2 + 14x - 3 = ?$
$$= (5x^2 + 15x) - (x + 3)$$
$$= 5x(x + 3) - (x + 3)$$
$$= (x + 3)(5x - 1)$$

1—Ans: $5x^2 + 15x - x - 3$

Section 6.4   Factoring Polynomials with Special Forms

1. Which of the following *does not* represent the difference of two squares?

(a) $81 - 49$ (b) $y^4 - 16$ (c) $x^2 - 16x$

(d) $(x - 2)^2 - 25$ (e) None of these

1—Ans: c

2. Which of the following *does not* represent the difference of two squares?

(a) $x^4 - 25$ (b) $100 - 64$ (c) $(z - 3)^2 - 36$

(d) $y^2 - 25y$ (e) None of these

1—Ans: d

3. Which of the following *does not* represent the difference of two squares?

(a) $z^4 - 81$ (b) $(x + 5)^2 - 81$ (c) $y^2 - 36y$

(d) $10^2 - 8^2$ (e) None of these

1—Ans: c

4. Which of the following *does not* represent the difference of two squares?

   (a) $z^2 - 49z$ (b) $4 - (x - 3)^2$ (c) $15^2 - 8^2$

   (d) $x^4 - (25)^2$ (e) None of these

   1—Ans: a

5. $49x^2 - 64y^2$ factors into:

   (a) $(7x + 8y)(7x + 8y)$ (b) $(7x - 8y)(7x + 8y)$ (c) $(7x - 8y)(7x - 8y)$

   (d) $(7x - 16y)(7x + 4y)$ (e) None of these

   1—Ans: b

6. $64x^2 - 49y^2$ factors into:

   (a) $(8y - 7x)(8y - 7x)$ (b) $(8y + 7x)(8y + 7x)$ (c) $(8y - 7x)(8y + 7x)$

   (d) $(16y - 7x)(4y + 7x)$ (e) None of these

   1—Ans: c

7. $36x^2 - 25y^2$ factors into:

   (a) $(6x - 5y)(6x + 5y)$ (b) $(6x - 5y)(6x - 5y)$ (c) $(9x - 5y)(4x + 5y)$

   (d) $(6x + 5y)(6x + 5y)$ (e) None of these

   1—Ans: a

8. $25x^2 - 36y^2$ factors into:

   (a) $(5x - 6y)(5x - 6y)$ (b) $(5x + 6y)(5x + 6y)$ (c) $(5x - 9y)(5x + 4y)$

   (d) $(5y - 6x)(5y + 6x)$ (e) None of these

   1—Ans: d

9. Factor the polynomial $49x^2 - 16y^2$.

   1—Ans: $(7x^2 - 4y)(7x^2 + 4y)$

10. Factor the polynomial $81x^2 - 64y^2$.

    1—Ans: $(9x - 8y)(9x + 8y)$

11. Factor the polynomial $\frac{1}{64}n^2 - \frac{1}{49}$.

    1—Ans: $\left(\frac{1}{8}n + \frac{1}{7}\right)\left(\frac{1}{8}n - \frac{1}{7}\right)$

12. Factor the polynomial $\frac{1}{36}n^2 - \frac{1}{25}$.

    1—Form: 6C—Ans: $\left(\frac{1}{6}n + \frac{1}{5}\right)\left(\frac{1}{6}n - \frac{1}{5}\right)$

13. Factor $(x + 3)^2 - 25$ and simplify.

   (a) $(x + 8)(x - 2)$ **(b)** $(x + 2)(x - 8)$ **(c)** $(x - 2)(x - 2)$

   (d) $(x + 4)(x - 4)$ **(e)** None of these

   2—Form: 6A—Ans: a

14. Factor $(x + 4)^2 - 25$ and simplify.

   (a) $(x + 1)(x - 9)$ **(b)** $(x + 3)(x - 3)$ **(c)** $(x + 9)(x - 1)$

   (d) $(x - 1)(x - 1)$ **(e)** None of these

   2—Form: 6B—Ans: c

15. Factor $(x - 5)^2 - 16$ and simplify.

   1—Ans: $[(x - 5) - 4][(x - 5 + 4] = (x - 9)(x - 1)$

16. Factor $(x + 5)^2 - 16$ and simplify.

   1—Ans: $[(x + 5) - 4][(x + 5) + 4] = (x + 1)(x + 9)$

17. When factored *completely*, the polynomial $x^4 - 16x^2$ gives:

   (a) $(x^2 - 4x)(x^2 + 4x)$ **(b)** $(x^3 + 4x^2)(x - 4)$ **(c)** $x^2(x - 4)(x + 4)$

   (d) $(x + 4)(x^3 - 4x^2)$ **(e)** None of these

   1—Ans: c

18. When factored *completely*, the polynomial $5x^3 - 80x$ gives:

   (a) $x(5x + 20)(x - 4)$ **(b)** $5x(x - 4)(x + 4)$ **(c)** $5(x^2 - 4x)(x + 4)$

   (d) $(5x^2 - 20x)(x + 4)$ **(e)** None of these

   1—Ans: b

19. When factored *completely*, the polynomial $3x^4 - 108x^2$ gives:

   (a) $3x^2(x - 6)(x + 6)$ **(b)** $x(3x - 18)(x^2 + 6x)$ **(c)** $3(x^2 - 6x)(x^2 + 6x)$

   (d) $(x - 6)(3x^3 + 18x)$ **(e)** None of these

   1—Ans: a

20. When factored *completely*, the polynomial $2x^3 - 72x$ gives:

   (a) $2(x^2 - 6x)(x + 6)$ **(b)** $(2x^2 - 12x)(x + 6)$ **(c)** $(2x - 12)(x^2 + 6x)$

   (d) $2x(x - 6)(x + 6)$ **(e)** None of these

   1—Ans: d

21. Factor $144x^3 - 16x$ *completely*.

   1—Ans: $16x(3x - 1)(3x + 1)$

22. Factor $9x^3 - 144x$ *completely.*

    1—Ans: $9x(x - 4)(x + 4)$

23. Factor $4y^4 - 64y^2$ *completely.*

    2—Ans: $4y^2(y + 4)(y - 4)$

24. Factor $5y^4 - 45y^2$ *completely.*

    2—Form: 6C—Ans: $5y^2(y + 3)(y - 3)$

25. Factor the binomial *completely*: $x^4 - 81$

    (a) $(x^2 - 9)(x^2 - 9)$ **(b)** $(x^2 + 9)(x^2 - 9)$ **(c)** $(x^2 + 9)(x - 3)(x + 3)$

    (d) $(x^2 - 3)(x^2 + 27)$ **(e)** None of these

    1—Ans: c

26. Factor the binomial *completely*: $256x^4 - 81$

    (a) $(16x^2 + 9)(4x + 3)(4x - 3)$ **(b)** $(16x^2 + 9)(16x^2 - 9)$ **(c)** $(16x^2 + 9)(16x^2 + 9)$

    (d) $(64x^2 + 9)(4x - 9)$ **(e)** None of these

    1—Ans: a

27. Factor the binomial *completely*: $a^4 - 625$

    (a) $(a^2 + 25)(a - 5)(a - 5)$ **(b)** $(a^2 + 25)(a - 5)(a + 5)$ **(c)** $(a + 5)(a + 5)(a + 5)(a - 5)$

    (d) $(a^2 + 25)(a^2 - 25)$ **(e)** None of these

    2—Form: 6A—Ans: b

28. Factor the binomial *completely*: $a^4 - 81$

    (a) $(a + 3)(a + 3)(a + 3)(a - 3)$ **(b)** $(a^2 + 9)(a^2 - 9)$ **(c)** $(a^2 + 9)(a + 3)(a - 3)$

    (d) $(a^2 + 9)(a - 3)(a - 3)$ **(e)** None of these

    2—Form: 6B—Ans: c

29. Factor the binomial $16x^2 - 81$ *completely.*

    1—Ans: $(4x^2 + 9)(2x + 3)(2x - 3)$

30. Factor the binomial $81x^4 - 16$ *completely.*

    1—Ans: $(9x^2 + 4)(3x - 2)(3x + 2)$

31. Factor the binomial $256x^2 - 81x^4$ *completely.*

    1—Ans: $(16 + 9x^2)(4 + 3x)(4 - 3x)$

32. Factor the binomial $81x^4 - 256$ *completely.*

1—Ans: $(9x^2 + 16)(3x + 4)(3x - 4)$

33. Identify which of the following polynomials is a perfect square trinomial.

(a) $4x^2 - 6x + 9$ **(b)** $y^2 - 6y - 9$ **(c)** $4x^2 - 4x + 1$

(d) $x^2 + 9$ **(e)** None of these

1—Ans: c

34. Identify which of the following polynomials is a perfect square trinomial.

(a) $4x^2 - 6x + 9$ **(b)** $y^2 - 6y + 9$ **(c)** $4x^2 - 4x - 1$

(d) $x^2 + 9$ **(e)** None of these

1—Ans: b

35. Identify which of the following polynomials is a perfect square trinomial.

(a) $4x^2 + 12x + 9$ **(b)** $4x^2 + 20x + 9$ **(c)** $4x^2 + 37x + 9$

(d) $4x^2 + 13x + 9$ **(e)** None of these

1—Form: 6A—Ans: a

36. Identify which of the following polynomials is a perfect square trinomial.

(a) $4x^2 + 101x + 25$ **(b)** $4x^2 + 25x + 25$ **(c)** $4x^2 + 29x + 25$

(d) $4x^2 + 20x + 25$ **(e)** None of these

1—Form: 6B—Ans: d

37. Which number or expression placed in the box will make the trinomial a perfect square?

$\boxed{} - 72x + 81$

(a) $36x^2$ **(b)** $9x^2$ **(c)** $4x^2$ **(d)** $16x^2$ **(e)** None of these

1—Ans: d

38. Which number or expression placed in the box will make the trinomial a perfect square?

$9x^2 + \boxed{} + 81$

(a) $27x$ **(b)** 54 **(c)** $54x$ **(d)** $27x^2$ **(e)** None of these

1—Ans: c

39. Which number or expression placed in the box will make the trinomial a perfect square?

$8x^2 - \boxed{} + 81$

(a) $18x$ **(b)** $-x^2$ **(c)** $54x$ **(d)** $36x$ **(e)** None of these

1—Ans: e, First term is not of the form a^2x^2.

40. Which number or expression placed in the box will make the trinomial a perfect square?

$9x^2 + 54x + $ ▨

(a) 18 **(b)** 81 **(c)** 9 **(d)** 36 **(e)** None of these

1—Ans: b

41. Find a number c so that the trinomial $x^2 - 8x + c$ is a perfect square trinomial.

1—Ans: $c = 16$

42. Find a number c so that the trinomial $x^2 - 12x + c$ is a perfect square trinomial.

1—Ans: $c = 36$

43. Place a number or expression in the box which will make the trinomial a perfect square.

$49x^2 - 56xy + $ ▨

1—Ans: $(16y^2)$

44. Place a number or expression in the box which will make the trinomial a perfect square.

$49x^2 + $ ▨ $ + 16y^2$

1—Ans: $(56xy$ or $-56xy)$

45. Factor the trinomial $9x^2 - 24x + 16$.

1—Ans: $(3x - 4)^2$

46. Factor the trinomial $25 - 60x + 36x^2$.

1—Ans: $(5 - 6x)^2$

47. Factor the trinomial $9x^2 + 24x + 16$.

1—Ans: $(3x + 4)^2$

48. Factor the trinomial $25 + 60x + 36x^2$.

1—Ans: $(5 + 6x)^2$

49. Factor $25x^2 - 30x + 9$ and write the result as the square of a binomial.

1—Ans: $(5x - 3)^2$

50. Factor $16x^2 - 40x + 25$ and write the result as the square of a binomial.

1—Form: 6C—Ans: $(4x - 5)^2$

51. Factor $125x^3 - 27$.

1—Ans: $(5x - 3)(25x^2 + 15x + 9)$

52. Factor $8y^3 - 125$.

    1—Ans: $(2y - 5)(4y^2 + 10y + 25)$

53. $27 - x^3$ factors into:

    (a) $(3 - x)(9 + 6x + x^2)$ **(b)** $(3 + x)(9 - 6x + x^2)$ **(c)** $(3 - x)(9 + 3x + x^2)$

    (d) $(3 + x)(9 - 3x + x^2)$ **(e)** None of these

    1—Ans: c

54. $27 + x^3$ factors into:

    (a) $(3 - x)(9 + 6x + x^2)$ **(b)** $(3 + x)(9 - 6x + x^2)$ **(c)** $(3 - x)(9 + 3x + x^2)$

    (d) $(3 + x)(9 - 3x + x^2)$ **(e)** None of these

    1—Ans: d

55. Factor $125x^3 + 27$.

    1—Ans: $(5x + 3)(25x^2 - 15x + 9)$

56. Factor $8y^3 + 125$.

    1—Ans: $(2y + 5)(4y^2 - 10y + 25)$

57. Factor the polynomial: $z^3 + 125$

    2—Ans: $(z + 5)(z^2 - 5z + 25)$

58. Factor the polynomial: $t^3 + 216$

    2—Ans: $(t + 6)(t^2 - 6t + 36)$

59. Find the missing factor: $2x^3 - 2 = 2(x - 1)(\quad)$

    2—Ans: $x^2 + x + 1$

60. Find the missing factor: $4x^3 - 4 = 4(\quad)(x^2 + x + 1)$

    2—Ans: $x - 1$

61. The polynomial $7x^3 - 42x^2 + 63x$, when *completely* factored, gives:

    (a) $7(x - 3)(x^2 + 3)$ **(b)** $7x(x^2 - 3x + 9)$ **(c)** $7x(x - 3)^2$

    (d) $7(x - 3)(x^2 + 3x + 9)$ **(e)** None of these

    2—Ans: c

62. The polynomial $7x^3 + 42x^2 + 63x$, when *completely* factored, gives:

(a) $7x(x + 3)^2$ (b) $7x(x^2 + 3x + 9)$ (c) $7(x + 3)(x^2 + 3)$

(d) $7(x + 3)(x^2 - 3x + 9)$ (e) None of these

2—Ans: a

63. The polynomial $5x^4 + 135x$, when *completely* factored, gives:

(a) $5x(x + 3)(x^2 + 9)$ (b) $5x(x + 3)(x^2 - 3x + 9)$ (c) $5x(x^2 - 3x + 9)$

(d) $5x(x + 3)(x^2 + 3x + 9)$ (e) None of these

2—Ans: b

64. The polynomial $5x^4 - 135x$, when *completely* factored, gives:

(a) $5x(x - 3)(x^2 + 9)$ (b) $5x(x - 3)(x^2 - 3x + 9)$ (c) $5x(x^2 - 3x + 9)$

(d) $5x(x - 3)(x^2 + 3x + 9)$ (e) None of these

2—Ans: d

65. Factor $8x^4 - 64x^3 + 128x^2$ *completely*.

2—Ans: $8x^2(x - 4)^2$

66. Factor $6x^4 - 48x^3 + 96x^2$ *completely*.

2—Ans: $6x^2(x - 4)^2$

Section 6.5   Polynomial Equations and Applications

1. Write the polynomial equation $y^2 - 4y = 5$ in standard form.

1—Ans: $y^2 - 4y - 5 = 0$

2. Write the polynomial equation $y^2 - 6y = 7$ in standard form.

1—Form: 6C—Ans: $y^2 - 6y - 7 = 0$

3. Find the solutions of $x^2 - x - 12 = (x - 4)(x + 3) = 0$.

(a) 4 and 3   (b) 4 and -3 (c) -4 and -3

(d) -4 and 3   (e) None of these

1—Ans: b

4. Find the solutions of $x^2 - 2x - 8 = (x - 4)(x + 2) = 0$.

(a) 4 and -2 (b) -4 and 2   (c) -4 and -2

(d) 4 and 2   (e) None of these

1—Ans: a

5. Find the solutions of $x^2 + 2x - 8 = (x + 4)(x - 2) = 0$.

   (a) 4 and -2 (b) -4 and -2 (c) -4 and 2

   (d) 4 and 2   (e) None of these

   1—Ans: c

6. Find the solutions of $x^2 + x - 12 = (x + 4)(x - 3) = 0$.

   (a) 4 and 3   (b) 4 and -3 (c) -4 and -3

   (d) -4 and 3   (e) None of these

   1—Ans: d

7. Solve the equation $x^2 + 3x - 10 = 0$.

   1—Ans: $x = 2$ and $x = -5$

8. Solve the equation $x^2 + 5x - 14 = 0$.

   1—Ans: $x = 2$ and $x = -7$

9. Solve the equation $3x^2 + x - 10 = 0$.

   1—Ans: $x = -2$ and $x = \frac{5}{3}$

10. Solve the equation $3x^2 - 11x + 10 = 0$.

    1—Ans: $x = 2$ and $x = \frac{5}{3}$

11. Solve for x: $6x^2 + 5x + 1 = 0$

    2—Ans: $x = -\frac{1}{3}, x = -\frac{1}{2}$

12. Solve for x: $8x^2 + 6x + 1 = 0$

    2—Ans: $x = -\frac{1}{4}, x = -\frac{1}{2}$

13. Find the solutions of $4x^2 = 12x - 9$.

    (a) $x = 0$ and $x = \frac{3}{2}$ (b) $x = -\frac{3}{2}$ only   (c) $x = \frac{3}{2}$ and $x = \frac{2}{3}$

    (d) $x = \frac{3}{2}$ only   (e) None of these

    1—Ans: d

14. Find the solutions of $9x^2 = 12x - 4$.

    (a) $x = 0$ and $x = \frac{2}{3}$ (b) $x = -\frac{2}{3}$ only   (c) $x = \frac{2}{3}$ only

    (d) $x = \frac{3}{2}$ and $x = \frac{2}{3}$ (e) None of these

    1—Ans: c

15. Find the solutions of $4x^2 + 12x = -9$.

    (a) $x = 0$ and $x = -\frac{3}{2}$ **(b)** $x = -\frac{3}{2}$ only   **(c)** $\frac{3}{2}$ only

    (d) $x = -\frac{3}{2}$ and $x = -\frac{2}{3}$ **(e)** None of these

    1—Ans: b

16. Find the solutions of $9x^2 + 12x = -4$.

    (a) $x = -\frac{2}{3}$ only   **(b)** $x = \frac{2}{3}$ only   **(c)** $x = -\frac{2}{3}$ and $x = -\frac{3}{2}$

    (d) $x = 0$ and $x = -\frac{2}{3}$ **(e)** None of these

    1—Ans: a

17. Solve the equation $2x^2 - 20x + 50 = 0$.

    2—Ans: $x = 5$

18. Solve the equation $2x^2 - 24x + 72 = 0$.

    2—Ans: $x = 6$

19. Solve the equation $16x^2 = 8x - 1$.

    1—Ans: $x = \frac{1}{4}$

20. Solve the equation $16x^2 + 8x = -1$.

    1—Ans: $x = -\frac{1}{4}$

21. Find the solutions of $3x^2 = 7x$.

    (a) $x = 0$ only   **(b)** $x = \frac{7}{3}$ only   **(c)** $x = 0$ and $x = \frac{7}{3}$

    (d) $x = 0$ and $x = \frac{3}{7}$ **(e)** None of these

    1—Ans: c

22. Find the solutions of $7x^2 = 3x$.

    (a) $x = 0$ only   **(b)** $x = 0$ and $x = \frac{3}{7}$ **(c)** $x = 0$ and $x = \frac{7}{3}$

    (d $x = \frac{3}{7}$ only   **(e)** None of these

    1—Ans: b

23. Find the solutions of $9x^2 = 5x$.

    (a) $x = 0$ only   **(b)** $x = \frac{5}{9}$ only   **(c)** $x = 0$ and $x = \frac{9}{5}$

    (d) $x = 0$ and $x = \frac{5}{9}$ **(e)** None of these

    1—Ans: d

24. Find the solutions of $5x^2 = 9x$.

    (a) $x = 0$ and $x = \frac{9}{5}$ **(b)** $x = 0$ only   **(c)** $x = \frac{9}{5}$ only

    (d) $x = 0$ and $x = \frac{5}{9}$ **(e)** None of these

    1—Ans: a

25. Find the solutions of $x^2 + 2x = 8$.

    (a) $x = 6$ and $x = 8$ **(b)** $x = -4$ and $x = 2$ **(c)** $x = -2$ and $x = 4$

    (d) $x = -2$ and $x = 8$ **(e)** None of these

    2—Form: 6A—Ans: b

26. Find the solutions of $x^2 + 3x = 10$.

    (a) $x = -2$ and $x = 5$ **(b)** $x = 7$ and $x = 10$ **(c)** $x = -3$ and $x = 10$

    (d) $x = -5$ and $x = 2$ **(e)** None of these

    2—Form: 6B—Ans: d

27. Find the solutions of $x^2 + 10x + 20 = 4$.

    (a) $x = -2$ only   **(b)** $x = -8$ only   **(c)** $x = -2$ and $x = -8$

    (d) $x = 2$ and $x = 8$ **(e)** None of these

    1—Ans: c

28. Find the solutions of $x^2 - 10x + 20 = 11$.

    (a) $x = -1$ and $x = -9$ **(b)** $x = 1$ and $x = 9$ **(c)** $x = 1$ only

    (d) $x = 9$ only   **(e)** None of these

    1—Ans: b

29. Find the solutions of $(x + 2)(x - 2) = 5$.

    (a) $x = 3$ and $x = 7$ **(b)** $x = 3$ only   **(c)** $x = -3$ and $x = 3$

    (d) $x = -3$ only   **(e)** None of these

    2—Form: 6A—Ans: c

30. Find the solutions of $(x + 1)(x - 1) = 3$.

    (a) $x = -2$ and $x = 2$ **(b)** $x = 2$ and $x = 4$ **(c)** $x = -2$ only

    (d) $x = 2$ only   **(e)** None of these

    2—Form: 6B—Ans: a

31. Find the solutions of $(x - 4)(x + 3) = 8$.

    (a) $x = 5$ and $x = -4$ **(b)** $x = -5$ and $x = 4$ **(c)** $x = -4$ and $x = 3$

    (d) $x = 4$ and $x = -3$ **(e)** None of these

    1—Ans: a

32. Find the solutions of $(x + 4)(x - 3) = 8$.

    (a) $x = 5$ and $x = -4$ **(b)** $x = -5$ and $x = 4$ **(c)** $x = -4$ and $x = 3$

    (d) $x = 4$ and $x = -3$ **(e)** None of these

    1—Ans: b

33. Find the solutions of $(x + 5)(x - 4) = -8$.

    (a) $x = 5$ and $x = -4$ **(b)** $x = -5$ and $x = 4$ **(c)** $x = -4$ and $x = 3$

    (d) $x = 4$ and $x = -3$ **(e)** None of these

    1—Ans: c

34. Find the solutions of $(x - 5)(x + 4) = -8$.

    (a) $x = 5$ and $x = -4$ **(b)** $x = -5$ and $x = 4$ **(c)** $x = -4$ and $x = 3$

    (d) $x = 4$ and $x = -3$ **(e)** None of these

    1—Ans: d

35. Solve the equation $x^2 - 12x + 20 = 9$.

    1—Ans: $x = 11$ and $x = 1$

36. Solve the equation $x^2 + 12x + 20 = 9$.

    1—Ans: $x = -1$ and $x = -11$

37. Solve the equation $x^2 + 12x + 20 = 33$.

    1—Ans: $x = 1$ and $x = -13$

38. Solve the equation $x^2 - 12x + 20 = 33$.

    1—Ans: $x = -1$ and $x = 13$

39. Solve the equation $(x + 1)(x - 4) = 14$.

    2—Form: 6C—Ans: $x = -3$ and $x = 6$

40. Solve the equation $(x + 2)(x + 5) = 4$.

    2—Ans: $x = -6$ and $x = -1$

41. Solve the equation $(x + 4)(x - 2) = 7$.

   1—Ans: $x = -5$ and $x = 3$

42. Solve the equation $(x - 4)(x + 2) = 7$.

   1—Ans: $x = -3$ and $x = 5$

43. Find the solutions of $9x^3 = 24x^2 - 16x$.

   (a) $x = 0$ and $x = \frac{3}{4}$ **(b)** $x = 0$ and $x = -\frac{4}{3}$ **(c)** $x = 0$ and $x = -\frac{3}{4}$

   (d) $x = 0$ and $x = \frac{4}{3}$ **(e)** None of these

   1—Ans: d

44. Find the solutions of $9x^3 + 24x^2 = -16x$.

   (a) $x = 0$ and $x = \frac{3}{4}$ **(b)** $x = 0$ and $x = -\frac{4}{3}$ **(c)** $x = 0$ and $x = -\frac{3}{4}$

   (d) $x = 0$ and $x = \frac{4}{3}$ **(e)** None of these

   1—Ans: b

45. Find the solutions of $16x^3 + 24x^2 = -9x$.

   (a) $x = 0$ and $x = \frac{3}{4}$ **(b)** $x = 0$ and $x = -\frac{4}{3}$ **(c)** $x = 0$ and $x = -\frac{3}{4}$

   (d) $x = 0$ and $x - \frac{4}{3}$ **(e)** None of these

   1—Ans: c

46. Find the solutions of $16x^3 = 24x^2 - 9x$.

   (a) $x = 0$ and $x = \frac{3}{4}$ **(b)** $x = 0$ and $x = -\frac{4}{3}$ **(c)** $x = 0$ and $x = -\frac{3}{4}$

   (d) $x = 0$ and $x = \frac{4}{3}$ **(e)** None of these

   1—Ans: a

47. Find the solutions of $x^3 = 3x^2 + 18x$.

   (a) $x = -3$ and $x = 6$ **(b)** $x = -6$ and $x = 0$ **(c)** $x = -6, x = 0$, and $x = 3$

   (d) $x = -3, x = 0$, and $x = 6$ **(e)** None of these

   2—Form: 6A—Ans: d

48. Find the solutions of $x^3 = 4x^2 + 12x$.

   (a) $x = -3$ and $x = 0$ **(b)** $x = -2, x = 0$, and $x = 6$ **(c)** $x = -6, x = 0$, and $x = 2$

   (d) $x = -2$ and $x = 6$ **(e)** None of these

   2—Form: 6B—Ans: b

49. Solve the equation $25x^3 = 9x$.

   1—Ans: $x = 0, x = \frac{3}{5}$, and $x = -\frac{3}{5}$

50. Solve the equation $9x^3 = 25x$.

   1—Ans: $x = 0$, $x = \frac{5}{3}$, and $x = -\frac{5}{3}$

51. A rectangular pen is 7 feet longer than it is wide. It encloses an area of 330 square feet. Its dimensions are:

   (a) 30 ft by 11 ft   **(b)** 25 ft by 18 ft   **(c)** 22 ft by 15 ft

   (d) 20 ft by 13 ft   **(e)** None of these

   1—Ans: c

52. A rectangular pen is 7 feet longer than it is wide. It encloses an area of 260 square feet. Its dimensions are:

   (a) 30 ft by 11 ft   **(b)** 25 ft by 18 ft   **(c)** 22 ft by 15 ft

   (d) 20 ft by 13 ft   **(e)** None of these

   1—Ans: d

53. A rectangular pen is 8 feet longer than it is wide. It encloses an area of 308 square feet. Its dimensions are:

   (a) 19 ft by 12 ft   **(b)** 22 ft by 14 ft   **(c)** 22 ft by 9 ft

   (d) 20 ft by 13 ft   **(e)** None of these

   1—Ans: b

54. A rectangular pen is 7 feet longer than it is wide. It encloses an area of 198 square feet. Its dimensions are:

   (a) 19 ft by 12 ft   **(b)** 22 ft by 14 ft   **(c)** 22 ft by 9 ft

   (d) 20 ft by 13 ft   **(e)** None of these

   1—Ans: e, The dimensions are 18 by 11 feet.

55. The product of two consecutive negative integers is 80. Write a polynomial equation and solve for the integers.

   2—Form: 6C—Ans: $x(x + 2) = 80$; $x = -10$ and $x = -8$

56. The product of two consecutive negative integers is 120. Write a polynomial equation and solve for the integers.

   2—Ans: $x(x + 2) = 120$; $x = 10$ and $x = 12$

57. A rock is dropped from a hot air balloon 1024 feet above the ground. Its height, H, after t seconds is given by the equation $H = 1024 - 16t^2$. Find the time when its height is 624 feet.

   2—Ans: 5 seconds

58. A rock is dropped from a hot air balloon 1024 feet above the ground. Its height, H, after t seconds is given by the equation $H = 1024 - 16t^2$. Find the time when its height is 768 feet.

   2—Ans: 4 seconds

59. An object is dropped from a bridge 144 feet above a river. Find the time, t, for the object to reach the river. The height, H, (in feet) of the object is modeled by the equation $H = -16t^2 + 144$, where t is measured in seconds.

   2—Ans: $t = 3$

60. An object is dropped from a bridge 400 feet above a river. Find the time, t, for the object to reach the river. The height, H, (in feet) of the object is modeled by the equation $H = -16t^2 + 400$, where t is measured in seconds.

   2—Ans: $t = 5$

CHAPTER 7
Systems of Equations

Section 7.1 Solving Systems of Equations by Graphing and Substitution

1. Determine which of the given points is a solution of the system of linear equations.

$$x + 2y = 1$$
$$2x - 3y = 16$$

(a) $(7, -2)$ **(b)** $(5, -2)$ **(c)** $(6, -1)$ **(d)** $(-4, 3)$ **(e)** None of these

1—Ans: b

2. Determine which of the given points is a solution of the system of linear equations.

$$x + 3y = 5$$
$$3x + 4y = 0$$

(a) $(7, -2)$ **(b)** $(5, -2)$ **(c)** $(6, -1)$ **(d)** $(-4, 3)$ **(e)** None of these

1—Ans: d

3. Determine which of the given points is a solution of the system of linear equations.

$$2x + 3y = 8$$
$$x - 3y = 13$$

(a) $(7, -2)$ **(b)** $(5, -2)$ **(c)** $(6, -1)$ **(d)** $(-4, 3)$ **(e)** None of these

1—Ans: a

4. Determine which of the given points is a solution of the system of linear equations.

$$2x + 7y = 5$$
$$x - 5y = 11$$

(a) $(7, -2)$ **(b)** $(5, -2)$ **(c)** $(6, -1)$ **(d)** $(-4, 3)$ **(e)** None of these

1—Ans: c

5. Determine which of the two points is a solution of the system of equations.

$$x + \ y = \ 0$$
$$3x - 2y = 15$$

Points $(3, -3)$ and $(2, 4)$.

1—Ans: $(3, -3)$ is a solution.

6. Determine which of the two points is a solution of the system of equations.

$$2x + \ y = 0$$
$$7x + 3y = 2$$

Points $(3, -6)$ and $(2, -4)$.

1—Ans: $(2, -4)$ is a solution.

7. $y = \frac{1}{2}x$

$y = 2 - \frac{1}{2}x$

Use the graph of the system as shown to solve the system.

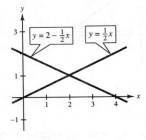

(a) $(-2, -1)$ **(b)** $(1, 2)$ **(c)** $(2, 1)$ **(d)** $(4, 0)$ **(e)** None of these

1—Ans: c

8. $y = \frac{2}{3}x + 2$

$y = -x + 1$

Use the graph of the system as shown to solve the system.

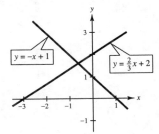

(a) $\left(-\frac{3}{5}, \frac{8}{5}\right)$ **(b)** $\left(\frac{8}{5}, \frac{3}{5}\right)$ **(c)** $\left(\frac{3}{5}, -\frac{8}{5}\right)$ **(d)** $\left(-\frac{8}{5}, -\frac{3}{5}\right)$ **(e)** None of these

1—Ans: a

9. $y = \frac{1}{2}x - 2$

$y = -2x + 3$

For the system of equations as shown, estimate the solution from the graph and check it in the equations.

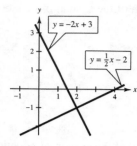

1—Ans: $(2, -1)$

10. $y = 3x + 3$

$y = -\frac{3}{4}x + 3$

For the system of equations as shown, estimate the solution from the graph and check it in the equation.

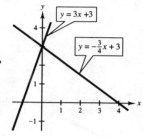

1—Ans: $(0, 3)$

11. Choose the best estimate listed for the solution of the linear system of equations as graphed.

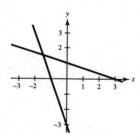

(a) $\left(\frac{3}{2}, -\frac{3}{2}\right)$ **(b)** $(1, -1)$ **(c)** $(0, -3)$ **(d)** $(-2, 2)$ **(e)** $\left(-\frac{3}{2}, \frac{3}{2}\right)$

1—Ans: e

12. Choose the best estimate listed for the solution of the linear system of equations as graphed.

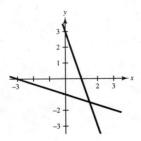

(a) $\left(\frac{3}{2}, -\frac{3}{2}\right)$ (b) $(-1, 1)$ (c) $(0, 3)$ (d) $(2, 2)$ (e) $\left(-\frac{3}{2}, \frac{3}{2}\right)$

1—Ans: a

13. Estimate the solution to the system of linear equations as graphed.

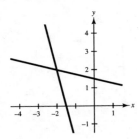

1—Ans: $(-2, 2)$

14. Estimate the solution to the system of linear equations as graphed.

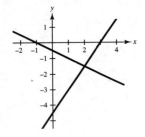

1—Ans: $\left(2, -\frac{3}{2}\right)$

15. For the system of equations

$$x + 5y = -2$$
$$2x - 7y = 4$$

which of the following cannot be derived by substituting from one equation into the other?

(a) $x + 5\left(\frac{2x + 4}{7}\right)y = -2$ (b) $\left(\frac{4 + 7y}{2}\right) + 5y = -2$ (c) $2x - 7\left(\frac{-2 - x}{5}\right) = 4$

(d) $2(-5y - 2) - 7y = 4$ (e) None of these

1—Ans: a

16. For the system of equations

$$3x + 5y = -1$$
$$x - 4y = 3$$

which of the following cannot be derived by substituting from one equation into the other?

(a) $3(4y + 3) + 5y = -1$ **(b)** $3x + 5\left(\dfrac{x + 3}{4}\right) = -1$ **(c)** $\left(\dfrac{-5y - 1}{3}\right) - 4y = 3$

(d) $x - 4\left(\dfrac{-3x - 1}{5}\right) = 3$ **(e)** None of these

1—Ans: b

17. For the system of equations

$$4x + y = -7$$
$$x - 6y = 5$$

eliminate y in the second equation by substitution from the first equation. Do not solve.

1—Ans: $x - 6(-7 - 4x) = 5$

18. For the system of equations

$$4x + y = -7$$
$$x - 6y = 5$$

eliminate x in the second equation by substitution from the first equation. Do not solve.

1—Ans: $\left(\dfrac{-y - 7}{4}\right) - 6y = 5$

19. For the system of linear equations

$$x + 3y = -7$$
$$2x + 8y = 4$$

substitution of x from the first equation into the second equation yields $2(7 - 3y) + 8y = 4$. Find the value of y.

(a) $y = 5$ **(b)** $y = -5$ **(c)** $y = -\dfrac{5}{7}$ **(d)** $y = \dfrac{5}{7}$ **(e)** None of these

1—Ans: b

20. For the system of linear equations

$$x + 3y = -7$$
$$2x + 8y = 4$$

substitution of y from the second equation into the first equation yields $x + 3\left(\dfrac{2 - x}{4}\right) = 7$. Find the value of x.

(a) $x = 22$ **(b)** $x = -22$ **(c)** $x = \dfrac{22}{7}$ **(d)** $x = \dfrac{34}{7}$ **(e)** None of these

1—Ans: a

21. For the system of linear equations

$$5x - 3y = 6$$
$$2x + 4y = 7$$

substituting for y into the second equation from the first equation yields $2x + 4\left(\dfrac{5x - 6}{3}\right) = 7.$

Complete the solution by calculating x and y.

1—Ans: $x = \dfrac{45}{26}, \ y = \dfrac{23}{26}$

22. For the system of linear equations

$$2x + 5y = 8$$
$$4x - 2y = 9$$

substituting for x into the first equation from the second equation yields $2\left(\dfrac{2y + 9}{4}\right) + 5y = 8.$

Complete the solution by calculating x and y.

1—Ans: $x = \dfrac{61}{24}, \ y = \dfrac{7}{12}$

23. For the system of linear equations

$$3x - 7y = \ \ 4$$
$$2x + 6y = -2$$

substituting for x into the first equation from the second equation yields $3\left(\dfrac{-6y - 2}{2}\right) - 7y = 4.$

Complete the solution by calculating x and y.

1—Ans: $x = \dfrac{5}{16}, \ y = -\dfrac{7}{16}$

24. For the system of linear equations

$$6x - 3y = 5$$
$$3x + 4y = 7$$

substituting for y into the second equation from the first equation yields $3x + 4\left(\dfrac{6x - 5}{3}\right) = 7.$

Complete the solution by calculating x and y.

1—Ans: $x = \dfrac{41}{33}, \ y = \dfrac{9}{11}$

25. Use the method of substitution to solve the system

$$x + 4y = 3$$
$$2x - \ y = 4.$$

(a) $\left(\dfrac{19}{9}, \dfrac{74}{9}\right)$ (b) $\left(\dfrac{19}{9}, \dfrac{2}{9}\right)$ (c) $\left(-\dfrac{13}{9}, -\dfrac{62}{9}\right)$

(d) $\left(\dfrac{13}{7}, \dfrac{2}{7}\right)$ (e) None of these

1—Ans: b

26. Use the method of substitution to solve the system

$$x + 4y = 3$$
$$2x - y = -4.$$

(a) $\left(-\frac{13}{9}, \frac{10}{9}\right)$ **(b)** $\left(-\frac{13}{9}, -\frac{62}{9}\right)$ **(c)** $\left(\frac{13}{7}, \frac{2}{7}\right)$

(d) $\left(\frac{19}{9}, \frac{2}{9}\right)$ **(e)** None of these

1—Ans: a

27. Use the method of substitution to solve the system

$$x + 3y = 4$$
$$3x - y = 6.$$

1—Ans: $x = \frac{11}{5}, \quad y = \frac{3}{5}$

28. Use the method of substitution to solve the system

$$x - 3y = 4$$
$$3x - y = 6.$$

1—Ans: $x = \frac{7}{4}, \quad y = -\frac{3}{4}$

29. Use the method of substitution to solve the system

$$x + 3y = 4$$
$$3x - y = -6.$$

1—Ans: $x = -\frac{7}{5}, \quad y = \frac{9}{5}$

30. Use the method of substitution to solve the system

$$x + 3y = -4$$
$$3x - y = 6.$$

1—Ans: $x = \frac{7}{5}, \quad y = -\frac{9}{5}$

31. A total of $13,000 is invested in two funds paying 7% and 9% simple interest. The combined annual interest for the two funds is $1020. If x represents the amount invested at 7% and y the amount at 9%, the mathematical model for this investment is represented by which system of equations?

(a) $0.09x + 0.07y = 1020$
      $x + y = 13,000$

(b) $0.07x + 0.09y = 13,000$
      $x + y = 1020$

(c) $0.07x + 0.09y = 1020$
      $x + y = 13,000$

(d) $0.09x + 0.07y = 13,000$
      $x + y = 1020$

(e) None of these

1—Ans: c

32. A total of $10,000 is invested in two funds paying 7% and 9% simple interest. The combined annual interest for the two funds is $1020. If x represents the amount invested at 7% and y the amount at 9%, the mathematical model for this investment is represented by which system of equations?

(a) $0.07x + 0.09y = 10,000$
      $x + \quad y = \quad 1020$

(b) $0.07x + 0.09y = \quad 1020$
      $x + \quad y = 10,000$

(c) $0.09x + 0.07y = 10,000$
      $x + \quad y = \quad 1020$

(d) $0.09x + 0.07y = \quad 1020$
      $x + \quad y = 10,000$

(e) None of these

1—Ans: b

33. A total of $15,000 is invested in two funds paying 8% and 10% simple interest. The combined interest for the two funds is $1310. Let x represent the amount invested at 8% and y the amount at 10%. Write a system of equations for this investment and solve for x and y.

2—Ans: $0.08x + 0.10y = \quad 1310$
            $x + \quad y = 15,000$
            $x = \quad 9500, \quad y = 5500$

34. A total of $14,000 is invested in two funds paying 8% and 10% simple interest. The combined interest for the two funds is $1240. Let x represent the amount invested at 8% and y the amount at 10%. Write a system of equations for this investment and solve for x and y.

2—Ans: $0.08x + 0.10y = \quad 1240$
            $x + \quad y = 14,000$
            $x = \quad 8000, \quad y = 6000$

35. The sum of two numbers is 111. One is twice the other. Choose the system of equations that represents these statements.

(a) $y = 2x$
      $x + y = 111$

(b) $2x + y = 111$
      $y = 2x$

(c) $x + y = 111$
      $x + 2 = y$

(d) $y = 2x$
      $x + \dfrac{y}{2} = 111$

(e) None of these

1—Ans: a

36. The sum of two numbers is 92. One is three times the other. Choose the system of equations that represents these statements.

    (a) $3x + y = 92$

               $y = 3x$

    (b) $x + y = 92$

            $x + 3 = y$

    (c) $x + y = 92$

             $y = 3x$

    (d) $y = 3x$

          $x + \dfrac{y}{3} = 92$

    (e) None of these

    1—Ans: c

37. The sum of two numbers is 123. One is one-half of the other. Choose the system of equations that represents these statements.

    (a) $y = 2x$

         $y + \dfrac{x}{2} = 123$

    (b) $x + y = 123$

            $y + 2 = x$

    (c) $2x + y = 123$

             $y = 2x$

    (d) $y = \dfrac{1}{2}x$

         $x + y = 123$

    (e) None of these

    1—Ans: d

38. The sum of two numbers is 212. One is three times the other. Choose the system of equations that represents these statements.

    (a) $x + y = 212$

            $x + 3 = y$

    (b) $y = 3x$

         $y + y = 212$

    (c) $3x + y = 212$

             $y = 3x$

    (d) $y = 3x$

         $x + \dfrac{y}{3} = 212$

    (e) None of these

    1—Ans: b

39. The sum of two numbers is 140. The larger number is five less than four times the smaller number. Find the numbers.

    1—Ans: 29 and 111

40. The sum of two numbers is 175. The larger number is three more than three times the smaller number. Find the numbers.

    1—Ans: 43 and 132

41. Use the graphing utility to determine which ordered pair is a solution of the system of equations.

$$2x + y = 1$$
$$-x + 2y = 7$$

(a) $(1, -1)$ (b) $(-1, 3)$ (c) $(-9, -1)$ (d) $(-1, 4)$ (e) None of these

1—T—Form: 7A—Ans: b

42. Use the graphing utility to determine which ordered pair is a solution of the system of equations.

$$5x + y = 11$$
$$3x - 2y = 4$$

(a) $\left(\frac{15}{13}, \frac{68}{13}\right)$ (b) $(2, 21)$ (c) $(2, 1)$ (d) $(-1, 16)$ (e) None of these

1—T—Form: 7B—Ans: c

43. Find the value of x in the solution of the system of equations.

$$0.25x - 0.75y = 3$$
$$3x - 2y = 71$$

(a) 5   (b) $-\frac{217}{7}$ (c) 27   (d) $\frac{61}{3}$ (e) None of these

2—Ans: c

44. Find the value of y in the solution of the system of equations.

$$0.25x - 0.75y = 3$$
$$3x - 2y = 71$$

(a) 5   (b) a (c) 27   (d) $\frac{61}{3}$ (e) None of these

2—Ans: a

45. Solve the system of equations by the method of substitution.

$$x^2 + 2y = 6$$
$$2x + y = 3$$

(a) $(4, -5)$ (b) $(2, 1)$ (c) $(0, 3)$

(d) $(0, 3)$ and $(4, -5)$ (e) None of these

2—Form: 7A—Ans: d

46. Solve the system of equations by the method of substitution.

$$x^2 + 2y = -6$$
$$x - y = 3$$

(a) $(-2, -5)$ (b) $(0, -3)$ (c) $(-2, -5)$ and $(0, -3)$

(d) $(4, 1)$ (e) None of these

2—Form: 7B—Ans: c

47. Use a graphing utility to solve the system of equations.

$$-x + 2y = 2$$
$$3x - y = 9$$

1—T—Ans: $(4, 3)$

48. Use a graphing utility to solve the system of equations.

$$3x + 4y = 2$$
$$2x + y = 3$$

1—T—Form: 7C—Ans: $(2, -1)$

49. Solve the system by the method of substitution.

$$2x^2 - y = -2$$
$$x - y = -2$$

2—Ans: $(0, 2)$ and $\left(\frac{1}{2}, \frac{5}{2}\right)$

50. Solve the system by the method of substitution.

$$x + y = 1$$
$$x^2 + 3y^2 = 21$$

2—Form: 7C—Ans: $\left(-\frac{3}{2}, \frac{5}{2}\right)$ and $(3, -2)$

51. Solve the system by the method of substitution.

$$0.1x - 0.3y = 1.2$$
$$3x - 2y = 71$$

(a) $(5, 27)$ **(b)** $(a, 5a)$ **(c)** $(27, 5)$ **(d)** $\left(\frac{61}{3}, 5\right)$ **(e)** None of these

2—Form: 7A—Ans: c

52. Solve the system by the method of substitution.

$$\frac{1}{3}x - \frac{3}{5}y = -2$$
$$2x - y = 14$$

(a) $\left(\frac{136}{23}, \frac{50}{23}\right)$ **(b)** $(12, 10)$ **(c)** $(12, -38)$ **(d)** No solution   **(e)** None of these

2—Form: 7B—Ans: b

53. Use a graphing utility to determine the solution to the system of equations.

$$x^2 - 4x + y = 0$$
$$x - y = 0$$

2—T—Form: 7C—Ans: $(0, 0)$ and $(3, 3)$

54. Use a graphing utility to determine the solution to the system of equations.

$$2x^2 - y - 1 = 0$$
$$2x^2 + y - 3 = 0$$

2—T—Ans: $(-1, 1)$ and $(1, 1)$

55. If the total cost of running a business is given by the equation $C = 450x + 1000$ and the revenue is given by the equation $R = 500x$, find the sales necessary to break even.

(a) 220   (b) 11   (c) 20   (d) 2000   (e) None of these

1—Ans: c

56. If the total cost of running a business is given by the equation $C = 4.16x + 75,000$ and the revenue is given by the equation $R = 7.91x$, find the sales necessary to break even.

(a) 6214   (b) 20,000   (c) 200   (d) 9482   (e) None of these

1—Ans: b

57. Choose the value of B such that the linear system

$$2x - 7y = -6$$
$$8x + By = -24$$

has infinitely many solutions.

2—Ans: $B = -28$

58. Choose the value of A such that the linear system

$$Ax + 5y = -7$$
$$-6x + 15y = -21$$

has infinitely many solutions.

2—Ans: $A = -2$

59. Which of the following is obtained when graphing a system of linear equations that has a single solution?

(a) Parallel lines   (b) Intersecting lines   (c) Coinciding lines

(d) No graph   (e) None of these

1—Ans: b

60. Which of the following is obtained when graphing a system of linear equations that has no solution?

(a) Parallel lines   (b) Intersecting lines   (c) Coinciding lines

(d) No graph   (e) None of these

1—Ans: a

61. Use a graphing utility to determine whether the system of linear equations has exactly one solution, infinitely many solutions, or no solutions (inconsistent).

$$3x + \ y = 7$$
$$x - 4y = 2$$

1—T—Ans: One solution

62. Use a graphing utility to determine whether the system of linear equations has exactly one solution, infinitely many solutions, or no solutions (inconsistent).

$$5x + \ y = 3$$
$$10x + 2y = 3$$

1—T—Ans: No solutions, inconsistent

63. $y = \frac{2}{3}x + 2$

$y = \frac{2}{3}x - 2$

Determine which of the following is true for the system of equations as graphed.

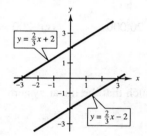

(a) There is a single unique solution.

(b) There is no solution; inconsistent.

(c) There are infinitely many solutions.

(d) There is a single solution point but it is well off the graph as shown.

(e) The graph is incorrect.

1—Ans: b

64. $y = 3x + 3$

$2y = 6x + 6$

Determine which of the following is true for the system of equations as graphed.

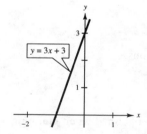

(a) There is a single unique solution.

(b) There is no solution; inconsistent.

(c) There are infinitely many solutions.

(d) There is a single solution point but it is well off the graph as shown.

(e) The graph is incorrect.

1—Ans: c

65. If a system of linear equations is consistent, and has a unique solution, what does its graph show?

1—Ans: Intersecting lines

66. If a system of linear equations is consistent but does not have a unique solution, what does its graph show?

1—Ans: The two lines coincide.

67. Use a graphing utility to graph the lines in the system of equations.

$$2x + 4y = 7$$
$$3x + 6y = 5$$

Use the graph to determine which choice describes the solution.

(a) Consistent, exactly one solution   **(b)** Consistent, infinitely many solutions

(c) Inconsistent

1—T—Form: 7A—Ans: c

68. Use a graphing utility to graph the lines in the system of equations.

$$6x - 5y = 4$$
$$3x + 2y = 1$$

Use the graph to determine which choice describes the solution.

(a) Consistent, exactly one solution   **(b)** Consistent, infinitely many solutions

(c) Inconsistent

1—T—Form: 7B—Ans: a

69. Use a graphing utility to graph the lines in the system of equations. Use the graphs to determine whether the solution is consistent or inconsistent. If it is inconsistent, determine the number of solutions.

$$\tfrac{1}{3}x - \tfrac{3}{5}y = -2$$
$$2x - y = 14$$

1—T—Form: 7C—Ans: Consistent, one solution

70. Use a graphing utility to graph the lines in the system of equations. Use the graphs to determine whether the solution is consistent or inconsistent. If it is inconsistent, determine the number of solutions.

$$6x - 8y = 2$$
$$\tfrac{9}{2}x - 6y = \tfrac{3}{2}$$

1—T—Ans: Consistent, infinitely many solutions

71. Suppose you are setting up a small business and have invested $18,000 to produce an item that will sell for $20.65. If each unit can be produced for $13.45, determine the number of units that you must sell in order to break even.

(a) 2500   **(b)** 872   **(c)** 1338   **(d)** 250   **(e)** $7.20

2—Ans: a

72. Suppose you are setting up a small business and have invested $5000 to produce an item that will sell for $9. If each unit can be produced for $7, how many units must you sell in order to break even?

2—Ans: 2500

73. A total of $50,000 is invested in two funds paying 8% and 10% simple interest. If the yearly interest for both funds totals $4660, determine the amount invested at 8%.

(a) $33,000 (b) $24,000 (c) $26,000

(d) $17,000 (e) $37,280

2—Ans: d

74. A total of $11,000 is invested in two funds paying 7% and 8% simple interest. If the yearly interest for both funds totals $865, determine the amount invested at 8%.

2—Ans: $9500

Section 7.2 Solving Systems of Equations by Elimination

1. A variable can be eliminated by adding the equations in which case?

(a) $2x + 3y = 10$
$3x - 2y = 7$

(b) $x + 4y = 8$
$2x + 4y = 7$

(c) $5x - y = 7$
$7x + y = 4$

(d) $8x + 7y = -1$
$2x + 4y = 3$

(e) None of these

1—Ans: c

2. A variable can be eliminated by adding the equations in which case?

(a) $8x - 4y = 9$
$2x + 7y = 10$

(b) $8x - 4y = 9$
$11x + 4y = 12$

(c) $7x + 4y = 1$
$7x + 8y = 2$

(d) $5x + 4y = 5$
$2x + 4y = 6$

(e) None of these

1—Ans: b

3. For what value of B could y be eliminated by adding the equations $6x + 3y = 10$ and $7x + By = -4$?

1—Ans: $B = -3$

4. For what value of B could y be eliminated by adding the equations $5x + 10y = 7$ and $3x + By = 4$?

1—Ans: $B = -10$

5. x can be eliminated from the system of equations

$$4x + 7y = 12$$
$$x + y = 4$$

by adding the equations after multiplying the second equation by which number?

(a) -7 **(b)** 7 **(c)** -4 **(d)** 4 **(e)** None of these

1—Ans: c

6. y can be eliminated from the system of equations

$$-2x + 4y = 1$$
$$x + 2y = 4$$

by adding the equations after multiplying the second equation by which number?

(a) -2 **(b)** 2 **(c)** 4 **(d)** -4 **(e)** None of these

1—Ans: a

7. x can be eliminated from the system of equations

$$3x + 4y = 8$$
$$x - 5y = 4$$

by adding the equations after multiplying the second equation by which number?

1—Ans: -3

8. y can be eliminated from the system of equations

$$3x + 4y = 8$$
$$2x - 5y = 4$$

by multiplying the first equation by 5, and multiplying the second equation by B, and adding the resulting two equations. Find B.

1—Ans: $B = 4$

9. Eliminating x from the linear system

$$5x - 2y = 7$$
$$6x - 3y = 4$$

leads to which of the following equations?

(a) $3y = 22$ **(b)** $27y = 22$ **(c)** $3y = 62$ **(d)** $27y = 62$ **(e)** None of these

2—Ans: b

10. Eliminating y from the linear system

$$7x - 3y = -4$$
$$2x + 5y = 5$$

leads to which of the following equations?

(a) $27x = -35$ **(b)** $41x = -35$ **(c)** $29x = -5$ **(d)** $41x = -5$ **(e)** None of these

2—Ans: d

11. Solve the system of linear equations.

$$5x + 2y = 4$$
$$3x + 3y = 1$$

(a) $x = -\frac{10}{9},\ y = -\frac{7}{9}$ **(b)** $x = \frac{10}{9},\ y = \frac{7}{9}$ **(c)** $x = \frac{10}{9},\ y = -\frac{7}{9}$

(d) $x = -\frac{10}{9},\ y = \frac{7}{9}$ **(e)** None of these

2—Ans: c

12. Solve the system of linear equations.

$$5x - 2y = -4$$
$$3x - 3y = -1$$

(a) $x = -\frac{10}{9},\ y = -\frac{7}{9}$ **(b)** $x = \frac{10}{9},\ y = \frac{7}{9}$ **(c)** $x = \frac{10}{9},\ y = -\frac{7}{9}$

(d) $x = -\frac{10}{9},\ y = \frac{7}{9}$ **(e)** None of these

2—Ans: a

13. Eliminate y from the linear system

$$4x - 7y = 2$$
$$2x + 6y = 5$$

to solve the resulting equation for x.

2—Ans: $38x = 47;\quad x = \frac{47}{38}$

14. Eliminate x from the linear system

$$6x - 2y = 5$$
$$2x + 8y = 7$$

to solve the resulting equation for y.

2—Ans: $-26y = -16;\quad y = \frac{8}{13}$

15. Solve the system of linear equations.

$$0.05x + 0.02y = -0.07$$
$$0.09x + 0.03y = -0.06$$

(a) $(3, 11)$ **(b)** $(3, -11)$ **(c)** $(-3, 11)$ **(d)** $(-3, -11)$ **(e)** None of these

2—Ans: b

16. Solve the system of linear equations.

$$0.05x - 0.02y = -0.07$$
$$0.09x - 0.03y = -0.06$$

  (a) $(3, 11)$ **(b)** $(3, -11)$ **(c)** $(-3, 11)$ **(d)** $(-3, -11)$ **(e)** None of these

  1—Ans: a

17. A bag contains 85 coins, all dimes and quarters. Find the number of dimes and the number of quarters if the value of the coins is $12.25.

  (a) 40 dimes and 45 quarters   **(b)** 45 dimes and 40 quarters   **(c)** 60 dimes and 25 quarters

  (d) 25 dimes and 60 quarters   **(e)** None of these

  1—Form: 7A—Ans: c

18. A bag contains 85 coins, all dimes and quarters. Find the number of dimes and the number of quarters if the value of the coins is $17.50.

  (a) 40 dimes and 45 quarters   **(b)** 45 dimes and 40 quarters   **(c)** 60 dimes and 25 quarters

  (d) 25 dimes and 60 quarters   **(e)** None of these

  1—Form: 7B—Ans: d

19. A box contains $28.45 in dimes and quarters. There are 160 coins in all. Write a system of linear equations describing this (assume x is the number of dimes and y is the number of quarters). Solve the system of equations.

  2—Ans: $0.10x + 0.25y = 28.45$
$$x + y = 160$$
$$x = 77 \quad \text{dimes}, \quad y = 83 \text{ quarters}$$

20. A box contains $26.80 in dimes and quarters. There are 160 coins in all. Write a system of linear equations describing this (assume x is the number of dimes and y is the number of quarters). Solve the system of equations.

  2—Ans: $0.10x + 0.25y = 26.80$
$$x + y = 160$$
$$x = 88 \quad \text{dimes}, \quad y = 72 \text{ quarters}$$

21. A 30% alcohol solution is mixed with an 80% solution to obtain a 60% solution. How many gallons of each must be used to produce 10 gallons of the mixture?

  2—Ans: 4 gallons of 30% and 6 gallons of 80%

22. A 30% alcohol solution is mixed with an 80% solution to obtain a 40% solution. How many gallons of each must be used to produce 10 gallons of the mixture?

  2—Ans: 8 gallons of 30% and 2 gallons of 80%

23. A cyclist travels for two hours at an average speed of 12 miles per hour, and then travels for t hours at an average speed of 20 miles per hour. The average speed for the entire trip is 15 miles per hour. If D is the total distance traveled, find the equivalent system of linear equations.

(a) $D = 12 + 20t$
$\quad\quad D = 15(t + 2)$

(b) $D = 24 + 20t$
$\quad\quad D = 15(t + 2)$

(c) $D = 40 + 12t$
$\quad\quad D = 15(t + 2)$

(d) $D = 24 + 20t$
$\quad\quad D = 15t + 2$

(e) None of these

2—Ans: b

24. x liters of 35% alcohol solution are mixed with y liters of a 60% alcohol solution to obtain 10 liters of a 40% alcohol solution. Find the equivalent system of linear equations.

(a) $0.35x + 0.60y = 10$
$\quad\quad x + \quad y = 0.40(10)$

(b) $0.60x + 0.35y = 10$
$\quad\quad x + \quad y = 0.40(10)$

(c) $0.60x + 0.35y = 0.40(10)$
$\quad\quad x + \quad y = 10$

(d) $0.35x + 0.60y = 0.40(10)$
$\quad\quad x + \quad y = 10$

(e) None of these

2—Ans: d

25. The sale price of a portable TV is $215.99. The discount is 28% of the usual selling price. Find the usual selling price.

1—Ans: $299.99

26. 400 theatrical tickets are sold raising total receipts of $2306.25. Adult tickets are $7.50 each and student tickets are $3.75 each. How many of each type of ticket are sold?

1—Ans: 215 adult and 185 student

27. The sale price of a portable TV is $197.76. The discount is 14% of the usual selling price. Find the usual selling price.

1—Ans: $229.95

28. A rectangle is two and one-half times as long as it is wide. Its perimeter is 434 inches. Find its length and width.

1—Ans: Length = 155 inches; Width = 62 inches

29. Use the method of elimination to find the value of x in the solution of the system of equations.

$$5x + 3y = 7$$
$$2x - 3y = 7$$

(a) -2 **(b)** -1 **(c)** 0   **(d)** 2   **(e)** None of these

1—Ans: d

30. Use the method of elimination to find the value of x in the solution of the system of equations.

$$4x - 2y = 12$$
$$2x + 2y = -9$$

(a) 2   **(b)** $\frac{1}{2}$ **(c)** -5 **(d)** $\frac{21}{2}$ **(e)** None of these

1—Ans: b

31. Use the method of elimination to find the value of y in the solution of the system of equations.

$$-2x + 3y = 5$$
$$3x - 2y = 0$$

(a) 0   **(b)** 1   **(c)** 3   **(d)** -1 **(e)** None of these

1—Ans: c

32. Use the method of elimination to find the value of y in the solution of the system of equations.

$$3x + 7y = 15$$
$$-5x + 2y = 16$$

(a) 3   **(b)** -2 **(c)** 2   **(d)** $\frac{6}{7}$ **(e)** None of these

1—Ans: a

33. Use the method of elimination to find the value of y in the solution of the system of equations.

$$5x + 2y = -1$$
$$-15x + 8y = 10$$

(a) $\frac{1}{2}$ **(b)** $\frac{9}{10}$ **(c)** $\frac{9}{14}$ **(d)** 0   **(e)** None of these

2—Form: 7A—Ans: a

34. Use the method of elimination to find the value of x in the solution of the system of equations.

$$7x + y = 3$$
$$21x + 5y = 11$$

(a) 1   **(b)** $\frac{2}{7}$ **(c)** $-\frac{3}{7}$ **(d)** -2 **(e)** None of these

2—Form: 7B—Ans: b

35. A twenty pound mixture of two kinds of candy sells for $30.52. One kind of candy in the mixture sells for $1.35 per pound. The other kind sells for $1.79 per pound. How much of the cheaper candy is in the mixture?

2—Form: 7C—Ans: 12 pounds

36. Suppose the demand and supply functions for a certain product are given by

$$p = 220 - 0.0002x \quad \text{Demand equation}$$

$$p = 90 + 0.0003x \quad \text{Supply equation}$$

where p is the price in dollars and x represents the number of units. Find the point of equilibrium.

2—Ans: $x = 260,000$ and $p = \$168$

37. Solve the system of linear equations.

$$0.06x + 0.02y = 0.08$$

$$0.09x + 0.05y = 0.16$$

2—Ans: $\left(\frac{2}{3}, 2\right)$

38. Solve the system of linear equations.

$$0.02x - 0.05y = -0.38$$

$$0.03x + 0.04y = 1.04$$

2—Form: 7C—Ans: $(16, 14)$

39. Solve the system of linear equations.

$$7x - 3y = 26$$

$$2x + 5y = 25$$

2—Ans: $(5, 3)$

40. Solve the system of linear equations.

$$5x + 3y = 9$$

$$2x - 4y = 14$$

2—Ans: $(3, -2)$

41. Use the method of elimination to find the value of y in the solution of the system of equations.

$$5x + 2y = 13$$

$$-15x + 8y = 10$$

(a) $\frac{1}{2}$ **(b)** $\frac{9}{10}$ **(c)** $\frac{9}{14}$ **(d)** 0 **(e)** $\frac{7}{2}$

1—Ans: e

42. Solve the system of equations by the method of elimination.

$$2x - 5y = -4$$

$$4x + 3y = 5$$

1—Ans: $\left(\frac{1}{2}, 1\right)$

43. Solve the system of equations.

$$\tfrac{1}{3}x - \tfrac{3}{5}y = -2$$
$$2x - y = 14$$

(a) $\left(\tfrac{136}{23}, \tfrac{50}{23}\right)$ **(b)** $(12, 10)$ **(c)** $(12, -38)$

(d) No solution   **(e)** Infinitely many solutions

2—Ans: b

44. Solve the system of equations.

$$x + y = 16$$
$$\tfrac{1}{2}x + \tfrac{1}{6}y = 2$$

(a) $(4, 12)$ **(b)** $(-2, 18)$ **(c)** $(-4, 20)$

(d) $(2, 14)$ **(e)** No solution

2—Ans: b

45. Use a graphing utility to determine the solution to the system of equations.

$$\tfrac{3}{4}x - \tfrac{2}{3}y = 2$$
$$-5x + 3y = -22$$

2—T—Ans: $(8, 6)$

Section 7.3   Linear Systems in Three Variables

1. Find the solutions to the system of linear equations.

$$x - 3y - 2z = -4$$
$$y + 3z = 7$$
$$z = -5$$

(a) $(10, 8, -5)$ **(b)** $(-38, -8, -5)$ **(c)** $(72, 22, -5)$

(d) $(52, 22, -5)$ **(e)** $(-4, 7, -5)$

1—Ans: d

2. Find the solutions to the system of linear equations.

$$x + 3y - 2z = -4$$
$$y - 3z = -7$$
$$z = -5$$

(a) $(-38, 8, -5)$ **(b)** $(52, -22, -5)$ **(c)** $(10, -8, -5)$

(d) $(72, -22, -5)$ **(e)** $(-4, -7, -5)$

1—Ans: b

3. Use back-substitution to solve the system of equations.

$$x - 5y - 2z = -24$$
$$y + 3z = -10$$
$$z = -6$$

1—Ans: $(4, 8, -6)$

4. Use back-substitution to solve the system of equations.

$$x + 5y + 2z = 24$$
$$y + 3z = -10$$
$$z = -6$$

1—Ans: $(-4, 8, -6)$

5. Use back-substitution to solve the system of equations.

$$x - 2y + 2z = 0$$
$$y - 3z = -10$$
$$z = 6$$

1—Ans: $(4, 8, 6)$

6. Use back-substitution to solve the system of equations.

$$x - 2y + 3z = 2$$
$$y - 2z = 4$$
$$z = -6$$

1—Ans: $(4, -8, -6)$

7. Find the solution to the system of linear equations.

$$x = -3$$
$$2x + 2y = 5$$
$$x - 3y + 2z = 2$$

(a) $\left(-3, \frac{11}{2}, \frac{43}{4}\right)$ **(b)** $\left(-3, \frac{11}{4}, -\frac{43}{2}\right)$ **(c)** $\left(-3, -\frac{11}{2}, \frac{5}{3}\right)$

(d) $\left(-3, -\frac{11}{3}, \frac{17}{6}\right)$ **(e)** None of these

1—Ans: a

8. Find the solution to the system of linear equations.

$$x \qquad\qquad = -3$$
$$2x + 4y \qquad = \quad 5$$
$$x - 6y - z = \quad 2$$

(a) $\left(-3, \frac{11}{2}, \frac{43}{4}\right)$ (b) $\left(-3, \frac{11}{4}, -\frac{43}{2}\right)$ (c) $\left(-3, -\frac{11}{2}, \frac{5}{3}\right)$

(d) $\left(-3, -\frac{11}{3}, \frac{17}{6}\right)$ (e) None of these

1—Ans: b

9. Find the solution to the system of linear equations.

$$x \qquad\qquad = -3$$
$$3x - 2y \qquad = \quad 2$$
$$2x - 4y - 3z = \quad 11$$

(a) $\left(-3, \frac{11}{2}, \frac{43}{4}\right)$ (b) $\left(-3, \frac{11}{4}, -\frac{43}{2}\right)$ (c) $\left(-3, -\frac{11}{2}, \frac{5}{3}\right)$

(d) $\left(-3, -\frac{11}{3}, \frac{17}{6}\right)$ (e) None of these

1—Ans: c

10. Find the solution to the system of linear equations.

$$x \qquad\qquad = -3$$
$$4x - 3y \qquad = -1$$
$$x - 4y - 2z = \quad 6$$

(a) $\left(-3, \frac{11}{2}, \frac{43}{4}\right)$ (b) $\left(-3, \frac{11}{4}, -\frac{43}{2}\right)$ (c) $\left(-3, -\frac{11}{2}, \frac{5}{3}\right)$

(d) $\left(-3, -\frac{11}{3}, \frac{17}{6}\right)$ (e) None of these

1—Ans: d

11. Solve the system of linear equations.

$$3x + 2y \qquad = \quad 7$$
$$y \qquad = -2$$
$$x - 2y - 3z = \quad 8$$

1—Ans: $\left(\frac{11}{3}, -2, -\frac{1}{9}\right)$

12. Solve the system of linear equations.

$$x \qquad\qquad = \quad 4$$
$$5x - 2y \qquad = \quad 5$$
$$3x - 4y - 4z = -3$$

1—Ans: $\left(4, \frac{15}{2}, -\frac{15}{4}\right)$

13. Find the solution to the system of equations.

$$2x + y + z = 4$$
$$x - 2y + z = 3$$
$$2x + y - z = 4$$

(a) $x = \frac{14}{13}$

$y = \frac{3}{13}$

$z = \frac{22}{13}$

(b) $x = 1$

$y = -3$

$z = 3$

(c) $x = -5$

$y = \frac{20}{3}$

$z = \frac{16}{3}$

(d) $x = \frac{11}{5}$

$y = -\frac{2}{5}$

$z = 0$

(e) None of these

2—Ans: d

14. Find the solution to the system of equations.

$$x + 2y - z = 3$$
$$x + y + z = 7$$
$$2x - y + 2z = -6$$

(a) $x = \frac{14}{13}$

$y = \frac{3}{13}$

$z = \frac{22}{13}$

(b) $x = 1$

$y = -3$

$z = 3$

(c) $x = -5$

$y = \frac{20}{3}$

$z = \frac{16}{3}$

(d) $x = \frac{11}{5}$

$y = -\frac{2}{5}$

$z = 0$

(e) None of these

2—Ans: c

15. Solve the system of linear equations.

$$-x + y - z = -6$$
$$2x + y - 2z = 2$$
$$x + 2y + z = 3$$

2—Ans: $x = \frac{13}{4}$, $y = -1$, $z = \frac{7}{4}$

16. Solve the system of linear equations.

$$-3x + y - z = 4$$
$$x + y + z = -2$$
$$2x + 2y + z = 1$$

2—Ans: $x = 1$, $y = 2$, $z = -5$

17. Solve the system of linear equations.

$$x + 2y + 3z = -1$$
$$2x + y + z = 1$$
$$3x - 2y - z = 3$$

2—Ans: $x = \frac{4}{5}$, $y = 0$, $z = -\frac{3}{5}$

18. Solve the system of linear equations.

$$x - 2y - z = -2$$
$$2x + y - 2z = 4$$
$$3x - y - 2z = -2$$

2—Ans: $x = -\frac{14}{5}$, $y = \frac{8}{5}$, $z = -4$

19. Find the solution to the system of equations.

$$x - y - 3z = 2$$
$$2x + y \qquad = 1$$
$$4x \qquad + z = 2$$

(a) $x = -\frac{16}{9}$ **(b)** $x = \frac{12}{13}$ **(c)** $x = \frac{3}{5}$

    $y = \frac{4}{3}$ $y = -\frac{35}{13}$ $y = -\frac{1}{5}$

    $z = \frac{40}{9}$ $z = \frac{15}{13}$ $z = -\frac{2}{5}$

(d) $x = 4$ **(e)** None of these

    $y = -6$

    $z = 5$

2—Ans: c

20. Find the solution to the system of equations.

$$2x - 2y - 3z = 5$$
$$x + y + z = 3$$
$$-3x + 2y \qquad = -24$$

(a) $x = -\frac{16}{9}$ **(b)** $x = \frac{12}{13}$ **(c)** $x = \frac{3}{5}$

    $y = \frac{4}{3}$ $y = -\frac{35}{13}$ $y = -\frac{1}{5}$

    $z = \frac{40}{9}$ $z = \frac{15}{13}$ $z = -\frac{2}{5}$

(d) $x = 4$ **(e)** None of these

    $y = -6$

    $z = 5$

2—Ans: d

21. Solve the system of linear equations.

$$x + 2y - 3z = -5$$
$$2x \qquad + \ z = \ \ 2$$
$$-x + 2y - 2z = \ \ 4$$

2—Ans: $x = -\frac{7}{4}, \quad y = \frac{53}{8}, \quad z = \frac{11}{2}$

22. Solve the system of linear equations.

$$x + 2y + 8z = -4$$
$$4x - \ y + 2z = -4$$
$$-3x + 2y \qquad = \ \ 3$$

2—Ans: $x = -\frac{1}{2}, \quad y = \frac{3}{4}, \quad z = -\frac{5}{8}$

23. Find the solution to the system of equations.

$$3x + y + 2z = 5$$
$$2x - y - 3z = 6$$
$$6x + y + 4z = 9$$

(a) $x = \frac{2}{5}$ **(b)** $x = -1$ **(c)** $x = 2$

$\quad\ y = \frac{3}{10}$ $\quad\ y = -1$ $\quad\ y = 1$

$\quad\ z = 0$ $\quad\ z = -2$ $\quad\ z = -1$

(d) $x = 6$ **(e)** None of these

$\quad\ y = -20$

$\quad\ z = -17$

2—Ans: c

24. Find the solution to the system of equations.

$$x + 2y - \ \ 3z = 1$$
$$6x + 2y - \ \ 8z = 3$$
$$8x + 6y - 18z = 5$$

(a) $x = \frac{2}{5}$ **(b)** $x = -1$ **(c)** $x = 2$

$\quad\ y = \frac{3}{10}$ $\quad\ y = -1$ $\quad\ y = 1$

$\quad\ z = 0$ $\quad\ z = -2$ $\quad\ z = -1$

(d) $x = 6$ **(e)** None of these

$\quad\ y = -20$

$\quad\ z = -17$

2—Ans: a

25. Solve the system of linear equations.

$$4x + y - 2z = 10$$
$$2x - y + 2z = -8$$
$$x + y + z = 6$$

1—Ans: $x = \frac{1}{3}$, $y = \frac{20}{3}$, $z = -1$

26. Solve the system of linear equations.

$$3x + 2y - z = 3$$
$$2x - y + z = -2$$
$$x + 2y - z = -1$$

1—Ans: $x = 2$, $y = -9$, $z = -15$

27. Choose the result from solving the system of equations.

$$x + y - z = 4$$
$$x - y + 2z = -2$$
$$3x - y + 3z = 0$$

  (a) No solution possible   **(b)** One unique solution   **(c)** Infinitely many solutions

  (d) Exactly two solutions   **(e)** None of these

  2—Ans: c

28. Choose the result from solving the system of equations.

$$x + 2y + 3z = 1$$
$$3x + 2y + z = 0$$
$$x + y + z = 1$$

  (a) Infinitely many solutions   **(b)** One unique solution   **(c)** Exactly two solutions

  (d) No solution possible   **(e)** None of these

  2—Ans: d

29. Solve the system of linear equations if possible. If not, so state.

$$2x - y + 2z = 1$$
$$-x + 2y - z = 0$$
$$x + y + z = -1$$

  2—Ans: Inconsistent, no solution possible.

30. Solve the system of linear equations if possible. If not, so state.

$$x + 2y + 3z = 2$$
$$y + 2z = 1$$
$$x + y + z = -1$$

2—Ans: Inconsistent, no solution possible.

31. Solve the system of linear equations if possible. If not, so state.

$$2x - y - z = -4$$
$$x + y - 2z = -5$$
$$x - 2y + z = 1$$

2—Ans: $x = a$, $y = a + 1$, $z = a + 3$; infinitely many solutions.

32. Solve the system of linear equations if possible. If not, so state.

$$x - 2y + z = 1$$
$$x + y - z = -1$$
$$2x - y = 0$$

2—Ans: $x = a$, $y = 2a$, $z = 3a + 1$; infinitely many solutions.

33. Find the equation of the parabola of the form $y = ax^2 + bx + c$ which passes through the three points $(0, 2)$, $(1, 1)$ and $(-1, -1)$.

(a) $y = 2x^2 + x - 2$ **(b)** $y = -2x^2 - x + 2$ **(c)** $y = 2x^2 - x - 2$

(d) $y = -2x^2 + x + 2$ **(e)** None of these

2—Ans: d

34. Find the equation of the parabola of the form $y = ax^2 + bx + c$ which passes through the three points $(0, -2)$, $(1, -1)$ and $(-1, 1)$.

(a) $y = 2x^2 + x - 2$ **(b)** $y = -2x^2 - x + 2$ **(c)** $y = 2x^2 - x - 2$

(d) $y = -2x^2 + x + 2$ **(e)** None of these

2—Ans: c

35. Find the equation of the parabola of the form $y = ax^2 + bx + c$ which passes through the three points $(0, -3)$, $(2, -1)$ and $(-2, 3)$.

2—Ans: $y = x^2 - x - 3$

36. Find the equation of the parabola of the form $y = ax^2 + bx + c$ which passes through the three points $(0, 3)$, $(2, 1)$ and $(-2, -3)$.

2—Ans: $y = -x^2 + x + 3$

37. Find the position equation $s = \frac{1}{2}at^2 + v_0t + s_0$ for an object that has the height ($s = 26$ feet when $t = \frac{1}{2}$ second; $s = 34$ feet when $t = 1$ second; and $s = 26$ feet when $t = 2$ seconds).

(a) $s = -16t^2 + 32t + 30$ (b) $s = -16t^2 + 28t + 24$ (c) $s = -16t^2 + 48t + 40$

(d) $s = -16t^2 + 40t + 10$ (e) None of these

2—Ans: d

38. Find the position equation $s = \frac{1}{2}at^2 + v_0t + s_0$ for an object that has the height ($s = 40$ feet when $t = 0$ seconds; $s = 72$ feet when $t = 1$ second; and $s = 72$ feet when $t = 2$ seconds).

(a) $s = -16t^2 + 32t + 30$ (b) $s = -16t^2 + 28t + 24$ (c) $s = -16t^2 + 48t + 40$

(d) $s = -16t^2 + 40t + 10$ (e) None of these

2—Ans: c

39. Find the position equation $s = \frac{1}{2}at^2 + v_0t + s_0$ for an object that has the indicated heights at the specified times. $s = 36$ feet when $t = 0$ seconds; $s = 70$ feet when $t = 1$ second; and $s = 72$ feet when $t = 2$ seconds.

2—Ans: $s = -16t^2 + 50t + 36$

40. Find the position equation $s = \frac{1}{2}at^2 + v_0t + s_0$ for an object that has the indicated heights at the specified times. $s = 44$ feet when $t = 0$ seconds; $s = 88$ feet when $t = 1$ second; and $s = 100$ feet when $t = 2$ seconds.

2—Ans: $s = -16t^2 + 60t + 44$

41. Use the method of back-substitution to find the value of x for the solution of the system of equations.

$$x + 2y + z = 15$$
$$5y - 2z = -16$$
$$z = 3$$

(a) 22   (b) 16   (c) $\frac{15}{7}$ (d) 8   (e) None of these

1—Ans: b

42. Use the method of back-substitution to find the value of x for the solution of the system of equations.

$$x + 2y - z = 26$$
$$y + 3z = 5$$
$$z = -2$$

(a) 4   (b) 26   (c) 6   (d) 2   (e) None of these

1—Ans: b

43. Use Gaussian elimination to solve the system of equations.

$$x - y + z = 2$$
$$2x + 3y + z = 7$$
$$3x + 2y + 2z = -8$$

(a) $(1, 0, 1)$ **(b)** $(6, 4, 4)$ **(c)** $(1, 2, 3)$

(d) No solution   **(e)** None of these

2—Ans: d

44. Use Gaussian elimination to solve the system of equations.

$$x - 6y + z = 1$$
$$-x + 2y - 4z = 3$$
$$7x - 10y + 3z = -25$$

(a) $(5, 1, 2)$ **(b)** $(-5, -1, 0)$ **(c)** $(-1, 3, 1)$

(d) No solution   **(e)** None of these

2—Ans: b

45. Solve the system of linear equations.

$$x - y + z = 5$$
$$3x + 2y - z = -2$$
$$2x + y + 3z = 10$$

(a) $(1, -1, 3)$ **(b)** $(2, -5, -2)$ **(c)** $(-1, 7, 13)$

(d) $(3, -9, -7)$ **(e)** No solution

2—Form: 7A—Ans: a

46. Solve the system of linear equations.

$$x + y + 3z = 0$$
$$2x - y - 3z = -9$$
$$x + 2y + 3z = 1$$

(a) $\left(-3a, a, \dfrac{2a}{3}\right)$ **(b)** $\left(-1, 2, -\dfrac{1}{3}\right)$ **(c)** $\left(-3, 1, \dfrac{2}{3}\right)$

(d) No solution   **(e)** None of these

2—Form: 7B—Ans: c

47. Solve the system of linear equations.

$$x - y - z = 0$$
$$2x + 4y + z = 0$$
$$3x + 4y - z = 0$$

2—Form: 7C—Ans: $(a, -a, 2a)$ where a is any real number

48. Solve the system of linear equations.

$$2x + 3y + 3z = 6$$
$$-x + y + z = 2$$

2—Ans: $(0, 2 - a, a)$

49. Solve the system of linear equations.

$$x - y + z = 2$$
$$2x + 3y + z = 7$$
$$3x + 2y + 2z = -8$$

(a) $(1, 0, 1)$ **(b)** $(6, 4, 4)$ **(c)** $(1, 2, 3)$ **(d)** No solution   **(e)** None of these

2—Form: 7A—Ans: d

50. Solve the system of linear equations.

$$2x + y - z = 3$$
$$x - 3y + z = 7$$
$$3x + 5y - 3z = 0$$

(a) $\left(a, \dfrac{3a - 10}{2}, \dfrac{7a - 16}{2}\right)$ **(b)** $\left(\dfrac{3a + 10}{3}, a, 6a - 21\right)$ **(c)** $(2, -2, -1)$

(d) No solution   **(e)** None of these

2—Form: 7B—Ans: d

51. Solve the system of linear equations.

$$x + y - 2z = 1$$
$$3x + y + z = 4$$
$$-x - 3y + 9z = 10$$

2—Ans: No solution

52. Solve the system of linear equations.

$$x - 2y - z = 7$$
$$-3x + 6y + 3z = 0$$

2—Form: 12C—Ans: No solution

53. Find a, b, and c for the quadratic equation $f(x) = ax^2 + bx + c$, such that $f(1) = -2, f(-2) = 19$, and $f(3) = 4$.

2—Ans: $a = 2, \quad b = -5, \quad c = 1$

54. Find an equation of the parabola $y = ax^2 + bx + c$ that passes through the points $(1, 4), (-1, 0)$, and $(2, -3)$.

2—Form: 7C—Ans: $y = -3x^2 + 2x + 5$

55. The sum of three positive numbers is 19. Find the second number if the third is three times the first and the second is one more than twice the first.

    (a) 7   **(b)** 13   **(c)** 1   **(d)** 9   **(e)** None of these

    2—Form: 7A—Ans: a

56. The sum of three positive numbers is 180. Find the first number if the third is four times the first and the second is thirty-six less than the third.

    (a) 12   **(b)** 36   **(c)** 24   **(d)** 60   **(e)** None of these

    2—Form: 7B—Ans: c

Section 7.4   Matrices and Linear Systems

1. Find the order of the matrix $\begin{bmatrix} 2 & 7 & -1 \\ 4 & 3 & 1 \end{bmatrix}$.

    (a) 3×2 **(b)** 2×3 **(c)** 6   **(d)** 1×3 **(e)** None of these

    1—Ans: b

2. Find the order of the matrix $\begin{bmatrix} 3 & -5 & 0 & 1 \\ 2 & 1 & 0 & -1 \\ 4 & 2 & 3 & 4 \end{bmatrix}$.

    (a) 3×4 **(b)** 4×3 **(c)** 3×3 **(d)** 12   **(e)** None of these

    1—Ans: a

3. Determine the order of the matrix $\begin{bmatrix} 9 & 1 & 7 \\ 3 & -8 & 5 \\ 0 & -2 & 4 \\ 1 & 1 & -5 \end{bmatrix}$.

    1—Ans: 4×3

4. Determine the order of the matrix $\begin{bmatrix} 7 & 1 & 4 & 2 & -1 \end{bmatrix}$.

    1—Ans: 1×5

5. Which of the following matrices is not a square matrix?

    (a) $\begin{bmatrix} 4 \end{bmatrix}$ **(b)** $\begin{bmatrix} 1 & 0 \\ 0 & 1 \end{bmatrix}$ **(c)** $\begin{bmatrix} 1 & 3 & 5 \\ -7 & 0 & 7 \\ -5 & -3 & -1 \end{bmatrix}$

    (d) $\begin{bmatrix} 36 & 25 \\ 16 & 9 \\ 4 & 1 \end{bmatrix}$ **(e)** None of these

    1—Ans: d

6. Which of the following matrices is not a square matrix?

(a) $\begin{bmatrix} 1 & 4 & 9 \\ 16 & 25 & 36 \end{bmatrix}$ **(b)** $[9]$ **(c)** $\begin{bmatrix} 0 & 1 \\ 1 & 0 \end{bmatrix}$

(d) $\begin{bmatrix} 2 & 4 & 6 \\ -8 & 0 & 8 \\ -6 & -4 & -2 \end{bmatrix}$ **(e)** None of these

   1—Ans: a

7. Write an example of a matrix of order 1×3.

   1—Ans: $[a \quad b \quad c]$; a, b, and c can be any numbers.

8. Write an example of a matrix of order 4×1.

   1—Ans: $\begin{bmatrix} a \\ b \\ c \\ d \end{bmatrix}$; a, b, c, and d can be any numbers.

9. Determine a matrix which is row-equivalent to $\begin{bmatrix} 2 & -1 & 7 \\ 0 & 1 & 4 \\ 2 & 3 & -2 \end{bmatrix}$.

(a) $\begin{bmatrix} 2 & 0 & 2 \\ -1 & 1 & 3 \\ 7 & 4 & -2 \end{bmatrix}$ **(b)** $\begin{bmatrix} 0 & 1 & 4 \\ 2 & -1 & 7 \\ 2 & 3 & -2 \end{bmatrix}$ **(c)** $\begin{bmatrix} 4 & -2 & 14 \\ 0 & 2 & 8 \\ 4 & 6 & 4 \end{bmatrix}$

(d) $\begin{bmatrix} 0 & 0 & 0 \\ 0 & 1 & 4 \\ 2 & 3 & -2 \end{bmatrix}$ **(e)** None of these

   2—Ans: b

10. Determine a matrix which is row-equivalent to $\begin{bmatrix} 2 & 1 & -4 \\ 3 & -2 & 1 \end{bmatrix}$.

(a) $\begin{bmatrix} 2 & 3 \\ 1 & -2 \\ -4 & 1 \end{bmatrix}$ **(b)** $\begin{bmatrix} 2 & -4 & 1 \\ 3 & 1 & -2 \end{bmatrix}$ **(c)** $\begin{bmatrix} 4 & 2 & -8 \\ 3 & -2 & 1 \end{bmatrix}$

(d) $\begin{bmatrix} 2 & 1 & -4 \\ 0 & 0 & 0 \end{bmatrix}$ **(e)** None of these

   2—Ans: c

11. Write a row-equivalent matrix to $\begin{bmatrix} 3 & 1 & 4 \\ 0 & -2 & 1 \\ 4 & -1 & 3 \end{bmatrix}$ by subtracting the first row from the third row.

1—Ans: $\begin{bmatrix} 3 & 1 & 4 \\ 0 & -2 & 1 \\ 1 & -2 & -1 \end{bmatrix}$

12. Write a row-equivalent matrix to $\begin{bmatrix} 4 & -1 & 3 \\ 1 & 2 & 0 \\ 4 & -2 & 1 \end{bmatrix}$ by multiplying the second row by 4.

1—Ans: $\begin{bmatrix} 4 & -1 & 3 \\ 4 & 8 & 0 \\ 4 & -2 & 1 \end{bmatrix}$

13. Write a row-equivalent matrix to $\begin{bmatrix} 7 & 2 & 4 \\ -1 & 0 & 3 \\ 4 & -1 & -2 \end{bmatrix}$ by interchanging the first and third rows.

1—Ans: $\begin{bmatrix} 4 & -1 & -2 \\ -1 & 0 & 3 \\ 7 & 2 & 4 \end{bmatrix}$

14. Write a row-equivalent matrix to $\begin{bmatrix} 2 & -1 & 3 \\ 5 & 1 & -2 \\ 3 & 2 & -1 \end{bmatrix}$ by adding three times the first row to the second row.

1—Ans: $\begin{bmatrix} 2 & -1 & 3 \\ 11 & -2 & 7 \\ 3 & 2 & -1 \end{bmatrix}$

15. Choose the coefficient matrix of the system of equations.

$$2x - 3y = 4$$
$$7x + 2y = 6$$

(a) $\begin{bmatrix} 2 & -3 & \vdots & 4 \\ 7 & 2 & \vdots & 6 \end{bmatrix}$ **(b)** $\begin{bmatrix} 2 & -3 \\ 7 & 2 \end{bmatrix}$ **(c)** $\begin{bmatrix} 2 & 7 \\ -3 & 2 \\ \cdots & \cdots \\ 4 & 6 \end{bmatrix}$

(d) $\begin{bmatrix} 2 & 7 \\ -3 & 2 \end{bmatrix}$ **(e)** None of these

1—Ans: b

16. Choose the coefficient matrix of the system of equations.

$$7x + 4y = 2$$
$$5x - 3y = 4$$

(a) $\begin{bmatrix} 7 & 4 \\ 5 & -3 \end{bmatrix}$

(b) $\begin{bmatrix} 7 & 4 & \vdots & 2 \\ 5 & -3 & \vdots & 4 \end{bmatrix}$

(c) $\begin{bmatrix} 7 & 5 \\ 4 & -3 \\ \hdotsfor{2} \\ 2 & 4 \end{bmatrix}$

(d) $\begin{bmatrix} 7 & 5 \\ 4 & 3 \end{bmatrix}$

(e) None of these

1—Ans: a

17. The augmented matrix for a system of linear equations in the variables x, y, and z is

$$\begin{bmatrix} 2 & -6 & 4 & \vdots & 1 \\ 1 & 3 & -5 & \vdots & 3 \\ 2 & -1 & 4 & \vdots & -4 \end{bmatrix}.$$

Write the system of equations.

1—Ans: $2x - 6y + 4z = 1$
$x + 3y - 5z = 3$
$2x - y + 4z = -4$

18. The augmented matrix for a system of linear equations in the variables x, y, and z is

$$\begin{bmatrix} 3 & -2 & 4 & \vdots & 7 \\ 1 & 3 & -1 & \vdots & 2 \\ 4 & 1 & -2 & \vdots & 4 \end{bmatrix}.$$

Write the system of equations.

1—Ans: $3x - 2y + 4z = 7$
$x + 3y - z = 2$
$4x + y - 2x = 4$

19. Which of the matrices is in row-echelon form?

(a) $\begin{bmatrix} 1 & 2 & 3 & 4 \\ 0 & 0 & 1 & 2 \\ 0 & 1 & 2 & 3 \end{bmatrix}$

(b) $\begin{bmatrix} 1 & -1 & 2 & -2 \\ 0 & 1 & -1 & 3 \\ 0 & 0 & 1 & -4 \end{bmatrix}$

(c) $\begin{bmatrix} 0 & 0 & 1 & -4 \\ 0 & 0 & -1 & 3 \\ 1 & -1 & 2 & -2 \end{bmatrix}$

(d) $\begin{bmatrix} 2 & 1 & 1 & 1 \\ 0 & 2 & 1 & 1 \\ 0 & 0 & 2 & 1 \end{bmatrix}$

(e) None of these

1—Ans: b

20. Which of the matrices is in row-echelon form?

(a) $\begin{bmatrix} 1 & 0 & -1 & 0 \\ 0 & 0 & 1 & 1 \\ 0 & 1 & 2 & -1 \end{bmatrix}$ (b) $\begin{bmatrix} 1 & 2 & 3 & 1 \\ 2 & -1 & 1 & 0 \\ -1 & 1 & 0 & 0 \end{bmatrix}$ (c) $\begin{bmatrix} 0 & 0 & 1 & -2 \\ 0 & 1 & 2 & 3 \\ 1 & -2 & -1 & 1 \end{bmatrix}$

(d) $\begin{bmatrix} 1 & 2 & -3 & 0 \\ 0 & 1 & -2 & 2 \\ 0 & 0 & 1 & 4 \end{bmatrix}$ (e) None of these

1—Ans: d

21. The row-echelon form of the augmented matrix of a system of linear equations in the variables x, y, and z is

$$\begin{bmatrix} 1 & -1 & -2 & \vdots & -5 \\ 0 & 1 & 2 & \vdots & 7 \\ 0 & 0 & 1 & \vdots & 4 \end{bmatrix}.$$

Find the solution of the system of equations.

1—Ans: $x = 2$, $y = -1$, $z = 4$

22. The row-echelon form of the augmented matrix of a system of linear equations in the variables x, y, and z is

$$\begin{bmatrix} 1 & -2 & 2 & \vdots & 3 \\ 0 & 1 & -3 & \vdots & 1 \\ 0 & 0 & 1 & \vdots & -3 \end{bmatrix}.$$

Find the solution of the system of equations.

1—Ans: $x = -7$, $y = -8$, $z = -3$

23. Which augmented matrix represents a system of equations with no solutions?

(a) $\begin{bmatrix} 3 & 7 & 1 & \vdots & -1 \\ 0 & 2 & 1 & \vdots & -2 \\ 0 & 0 & 1 & \vdots & 3 \end{bmatrix}$ (b) $\begin{bmatrix} 1 & 0 & 0 & \vdots & 4 \\ 0 & 1 & 0 & \vdots & -2 \\ 0 & 0 & 1 & \vdots & 3 \end{bmatrix}$ (c) $\begin{bmatrix} 2 & 1 & 4 & \vdots & 2 \\ 0 & 1 & 3 & \vdots & -1 \\ 0 & 0 & 0 & \vdots & 2 \end{bmatrix}$

(d) $\begin{bmatrix} 3 & -1 & 4 & \vdots & -2 \\ 0 & 2 & 4 & \vdots & 1 \\ 0 & 0 & 0 & \vdots & 0 \end{bmatrix}$ (e) None of these

1—Ans: c

24. Which augmented matrix represents a system of equations with infinitely many solutions?

(a) $\begin{bmatrix} 2 & 6 & -1 & \vdots & 2 \\ 0 & 2 & 4 & \vdots & 3 \\ 0 & 0 & 0 & \vdots & 0 \end{bmatrix}$ (b) $\begin{bmatrix} 1 & 4 & -3 & \vdots & 1 \\ 0 & 1 & 5 & \vdots & 2 \\ 0 & 0 & 0 & \vdots & 4 \end{bmatrix}$ (c) $\begin{bmatrix} 1 & 0 & 0 & \vdots & -2 \\ 0 & 1 & 0 & \vdots & 4 \\ 0 & 0 & 1 & \vdots & -1 \end{bmatrix}$

(d) $\begin{bmatrix} 2 & 1 & 4 & \vdots & 0 \\ 0 & 1 & -3 & \vdots & 2 \\ 0 & 0 & -1 & \vdots & 2 \end{bmatrix}$ (e) None of these

1—Ans: a

25. Write the set of linear equations in the variables x, y, and z which has the following augmented matrix.

$$\begin{bmatrix} 2 & -1 & 3 & \vdots & 7 \\ 2 & -3 & 7 & \vdots & 4 \\ 5 & 6 & -3 & \vdots & 2 \end{bmatrix}$$

1—Ans: $2x - y + 3z = 7$

$\qquad\quad 2x - 3y + 7z = 4$

$\qquad\quad 5x + 6y - 3z = 2$

26. Write the set of linear equations in the variables x, y, and z which has the following augmented matrix.

$$\begin{bmatrix} 5 & 3 & 1 & \vdots & -4 \\ 2 & 4 & 6 & \vdots & 5 \\ 6 & -1 & 2 & \vdots & 0 \end{bmatrix}$$

1—Ans: $5x + 3y + z = -4$

$\qquad\quad 2x + 4y + 6z = 5$

$\qquad\quad 6x - y + 2z = 0$

27. The augmented matrix of a system of linear equations in the variables x and y is

$$\begin{bmatrix} 2 & 5 & \vdots & 7 \\ 1 & -3 & \vdots & 2 \end{bmatrix}.$$

Find the solution of the system of equations.

(a) $x = \frac{31}{11}$ **(b)** $x = -\frac{31}{11}$ **(c)** $x = -\frac{31}{11}$ **(d)** $x = \frac{31}{11}$ **(e)** None of these

$\quad\ y = -\frac{3}{11}$ $y = -\frac{3}{11}$ $y = \frac{3}{11}$ $y = \frac{3}{11}$

1—Ans: d

28. The augmented matrix of a system of linear equations in the variables x and y is

$$\begin{bmatrix} 2 & -5 & \vdots & -7 \\ 1 & 3 & \vdots & -2 \end{bmatrix}.$$

Find the solution of the system of equations.

(a) $x = \frac{31}{11}$ **(b)** $x = -\frac{31}{11}$ **(c)** $x = -\frac{31}{11}$ **(d)** $x = \frac{31}{11}$ **(e)** None of these

$\quad\ y = -\frac{3}{11}$ $y = -\frac{3}{11}$ $y = \frac{3}{11}$ $y = \frac{3}{11}$

1—Ans: c

29. The augmented matrix of a system of linear equations in the variables x and y is

$$\begin{bmatrix} 3 & -7 & \vdots & 2 \\ 5 & 3 & \vdots & 1 \end{bmatrix}.$$

Solve the system of equations.

1—Ans: $x = \frac{13}{44}, \quad y = -\frac{7}{44}$

30. The augmented matrix of a system of linear equations in the variables x and y is

$$\begin{bmatrix} 2 & 3 & \vdots & -2 \\ 9 & -4 & \vdots & 5 \end{bmatrix}.$$

Solve the system of equations.

1—Ans: $x = \frac{1}{5},\quad y = -\frac{4}{5}$

31. The augmented matrix of a system of linear equations in the variables x and y is

$$\begin{bmatrix} 3 & 5 & \vdots & -2 \\ -2 & 4 & \vdots & 7 \end{bmatrix}.$$

Solve the system of equations.

1—Ans: $x = -\frac{43}{22},\quad y = \frac{17}{22}$

32. The augmented matrix of a system of linear equations in the variables x and y is

$$\begin{bmatrix} 4 & -5 & \vdots & 6 \\ 3 & 8 & \vdots & 2 \end{bmatrix}.$$

Solve the system of equations.

1—Ans: $x = \frac{58}{47},\quad y = -\frac{10}{47}$

33. The augmented matrix of a system of linear equations in the variables x, y, and z is

$$\begin{bmatrix} 3 & 4 & 1 & \vdots & 5 \\ 1 & -1 & -1 & \vdots & 1 \\ 1 & -3 & -3 & \vdots & -3 \end{bmatrix}.$$

Find the solution of the system of equations.

(a) $x = -3$	**(b)** $x = 3$	**(c)** $x = -3$	**(d)** $x = 3$	**(e)** None of these
$y = -2$	$y = -2$	$y = 2$	$y = -2$	
$z = -4$	$z = 4$	$z = 4$	$z = -4$	

2—Ans: b

34. The augmented matrix of a system of linear equations in the variables x, y, and z is

$$\begin{bmatrix} 3 & 4 & -1 & \vdots & -5 \\ 1 & -1 & 1 & \vdots & -1 \\ 1 & -3 & 3 & \vdots & 3 \end{bmatrix}.$$

Find the solution of the system of equations.

(a) $x = -3$	**(b)** $x = 3$	**(c)** $x = -3$	**(d)** $x = 3$	**(e)** None of these
$y = -2$	$y = -2$	$y = 2$	$y = -2$	
$z = -4$	$z = 4$	$z = 4$	$z = -4$	

2—Ans: c

35. The augmented matrix of a system of linear equations in the variables x, y, and z is

$$\begin{bmatrix} 3 & -4 & 1 & \vdots & -5 \\ 1 & 1 & -1 & \vdots & -1 \\ 1 & 3 & -3 & \vdots & 3 \end{bmatrix}.$$

Find the solution of the system of equations.

(a) $x = -3$ (b) $x = 3$ (c) $x = -3$ (d) $x = 3$ (e) None of these

$y = -2$ $y = -2$ $y = 2$ $y = -2$

$z = -4$ $z = 4$ $z = 4$ $z = -4$

2—Ans: a

36. The augmented matrix of a system of linear equations in the variables x, y, and z is

$$\begin{bmatrix} 3 & 4 & -1 & \vdots & 5 \\ 1 & -1 & 1 & \vdots & 1 \\ 1 & -3 & 3 & \vdots & -3 \end{bmatrix}.$$

Find the solution of the system of equations.

(a) $x = -3$ (b) $x = 3$ (c) $x = -3$ (d) $x = 3$ (e) None of these

$y = -2$ $y = -2$ $y = 2$ $y = -2$

$z = 4$ $z = 4$ $z = 4$ $z = -4$

2—Ans: d

37. The augmented matrix of a system of linear equations in the variables x, y, and z is

$$\begin{bmatrix} 2 & 2 & -1 & \vdots & -2 \\ 1 & -1 & 3 & \vdots & 1 \\ 2 & 3 & 1 & \vdots & 2 \end{bmatrix}.$$

Solve the system of equations.

2—Ans: $x = -\frac{5}{3}$, $y = \frac{4}{3}$, $z = \frac{4}{3}$

38. The augmented matrix of a system of linear equations in the variables x, y, and z is

$$\begin{bmatrix} 2 & 2 & 1 & \vdots & 2 \\ 1 & -1 & -3 & \vdots & -1 \\ 2 & 3 & -1 & \vdots & -2 \end{bmatrix}.$$

Solve the system of equations.

2—Ans: $x = \frac{5}{3}$, $y = -\frac{4}{3}$, $z = \frac{4}{3}$

39. Fill in the box by using elementary row operations to form a row-equivalent matrix.

$$\begin{bmatrix} 1 & 2 & -5 \\ -3 & 2 & 1 \end{bmatrix} \begin{bmatrix} 1 & 2 & -5 \\ 0 & 8 & \blacksquare \end{bmatrix}$$

(a) -14 (b) 16 (c) -8 (d) -4 (e) None of these

1—Form: 7A—Ans: a

40. Find the number that belongs in the box by using elementary row operations to form a row-equivalent matrix.

$$\begin{bmatrix} 1 & -3 & 4 \\ -2 & 7 & 1 \end{bmatrix} \begin{bmatrix} 1 & -3 & 4 \\ 0 & 1 & \blacksquare \end{bmatrix}$$

(a) 5 **(b)** −7 **(c)** 8 **(d)** 0 **(e)** None of these

1—Form: 7B—Ans: e

41. Form the augmented matrix of the system of equations.

$$y - 3z = 5$$
$$2x + z = -1$$
$$4x - y = 0$$

(a) $\begin{bmatrix} 1 & -3 \\ 2 & 1 \\ 4 & -1 \end{bmatrix}$

(b) $\begin{bmatrix} 1 & -3 & \vdots & 5 \\ 2 & 1 & \vdots & -1 \\ 4 & -1 & \vdots & 0 \end{bmatrix}$

(c) $\begin{bmatrix} 0 & 1 & -3 \\ 2 & 0 & 1 \\ 4 & -1 & 0 \end{bmatrix}$

(d) $\begin{bmatrix} 0 & 1 & -3 & \vdots & 5 \\ 2 & 0 & 1 & \vdots & -1 \\ 4 & -1 & 0 & \vdots & 0 \end{bmatrix}$

(e) None of these

1—Form: 7A—Ans: d

42. Form the augmented matrix of the system of equations.

$$x + 2z = 7$$
$$y - z = -5$$
$$3x - y = 2$$

(a) $\begin{bmatrix} 1 & 2 & \vdots & 7 \\ 1 & -1 & \vdots & -5 \\ 3 & -1 & \vdots & 2 \end{bmatrix}$

(b) $\begin{bmatrix} 1 & 0 & 2 \\ 0 & 1 & -1 \\ 3 & -1 & 0 \end{bmatrix}$

(c) $\begin{bmatrix} 1 & 0 & 2 & \vdots & 7 \\ 0 & 1 & -1 & \vdots & -5 \\ 3 & -1 & 0 & \vdots & 2 \end{bmatrix}$

(d) $\begin{bmatrix} 1 & 2 \\ 1 & -1 \\ 3 & -1 \end{bmatrix}$

(e) None of these

1—Form: 7B—Ans: c

43. Use the variables x, y, and z to write the system of linear equations represented by the augmented matrix $\begin{bmatrix} 2 & -1 & 0 & \vdots & 4 \\ 0 & 3 & 1 & \vdots & -2 \\ 1 & -3 & 1 & \vdots & 1 \end{bmatrix}$.

1—Form: 7C—Ans:
$$2x - y = 4$$
$$3y + z = -2$$
$$x - 3y + z = 1$$

44. Use the variables x, y, and z to write the system of linear equations represented by the augmented matrix $\begin{bmatrix} 0 & 2 & -3 & \vdots & 9 \\ 0 & 3 & 1 & \vdots & -3 \\ 4 & -2 & 0 & \vdots & 11 \end{bmatrix}$.

1—Form: 7C—Ans:
$$2y - 3z = 9$$
$$3y + z = -3$$
$$4x - 2y = 11$$

45. Determine which matrix is in row-echelon form.

(a) $\begin{bmatrix} 1 & 5 \\ 0 & 1 \\ 0 & 0 \end{bmatrix}$ 　　　 **(b)** $\begin{bmatrix} 0 & 0 & 0 \\ 0 & 1 & 2 \end{bmatrix}$ 　　　 **(c)** $\begin{bmatrix} 1 & -4 & 3 & 7 \\ 0 & 1 & 2 & -1 \\ 0 & 0 & 3 & 5 \end{bmatrix}$

(d) $[3]$ 　　　 **(e)** None of these

1—Ans: a

46. Determine which matrix is in row-echelon form.

(a) $\begin{bmatrix} 1 & -2 \\ 0 & 1 \\ 0 & 0 \end{bmatrix}$ 　　　 **(b)** $\begin{bmatrix} 1 & 0 & 4 & -2 \\ 0 & 1 & 7 & 5 \\ 0 & 0 & 0 & 0 \end{bmatrix}$ 　　　 **(c)** $\begin{bmatrix} 1 & -6 & 2 \\ 0 & 1 & 4 \end{bmatrix}$

(d) $\begin{bmatrix} 1 & 1 \\ 0 & 1 \end{bmatrix}$ 　　　 **(e)** None of these

1—Ans: b

47. Find the solution to the system of linear equations with the augmented matrix

$$\begin{bmatrix} 1 & 2 & -1 & 4 \\ 0 & 2 & 1 & -3 \\ 0 & 0 & 2 & -4 \end{bmatrix}.$$

1—Form: 7C—Ans: $\left(3, -\frac{1}{2}, -2\right)$

48. Find the solution to the system of linear equations with the augmented matrix

$$\begin{bmatrix} 1 & 0 & 1 & 0 \\ 0 & 1 & -2 & 1 \end{bmatrix}.$$

2—Ans: $(-a, 2a + 1, a)$

49. Use matrices to solve the system of linear equations.

$$x + 2y + z = 5$$
$$2x - y - 3z = 5$$
$$-2x + 3y + z = -11$$

2—Ans: $(5, -1, 2)$

50. Use matrices to solve the system of linear equations.

$$3x + 2y - 5z = -10$$
$$2x + 4y + \ z = \ \ \ 0$$
$$x - 6y - 4z = \ -3$$

2—Ans: $\left(\frac{1}{2}, -\frac{3}{4}, 2\right)$

51. The fraction $\dfrac{5x^2 + 20x + 6}{x(x + 1)^2}$ can be written as the sum of three fractions as follows.

$$\frac{5x^2 + 20x + 6}{x(x + 1)^2} = \frac{A}{x} + \frac{B}{x + 1} + \frac{C}{(x + 1)^2}$$

where A, B, and C are the solutions of the system.

$$A + B \ \ \ \ \ \ = \ 5$$
$$2A + B + C = 20$$
$$A \ \ \ \ \ \ \ \ \ = \ 6$$

Solve the system.

2—Ans: $A = 6$, $B = -1$, and $C = 9$

52. The fraction $\dfrac{3x + 4}{x^3 - 2x - 4}$ can be written as the sum of two fractions as follows.

$$\frac{3x + 4}{x^3 - 2x - 4} = \frac{A}{x - 2} + \frac{Bx + C}{x^2 + 2x + 2}$$

where A, B, and C are the solutions of the system.

$$A + \ B \ \ \ \ \ \ = 0$$
$$2A - 2B + \ C = 3$$
$$2A \ \ \ \ \ \ - 2C = 4$$

Solve the system.

2—Form: 7C—Ans: $A =$, $B = -1$, and $C = -1$

53. The fraction $\dfrac{x^2 - x + 2}{x^3 - x^2 + x - 1}$ can be written as the sum of two fractions as follows.

$$\frac{x^2 - x + 2}{x^3 - x^2 + x - 1} = \frac{A}{x - 1} + \frac{Bx + C}{x^2 + 1}$$

where A, B, and C are the solutions of the system.

$$\begin{aligned} A + B \quad\quad &= \quad 1 \\ -B + C &= -1 \\ A \quad\quad - C &= \quad 2 \end{aligned}$$

Solve the system.

(a) $A = -1, B = 1, C = 0$ (b) $A = 1, B = 0, C = -1$ (c) $A = 1, B = -1, C = 2$

(d) $A = 1, B = -1, C = 0$ (e) $A = 0, B = 0, C = -2$

2—Form: 7A—Ans: b

54. The fraction $\dfrac{16x}{x^3 - 10x^2}$ can be written as the sum of three fractions as follows.

$$\frac{16x}{x^3 - 10x^2} = \frac{A}{x} + \frac{B}{x^2} + \frac{C}{x - 10}$$

where A, B, and C are the solutions of the system.

$$\begin{aligned} A \quad\quad + C &= \quad 0 \\ -10A + B \quad\quad &= \quad 16 \\ -10B \quad\quad &= \quad 0 \end{aligned}$$

Solve the system.

(a) $A = 0, B = 16, C = 0$ (b) $A = -\frac{8}{5}, B = 0, C = 0$ (c) $A = 0, B = -\frac{8}{5}, C = \frac{8}{5}$

(d) $A = \frac{8}{5}, B = \frac{8}{5}, C = -\frac{8}{5}$ (e) $A = -\frac{8}{5}, B = 0, C = \frac{8}{5}$

2—Form: 7B—Ans: e

55. Use matrices to solve the system of linear equations.

$$\begin{aligned} 10x + 5y &= 9.2 \\ 30x + 10y &= 21.1 \end{aligned}$$

1—Ans: $(0.27, 1.3)$

56. Use matrices to solve the system of linear equations.

$$\begin{aligned} 10x + 5y &= 12.3 \\ 30x + 10y &= 29.1 \end{aligned}$$

(a) $(0.45, 1.56)$ (b) $(0.26, 1.94)$ (c) $(0.6, 1.26)$

(d) $(3.2, -3.94)$ (e) No solution

1—Ans: a

57. Use matrices to solve the system of linear equations.

$$\begin{aligned} x - y + z &= 2 \\ 2x + 3y + z &= 7 \\ 3x + 2y + 2z &= -8 \end{aligned}$$

(a) $(1, 0, 1)$

(b) $(6, 4, 4)$

(c) $(1, 2, 3)$

(d) No solution

(e) $(2, 7, -8)$

1—Ans: d

58. Use matrices to solve the system of linear equations.

$$\begin{aligned} x - 3y + 2z &= -11 \\ x + 4y - 5z &= 17 \\ -2x + y - z &= 6 \end{aligned}$$

1—Ans: $(-1, 2, -2)$

59. Find an equation of the parabola, $y = ax^2 + bx + c$, that passes through the points $(1, 4)$, $(-1, 0)$, and $(2, -3)$.

(a) $y = 4x^2 + 2x - 2$

(b) $y = 3x^2 + 2x - 7$

(c) $y = -3x^2 + 2x + 5$

(d) $y = 4x^2$

(e) $x = 4y^2$

2—Ans: c

60. Find an equation of the parabola, $y = ax^2 + bx + c$, that passes through the points $(0, 5)$, $(2, -5)$, and $(-3, -40)$.

(a) $y = 3x^2 - 2x - 7$

(b) $y = -4x^2 + 3x + 5$

(c) $y = 4x^2 + 3x + 5$

(d) $y = 9x^2 - 121$

(e) $y = 3x^2 - 2x + 5$

2—Ans: b

61. Find an equation of the parabola, $y = ax^2 + bx + c$, that passes through the points $(0, -5)$, $(2, 1)$, and $(-1, -14)$.

2—Ans: $y = -2x^2 + 7x - 5$

62. Find an equation of the parabola, $y = ax^2 + bx + c$, that passes through the points $(1, 1)$, $(-1, 11)$, and $(3, 23)$.

2—Ans: $y = 4x^2 - 5x + 2$

63. The sum of three positive numbers is 19. Find the second number if the third is three times the first and the second is one more than twice the first.

(a) 7

(b) 13

(c) 1

(d) 9

(e) 10

1—Ans: a

64. The sum of three positive numbers is 180. Find the first number if the third is four times the first and the second is thirty-six less than the third.

(a) 12   (b) 36   (c) 24   (d) 60   (e) 6

1—Ans: c

65. Find an equation of the circle, $x^2 + y^2 + Dx + Ey + F = 0$, that passes through the points $(9, -3)$, $(2, 4)$, and $(-5, -3)$.

(a) $x^2 + y^2 + 3x - 2y + 10 = 0$ (b) $x^2 + y^2 - 4x + 6y - 36 = 0$

(c) $x^2 + y^2 - 8x + 2y - 12 = 0$ (d) $x^2 + y^2 + 2x - 7y + 1 = 0$

(e) $x^2 + y^2 - 5x + y + 1 = 0$

2—Ans: b

Section 7.5   Determinants and Linear Systems

1. Find the value of the determinant of the matrix $\begin{bmatrix} 2 & -4 \\ 8 & 3 \end{bmatrix}$.

(a) -26 (b) -38 (c) 26   (d) 38   (e) None of these

1—Ans: d

2. Find the value of the determinant of the matrix $\begin{bmatrix} 3 & -7 \\ 2 & 5 \end{bmatrix}$.

(a) -29 (b) -1 (c) 29   (d) 1   (e) None of these

1—Ans: c

3. Evaluate the determinant of the matrix $\begin{bmatrix} 2 & 8 \\ -4 & 6 \end{bmatrix}$.

1—Ans: 44

4. Evaluate the determinant of the matrix $\begin{bmatrix} -7 & -3 \\ -2 & 6 \end{bmatrix}$.

1—Ans: -48

5. Evaluate the determinant of the matrix $\begin{bmatrix} 6 & 5 \\ -3 & 2 \end{bmatrix}$.

1—Ans: 27

6. Evaluate the determinant of the matrix $\begin{bmatrix} 2 & 6 \\ -3 & 7 \end{bmatrix}$.

1—Ans: 32

7. Find the value of the determinant of the matrix $\begin{bmatrix} 2 & 0 & 3 \\ 1 & 2 & -1 \\ -4 & 1 & 2 \end{bmatrix}$.

   (a) 37   **(b)** -15 **(c)** 33   **(d)** 31   **(e)** None of these

   1—Ans: a

8. Find the value of the determinant of the matrix $\begin{bmatrix} 2 & 1 & -1 \\ 0 & 4 & 1 \\ 3 & -1 & 2 \end{bmatrix}$.

   (a) 5   **(b)** 33   **(c)** 29   **(d)** 27   **(e)** None of these

   1—Ans: b

9. Find the value of the determinant of the matrix $\begin{bmatrix} 2 & 2 & -1 \\ 1 & -3 & 1 \\ 0 & -2 & 1 \end{bmatrix}$.

   (a) -6 **(b)** -14 **(c)** -2 **(d)** 6   **(e)** None of these

   1—Ans: c

10. Find the value of the determinant of the matrix $\begin{bmatrix} 2 & -2 & 1 \\ 1 & 3 & -1 \\ -2 & 1 & 0 \end{bmatrix}$.

   (a) -11 **(b)** 1   **(c)** -13 **(d)** 5   **(e)** None of these

   1—Ans: d

11. Evaluate the determinant of the matrix $\begin{bmatrix} 2 & 1 & 4 \\ -2 & -1 & 0 \\ 1 & -2 & 3 \end{bmatrix}$.

   1—Ans: 20

12. Evaluate the determinant of the matrix $\begin{bmatrix} 2 & 0 & -3 \\ 4 & 1 & -2 \\ -1 & 2 & 3 \end{bmatrix}$.

   1—Ans: -13

13. Find the value of the determinant $\begin{vmatrix} 4 & 3 & 2 \\ 5 & -1 & -2 \\ 1 & 1 & 1 \end{vmatrix}$.

   (a) 5   **(b)** -25 **(c)** -5 **(d)** -41 **(e)** None of these

   1—Ans: c

14. Find the value of the determinant $\begin{vmatrix} 1 & 2 & 4 \\ 1 & -3 & 2 \\ 1 & 5 & -1 \end{vmatrix}$.

(a) 31 (b) 23 (c) −31 (d) −11 (e) None of these

1—Ans: a

15. Evaluate the determinant $\begin{vmatrix} 1 & 4 & 3 \\ 3 & -1 & -2 \\ 2 & -1 & 1 \end{vmatrix}$.

1—Ans: −34

16. Evaluate the determinant $\begin{vmatrix} 3 & -2 & 1 \\ -1 & 5 & 4 \\ 2 & 1 & 3 \end{vmatrix}$.

1—Ans: 0

17. Find the determinant of coefficients of the system of linear equations.

$$3x + 4y - z = 7$$
$$2x - 3y + 2z = -8$$
$$5x + y - 3z = 5$$

(a) $\begin{vmatrix} 3 & 4 & -1 & 7 \\ 2 & -3 & 2 & -8 \\ 5 & 1 & -3 & 5 \end{vmatrix}$

(b) $\begin{vmatrix} 7 & 4 & -1 \\ -8 & -3 & 2 \\ 5 & 1 & 3 \end{vmatrix}$

(c) $\begin{vmatrix} 3 & 4 & 7 \\ 2 & -3 & -8 \\ 5 & 1 & 5 \end{vmatrix}$

(d) $\begin{vmatrix} 3 & 4 & -1 \\ 2 & -3 & 2 \\ 5 & 1 & -3 \end{vmatrix}$

(e) None of these

1—Ans: d

18. Find the determinant of coefficients of the system of linear equations.

$$5x - 7y + 4z = 3$$
$$-x + 2y + 3z = -2$$
$$3x - 5y - 7z = 4$$

(a) $\begin{vmatrix} 5 & -7 & 4 & 3 \\ -1 & 2 & 3 & -2 \\ 3 & -5 & -7 & 4 \end{vmatrix}$

(b) $\begin{vmatrix} 3 & -7 & 4 \\ -2 & 2 & 3 \\ 4 & -5 & -7 \end{vmatrix}$

(c) $\begin{vmatrix} 5 & -7 & 4 \\ -1 & 2 & 3 \\ 3 & -5 & -7 \end{vmatrix}$

(d) $\begin{vmatrix} 5 & -7 & 3 \\ -1 & 2 & -2 \\ 3 & -5 & 4 \end{vmatrix}$

(e) None of these

1—Ans: c

19. Use Cramer's Rule to solve the system of linear equations.

$$3x + 9y = 7$$
$$8x - 5y = -7$$

2—Ans: $x = -\frac{28}{87}, \; y = \frac{77}{87}$

20. Use Cramer's Rule to solve the system of linear equations.

$$11x + 9y = 4$$
$$9x - 6y = 5$$

2—Ans: $x = \frac{23}{49}, \; y = -\frac{19}{147}$

21. Use Cramer's Rule to solve the system of linear equations.

$$8x - 12y = 3$$
$$7x + 5y = -4$$

2—Ans: $x = -\frac{33}{124}, \; y = -\frac{53}{124}$

22. Use Cramer's Rule to solve the system of linear equations.

$$10x - 7y = 3$$
$$7x + 9y = -4$$

2—Ans: $x = -\frac{1}{139}, \; y = -\frac{61}{139}$

23. Choose an expression for x if Cramer's Rule is used to solve

$$7x - 5y = 2$$
$$5x + 3y = 4.$$

(a) $x = \dfrac{\begin{vmatrix} 7 & -5 \\ 5 & 3 \end{vmatrix}}{\begin{vmatrix} 2 & -5 \\ 4 & 3 \end{vmatrix}}$

(b) $x = \dfrac{\begin{vmatrix} 2 & -5 \\ 4 & 3 \end{vmatrix}}{\begin{vmatrix} 7 & -5 \\ 5 & 3 \end{vmatrix}}$

(c) $x = \dfrac{\begin{vmatrix} 7 & 2 \\ 5 & 4 \end{vmatrix}}{\begin{vmatrix} 7 & -5 \\ 5 & 3 \end{vmatrix}}$

(d) $x = \begin{vmatrix} 2 & -5 \\ 4 & 3 \end{vmatrix}$

(e) None of these

1—Ans: b

24. Choose an expression for y if Cramer's Rule is used to solve

$$8x - 5y = -7$$
$$3x + 7y = 4.$$

(a) $y = \begin{vmatrix} 8 & -7 \\ 3 & 4 \end{vmatrix}$

(b) $y = \dfrac{\begin{vmatrix} 8 & -5 \\ 3 & 7 \end{vmatrix}}{\begin{vmatrix} 8 & -7 \\ 3 & 4 \end{vmatrix}}$

(c) $y = \dfrac{\begin{vmatrix} 8 & -7 \\ 3 & 4 \end{vmatrix}}{\begin{vmatrix} 8 & -5 \\ 3 & 7 \end{vmatrix}}$

(d) $y = \dfrac{\begin{vmatrix} -7 & -5 \\ 4 & 7 \end{vmatrix}}{\begin{vmatrix} 8 & -5 \\ 3 & 7 \end{vmatrix}}$

(e) None of these

1—Ans: c

25. Find the value of x for the given system using Cramer's Rule and given that $D = 98$.

$$3x + 7y - 4z = 3$$
$$-2x + 2y + 5z = -1$$
$$4x + 2y - 3z = 4$$

1—Ans: $x = \frac{111}{98}$

26. Find the value of y for the given system using Cramer's Rule and given that $D = 98$.

$$3x + 7y - 4z = 3$$
$$-2x + 2y + 5z = -1$$
$$4x + 2y - 3z = 4$$

1—Ans: $y = \frac{7}{98} = \frac{1}{14}$

27. Find the value of z for the given system using Cramer's Rule and given that $D = 98$.

$$3x + 7y - 4z = 3$$
$$-2x + 2y + 5z = -1$$
$$4x + 2y - 3z = 4$$

1—Ans: $z = \frac{22}{98} = \frac{11}{49}$

28. Which coefficient matrix D would represent a system of two linear equations not solvable using Cramer's Rule?

(a) $D = \begin{vmatrix} 1 & 7 \\ 2 & 4 \end{vmatrix}$

(b) $D = \begin{vmatrix} 7 & 1 \\ -3 & 2 \end{vmatrix}$

(c) $D = \begin{vmatrix} 2 & 4 \\ 4 & 8 \end{vmatrix}$

(d) $D = \begin{vmatrix} 2 & -4 \\ 4 & 8 \end{vmatrix}$

(e) None of these

1—Ans: c

29. Which coefficient matrix D would represent a system of two linear equations not solvable using Cramer's Rule?

(a) $D = \begin{vmatrix} 3 & 4 \\ 8 & 6 \end{vmatrix}$
  (b) $D = \begin{vmatrix} 3 & 6 \\ -4 & 8 \end{vmatrix}$
  (c) $D = \begin{vmatrix} 3 & -4 \\ 6 & 8 \end{vmatrix}$

(d) $D = \begin{vmatrix} 3 & 4 \\ 6 & 8 \end{vmatrix}$
  (e) None of these

1—Ans: d

30. Use Cramer's Rule to solve the system of linear equations.

$$3x - 7y = 4$$
$$2x + 3y = -2$$

2—Ans: $x = -\frac{2}{23}$, $y = -\frac{14}{23}$

31. Use Cramer's Rule to solve the system of linear equations.

$$5x + 9y = -4$$
$$2x - 7y = 8$$

2—Ans: $x = \frac{44}{53}$, $y = -\frac{48}{53}$

32. Find the area of the triangle with vertices $(-2, 1)$, $(3, 5)$, and $(1, -3)$.

(a) 32 (b) 2 (c) 16 (d) 4 (e) None of these

2—Ans: c

33. Find the area of the triangle with vertices $(-3, -2)$, $(-1, 4)$, and $(3, -1)$.

(a) 17 (b) 34 (c) 16 (d) 0 (e) None of these

2—Ans: a

34. Use a determinant to find an equation of the line through points $(-3, 5)$ and $(2, -7)$.

2—Ans: $\begin{vmatrix} x & y & 1 \\ 2 & -7 & 1 \\ -3 & 5 & 1 \end{vmatrix} = 0, \quad 12x + 5y + 11 = 0$

35. Use a determinant to find an equation of the line through points $(5, -2)$ and $(7, -6)$.

2—Ans: $\begin{vmatrix} x & y & 1 \\ 5 & -2 & 1 \\ 7 & -6 & 1 \end{vmatrix} = 0, \quad 4x + 2y - 16 = 0$

36. Use a determinant to determine which of the given points is collinear with
$(-2, 4)$ and $(3, -7)$.

   (a) $(2, 7)$ **(b)** $(-1, 2)$ **(c)** $(8, 15)$ **(d)** $\left(-1, \frac{9}{5}\right)$ **(e)** None of these

2—Ans: d

37. Use a determinant to determine which of the given points is collinear with
$(-3, 6)$ and $(2, -3)$.

   (a) $\left(\frac{4}{3}, 2\right)$ **(b)** $(7, -12)$ **(c)** $(2, 0)$ **(d)** $(7, 15)$ **(e)** None of these

2—Ans: b

38. If the three points $(-2, -4)$, $(2, 1)$, and $(5, 8)$ form a triangle, find its area. If not,
find the equation of the line containing the three points.

2—Ans: They form a triangle of area $\frac{13}{2}$.

39. If the three points $\left(-\frac{3}{2}, -7\right)$ $\left(\frac{3}{5}, 0\right)$ and $(3, 8)$ form a triangle, find its area. If not,
find the equation of the line containing the three points.

2—Ans: No triangle. They lie on the line $10x - 3y - 6 = 0$.

40. Evaluate the determinant of the matrix.
$$\begin{bmatrix} 3 & 1 & -2 \\ 0 & 2 & 3 \\ 1 & -2 & -2 \end{bmatrix}$$

   (a) 13   **(b)** 5   **(c)** -31 **(d)** 9   **(e)** None of these

1—Form: 7A—Ans: a

41. Evaluate the determinant of the matrix.
$$\begin{bmatrix} -2 & 1 & 3 \\ 3 & 0 & -1 \\ 4 & -2 & 1 \end{bmatrix}$$

   (a) 7   **(b)** -21 **(c)** 0   **(d)** 21   **(e)** None of these

1—Form: 7B—Ans: b

42. Find the value of the determinant of the coefficient matrix of the system.
$$x - 4y = 1$$
$$3x + 2y = 10$$

   (a) 3   **(b)** 42   **(c)** 14   **(d)** -10 **(e)** None of these

1—Ans: c

43. Use Cramer's Rule to find the value of x for the solution of the system of equations.

$$x - 4y = 1$$
$$3x + 2y = 10$$

(a) 3   **(b)** $\frac{1}{2}$ **(c)** 14   **(d)** 1   **(e)** None of these

1—Ans: a

44. Evaluate the determinant of the matrix.

$$\begin{bmatrix} 1 & 3 & 1 \\ 2 & -2 & 0 \\ -3 & 2 & 1 \end{bmatrix}$$

1—Ans: -10

45. Find the determinant of the matrix: $\begin{bmatrix} 3 & -1 & 6 \\ 2 & 0 & 4 \\ 1 & 6 & 2 \end{bmatrix}$

1—Form: 7C—Ans: 0

46. Use Cramer's Rule to solve the system of equations.

$$x - 4y = 1$$
$$3x + 2y = 10$$

2—Ans: $\left(3, \frac{1}{2}\right)$

47. Use Cramer's Rule to solve the system of equations.

$$5x + 3y = 9$$
$$2x - 4y = 14$$

2—Ans: $(3, -2)$

48. Use a graphing utility to evaluate the determinant of the matrix.

$$\begin{bmatrix} 0 & 2 & 3 \\ 1 & -1 & 4 \\ 3 & 0 & 2 \end{bmatrix}$$

(a) 9   **(b)** 19   **(c)** 29   **(d)** 0   **(e)** None of these

2—T—Form: 7A—Ans: c

49. Use a graphing utility to evaluate the determinant of the matrix.

$$\begin{bmatrix} 0 & -1 & 2 \\ 3 & 5 & 0 \\ 1 & -1 & 3 \end{bmatrix}$$

(a) 25   **(b)** -25 **(c)** 7   **(d)** -7 **(e)** None of these

2—T—Form: 7B—Ans: d

50. Use a graphing utility to evaluate the determinant of the matrix.

$$\begin{bmatrix} 2 & 3 & -1 \\ 0 & 5 & 0 \\ -1 & 1 & 2 \end{bmatrix}$$

2—T—Form: 7C—Ans: 15

51. Use a graphing utility to evaluate the determinant of the matrix.

$$\begin{bmatrix} 3 & 0 & 1 \\ -1 & 4 & -1 \\ 5 & -2 & 0 \end{bmatrix}$$

2—T—Ans: -24

52. Use a graphing utility and Cramer's rule to find the value of y in the solution of the system of equations.

$$2x - 3y = 5$$
$$2x + 3y = -3$$

(a) $\frac{1}{2}$ **(b)** $-\frac{3}{4}$ **(c)** $-\frac{4}{3}$ **(d)** $\frac{4}{3}$ **(e)** None of these

1—T—Form: 7A—Ans: c

53. Use a graphing utility and Cramer's rule to find the value of x in the solution of the system of equations.

$$2x - y = 6$$
$$2x + 2y = -9$$

(a) 2   **(b)** $\frac{1}{2}$ **(c)** -5 **(d)** $\frac{21}{2}$ **(e)** None of these

1—T—Form: 7B—Ans: b

54. Use a graphing utility and Cramer's rule to find the value of x in the solution of the system of equations.

$$2x - 3y = 5$$
$$2x + 3y = -3$$

1—T—Form: 7C—Ans: $\frac{1}{2}$

55. Use a graphing utility and Cramer's rule to find the value of y in the solution of the system of equations.

$$2x - y = 6$$
$$2x + 2y = -9$$

1—T—Ans: -5

CHAPTER 8
Rational Expressions, Equations, and Functions

Section 8.1   Rational Expressions and Functions

1. Find the domain of the function $\dfrac{3}{x-5}$.

   (a) $x = 5$ **(b)** All real x such that $x \neq 5$ **(c)** $x = 3$

   (d) All real x such that $x \neq 3$ **(e)** None of these

   1—Ans: b

2. Find the domain of the function $\dfrac{x-1}{2x-1}$.

   (a) All real x such that $x \neq 1$ **(b)** $x = 1$ **(c)** $x = \dfrac{1}{2}$

   (d) All real x such that $x \neq \dfrac{1}{2}$ **(e)** None of these

   1—Ans: d

3. Find the domain of the function $\dfrac{x-2}{x^2+1}$.

   1—Ans: $(-\infty, \infty)$

4. Find the domain of the function $\dfrac{x+2}{x^2-4}$.

   1—Ans: $(-\infty, -2) \cup (-2, 2) \cup (2, \infty)$

5. Find the domain of the function $\dfrac{3}{x(x-3)}$.

   1—Ans: $(-\infty, 0) \cup (0, 3) \cup (3, \infty)$

6. Find the domain of the function $\dfrac{7(x^2-9)}{9}$.

   1—Ans: $(-\infty, \infty)$

7. Which of the following is not a valid use of cancellation?

  (a) $\dfrac{3x}{x^2 - x} = \dfrac{3\cancel{x}}{\cancel{x}(x - 1)} = \dfrac{3}{x - 1}, x \neq 0$

  (b) $\dfrac{x - 3}{x^2 - 9} = \dfrac{\cancel{(x - 3)} \cdot 1}{\cancel{(x - 3)}(x + 3)} = \dfrac{1}{x + 3}, x \neq 3$

  (c) $\dfrac{5xy}{10y^2} = \dfrac{\cancel{5}x\cancel{y}}{\underset{2}{\cancel{10}}y\underset{1}{\cancel{y}}} = \dfrac{x}{2y}$

  (d) $\dfrac{\cancel{4}x}{\cancel{4}y^2 + 1} = \dfrac{x}{y^2 + 1}$

  (e) None of these

2—Ans: d

8. Which of the following is not a valid use of cancellation?

  (a) $\dfrac{(x + 2)(x - 3)}{(x - 3)(x + 4)} = \dfrac{(x + 2)\cancel{(x - 3)}}{\cancel{(x - 3)}(x + 4)} = \dfrac{x + 2}{x + 4}, x \neq 3$

  (b) $\dfrac{2x + 1}{2 - x} = \dfrac{2\cancel{x} + 1}{2 - \cancel{x}} = \dfrac{3}{2}$

  (c) $\dfrac{7xy^2}{21x^2y} = \dfrac{\cancel{7}x\overset{1}{y\cancel{2}}}{\underset{3\ 1}{2\cancel{1}x\cancel{2}\cancel{y}}} = \dfrac{y}{3x}, y \neq 0$

  (d) $\dfrac{x^2 - x}{2x} = \dfrac{\cancel{x}(x - 1)}{2\cancel{x}} = \dfrac{x - 1}{2}, x \neq 0$

  (e) None of these

2—Ans: b

9. Simplify the expression $\dfrac{x^2 - 3}{2x - x^2}$.

  1—Ans: $\dfrac{x - 3}{2 - x}, \ x \neq 0$

10. Simplify the expression $\dfrac{5x + 5}{15x + 5}$.

  1—Ans: $\dfrac{x + 1}{3x + 1}$

11. Which algebraic expression can be simplified?

  (a) $\dfrac{x^2 - 2}{x^2 + 3x}$ (b) $\dfrac{x - 1}{x^2 - 1}$ (c) $\dfrac{3}{x^2 - 3}$ (d) $\dfrac{x}{x + 2}$ (e) None of these

  1—Ans: b

12. Which algebraic expression can be simplified?

  (a) $\dfrac{x^2 - 3}{x^2 + 2x}$ (b) $\dfrac{5}{5 + 3x}$ (c) $\dfrac{2x}{x + 2}$ (d) $\dfrac{x^2 - 2x}{x^2 + 3x}$ (e) None of these

  1—Ans: d

13. Simplify the expression $\dfrac{3x^3 - 6x^2 + 9x}{3x}$.

  2—Ans: $x^2 - 2x + 3, \ x \neq 0$

14. Simplify the expression $\dfrac{3x^3 - 6x^2 - 9x}{3x^2}$.

   2—Ans: $\dfrac{x^2 - 2x - 3}{x}$

15. Simplify the expression $\dfrac{x^4 - x^2}{x^2 - 1}$, properly restricting the domain.

   1—Ans: x^2, $x \neq \pm 1$

16. Simplify the expression $\dfrac{x^4 - x^2}{x - 1}$, properly restricting the domain.

   1—Ans: $x^2(x + 1)$, $x \neq 1$

17. Simplify the expression $\dfrac{x^4 - x^2}{x + 1}$, properly restricting the domain.

   1—Ans: $x^2(x - 1)$, $x \neq -1$

18. Simplify the expression $\dfrac{x^4 - x^2}{x^2 - x}$, properly restricting the domain.

   1—Ans: $x(x + 1)$, $x \neq 0$ and $x \neq 1$

19. Which of the following simplifications is not valid?

   (a) $\dfrac{2 - x}{x - 2} = -1$, $x \neq 2$ **(b)** $\dfrac{4 - x^2}{x - 2} = x + 2$, $x \neq 2$ **(c)** $\dfrac{x^2 - 9}{3 - x} = -(x + 3)$, $x \neq 3$

   (d) $-\dfrac{9 - x^2}{3 + x} = x - 3$, $x \neq -3$ **(e)** None of these

   1—Ans: b

20. Which of the following simplifications is not valid?

   (a) $\dfrac{4 - x^2}{x - 2} = x + 2$, $x \neq 2$ **(b)** $\dfrac{x^2 - 9}{3 - x} = -(x + 3)$, $x \neq 3$ **(c)** $-\dfrac{9 - x^2}{3 + x} = x - 3$, $x \neq -3$

   (d) $\dfrac{2 - x}{x - 2} = -1$, $x \neq 2$ **(e)** None of these

   1—Ans: a

21. Which of the following simplifications is not valid?

   (a) $\dfrac{x^2 - 9}{3 - x} = -(x + 3)$, $x \neq 3$ **(b)** $-\dfrac{9 - x^2}{3 + x} = x - 3$, $x \neq -3$ **(c)** $\dfrac{2 - x}{x - 2} = -1$, $x \neq 2$

   (d) $\dfrac{4 - x^2}{x - 2} = x + 2$, $x \neq 2$ **(e)** None of these

   1—Ans: d

22. Which of the following simplifications is not valid?

(a) $-\dfrac{9 - x^2}{3 + x} = x - 3,\ x \neq -3$ (b) $\dfrac{2 - x}{x - 2} = -1,\ x \neq 2$ (c) $\dfrac{4 - x^2}{x - 2} = x + 2,\ x \neq 2$

(d) $\dfrac{x^2 - 9}{3 - x} = -(x + 3),\ x \neq 3$ (e) None of these

1—Ans: c

23. Simplify the expression $\dfrac{2 - x - x^2}{x^2 - x}$.

2—Ans: $-\dfrac{x + 2}{x},\ x \neq 1$

24. Simplify the expression $\dfrac{6 + x - x^2}{x^2 - 9}$.

2—Ans: $-\dfrac{x + 2}{3 + x},\ x \neq 3$

25. Which of the following is not correct?

(a) $-\dfrac{(5 - x)}{x - 5} = 1,\ x \neq 5$ (b) $\dfrac{5 - x}{-(x - 5)} = 1,\ x \neq 5$ (c) $\dfrac{25 - x^2}{5 - x} = x + 5,\ x \neq 5$

(d) $\dfrac{25 - x^2}{5 + x} = x - 5,\ x \neq -5$ (e) None of these

1—Ans: d

26. Which of the following is not correct?

(a) $\dfrac{(5 - x)}{x - 5} = -1,\ x \neq 5$ (b) $\dfrac{25 - x^2}{-5 + x} = x + 5,\ x \neq 5$ (c) $\dfrac{25 - x^2}{5 + x} = 5 - x,\ x \neq -5$

(d) $-\dfrac{5 - x}{x - 5} = 1,\ x \neq 5$ (e) None of these

1—Ans: b

27. Find the missing factor: $\dfrac{2 - z}{z} = \dfrac{(2 - z)\,\rule{0.5cm}{0.3cm}}{z^2 + z}$.

1—Ans: $(z + 1)$

28. Find the missing factor: $\dfrac{5x}{(2x - 3)} = \dfrac{5x\,\rule{0.5cm}{0.3cm}}{2x^2 + 3x - 9}$.

1—Ans: $(x + 3)$

29. Find the missing factor: $\dfrac{3x^2}{x^2 - x + 1} = \dfrac{3x^2\,\rule{0.5cm}{0.3cm}}{x^3 + 1}$.

1—Ans: $(x + 1)$

30. Find the missing numerator: $\dfrac{(2x - 3)}{x^2 + 2x + 4} = \dfrac{}{x^3 - 8}$.

1—Ans: $(2x^2 - 7x + 6)$

31. Simplify $\dfrac{2x - 4z}{4x^2 - 16xz + 16z^2}$.

(a) $\dfrac{2}{x - 2z}$ **(b)** $\dfrac{1}{2(x + 2z)}$ **(c)** $\dfrac{1}{2(x - 2z)}$

(d) $\dfrac{2}{4x - 8z}$ **(e)** None of these

1—Ans: c

32. Simplify $\dfrac{2x + 4z}{4x^2 + 16xz + 16z^2}$.

(a) $\dfrac{2}{x - 2z}$ **(b)** $\dfrac{1}{2(x + 2z)}$ **(c)** $\dfrac{1}{2(x - 2z)}$

(d) $\dfrac{2}{4x + 8z}$ **(e)** None of these

1—Ans: b

33. Simplify $\dfrac{4x + 8z}{2x^2 - 8z^2}$.

(a) $\dfrac{2}{x - 2z},\ x \neq -2z$ **(b)** $\dfrac{1}{2(x + 2z)},\ x \neq 2z$ **(c)** $\dfrac{1}{2(x - 2z)},\ x \neq -2z$

(d) $\dfrac{4}{2x - 4z},\ x \neq -2z$ **(e)** None of these

1—Ans: a

34. Simplify $\dfrac{4x - 8z}{2x^2 - 8z^2}$.

(a) $\dfrac{2}{x - 2z},\ x \neq -2z$ **(b)** $\dfrac{4}{2x + 4z},\ x \neq 2z$ **(c)** $\dfrac{1}{2(x - 2z)},\ x \neq -2z$

(d) $\dfrac{2}{x + 2z},\ x \neq 2z$ **(e)** None of these

1—Ans: d

35. Simplify the expression $\dfrac{y^3 + xy^2 - xy - x^2}{y^2 - x^2}$.

2—Ans: $\dfrac{y^2 - x}{y - x},\ y \neq -x$

36. Simplify the expression $\dfrac{y^3 + xy^2 - xy - x^2}{y^2 + 2xy + x^2}$.

2—Ans: $\dfrac{y^2 - x}{y + x}$

37. A machine shop has a set-up cost of \$4000 for the production of a new product. The cost of labor and materials for producing each unit is \$8.25. When x units are produced, find the average cost per unit.

(a) \$8.25

(b) $\dfrac{4000 + 8.25x}{x}$

(c) $\dfrac{4000}{x}$

(d) $\dfrac{4000}{x} + 8.25x$

(e) None of these

2—Ans: b

38. A machine shop has a set-up cost of \$4800 for the production of a new product. The cost of labor and materials for producing each unit is \$7.75. When x units are produced, find the average cost per unit.

(a) $\dfrac{4800}{x}$

(b) $\dfrac{4800}{x} + 7.75$

(c) \$7.75

(d) $\dfrac{4800 + 7.75x}{x}$

(e) None of these

2—Ans: d

39. Suppose you start a trip on a bicycle and average 12 miles per hour. A friend starts at the same place $2\frac{1}{2}$ hours later, and follows your path at 16 miles per hour. Find a polynomial expression for the distance between you and your friend in terms of t, the time your friend has been traveling. How long does it take your friend to catch you?

2—Ans: $12\left(t + \frac{5}{2}\right) - 16t$ or $30 - 4t$; $7\frac{1}{2}$ hours

40. Suppose you start a trip on a bicycle and average 14 miles per hour. A friend starts at the same place 3 hours later, and follows your path at 17 miles per hour. Find a polynomial expression for the distance between you and your friend in terms of t, the time your friend has been traveling. How long does it take your friend to catch you?

2—Ans: $14(t + 3) - 17t$ or $42 - 3t$;   14 hours

41. Find the domain: $\dfrac{x}{x + 3}$.

(a) $(-\infty, 3) \cup (3, \infty)$

(b) $(-\infty, 0) \cup (0, \infty)$

(c) $(-\infty, -3) \cup (-3, \infty)$

(d) $(-\infty, -3) \cup (-3, 0) \cup (0, 3) \cup (3, \infty)$

(e) None of these

1—Ans: c

42. Find the domain: $\dfrac{x-1}{x-2}$.

(a) $(-\infty, 1) \cup (1, \infty)$

(b) $(-\infty, 2) \cup (2, \infty)$

(c) $(-\infty, -2) \cup (-2, \infty)$

(d) $(-\infty, 1) \cup (1, 2) \cup (2, \infty)$

(e) None of these

1—Ans: b

43. Find the domain: $\dfrac{x+4}{(x+4)(x-1)}$.

(a) $(-\infty, -4) \cup (-4, \infty)$

(b) $(-\infty, 1) \cup (1, \infty)$

(c) $(-\infty, -4) \cup (-4, 1) \cup (1, \infty)$

(d) $(-\infty, \infty)$

(e) None of these

1—Form: 8A—Ans: c

44. Find the domain: $\dfrac{x+3}{(x+3)(x-1)}$.

(a) $(-\infty, -3) \cup (-3, 1) \cup (1, \infty)$

(b) $(-\infty, 1) \cup (1, \infty)$

(c) $(-\infty, \infty)$

(d) $(-\infty, -3) \cup (-3, \infty)$

(e) None of these

1—Form: 8B—Ans: a

45. Simplify $\dfrac{24x^5 + 18x^3}{12x^2}$.

(a) $20x^3$　　(b) $12x^5 + 3x$　　(c) $\dfrac{1}{2}(4x^2 + 3)$　　(d) $\dfrac{x(4x^2 + 3)}{2}$　　(e) None of these

1—Ans: d

46. Simplify $\dfrac{3x(x+5)^3}{12x^2(x+5)}$.

(a) $\dfrac{(x+5)^2}{9x}$　　(b) $\dfrac{x+5}{4x}$　　(c) $\dfrac{5}{4}$　　(d) $\dfrac{(x+5)^2}{4x}$　　(e) None of these

1—Ans: d

47. Simplify $\dfrac{x^2 + 4x - 21}{x^2 - 9}$.

(a) $\dfrac{x+7}{x+3}$　　(b) $\dfrac{7}{3}$　　(c) $\dfrac{4x-21}{-9}$　　(d) $\dfrac{x-7}{x-3}$　　(e) None of these

2—Ans: a

48. Simplify $\dfrac{x^2 - 5x - 14}{x^2 - 4}$.

(a) $\dfrac{5x + 14}{14}$ 　　(b) $\dfrac{x + 7}{x + 2}$ 　　(c) $\dfrac{x - 7}{x - 2}$ 　　(d) $\dfrac{7}{2}$ 　　(e) None of these

2—Ans: c

49. Simplify $\dfrac{1 - 2x}{2x^2 + 5x - 3}$.

(a) $\dfrac{1}{6x - 3}$ 　　　　(b) $\dfrac{1}{x + 3}$ 　　　　(c) $\dfrac{1 - 2x}{2x^2 + 5x - 3}$

(d) $\dfrac{-1}{x + 3}$ 　　　　(e) None of these

2—Form: 8A—Ans: d

50. Simplify $\dfrac{3 - 2x}{2x^2 - x - 3}$.

(a) 1 　　　　(b) $-\dfrac{1}{x^2}$ 　　　　(c) $-\dfrac{1}{x + 1}$ 　　(d) $\dfrac{3 - 2x}{2x^2 - x - 3}$ 　　(e) None of these

2—Form: 8B—Ans: c

51. Find the domain: $\dfrac{x + 3}{x + 2}$.

1—Ans: $(-\infty, -2) \cup (-2, \infty)$

52. Find the domain: $\dfrac{5}{2 - x}$.

1—Ans: $(-\infty, 2) \cup (2, \infty)$

53. Find the domain: $\dfrac{x}{x^2 + x}$.

1—Ans: $(-\infty, -1) \cup (-1, 0) \cup (0, \infty)$

54. Find the domain: $\dfrac{x + 3}{x^2 + 3x}$.

1—Form: 8C—Ans: $(-\infty, -3) \cup (-3, 0) \cup (0, \infty)$

55. Simplify $\dfrac{6x^2(x - 2)^3}{x(x - 2)^6}$.

1—Ans: $\dfrac{6x}{(x - 2)^4}$

56. Simplify $\dfrac{3x(x + 1)^4}{12x^3(x + 1)}$.

1—Ans: $\dfrac{(x + 1)^3}{4x^2}$

57. Simplify $\dfrac{2x^2 - 5x - 3}{x^2 - 9}$.

2—Ans: $\dfrac{2x + 1}{x + 3}$

58. Simplify $\dfrac{12 - 5x - 2x^2}{4x^2 - 9}$.

2—Form: 8C—Ans: $-\dfrac{x + 4}{2x + 3}$

59. Find the domain of $f(x) = \dfrac{1}{x^2 + x}$.

(a) All real values of x

(b) All real values of x such that $x \neq 0$

(c) All real values of x such that $x \neq -1$

(d) All real values of x such that $x \neq -1, 0$

(e) None of these

2—Ans: d

60. Find the domain of $f(x) = \dfrac{3 + 4x}{1 - 2x}$.

(a) All real values of x such that $x \neq -\dfrac{3}{4}$

(b) All real values of x such that $x \neq -\dfrac{3}{4}, \dfrac{1}{2}$

(c) All real values of x

(d) All real values of x such that $x \neq \dfrac{1}{2}$

(e) None of these

1—Ans: d

61. Find the domain: $\dfrac{x}{x^2 + 4}$.

1—Ans: $(-\infty, \infty)$

62. Find the domain: $\dfrac{3x}{x^2 - 8x + 16}$.

1—Ans: $(-\infty, 4) \cup (4, \infty)$

63. Find $f\left(\dfrac{1}{2}\right)$ for the function $f(x) = \dfrac{2x-1}{2x+1}$.

(a) $\dfrac{1}{2}$ (b) 2   (c) Undefined   (d) $\dfrac{1}{4}$ (e) 0

1—Form: 8A—Ans: e

64. Find $f(4)$ for the function $f(t) = \dfrac{t-2}{3t^2-11t-4}$.

(a) 2   (b) 0   (c) Undefined   (d) $\dfrac{2}{13}$ (e) $\dfrac{1}{13}$

1—Form: 8B—Ans: c

65. Find $f(-1)$ for the function $f(s) = \dfrac{3s^2}{1-2s-s^2}$.

1—Form: 8C—Ans: $\dfrac{3}{2}$

66. Find $f(-2)$ for the function $f(u) = \dfrac{u^3-8}{u^2+1}$.

1—Ans: $-\dfrac{16}{5}$

67. Use the table feature of a graphing utility to complete the table. What can you conclude?

x	-2	-1	0	1	2	3	4
$\dfrac{3x-x^2}{x}$							
$3-x$							

1—T—Ans:

x	-2	-1	0	1	2	3	4
$\dfrac{3x-x^2}{x}$	5	4	Undefined	2	1	0	-1
$3-x$	5	4	3	2	1	0	-1

The two expressions are equal for all real numbers except 0.

68. Use the table feature of a graphing utility to complete the table. What can you conclude?

x	-2	-1	0	1	2	3	4
$\dfrac{3x^2 - 2x - 16}{x - 2}$							
$3x + 8$							

1—T—Ans:

x	-2	-1	0	1	2	3	4
$\dfrac{3x^2 - 2x - 16}{x - 2}$	2	5	8	11	Undefined	17	20
$3x + 8$	2	5	8	11	14	17	20

The two expressions are equal for all real numbers except 2.

69. The cost of producing x units of a product is $C = 150{,}000 + 0.25x$. Find the average cost for producing 10,000 units.

2—Ans: $15.25

70. The cost in millions of dollars for the federal government to seize p percent of a certain illegal drug as it enters the country is $C = \dfrac{528p}{100 - p}$, $0 \le p < 100$. Find the cost of seizing 40%.

2—T—Ans: $352,000,000

71. The cost in dollars for removing p percent of the air pollutants in the stack emission of a utility company that burns coal to generate electricity is $C = \dfrac{80{,}000p}{100 - p}$, $0 \le p < 100$. Find the cost of removing 20%.

2—T—Ans: $20,000

72. The game commission introduces 50 deer into newly acquired state game lands. The population of the herd is given by $N = \dfrac{10(5 + 3t)}{1 + 0.04t}$, $t > 0$ where t is time in years. Find the population when t is 15.

2—T—Ans: 312 deer

73. The game commission introduces 40 elk into newly acquired state game lands. The population of the herd is given by $N = \dfrac{10(4 + 2t)}{1 + 0.03t}$, $t \ge 0$ where t is time in years. Find the population when t is 8.

2—T—Ans: 161 elk

74. The cost of producing x units is $C = 250,000 + 3x$. Find the average cost of producing $x = 2000$ units.

2—T—Ans: $128

75. The cost of recycling a waste product is $C = 350,000 + 5x$. Find the average cost of recycling for $x = 2000$ lbs.

2—T—Ans: $180

Section 8.2   Multiplying and Dividing Rational Expressions

1. Choose the missing expression to make the two fractions equivalent.

$$\frac{(x - 3)(x + 4)}{(x - 1)(x + 2)} \cdot \frac{(x + 2)}{(x - 3)} = \frac{\rule{2cm}{0.3cm}}{x - 1}$$

(a) $x - 3$ **(b)** $x + 4$ **(c)** $x - 1$ **(d)** $x + 2$ **(e)** None of these

1—Ans: b

2. Choose the missing expression to make the two fractions equivalent.

$$\frac{(x - 3)(x + 4)}{(x - 1)(x + 2)} \cdot \frac{(x - 1)}{(x + 4)} = \frac{\rule{2cm}{0.3cm}}{x + 2}$$

(a) $x - 3$ **(b)** $x + 4$ **(c)** $x - 1$ **(d)** $x + 2$ **(e)** None of these

1—Ans: a

3. Multiply and simplify: $\dfrac{(2x - 1)(3x + 2)}{(x - 4)(2x + 1)} \cdot \dfrac{2x + 1}{2x - 1}$.

1—Ans: $\dfrac{3x + 2}{x - 4}$

4. Multiply and simplify: $\dfrac{(5x + 2)(3x + 2)}{(2x - 1)(3x - 4)} \cdot \dfrac{2x - 1}{5x + 2}$.

1—Ans: $\dfrac{3x + 2}{3x - 4}$

5. Multiply and simplify: $\dfrac{(2x - 5)(2x - 3)}{(4x + 3)(2x - 1)} \cdot \dfrac{4x + 3}{2x - 3}$.

1—Ans: $\dfrac{2x - 5}{2x - 1}$

6. Multiply and simplify: $\dfrac{(3x + 5)(3x - 1)}{(3x + 1)(5x - 2)} \cdot \dfrac{3x + 1}{3x + 5}$.

1—Ans: $\dfrac{3x - 1}{5x - 2}$

7. Multiply $\dfrac{5x^2y^3}{8xy^2}$ by $\dfrac{4x^3y}{10x^2y^2}$ and simplify.

   (a) $\dfrac{20x^5y^4}{80x^3y^5}$ **(b)** $\dfrac{4}{x^2}$ **(c)** $\dfrac{x^2}{4}$ **(d)** $\dfrac{x^8y^8}{4}$ **(e)** None of these

   1—Ans: c

8. Multiply $\dfrac{12xy^4}{6x^3y^3}$ by $\dfrac{4x^3y}{3x^2y^2}$ and simplify.

   (a) $\dfrac{48x^4y^5}{18x^5y^5}$ **(b)** $\dfrac{8}{3x}$ **(c)** $\dfrac{8x^9y^{10}}{3}$ **(d)** $\dfrac{8x}{3}$ **(e)** None of these

   1—Ans: b

9. Multiply $\dfrac{15x^3y^4}{21x^2y^2}$ by $\dfrac{14x^2y^3}{6xy^2}$ and simplify.

   (a) $\dfrac{5x^2y^3}{3}$ **(b)** $\dfrac{210x^5y^7}{126x^3y^4}$ **(c)** $\dfrac{5}{3x^2y^3}$ **(d)** $\dfrac{5x^8y^{11}}{3}$ **(e)** None of these

   1—Ans: a

10. Multiply $\dfrac{12x^4y^3}{9x^3y^4}$ by $\dfrac{4x^5y^2}{8x^6}$ and simplify.

   (a) $\dfrac{2}{3y^5}$ **(b)** $\dfrac{48x^9y^5}{72xy}$ **(c)** $\dfrac{3x^{18}}{2y^9}$ **(d)** $\dfrac{2y}{3}$ **(e)** None of these

   1—Ans: d

11. Multiply and simplify: $\dfrac{18x^4y^2}{12xy^5} \cdot \dfrac{8x^3y^3}{9y^4}$.

   1—Ans: $\dfrac{4x^6}{3y^4}$

12. Multiply and simplify: $\dfrac{27x^6y^4}{15x^2y^3} \cdot \dfrac{12x^3y^4}{36y^4y}$.

   1—Ans: $\dfrac{3x^3y^4}{5}$

13. Multiply and simplify: $\dfrac{6x}{4 - x^2} \cdot \dfrac{-(x + 2)^2}{x^2 + 2x}$.

(a) $6(x + 2)$ (b) $\dfrac{6}{x - 2}$ (c) $\dfrac{-6}{x + 2}$ (d) $\dfrac{6x}{x + 2}$ (e) None of these

1—Ans: b

14. Multiply and simplify: $\dfrac{6x}{4 - x^2} \cdot \dfrac{-(x + 2)^2}{x^2 - 2x}$.

(a) $6(x - 2)$ (b) $\dfrac{6}{x - 2}$ (c) $\dfrac{-6}{x + 2}$ (d) $\dfrac{6}{x + 2}$ (e) None of these

1—Ans: d

15. Multiply and simplify the algebraic fraction: $\dfrac{-3x + 9}{x^2 - 9} \cdot \dfrac{3x^2(x + 3)^2}{x^2 + 3x}$.

2—Ans: $-9x$

16. Multiply and simplify the algebraic fraction: $\dfrac{9 - 3x}{x^2 - 9} \cdot \dfrac{3x(x - 3)^2}{x^3 - 3x^2}$.

2—Ans: $\dfrac{-9(x - 3)}{x(x + 3)}$

17. Multiply and simplify the algebraic fraction: $\dfrac{(9 + 3x)}{x^2 - 9} \cdot \dfrac{3x(x + 3)}{x^3 + 3x^2}$.

2—Ans: $\dfrac{9}{x(x - 3)}$

18. Multiply and simplify the algebraic fraction: $\dfrac{(3x + 9)}{x^2 - 9} \cdot \dfrac{3x(x + 3)}{x^2(x - 3)^2}$.

2—Ans: $\dfrac{9(x + 3)}{x(x - 3)^3}$

19. Multiply and simplify the expression $\dfrac{x^2 - 3x - 4}{2 - x - x^2} \cdot \dfrac{x^2 - 4}{2x^2 - x - 3}$.

(a) $-\dfrac{(x - 4)(x - 2)}{(x - 1)(2x - 3)}$ (b) $\dfrac{x - 4}{2x - 3}$ (c) $-\dfrac{x - 2}{x - 1}$

(d) $\dfrac{(x + 1)(x + 2)}{(x - 1)(2x - 3)}$ (e) None of these

2—Ans: a

20. Multiply and simplify the expression $\dfrac{x^2 - 9}{x^2 - 5x + 6} \cdot \dfrac{(x - 2)^2}{3x^2 + 9x}$.

    (a) $\dfrac{(x + 2)}{x(x - 2)}$ **(b)** $\dfrac{x - 2}{3x}$ **(c)** $\dfrac{3x}{x - 2}$

    (d) $\dfrac{(x - 2)}{(x + 3)(x - 3)}$ **(e)** None of these

    2—Ans: b

21. Multiply and simplify the expression $\dfrac{(2x - 1)^2}{x^2 - x} \cdot \dfrac{2x^2 - x - 1}{4x^2 - 1}$.

    (a) $\dfrac{2x - 1}{2x + 1}$ **(b)** $\dfrac{2x + 1}{x(2x - 1)}$ **(c)** $\dfrac{2x - 1}{x}$

    (d) $\dfrac{2x + 1}{x}$ **(e)** None of these

    2—Ans: c

22. Multiply and simplify the expression $\dfrac{(2x + 1)^2}{x^2 + x} \cdot \dfrac{2x^2 + x - 1}{4x^2 - 1}$.

    (a) $\dfrac{2x - 1}{x}$ **(b)** $\dfrac{2x + 1}{x(2x - 1)}$ **(c)** $\dfrac{2x + 1}{2x - 1}$

    (d) $\dfrac{2x + 1}{x}$ **(e)** None of these

    2—Ans: d

23. Multiply and simplify the expression $\dfrac{(x + 2)^2}{3 - x} \cdot \dfrac{x - 3}{x^2 - 4}$.

    1—Ans: $\dfrac{x + 2}{2 - x}$

24. Multiply and simplify the expression $\dfrac{(x - 2)^2}{x + 3} \cdot \dfrac{3 - x}{x^2 - 4} \cdot \dfrac{x + 2}{2 - x}$.

    1—Ans: $\dfrac{x - 3}{x + 3}$

25. Divide the algebraic fractions as indicated: $\dfrac{x + 2}{x - 3} \div \dfrac{x + 2}{x + 3}$.

    (a) $\dfrac{(x + 2)^2}{x^2 - 9}$ **(b)** $\dfrac{x - 3}{x + 3}$ **(c)** $\dfrac{x + 3}{x - 3}$ **(d)** $\dfrac{x^2 - 9}{(x + 2)^2}$ **(e)** None of these

    1—Ans: c

26. Divide the algebraic fractions as indicated: $\dfrac{x+2}{x+3} \div \dfrac{x+2}{x-3}$.

(a) $\dfrac{(x+2)^2}{x^2-9}$ (b) $\dfrac{x-3}{x+3}$ (c) $\dfrac{x+3}{x-3}$ (d) $\dfrac{x^2-9}{(x+2)^2}$ (e) None of these

1—Ans: b

27. Divide and simplify: $\dfrac{x-4}{x+2} \div \dfrac{x-4}{x-2}$.

1—Ans: $\dfrac{x-2}{x+2}$

28. Divide and simplify: $\dfrac{x-4}{x-2} \div \dfrac{x-4}{x+2}$.

1—Ans: $\dfrac{x+2}{x-2}$

29. Divide and simplify: $\dfrac{t^2+t-6}{t^2+6t+9} \div \dfrac{t^2-4}{t+3}$.

(a) $\dfrac{t-3}{t+2}$ (b) $\dfrac{1}{t-2}$ (c) $\dfrac{1}{t+2}$ (d) $\dfrac{t+3}{t-2}$ (e) None of these

1—Ans: c

30. Divide and simplify: $\dfrac{t^2-t-6}{t^2-6t+9} \div \dfrac{t^2-4}{t-3}$.

(a) $\dfrac{t-3}{t+2}$ (b) $\dfrac{1}{t-2}$ (c) $\dfrac{1}{t+2}$ (d) $\dfrac{t+3}{t-2}$ (e) None of these

1—Ans: b

31. Divide and simplify: $\dfrac{r^2-r-12}{r^2+6r+9} \div \dfrac{r^2-4r}{r^2-9}$.

1—Ans: $\dfrac{r-3}{r}$

32. Divide and simplify: $\dfrac{r^2+6r+9}{r^2-r-12} \div \dfrac{r+3}{r+2}$.

1—Ans: $\dfrac{r+2}{r-4}$

33. Divide and simplify: $\dfrac{4x-6y}{x+y} \div \dfrac{2x-3y}{y^2-x^2}$.

(a) $\dfrac{1}{2(x-y)}$ (b) $2(y-x)$ (c) $-\dfrac{1}{2(x+y)}$ (d) $2(x+y)$ (e) None of these

1—Ans: b

34. Divide and simplify: $\dfrac{x + y}{4x + 6y} \div \dfrac{x^2 - y^2}{2x + 3y}$.

    (a) $\dfrac{1}{2(x - y)}$ **(b)** $2(y - x)$ **(c)** $-\dfrac{1}{2(x + y)}$ **(d)** $2(x + y)$ **(e)** None of these

    1—Ans: a

35. Divide and simplify: $\dfrac{(x - y)^2}{y^2 - x^2} \div \dfrac{x - y}{x^3y - xy^3}$.

    1—Ans: $xy(y - x)$

36. Divide and simplify: $\dfrac{x - y}{x^3y - xy^3} \div \dfrac{(x - y)^2}{x^2 - y^2}$.

    1—Ans: $\dfrac{1}{xy(x - y)}$

37. Perform the indicated operations and simplify: $\left[\dfrac{x^2 + 2x}{4} \cdot \dfrac{xy - y}{3x}\right] \div \dfrac{y - xy}{x - 2}$.

    (a) $\dfrac{x^2 - 4}{12}$ **(b)** $-\dfrac{x^2 - 4}{12}$ **(c)** $-\dfrac{(x - 2)^2}{12}$ **(d)** $\dfrac{(x + 2)^2}{12}$ **(e)** None of these

    2—Ans: b

38. Perform the indicated operations and simplify: $\left[\dfrac{x^2 + 2x}{3} \cdot \dfrac{y - xy}{4x}\right] \div \dfrac{xy - y}{2 - x}$.

    (a) $\dfrac{x^2 - 4}{12}$ **(b)** $-\dfrac{x^2 - 4}{12}$ **(c)** $-\dfrac{(x - 2)^2}{12}$ **(d)** $\dfrac{(x + 2)^2}{12}$ **(e)** None of these

    2—Ans: a

39. Perform the operations and simplify: $\left[\dfrac{x - 2}{3x} \cdot \dfrac{x + 3}{2x}\right] \div \dfrac{8 - 4x}{12x^3}$.

    2—Ans: $\dfrac{-x(x + 3)}{2}$

40. Perform the operations and simplify: $\left[\dfrac{x - 2}{3x} \cdot \dfrac{x + 3}{2x}\right] \div \dfrac{3x + 9}{12x^3}$.

    2—Ans: $\dfrac{2x(x - 2)}{3}$

41. Multiply and simplify: $\dfrac{12x^2y}{5y^2} \cdot \dfrac{2xy}{3x^2}$.

    (a) $\dfrac{8x}{5y}$ **(b)** $\dfrac{8}{5}$ **(c)** $\dfrac{8x}{5}$ **(d)** $\dfrac{24x}{15y}$ **(e)** None of these

    1—Ans: c

42. Multiply and simplify: $\dfrac{4y^2}{9x} \cdot \dfrac{27}{16xy^2}$.

(a) $\dfrac{3}{4}$ (b) $\dfrac{3y^4}{4}$ (c) $\dfrac{81}{4x^2}$ (d) $\dfrac{3}{4x^2}$ (e) None of these

1—Ans: d

43. Multiply and simplify: $\dfrac{x^2 - 2x}{(x + 1)^2} \cdot \dfrac{x^2 + 4x + 3}{x(x + 3)}$.

(a) $\dfrac{x - 2}{x + 1}$ (b) $\dfrac{x^2 - 2x}{x(x + 1)}$ (c) $\dfrac{3 - x}{2x + 1}$ (d) $\dfrac{-2x^2 - 6x}{2x + 1}$ (e) None of these

2—Ans: a

44. Multiply and simplify: $\dfrac{x^2 - 2x - 3}{x^2 - x} \cdot \dfrac{x^2}{x^2 - 3x}$.

(a) $\dfrac{2x + 3}{3x^2}$ (b) $\dfrac{x + 1}{x - 1}$ (c) -1 (d) $\dfrac{x + 3}{x - 3}$ (e) None of these

2—Ans: b

45. Divide and simplify: $\dfrac{5t^2}{8} \div \dfrac{15t^5}{12}$.

(a) $\dfrac{75t^7}{96}$ (b) $\dfrac{75t^{10}}{96}$ (c) $\dfrac{1}{t^{5/2}}$ (d) $\dfrac{1}{2t^3}$ (e) None of these

1—Ans: d

46. Divide and simplify: $\dfrac{4x^2}{y} \div \dfrac{3xy}{5}$.

(a) $\dfrac{20x}{3y^2}$ (b) $\dfrac{12x^3}{5}$ (c) $\dfrac{20x}{3}$ (d) $\dfrac{15x}{4y^2}$ (e) None of these

1—Ans: a

47. Divide and simplify: $\dfrac{x^3 - 8}{64x} \div \dfrac{x^2 - x - 2}{16x^2}$.

(a) $\dfrac{x^3}{4}$ (b) $\dfrac{x(x^2 + 2x + 4)}{4(x + 1)}$ (c) $\dfrac{x^2 + x}{4}$

(d) $\dfrac{-2(x^3 - 8)}{4}$ (e) None of these

2—Ans: b

48. Divide and simplify: $\dfrac{t^3 + 8}{2t^2} \div \dfrac{(t + 2)^2}{8t}$.

(a) $\dfrac{4(t^2 - 2t + 4)}{t(t + 2)}$ (b) -16 (c) $4t$

(d) $\dfrac{4(t - 2)}{t}$ (e) None of these

2—Ans: a

49. Simplify: $\dfrac{\left(\dfrac{3}{x - 1}\right)}{\left(\dfrac{x}{x^2 - 1}\right)}$.

(a) 4 (b) $\dfrac{3(x + 1)}{x}$ (c) $\dfrac{3x}{(x - 1)(x^2 - 1)}$

(d) 3 (e) None of these

2—Form: 8A—Ans: b

50. Simplify: $\dfrac{\left(\dfrac{x^2}{x^2 - 1}\right)}{\left(\dfrac{3x}{x + 1}\right)}$.

(a) $-\dfrac{1}{3}$ (b) $\dfrac{3x^3}{(x^2 - 1)(x + 1)}$ (c) $\dfrac{x}{3(x - 1)}$

(d) $\dfrac{1}{x(x - 1)}$ (e) None of these

2—Form: 8B—Ans: c

51. Multiply and simplify: $\dfrac{2}{u - 3} \cdot \dfrac{3 - u}{8}$.

1—Ans: $-\dfrac{1}{4}$

52. Multiply and simplify: $\dfrac{4 - t}{6} \cdot \dfrac{9}{t - 4}$.

1—Ans: $-\dfrac{3}{2}$

53. Multiply and simplify: $\dfrac{x^2 + 2x - 3}{x + 2} \cdot \dfrac{x^2 + 2x}{x^2 - 1}$.

2—Ans: $\dfrac{x(x + 3)}{x + 1}$

54. Multiply and simplify: $\dfrac{x^2 - 4}{x^2 - 3x} \cdot \dfrac{x - 3}{x^2 + 3x - 10}$.

2—Ans: $\dfrac{x + 2}{x(x + 5)}$

55. Divide and simplify: $\dfrac{4y^2}{9x} \div \dfrac{16}{27xy^2}$.

1—Ans: $\dfrac{3y^4}{4}$

56. Divide and simplify: $\dfrac{12x^2}{49y} \div \dfrac{16}{21x^2y}$.

1—Ans: $\dfrac{9x^4}{28}$

57. Divide and simplify: $\dfrac{8x^3 + 27}{2x^2 + 3x} \cdot \dfrac{4x^2 - 6x + 9}{3x^3}$.

2—Ans: $3x^2$

58. Divide and simplify: $\dfrac{3x^2 - x - 2}{x^2 - 8x + 16} \div \dfrac{3x^2 + 2x}{x^3 - 64}$.

2—Form: 8C—Ans: $\dfrac{(x^2 + 4x - 16)(x - 1)}{x(x - 4)}$

59. Simplify: $\dfrac{\left(\dfrac{2}{t^2 + t + 2}\right)}{\left(\dfrac{4}{t^2 - t - 6}\right)}$.

2—Ans: $\dfrac{t - 3}{2(t - 1)}$

60. Simplify: $\dfrac{\left(\dfrac{24}{x^2 + 4x + 3}\right)}{\left(\dfrac{56}{x^2 - 2x - 15}\right)}$.

2—Ans: $\dfrac{3(x - 5)}{7(x + 1)}$

61. Multiply and simplify: $\dfrac{2 - x}{x^2 + 4} \cdot \dfrac{x + 2}{x^2 + 5x - 14}$.

(a) $-\dfrac{x + 2}{(x^2 + 4)(x + 7)}$

(b) $\dfrac{1}{(x + 2)(x + 7)}$

(c) $\dfrac{x + 2}{(x^2 + 4)(x + 7)}$

(d) $\dfrac{-1}{(x + 2)(x + 7)}$

(e) None of these

2—Ans: a

62. Divide and simplify: $\dfrac{x + 1}{x^2 - 1} \div \dfrac{x^2 + 1}{x - 1}$.

(a) $-\dfrac{1}{x^2 + 1}$

(b) $\dfrac{1}{x^2 + 1}$

(c) $\dfrac{x^3 + 1}{x^3 - 1}$

(d) -1

(e) None of these

1—Ans: b

63. Simplify: $\left[\dfrac{(x + 2)^2}{x} \cdot \dfrac{3x^2}{x^2 - 4} \right] \div \dfrac{9x^3}{x - 2}$.

(a) $\dfrac{x + 2}{3x^2}$

(b) $\dfrac{27x^4}{2 - x}$

(c) $\dfrac{4(x - 2)}{3x}$

(d) $-\dfrac{8}{3}$

(e) None of these

2—Ans: a

64. Perform the operation and simplify: $\dfrac{4u^3 - 5u^4}{u^2 + 2u + 1} \div \left(\dfrac{u^2}{5u^2 + u - 4} \right)^2$.

2—Ans: $\dfrac{(4u - 5)(5u - 4)^2}{u}$

65. Use a graphing utility to graph the equation $y_1 = \dfrac{6x}{4 - x^2} \cdot \dfrac{(x - 2)^2}{x^2 - 2x}$. Then graph each of the choices for y_2 and use the results to decide which is equivalent to y_1.

(a) $y_2 = 6(2 - x)$

(b) $y_2 = \dfrac{6x}{2 - x}$

(c) $y_2 = \dfrac{-6}{x + 2}$

(d) $y_2 = \dfrac{6}{x + 2}$

(e) $y_2 = \dfrac{6x}{x - 2}$

2—T—Form: 8A—Ans: c

66. Use a graphing utility to graph the equation $y_1 = \dfrac{x^2 + x - 12}{x^2 + x - 6} \cdot \dfrac{x - 1}{x + 4}$. Then graph each of the choices for y_2 and use the results to decide which is equivalent to y_1.

(a) $y_2 = \dfrac{x + 4}{x - 3}$

(b) $y_2 = \dfrac{x - 1}{x + 4}$

(c) $y_2 = \dfrac{x + 4}{x - 1}$

(d) $y_2 = \dfrac{x + 4}{x + 2}$

(e) $y_2 = \dfrac{(x - 3)^2(x + 4)}{(x - 1)(x + 2)^2}$

2—T—Form: 8B—Ans: c

67. Use a graphing utility to graph the two equations in the same viewing rectangle. Use the graphs to determine whether the expressions are equivalent.

$$y_1 = \frac{2 - x}{x + 2} \cdot \frac{x + 3}{x^2 - 4} \cdot \frac{(x + 2)^2}{3 - x} \qquad \text{and} \qquad y_2 = \frac{x - 3}{x + 3}$$

1—T—Form: 8C—Ans: $y_1 \neq y_2$

68. Use a graphing utility to graph the two equations in the same viewing rectangle. Use the graphs to determine whether the expressions are equivalent.

$$y_1 = \frac{3 - x}{x + 3} \cdot \frac{x + 2}{x^2 - 9} \cdot \frac{(x + 3)^2}{2 - x} \qquad \text{and} \qquad y_2 = \frac{x + 2}{x - 2}$$

1—T—Ans: $y_1 = y_2$

69. Use a graphing utility to graph the two equations in the same viewing rectangle. Use the graphs to determine whether the expressions are equivalent.

$$y_1 = \frac{x - 1}{4x + 6} \div \frac{1 - x^2}{2x + 3} \qquad \text{and} \qquad y_2 = \frac{1}{2(x + 7)}$$

1—T—Ans: $y_1 \neq y_2$

70. Use a graphing utility to graph the two equations in the same viewing rectangle. Use the graphs to determine whether the expressions are equivalent.

$$y_1 = \frac{x^2 + x - 6}{x^2 + 6x + 9} \div \frac{x^2 - 4}{x^2 - 9} \qquad \text{and} \qquad y_2 = \frac{x - 3}{x + 2}$$

1—T—Ans: $y_1 = y_2$

71. Use a graphing utility to graph the equation $y_1 = \dfrac{x^2 - x - 6}{x^2 - 6x + 9} \div \dfrac{x^2 - 4}{x^2 - 9}$. Then graph each of the choices for y_2 and use the results to decide which is equivalent to y_1.

(a) $y_2 = \dfrac{x - 3}{x + 2}$ **(b)** $y_2 = \dfrac{1}{x - 2}$ **(c)** $y_2 = \dfrac{1}{x + 2}$

(d) $y_2 = \dfrac{x + 3}{x - 2}$ **(e)** $y_2 = \dfrac{x - 3}{x - 2}$

1—T—Ans: d

72. Use a graphing utility to graph the equation $y_1 = \dfrac{4x + 6}{1 - x} \div \dfrac{2x + 3}{1 - x^2}$. Then graph each of the choices for y_2 and use the results to decide which is equivalent to y_1.

(a) $y_2 = \dfrac{1}{2(x - 1)}$ **(b)** $y_2 = 2(1 - x)$ **(c)** $y_2 = \dfrac{1}{2(x + 1)}$

(d) $y_2 = 2(x + 1)$ **(e)** $y_2 = \dfrac{2}{(1 - x)^2}$

1—T—Ans: d

Section 8.3 Adding and Subtracting Rational Expressions

1. Combine and simplify: $\dfrac{2 - 3x}{5} + \dfrac{2x - 1}{5}$.

   (a) $\dfrac{1 - 5x}{5}$ **(b)** $\dfrac{1 - x}{5}$ **(c)** $\dfrac{4x - 4}{5}$

   (d) $\dfrac{1 - x}{25}$ **(e)** None of these

   1—Ans: b

2. Combine and simplify: $\dfrac{5 - 2x}{4} + \dfrac{3x - 2}{4}$.

   (a) $\dfrac{3 + x}{4}$ **(b)** $\dfrac{8x - 4}{4}$ **(c)** $\dfrac{3 + x}{16}$

   (d) $\dfrac{7 - 5x}{4}$ **(e)** None of these

   1—Ans: a

3. Add the fractions: $\dfrac{2 - 3x}{x + 5} + \dfrac{1 + x}{x + 5}$.

   1—Ans: $\dfrac{3 - 2x}{x + 5}$

4. Add the fractions: $\dfrac{4 - 3x}{2x + 1} + \dfrac{x - 2}{2x + 1}$.

   1—Ans: $\dfrac{2 - 2x}{2x + 1}$

5. Add the fractions: $\dfrac{5 - 2x}{3x - 1} + \dfrac{3x - 2}{3x - 1}$.

   1—Ans: $\dfrac{3 + x}{3x - 1}$

6. Add the fractions: $\dfrac{4x + 2}{x + 3} + \dfrac{5 - 2x}{x + 3}$.

   1—Ans: $\dfrac{2x + 7}{x + 3}$

7. Add and simplify: $\dfrac{3x - 7}{x^2 - 9} + \dfrac{1 - x}{x^2 - 9}$.

   (a) $\dfrac{2}{x - 3}$ **(b)** $\dfrac{2}{x + 3}$ **(c)** $\dfrac{4x - 8}{x^2 - 9}$ **(d)** $\dfrac{2x}{x + 3}$ **(e)** None of these

   1—Ans: b

8. Add and simplify: $\dfrac{2x - 1}{4x^2 - 1} + \dfrac{4x - 2}{4x^2 - 1}$.

(a) $\dfrac{3}{2x - 1}$ (b) $\dfrac{-1}{2x + 1}$ (c) $\dfrac{6x}{4x^2 - 1}$ (d) $\dfrac{3}{2x + 1}$ (e) None of these

1—Ans: d

9. Add and simplify: $\dfrac{2x - 1}{1 - 4x^2} + \dfrac{4x - 2}{1 - 4x^2}$.

1—Ans: $\dfrac{-3}{1 + 2x}$

10. Add and simplify: $\dfrac{x - 7}{4 - x^2} + \dfrac{2x + 1}{4 - x^2}$.

1—Ans: $\dfrac{-3}{x + 2}$

11. Subtract and simplify: $\dfrac{3 + 4x}{2x + x^2} - \dfrac{2x + 3}{2x + x^2}$.

(a) $\dfrac{2}{x + 2}$ (b) $\dfrac{2x + 6}{x(x + 2)}$ (c) $\dfrac{6(x + 1)}{2x + x^2}$ (d) $\dfrac{6}{x + 2}$ (e) None of these

1—Ans: a

12. Subtract and simplify: $\dfrac{3 + 4x}{2x + x^2} - \dfrac{x - 3}{2x + x^2}$.

(a) $\dfrac{3x}{2x + x^2}$ (b) $\dfrac{3}{2 + x}$ (c) $\dfrac{3}{x}$ (d) $\dfrac{3x}{x + 2}$ (e) None of these

1—Ans: c

13. Subtract and simplify: $\dfrac{x - 5}{x^2 - 1} - \dfrac{-1 - 3x}{x^2 - 1}$.

1—Ans: $\dfrac{4}{x + 1}$

14. Subtract and simplify: $\dfrac{5 - x}{1 - x^2} - \dfrac{1 - 5x}{1 - x^2}$.

1—Ans: $\dfrac{4}{1 - x}$

15. The least common multiple of x^2, $x^2 - 2x$, and $x^2 - 4$ is:

(a) $x^3(x - 2)(x^2 - 4)$ (b) $x(x + 2)(x - 2)$ (c) $x^2(x^2 - 4)$

(d) $x^2(x - 2)^2(x + 2)$ (e) None of these

1—Ans: c

16. The least common multiple of $x^2 - 9$, $x^3 + 3x^2$, and $(x - 3)^3$ is:

(a) $x^2(x - 3)^4(x + 3)^2$ (b) $(x^2 - 9)(x^3 + 3x^2)(x - 3)^3$ (c) $x^2(x + 3)(x - 3)$

(d) $x^2(x + 3)(x - 3)^3$ (e) None of these

1—Ans: d

17. Find the least common multiple of $8(x^2 - 9)$, $3(9 - x^2)$, and $6(x + 3)^2$.

1—Ans: $24(x - 3)(x + 3)^2$; (-1) in multiplier is optional.

18. Find the least common multiple of $4x^2(x^2 - 1)$, $6x(x - 1)^2$, and $3(x^2 + x)$.

1—Ans: $12x^2(x + 1)(x - 1)^2$

19. Add: $\dfrac{7}{5x} + \dfrac{4}{3x}$.

(a) $\dfrac{11}{8x}$ (b) $\dfrac{11}{18x^2}$ (c) $\dfrac{11}{15x}$ (d) $\dfrac{41}{15x}$ (e) None of these

1—Ans: d

20. Add: $\dfrac{3}{8x} + \dfrac{5}{7x}$.

(a) $\dfrac{8}{15x}$ (b) $\dfrac{8}{15x^2}$ (c) $\dfrac{61}{56x}$ (d) $\dfrac{8}{56x}$ (e) None of these

1—Ans: c

21. Add: $\dfrac{9}{2x} + \dfrac{7}{3x}$.

1—Ans: $\dfrac{41}{6x}$

22. Add: $\dfrac{11}{4x} + \dfrac{5}{6x}$.

1—Ans: $\dfrac{43}{12x}$

23. Add: $\dfrac{3}{7x} + \dfrac{8}{5x}$.

1—Ans: $\dfrac{71}{35x}$

24. Add: $\dfrac{5}{4x} + \dfrac{7}{10x}$.

1—Ans: $\dfrac{39}{20x}$

25. Subtract and simplify: $\dfrac{3}{x+3} - \dfrac{2}{x-1}$.

(a) $\dfrac{1}{(x+3)(x-1)}$ **(b)** $\dfrac{x-9}{(x+3)(x-1)}$ **(c)** $\dfrac{1}{4}$

(d) $\dfrac{5x+3}{(x+3)(x-1)}$ **(e)** None of these

1—Ans: b

26. Subtract and simplify: $\dfrac{5}{x-2} - \dfrac{3}{x+2}$.

(a) $\dfrac{2}{-4} = -\dfrac{1}{2}$ **(b)** $\dfrac{2}{(x-2)(x+2)}$ **(c)** $\dfrac{2x+16}{(x-2)(x+2)}$

(d) $\dfrac{8}{(x-2)(x+2)}$ **(e)** None of these

1—Ans: c

27. Subtract and simplify: $\dfrac{7}{2x-1} - \dfrac{3}{x+3}$.

1—Ans: $\dfrac{x+24}{(2x-1)(x+3)}$

28. Subtract and simplify: $\dfrac{8}{x-3} - \dfrac{3}{2x+5}$.

1—Ans: $\dfrac{13x+49}{(x-3)(2x+5)}$

29. Add and simplify: $\dfrac{3x}{x^2-4} + \dfrac{3}{2-x}$.

(a) $\dfrac{3x+3}{(x^2-4)(2-x)}$ **(b)** $\dfrac{-6}{x+2}$ **(c)** $\dfrac{6}{4-x^2}$

(d) $\dfrac{3x+3}{x^2-x-2}$ **(e)** None of these

2—Ans: c

30. Add and simplify: $\dfrac{3x}{4-x^2} + \dfrac{3}{x+2}$.

(a) $\dfrac{3x+3}{(4-x^2)(x+2)}$ **(b)** $\dfrac{6}{4-x^2}$ **(c)** $\dfrac{3x+3}{6+x-x^2}$

(d) $\dfrac{6}{x+2}$ **(e)** None of these

2—Ans: b

31. Combine the fractions and simplify: $\dfrac{x-2}{3x^2-2x} - \dfrac{6}{x} + \dfrac{2}{3x-2}$.

2—Ans: $-\dfrac{5}{x}$

32. Combine the fractions and simplify: $\dfrac{6}{x} - \dfrac{2}{3x+2} - \dfrac{x+2}{3x^2+2x}$.

2—Ans: $\dfrac{5}{x}$

33. Combine the fractions and simplify: $\dfrac{5}{2x^2-5x} - \dfrac{3}{x} - \dfrac{2}{2x-5}$.

2—Ans: $\dfrac{-4}{x}$

34. Combine the fractions and simplify: $\dfrac{3}{x} - \dfrac{15}{2x^2+5x} + \dfrac{2}{2x+5}$.

2—Ans: $\dfrac{8}{2x+5}$

35. Simplify the complex fraction: $\dfrac{\left(\dfrac{2}{x}-\dfrac{1}{2}\right)}{\left(\dfrac{2}{3}+\dfrac{1}{x}\right)}$.

(a) $\dfrac{2-x}{2x+3}$ **(b)** $\dfrac{4-x}{2x+3}$ **(c)** $\dfrac{2x-1}{6+x}$ **(d)** $\dfrac{3(4-x)}{2(2x+3)}$ **(e)** None of these

2—Ans: d

36. Simplify the complex fraction: $\dfrac{\left(\dfrac{4}{x}-\dfrac{2}{3}\right)}{\left(\dfrac{1}{2}-\dfrac{3}{x}\right)}$.

(a) $\dfrac{12-2x}{x-6}$ **(b)** $\dfrac{-4}{3}$ **(c)** $\dfrac{4x-6}{2-3x}$ **(d)** $\dfrac{4-2x}{x-3}$ **(e)** None of these

2—Ans: b

37. Simplify the complex fraction: $\dfrac{\left(\dfrac{3}{x-2}+1\right)}{\left(\dfrac{9}{x-2}-\dfrac{3}{x}\right)}$.

2—Ans: $\dfrac{x}{6}$

38. Simplify the complex fraction: $\dfrac{\left(\dfrac{3}{x-2} - \dfrac{2}{x+2}\right)}{\left(\dfrac{2}{x+2} - \dfrac{1}{x-2}\right)}$.

2—Ans: $\dfrac{x+10}{x-6}$

39. Simplify the complex fraction: $\dfrac{\left(\dfrac{2}{x-3} + \dfrac{3}{x}\right)}{\left(\dfrac{1}{x-3} - \dfrac{4}{x}\right)}$.

2—Ans: $\dfrac{5x-9}{3(4-x)}$

40. Simplify the complex fraction: $\dfrac{\left(\dfrac{2x}{x+1} + \dfrac{1}{x-2}\right)}{\left(\dfrac{2x}{x-2} + \dfrac{1}{x+1}\right)}$.

2—Ans: $\dfrac{x-1}{x+2}$

41. Subtract and simplify: $\dfrac{2x}{2x^2+x-6} - \dfrac{3}{2x^2+x-6}$.

(a) $\dfrac{2x-3}{2x^2+x-6}$ (b) $\dfrac{-3}{2x-6}$ (c) $\dfrac{1}{x+2}$

(d) $\dfrac{1}{2x+2}$ (e) None of these

1—Ans: c

42. Subtract and simplify: $\dfrac{2x-3}{2x^2+5x-25} - \dfrac{2}{2x^2+5x-25}$.

(a) $\dfrac{2x-5}{2x^2+5x-25}$ (b) $\dfrac{1}{x^2+10}$ (c) $\dfrac{2x-1}{2x^2+5x-25}$

(d) $\dfrac{1}{x+5}$ (e) None of these

1—Ans: d

43. Add and simplify: $\dfrac{x}{x-1} + \dfrac{3x}{x^2-1}$.

(a) $-4x$ (b) $\dfrac{4-x}{x-1}$ (c) $\dfrac{4x}{x^2-1}$

(d) $\dfrac{x^2+4x}{x^2-1}$ (e) None of these

1—Form: 8A—Ans: d

44. Add and simplify: $\dfrac{5}{x+2} + \dfrac{3}{x-1}$.

(a) $\dfrac{8x+1}{(x-1)(x+2)}$ (b) $\dfrac{8x+5}{(x-1)(x+2)}$ (c) $\dfrac{8}{(x-1)(x+2)}$

(d) $\dfrac{8x-3}{(x-1)(x+2)}$ (e) None of these

    1—Form: 8B—Ans: a

45. Simplify: $\dfrac{\left(1+\dfrac{1}{x}\right)}{\left(1-\dfrac{1}{x}\right)}$.

(a) $\dfrac{x+1}{x-1}$ (b) $\dfrac{x-1}{x+1}$ (c) 1   (d) -1 (e) None of these

    2—Form: 8A—Ans: a

46. Simplify: $\dfrac{\left(2-\dfrac{1}{x}\right)}{x}$.

(a) 1   (b) $\dfrac{2x-1}{x^2}$ (c) $\dfrac{2x-1}{x}$ (d) $2x-1$ (e) None of these

    2—Form: 8B—Ans: b

47. Combine and simplify: $\dfrac{4x}{x^2-4} - \dfrac{3}{x+2}$.

    1—Ans: $\dfrac{x+6}{x^2-4}$

48. Combine and simplify: $\dfrac{x-1}{x^2-9} - \dfrac{2}{x-3}$.

    1—Ans: $\dfrac{x+7}{9-x^2}$

49. Combine and simplify: $\dfrac{1}{2} + \dfrac{2}{x} + \dfrac{3}{x^2}$.

    1—Ans: $\dfrac{x^2+4x+6}{2x^2}$

50. Combine and simplify: $\dfrac{1}{3} - \dfrac{2}{x} + \dfrac{3}{x^2}$.

    1—Ans: $\dfrac{x^2-6x+9}{3x^2}$

51. Simplify: $\dfrac{\left(\dfrac{6}{x-1}-3\right)}{\dfrac{3}{x}}$.

2—Ans: $\dfrac{x(3-x)}{x-1}$

52. Simplify: $\dfrac{\left(2-\dfrac{4}{3-x}\right)}{\dfrac{6}{x}}$.

2—Form: 8C—Ans: $\dfrac{x-x^2}{3(3-x)}$

53. Subtract and simplify: $\dfrac{3}{x^2+2x+1}-\dfrac{1}{x+1}$.

(a) $\dfrac{4-x}{x^2+2x+1}$ (b) $\dfrac{-x^2+5x+2}{(x+1)(x^2+2x+1)}$ (c) $\dfrac{-x^2+x+2}{(x^2+2x+1)(x+1)}$

(d) $\dfrac{2-x}{x^2+2x+1}$ (e) None of these

2—Ans: d

54. Combine and simplify: $\dfrac{5}{x+2}-\dfrac{6}{x^2+4x+4}$.

2—Ans: $\dfrac{5x+4}{(x+2)^2}$

55. Use a graphing utility to graph the equation $y_1=\dfrac{9}{5x}+\dfrac{5}{4x}$. Then graph each of the choices for y_2 and use the results to decide which is equivalent to y_1.

(a) $y_2=\dfrac{14}{9x}$ (b) $y_2=\dfrac{14}{20}x$ (c) $y_2=\dfrac{61}{20x}$

(d) $y_2=\dfrac{14}{20x^2}$ (e) $y_2=\dfrac{9}{4x}$

1—T—Ans: c

56. Use a graphing utility to graph the equation $y_1 = \dfrac{8}{5x} + \dfrac{5}{8x}$. Then graph each of the choices for y_2 and use the results to decide which is equivalent to y_1.

   (a) $y_2 = \dfrac{1}{x}$ **(b)** $y_2 = \dfrac{89}{40x}$ **(c)** $y_2 = \dfrac{13}{40x^2}$

   (d) $y_2 = \dfrac{13}{40x}$ **(e)** $y_2 = \dfrac{1}{x^2}$

   1—T—Ans: b

57. Use a graphing utility to graph the two equations in the same viewing rectangle. Use the graphs to determine whether the expressions are equivalent.

$$y_1 = \frac{3}{2-x} - \frac{3x}{4-x^2} \quad \text{and} \quad y_2 = \frac{6}{4-x^2}$$

   1—T—Ans: $y_1 = y_2$

58. Use a graphing utility to graph the two equations in the same viewing rectangle. Use the graphs to determine whether the expressions are equivalent.

$$y_1 = \frac{3}{x+2} - \frac{3x}{x^2-4} \quad \text{and} \quad y_2 = \frac{6}{x^2-4}$$

   1—T—Ans: $y_1 \neq y_2$

59. Simplify the complex fraction: $\dfrac{\left(\dfrac{1}{x} - \dfrac{1}{y}\right)}{\left(\dfrac{x-y}{x^3 + x^2 y}\right)}$.

   2—Ans: $\dfrac{-x(x+y)}{y}$

60. Simplify the complex fraction: $\dfrac{\left(\dfrac{1}{y} - \dfrac{1}{x}\right)}{\left(\dfrac{1}{3y^2} - \dfrac{1}{3x^2}\right)}$.

   2—Ans: $\dfrac{3xy}{x+y}$

61. Use the table feature of a graphing utility to complete the table. What can you conclude?

x	-3	-2	-1	0	1	2	3
$\dfrac{\left(\dfrac{1}{x}-1\right)}{\dfrac{1}{x^2}}$							
$x(1-x)$							

2—T—Ans:

x	-3	-2	-1	0	1	2	3
$\dfrac{\left(\dfrac{1}{x}-1\right)}{\dfrac{1}{x^2}}$	-12	-6	-2	Undefined	0	-2	-6
$x(1-x)$	-12	-6	-2	0	0	-2	-6

The two expressions are equal for all real numbers except 0.

62. Use the table feature of a graphing utility to complete the table. What can you conclude?

x	-3	-2	-1	0	1	2	3
$\dfrac{\left(\dfrac{1}{x^2}-1\right)}{\left(\dfrac{1}{x}-1\right)}$							
$\dfrac{1+x}{x}$							

2—T—Ans:

x	-3	-2	-1	0	1	2	3
$\dfrac{\left(\dfrac{1}{x^2}-1\right)}{\left(\dfrac{1}{x}-1\right)}$	$\dfrac{2}{3}$	$\dfrac{1}{2}$	0	Undefined	Undefined	$\dfrac{3}{2}$	$\dfrac{4}{3}$
$\dfrac{1+x}{x}$	$\dfrac{2}{3}$	$\dfrac{1}{2}$	0	Undefined	2	$\dfrac{3}{2}$	$\dfrac{4}{3}$

The two expressions are equal for all real numbers except 1.

63. Find and simplify the expression $\dfrac{f(2+h)-f(2)}{h}$ for the function $f(x)=\dfrac{1}{1-x}$.

2—Ans: $\dfrac{\dfrac{1}{1-(2-h)}-1}{h}=\dfrac{1}{1+h}$

64. Find and simplify the expression $\dfrac{f(2 + h) - f(2)}{h}$ for the function $f(x) = \dfrac{x}{x + 1}$.

2—Form: 8C—Ans: $\dfrac{\dfrac{2 + h}{(2 + h) + 1} - \dfrac{2}{3}}{h} = \dfrac{1}{3(3 + h)}$

65. Find $\dfrac{f(2 + h) - f(2)}{h}$ for the function $f(x) = \dfrac{1}{1 + x}$.

 (a) $\dfrac{-1}{3(3 + h)}$ **(b)** -1 **(c)** $\dfrac{1}{3(3 + h)}$ **(d)** $\dfrac{1}{3 + h}$ **(e)** $\dfrac{1}{3h(3 + h)}$

2—Form: 8A—Ans: a

66. Find $\dfrac{f(2 + h) - f(2)}{h}$ for the function $f(x) = \dfrac{1}{x + 2}$.

 (a) -1 **(b)** $\dfrac{1}{4 + h}$ **(c)** $\dfrac{-1}{4(4 + h)}$ **(d)** $\dfrac{-1}{4h(4 + h)}$ **(e)** $\dfrac{1}{4(4 + h)}$

2—Form: 8B—Ans: c

67. Combine and simplify: $\dfrac{5}{x} - \dfrac{1}{3}$.

1—Ans: $\dfrac{15 - x}{3x}$

68. Combine and simplify: $\dfrac{4}{x} - \dfrac{2}{3}$.

1—Ans: $\dfrac{12 - 2x}{3x}$

69. Combine and simplify: $\dfrac{2}{x + 2} - \dfrac{x}{x^2 - 4} + \dfrac{x}{x - 2}$.

2—Ans: $\dfrac{3x^2 + x - 4}{x^2 - 4}$

70. Combine and simplify: $\dfrac{x}{x + 3} - \dfrac{2}{x^2 - 9} + \dfrac{x}{x - 3}$.

2—Ans: $\dfrac{2x^2 - 2}{x^2 - 9}$

71. Combine and simplify: $\dfrac{2}{x^2 + x} + \dfrac{3}{x^2 - 1} - \dfrac{5}{x^2 - x}$.

2—Form: 8C—Ans: $\dfrac{-7}{x(x^2 - 1)}$

72. Combine and simplify: $\dfrac{1}{x^2 - 4x} - \dfrac{5}{x^2 - 16} - \dfrac{2}{x^2 + 4x}$.

   2—Ans: $\dfrac{12 - 6x}{x(x^2 - 4)}$

Section 8.4   Solving Rational Equations

1. Solve: $\dfrac{x}{7} - 3 = \dfrac{x}{2}$.

   (a) $x = \dfrac{42}{5}$ **(b)** $x = \dfrac{5}{42}$ **(c)** $x = -\dfrac{42}{5}$ **(d)** $x = -\dfrac{5}{42}$ **(e)** None of these

   1—Ans: c

2. Solve: $\dfrac{x}{5} = 6 - \dfrac{x}{15}$.

   (a) $x = \dfrac{45}{2}$ **(b)** $x = \dfrac{2}{45}$ **(c)** $x = -\dfrac{45}{2}$ **(d)** $x = -\dfrac{2}{45}$ **(e)** None of these

   1—Ans: a

3. Solve: $\dfrac{x}{6} - \dfrac{3}{2} = \dfrac{2x}{3}$.

   (a) $x = \dfrac{1}{3}$ **(b)** $x = -3$ **(c)** $x = -\dfrac{1}{3}$ **(d)** $x = 3$ **(e)** None of these

   1—Ans: b

4. Solve: $\dfrac{3x}{4} + \dfrac{2}{3} = -\dfrac{5x}{6}$.

   (a) $x = \dfrac{8}{19}$ **(b)** $x = \dfrac{19}{8}$ **(c)** $x = -\dfrac{19}{8}$ **(d)** $x = -\dfrac{8}{19}$ **(e)** None of these

   1—Ans: d

5. Solve: $\dfrac{4x}{3} + \dfrac{7}{4} = \dfrac{5x}{6}$.

   1—Ans: $x = -\dfrac{7}{2}$

6. Solve: $\dfrac{2x}{9} = \dfrac{5x}{6} - \dfrac{7}{2}$.

   1—Ans: $x = \dfrac{63}{11}$

7. Solve: $\dfrac{x-1}{3} + \dfrac{3x-1}{12} = -\dfrac{7}{4}$.

   (a) $x = \dfrac{7}{16}$ **(b)** $x = -\dfrac{19}{7}$ **(c)** $x = -\dfrac{16}{7}$ **(d)** $x = \dfrac{16}{7}$ **(e)** None of these

   1—Ans: c

8. Solve: $\dfrac{2x-1}{3} - \dfrac{2-3x}{4} = \dfrac{5}{6}$.

   (a) $x = 4$ **(b)** $x = \dfrac{17}{20}$ **(c)** $x = \dfrac{20}{11}$ **(d)** $x = \dfrac{20}{17}$ **(e)** None of these

   1—Ans: d

9. Solve: $\dfrac{x+2}{3} - \dfrac{2x-1}{2} = \dfrac{2}{3}$.

   1—Ans: $x = \dfrac{3}{4}$

10. Solve: $\dfrac{2x-1}{3} - \dfrac{1-3x}{2} = \dfrac{3}{2}$.

   1—Ans: $x = \dfrac{14}{13}$

11. Solve: $\dfrac{2}{x} - \dfrac{3}{4} = \dfrac{5}{x}$.

   (a) $x = 6$ **(b)** $x = -4$ **(c)** $x = -\dfrac{1}{4}$ **(d)** $x = 4$ **(e)** None of these

   1—Ans: b

12. Solve: $\dfrac{5}{x} - \dfrac{4}{3} = \dfrac{2}{x}$.

   (a) $x = \dfrac{4}{9}$ **(b)** $x = -\dfrac{9}{4}$ **(c)** $x = \dfrac{5}{4}$ **(d)** $x = \dfrac{9}{4}$ **(e)** None of these

   1—Ans: d

13. Solve: $\dfrac{3}{x} - \dfrac{4}{5} = \dfrac{6}{x}$.

   (a) $x = -\dfrac{15}{4}$ **(b)** $x = \dfrac{15}{4}$ **(c)** $x = \dfrac{45}{4}$ **(d)** $x = -\dfrac{45}{4}$ **(e)** None of these

   1—Ans: a

14. Solve: $\dfrac{4}{x} - \dfrac{3}{2} = \dfrac{5}{x}$.

    (a) $x = \dfrac{2}{3}$ **(b)** $x = -\dfrac{3}{2}$ **(c)** $x = -\dfrac{2}{3}$ **(d)** $x = \dfrac{3}{2}$ **(e)** None of these

    1—Ans: c

15. Solve: $\dfrac{5}{x} + \dfrac{4}{3} + \dfrac{2}{x} = 0$.

    1—Ans: $x = -\dfrac{21}{4}$

16. Solve: $\dfrac{3}{4} - \dfrac{2}{x} - \dfrac{5}{x} = 0$.

    1—Ans: $x = \dfrac{28}{3}$

17. Solve: $\dfrac{3x}{x + 2} - \dfrac{2}{x - 2} = 3$.

    (a) $x = -9$ **(b)** $x = 1$ **(c)** $x = \dfrac{2}{7}$ **(d)** $x = -\dfrac{2}{3}$ **(e)** None of these

    1—Ans: b

18. Solve: $\dfrac{2x}{x - 2} + \dfrac{3}{x + 1} = 2$.

    (a) $x = -9$ **(b)** $x = 1$ **(c)** $x = \dfrac{2}{7}$ **(d)** $x = -\dfrac{2}{3}$ **(e)** None of these

    1—Ans: c

19. Solve: $\dfrac{x}{x + 4} - \dfrac{2}{x - 1} = 1$.

    (a) $x = -9$ **(b)** $x = 1$ **(c)** $x = \dfrac{2}{7}$ **(d)** $x = -\dfrac{2}{3}$ **(e)** None of these

    1—Ans: d

20. Solve: $\dfrac{2x}{x - 1} - \dfrac{1}{x + 4} = 2$.

    (a) $x = -9$ **(b)** $x = 1$ **(c)** $x = \dfrac{2}{7}$ **(d)** $x = -\dfrac{2}{7}$ **(e)** None of these

    1—Ans: a

21. Find and check any possible solutions of $\dfrac{2x}{x + 1} = 3 - \dfrac{2}{x + 1}$.

    1—Ans: Trial solution, $x = -1$, doesn't check. No solution.

22. Find and check any possible solutions of $\dfrac{x+4}{x+3} = \dfrac{1}{x+3} - 1$.

1—Ans: Trial solution, $x = -3$, doesn't check. No solution.

23. Solve: $\dfrac{2x}{x+1} = \dfrac{4}{x+3}$.

(a) $x = -1$ and $x = -3$ (b) $x = 2$ and $x = -2$ (c) $x = 1$ and $x = 2$

(d) $x = -2$ and $x = 1$ (e) None of these

1—Ans: d

24. Solve: $\dfrac{3x}{x-2} = 2 - \dfrac{1}{x+2}$.

(a) $x = -1$ and $x = 2$ (b) $x = -1$ and $x = -6$ (c) $x = -6$ and $x = 2$

(d) $x = 1$ and $x = 6$ (e) None of these

1—Ans: b

25. Solve: $\dfrac{x}{x+2} - 4 = \dfrac{4}{x-1}$.

(a) $x = -3$ and $x = -2$ (b) $x = 0$ and $x = 1$ (c) $x = 0$ and $x = -3$

(d) $x = 3$ and $x = 0$ (e) None of these

1—Ans: c

26. Solve: $\dfrac{4x}{x+1} - 2 = \dfrac{1}{x-2}$.

(a) $x = 3$ and $x = \dfrac{1}{2}$ (b) $x = \dfrac{1}{2}$ and $x = 0$ (c) $x = -1$ and $x = 3$

(d) $x = 2$ and $x = 3$ (e) None of these

1—Ans: a

27. Solve: $\dfrac{x^2}{x+3} = \dfrac{9}{x+3} - 1$.

1—Ans: $x = 2$ is the only solution.

28. Solve: $\dfrac{x^2}{x-2} = -1 + \dfrac{4}{x-2}$.

1—Ans: $x = -3$ is the only solution.

29. Solve: $\dfrac{3}{x-1} + \dfrac{2}{x+3} = \dfrac{5}{(x-1)(x+3)}$.

    (a) $x = -\dfrac{2}{5}$ **(b)** $x = -3$ **(c)** $x = \dfrac{2}{5}$ **(d)** $x = 2$ **(e)** None of these

    2—Ans: a

30. Solve: $\dfrac{2}{x+2} - \dfrac{3}{x-3} = \dfrac{6}{(x+2)(x-3)}$.

    (a) $x = 4$ **(b)** $x = 18$ **(c)** $x = -4$ **(d)** $x = -18$ **(e)** None of these

    2—Ans: d

31. Solve: $y = -\dfrac{2}{3} \cdot \dfrac{y-2}{y-1}$.

    2—Ans: $y = \dfrac{4}{3}$ and $y = -1$

32. Solve: $\dfrac{3y}{y+3} = \dfrac{16}{y+2}$.

    2—Ans: $y = 6$ and $y = -\dfrac{8}{3}$

33. Twelve is divided by a number and the result is added to five times the number. The result is 32. If the number is an integer, it is:

    (a) 4   **(b)** $\frac{2}{5}$ **(c)** $\frac{3}{5}$ **(d)** 6   **(e)** None of these

    2—Ans: d

34. Twelve is divided by a number and the result is added to five times the number. The result is 32. If the number is not an integer, it is:

    (a) 4   **(b)** $\frac{2}{5}$ **(c)** $\frac{3}{5}$ **(d)** 6   **(e)** None of these

    2—Ans: b

35. You travel 350 miles in the same amount of time it takes a friend to travel 400 miles. Your friend's average speed is 4 miles per hour greater than your average speed. Find your average speed.

    2—Ans: 28 mph

36. You travel 350 miles in the same amount of time it takes a friend to travel 400 miles. Your friend's average speed is 4 miles per hour greater than your average speed. Find your friend's average speed.

    2—Ans: 32 mph

37. The average cost $\overline{C}$ of producing x units of a product is given by $\overline{C} = \frac{3}{4} + \frac{3000}{x}$.

    The number of units that must be produced to obtain an average cost of \$3.25 per unit is:

    (a) 800   **(b)** 1200   **(c)** 1250   **(d)** 1500   **(e)** None of these

    1—Ans: b

38. The average cost $\overline{C}$ of producing x units of a product is given by $\overline{C} = \frac{3}{4} + \frac{3000}{x}$.

    The number of units that must be produced to obtain an average cost of \$4.50 per unit is:

    (a) 800   **(b)** 1200   **(c)** 1250   **(d)** 1500   **(e)** None of these

    1—Ans: a

39. After 180 times at bat a baseball player has 45 hits for a batting average of 0.250. How many additional consecutive hits must the player get to raise his batting average to at least 0.300?

    1—Ans: 13

40. After 180 times at bat a baseball player has 45 hits for a batting average of 0.250. How many additional consecutive hits must the player get to raise his batting average to at least 0.290?

    1—Ans: 11

41. Solve: $\frac{3}{x} - \frac{2}{x+1} = \frac{4}{x}$.

    (a) 3   **(b)** $-\frac{1}{3}$ **(c)** 0   **(d)** 1   **(e)** None of these

    2—Ans: b

42. Solve: $\frac{4}{x} - \frac{1}{x+2} = \frac{2}{x}$.

    (a) 0   **(b)** 2   **(c)** -4 **(d)** -2 **(e)** None of these

    2—Ans: c

43. Solve: $\frac{1}{x-2} + \frac{1}{x+2} = \frac{4}{x^2-4}$.

    (a) 2   **(b)** -2 **(c)** 2, -2 **(d)** 4   **(e)** None of these

    2—Form: 8A—Ans: e

44. Solve: $\frac{1}{x-2} + \frac{1}{x+3} = \frac{5}{x^2+x-6}$.

    (a) 2   **(b)** -3 **(c)** 3   **(d)** 2, -3 **(e)** None of these

    2—Form: 8B—Ans: e

45. Solve: $\dfrac{2}{x+3} + 5 = \dfrac{3}{x+3}$.

    (a) -1 **(b)** 0 **(c)** $-\dfrac{12}{7}$ **(d)** $-\dfrac{4}{3}$ **(e)** None of these

    1—Ans: c

46. Solve: $\dfrac{3}{x-1} - 6 = \dfrac{5x}{x-1}$.

    (a) $\dfrac{2}{11}$ **(b)** $\dfrac{9}{11}$ **(c)** $-\dfrac{3}{5}$ **(d)** $\dfrac{3}{4}$ **(e)** None of these

    1—Ans: b

47. The average cost $\overline{C}$ for producing x units of a product is given by $\overline{C} = \dfrac{4000}{x} + \dfrac{1}{4}$.
Determine the number of units that must be produced to obtain the average cost of \$2.25 per unit.

    (a) 500   **(b)** 200   **(c)** 1600   **(d)** 2000   **(e)** None of these

    2—Ans: d

48. The markup rate for an item that sells for \$560 is given by

$$\text{Markup rate} = \dfrac{560}{C} - 1$$

where C is the wholesale cost. Find the wholesale cost if the markup rate is 75%.

    (a) \$224   **(b)** \$73.68   **(c)** \$320   **(d)** \$319.43   **(e)** None of these

    2—Ans: c

49. Solve: $\dfrac{5}{x} = \dfrac{2}{x+3} - \dfrac{3}{x}$.

    2—Ans: -4

50. Solve: $\dfrac{5}{x} + \dfrac{2}{x+3} = \dfrac{3}{x}$.

    2—Ans: $-\dfrac{3}{2}$

51. Solve: $\dfrac{1}{x-2} + \dfrac{1}{x+3} = \dfrac{17}{x^2+x-6}$.

    2—Ans: 8

52. Solve: $\dfrac{1}{x+3} - \dfrac{4}{x+4} = \dfrac{5}{x^2+7x+12}$.

    2—Ans: $-\dfrac{13}{3}$

53. Solve: $\dfrac{3}{x-2} = 5 - \dfrac{2}{x-2}$.

1—Ans: 3

54. Solve: $\dfrac{4}{x+2} = 6 + \dfrac{1}{x+2}$.

1—Ans: $-\dfrac{3}{2}$

55. Determine a number that can be added to its reciprocal to obtain $\dfrac{25}{12}$.

(a) $\dfrac{5}{6}$ (b) $\dfrac{3}{4}$ (c) 2   (d) $\dfrac{13}{12}$ (e) $\dfrac{4}{7}$

2—Ans: b

56. Determine a number that can be added to its reciprocal to obtain $\dfrac{34}{15}$.

(a) $\dfrac{5}{3}$ (b) $\dfrac{16}{15}$ (c) $\dfrac{15}{9}$ (d) $\dfrac{17}{15}$ (e) $\dfrac{33}{15}$

2—Ans: a

57. Determine a number that can be added to its reciprocal to obtain $\dfrac{41}{20}$.

2—Form: 8C—Ans: $\dfrac{4}{5}$ or $\dfrac{5}{4}$

58. Determine a number that can be added to its reciprocal to obtain $\dfrac{29}{10}$.

2—Ans: $\dfrac{2}{5}$ or $\dfrac{5}{2}$

59. Solve: $\dfrac{x}{3} = \dfrac{2}{7}$.

(a) -1 (b) $\dfrac{5}{7}$ (c) $\dfrac{6}{7}$ (d) $\dfrac{7}{6}$ (e) 42

1—Ans: c

60. Solve: $\dfrac{3}{x} = \dfrac{2}{9}$.

(a) 9   (b) $\dfrac{2}{3}$ (c) $\dfrac{2}{27}$ (d) 6   (e) $\dfrac{27}{2}$

1—Ans: e

61. Solve: $\dfrac{x}{4} = \dfrac{4}{x}$.

1—Ans: -4 and 4

62. Solve: $\dfrac{5}{11} = \dfrac{x}{3}$.

1—Ans: $\dfrac{15}{11}$

63. Use a graphing utility to determine the x-intercepts of the graph of the equation
$y = \dfrac{9}{x - 5} + \dfrac{6}{x}$.

  (a) $(3, 0)$ **(b)** $(0, 3)$ **(c)** $(0, 0)$ **(d)** $(2, 0)$ **(e)** There are none

1—T—Form: 8A—Ans: d

64. Use a graphing utility to determine the x-intercepts of the graph of the equation
$y = \dfrac{1}{x - 6} + \dfrac{2}{x}$.

  (a) $(0, 0)$ **(b)** $(4, 0)$ **(c)** $\left(\dfrac{1}{2}, 0\right)$ **(d)** $\left(0, \dfrac{1}{2}\right)$ **(e)** $(0, 4)$

1—T—Form: 8B—Ans: b

65. Use a graphing utility to determine the x-intercepts of the graph of the equation
$y = x - 3 + \dfrac{2}{x}$.

2—T—Form: 8C—Ans: $(1, 0)$ and $(2, 0)$

66. Use a graphing utility to determine the x-intercepts of the graph of the equation
$y = x - 5 + \dfrac{6}{x}$.

2—T—Ans: $(2, 0)$ and $(3, 0)$

67. Use a graphing utility to determine the x-intercepts of the graph of the equation
$y = x + 3 - \dfrac{10}{x}$.

1—T—Ans: $(-5, 0)$ and $(2, 0)$

68. Use a graphing utility to determine the x-intercepts of the graph of the equation
$y = x + 1 - \dfrac{12}{x}$.

1—T—Ans: $(-4, 0)$ and $(3, 0)$

69. Use a graphing utility to determine any *x*-intercepts. Then set $y = 0$ and solve the resulting equation to confirm your results.

$$y = \frac{x - 1}{x + 2}$$

1—T—Ans: $(1, 0)$

70. Use a graphing utility to determine any *x*-intercepts. Then set $y = 0$ and solve the resulting equation to confirm your results.

$$y = \frac{x + 3}{x + 5}$$

1—T—Ans: $(-3, 0)$

71. The sum of 3 times a number and 2 times its reciprocal is $\frac{55}{3}$. Find the number.

2—Ans: 6 or $\frac{1}{9}$

72. The sum of 4 times a number and 3 times its reciprocal is $\frac{103}{5}$. Find the number.

2—Ans: 5 or $\frac{3}{20}$

Section 8.5   Graphs of Rational Functions

1. Find the domain of $f(x) = \dfrac{x - 1}{x - 2}$.

  (a) $(-\infty, 1) \cup (1, \infty)$ **(b)** $(-\infty, 2) \cup (2, \infty)$ **(c)** $(-\infty, -2) \cup (-2, \infty)$

  (d) $(-\infty, 1) \cup (1, 2) \cup (2, \infty)$ **(e)** None of these

1—Ans: b

2. Find the domain of $f(x) = \dfrac{x + 3}{(x + 3)(x - 1)}$.

  (a) $(-\infty, -3) \cup (-3, 1) \cup (1, \infty)$ **(b)** $(-\infty, 1) \cup (1, \infty)$

  (c) $(-\infty, \infty)$ **(d)** $(-\infty, -3) \cup (-3, \infty)$

  (e) None of these

1—Ans: a

3. Find the domain of $f(x) = \dfrac{1}{x^2 + x}$.

  (a) $(-\infty, \infty)$ **(b)** $(-\infty, 0) \cup (0, \infty)$

  (c) $(-\infty, -1) \cup (-1, \infty)$ **(d)** $(-\infty, -1) \cup (-1, 0) \cup (0, \infty)$

  (e) None of these

1—Ans: d

4. Find the domain of $f(x) = \dfrac{3 + 4x}{1 - 2x}$.

(a) $\left(-\infty, -\dfrac{3}{4}\right) \cup \left(-\dfrac{3}{4}, \infty\right)$

(b) $\left(-\infty, -\dfrac{3}{4}\right) \cup \left(-\dfrac{3}{4}, \dfrac{1}{2}\right) \cup \left(\dfrac{1}{2}, \infty\right)$

(c) $(-\infty, \infty)$

(d) $\left(-\infty, \dfrac{1}{2}\right) \cup \left(\dfrac{1}{2}, \infty\right)$

(e) None of these

1—Ans: d

5. Find the domain of $f(x) = \dfrac{x}{x^2 + 4}$.

1—Ans: $(-\infty, \infty)$

6. Find the domain of $f(x) = \dfrac{3x}{x^2 - x - 6}$.

1—Ans: $(-\infty, -2) \cup (-2, 3) \cup (3, \infty)$

7. Find all intercepts: $f(x) = \dfrac{x - 1}{x + 3}$.

(a) $(1, 0), \left(0, -\dfrac{1}{3}\right)$

(b) $(1, 0)$

(c) $(-3, 0), (1, 0)$

(d) $(-3, 0), \left(0, -\dfrac{1}{3}\right)$

(e) None of these

1—Ans: a

8. Find all intercepts: $f(x) = \dfrac{-4x}{x^2 + 1}$.

(a) $(0, 0), (-1, 0), (1, 0)$

(b) $(-1, 0), (1, 0)$

(c) $(0, 0)$

(d) $(0, -4)$

(e) None of these

1—Ans: c

9. Find all intercepts: $f(x) = \dfrac{3x - 2}{x}$.

1—Ans: $\left(\dfrac{2}{3}, 0\right)$

10. Find all intercepts: $g(t) = \dfrac{1}{t + 3} - 1$.

2—Ans: $(-2, 0), \left(0, -\dfrac{2}{3}\right)$

11. Find the vertical asymptote: $f(x) = \dfrac{7}{x+2}$.

    (a) $x = -2$ **(b)** $x = 2$ **(c)** $(0, -2)$ **(d)** $y = 0$ **(e)** None of these

    1—Ans: a

12. Find the vertical asymptote(s): $f(x) = \dfrac{1}{(x+2)(x-5)}$.

    (a) $x = 2, x = -5$ **(b)** $y = 0$ **(c)** $x = -2, x = 5$

    (d) $y = 1$ **(e)** None of these

    1—Form: 8A—Ans: c

13. Find the vertical asymptote(s): $f(x) = \dfrac{x}{(x+1)^2}$.

    (a) $x = 0$ **(b)** $x = -1, x = 1$ **(c)** $x = -1$

    (d) $y = 0$ **(e)** None of these

    1—Form: 8B—Ans: c

14. Find the vertical asymptote(s): $f(x) = \dfrac{3x^2}{x^2 + 9}$.

    (a) $x = 0$ **(b)** $y = 3$ **(c)** $x = 3, x = -3$

    (d) $y = \dfrac{1}{3}$ **(e)** None of these

    1—Ans: e

15. Find the vertical asymptote(s): $f(x) = \dfrac{x-3}{x+2}$.

    1—Ans: $x = -2$

16. Find the vertical asymptote(s): $f(x) = \dfrac{2x+1}{x-3}$.

    1—Form: 8C—Ans: $x = 3$

17. Find the horizontal asymptote (if any): $f(x) = \dfrac{-3}{x+4}$.

    (a) $x = -3$ **(b)** $y = 0$ **(c)** $x = -4$ **(d)** $y = -\dfrac{3}{4}$ **(e)** None of these

    1—Ans: b

18. Find the horizontal asymptote (if any): $f(x) = \dfrac{x^2 + 1}{x - 2}$.

   (a) $x = 2$ **(b)** $y = 1$ **(c)** $y = -\dfrac{1}{2}$ **(d)** $x = 1$ **(e)** None of these

   1—Ans: e

19. Find the horizontal asymptote (if any): $f(x) = \dfrac{5x}{x - 1}$.

   (a) $x = 1$ **(b)** $x = 0$ **(c)** $y = 0$ **(d)** $y = 5$ **(e)** None of these

   2—Form: 8A—Ans: d

20. Find the horizontal asymptote (if any): $f(x) = \dfrac{2x + 7}{3 - x}$.

   (a) $x = 3$ **(b)** $y = \dfrac{2}{3}$ **(c)** $y = -2$ **(d)** $x = -\dfrac{7}{2}$ **(e)** None of these

   2—Form: 8B—Ans: c

21. Find the horizontal asymptote (if any): $f(x) = \dfrac{3x - 16}{2x - 7}$.

   1—Ans: $y = \dfrac{3}{2}$

22. Find the horizontal asymptote (if any): $f(x) = \dfrac{2x - 5}{1 - 3x}$.

   1—Form: 8C—Ans: $y = -\dfrac{2}{3}$

23. Which of the following functions has a horizontal asymptote at $y = 2$?

   (a) $\dfrac{x - 2}{3x - 5}$ **(b)** $\dfrac{2x}{x^2 - 2}$ **(c)** $\dfrac{2x^2 - 6x + 1}{1 + x^2}$

   (d) $\dfrac{2x - 1}{x^2 + 1}$ **(e)** $\dfrac{2x + 1}{1 - x}$

   1—Ans: c

24. Which of the following functions has a horizontal asymptote at $y = -\dfrac{1}{2}$?

   (a) $f(x) = \dfrac{x^2}{1 - 2x^2}$ **(b)** $f(x) = \dfrac{-x^2}{2 + x^2}$ **(c)** $f(x) = \dfrac{2x^2 - 6x + 1}{1 + x^2}$

   (d) $f(x) = \dfrac{x - 1}{2x^2 + 1}$ **(e)** None of these

   1—Ans: a

25. Use a graphing utility to match the graph with the correct function.

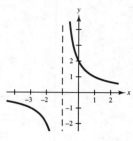

   (a) $f(x) = \dfrac{1}{x-1}$ **(b)** $f(x) = \dfrac{2}{x+1}$ **(c)** $f(x) = \dfrac{2}{x-1}$

   (d) $f(x) = \dfrac{x+2}{x+1}$ **(e)** None of these

   2—T—Ans: b

26. Use a graphing utility to match the graph with the correct function.

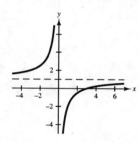

   (a) $f(x) = \dfrac{x-3}{x}$ **(b)** $f(x) = \dfrac{x+3}{x}$ **(c)** $f(x) = \dfrac{x-3}{x-1}$

   (d) $f(x) = \dfrac{x}{x-3}$ **(e)** None of these

   2—T—Form: 8A—Ans: b *a)*

27. Use a graphing utility to match the graph with the correct function.

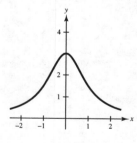

   (a) $f(x) = \dfrac{0}{x^2+1}$ **(b)** $f(x) = \dfrac{3}{x^2+1}$ **(c)** $f(x) = \dfrac{x-3}{x^2+1}$

   (d) $f(x) = \dfrac{3}{x^2-1}$ **(e)** None of these

   2—T—Ans: b

28. Use a graphing utility to match the graph with the correct function.

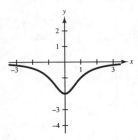

(a) $f(x) = \dfrac{x - 2}{x + 1}$ **(b)** $f(x) = \dfrac{2}{x^2 + 1}$ **(c)** $f(x) = \dfrac{-2}{x^2 + 1}$

(d) $f(x) = \dfrac{-2}{x^2 - 1}$ **(e)** $f(x) = \dfrac{x + 2}{x - 1}$

2—T—Form: 8B—Ans: c

29. Sketch the graph of the rational function: $f(x) = \dfrac{2}{4 - x}$. Find intercepts, vertical asymptotes, and horizontal asymptotes.

2—Form: 8C—Ans: Intercept: $\left(0, \dfrac{1}{2}\right)$

Vertical asymptote: $x = 4$

Horizontal asymptote: $y = 0$

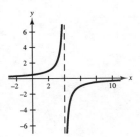

30. Sketch the graph of the rational function: $f(x) = \dfrac{2x}{4 - x}$. Find intercepts, vertical asymptotes, and horizontal asymptotes.

2—Ans: Intercept: $(0, 0)$

Vertical asymptote: $x = 4$

Horizontal asymptote: $y = -2$

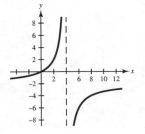

31. Find all intercepts: $g(t) = \dfrac{1}{t-5} - 2$

(a) $\left(0, -\dfrac{15}{11}\right), \left(\dfrac{2}{11}, 0\right)$

(b) $(5, 2)$

(c) $(5, 0), (0, -2)$

(d) $\left(0, -\dfrac{11}{5}\right), \left(\dfrac{11}{2}, 0\right)$

(e) None of these

2—Ans: d

32. Find all intercepts: $f(x) = 1 - \dfrac{8}{x^3}$

(a) $(0, 1)$

(b) $(2, 0)$

(c) $(8, 0)$

(d) $(2, 0), (-2, 0)$

(e) None of these

2—Ans: b

33. Which of the following functions has a horizontal asymptote at $y = -1$?

(a) $f(x) = \dfrac{-2x^2}{1 - 2x^2}$

(b) $f(x) = \dfrac{-x^2}{2 + x^2}$

(c) $f(x) = \dfrac{2x^2 - 6x + 1}{1 + 2x^2}$

(d) $f(x) = \dfrac{x - 1}{2x^2 + 1}$

(e) None of these

2—Ans: b

34. Match the graph with the correct function.

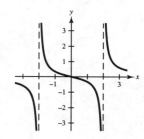

(a) $f(x) = \dfrac{1}{x^2 - 4}$

(b) $f(x) = \dfrac{x^2}{x^2 - 4}$

(c) $f(x) = \dfrac{x}{x^2 + 4}$

(d) $f(x) = \dfrac{x}{x^2 - 4}$

(e) None of these

2—Ans: d

35. Match the graph with the correct function.

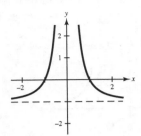

(a) $f(x) = \dfrac{1}{x^2 - 1}$ **(b)** $f(x) = \dfrac{1}{x^2} + 1$ **(c)** $f(x) = \dfrac{1}{x^2 + 1}$

(d) $f(x) = \dfrac{1}{x^2} - 1$ **(e)** None of these

2—Ans: d

36. Match the rational function with the correct graph: $f(x) = \dfrac{3 + x}{x - 1}$

(a)

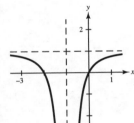

(b)

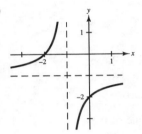

(c)

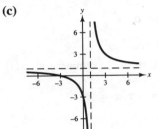

(d)

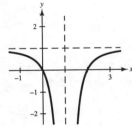

(e) None of these

2—Ans: c

37. Which of the following is the correct sketch of the graph of the function:

$$f(x) = \frac{1}{(x-2)^2}?$$

(a)

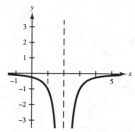

(b)

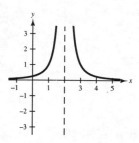

(c)

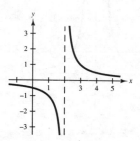

(d)

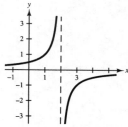

(e) None of these

1—Ans: b

38. Find the vertical asymptote(s): $f(x) = x + 2 - \dfrac{3}{x}$

(a) $x = -2, x = 0$ **(b)** $y = 0$ **(c)** $y = -2$

(d) $x = 0$ **(e)** None of these

1—Ans: d

39. Find the horizontal asymptote(s): $f(x) = \dfrac{x - 1}{x^2 + 9}$

(a) $y = 1$ **(b)** $y = 0$ **(c)** $x = 1$ **(d)** $x = \pm 1$ **(e)** None of these

1—Ans: b

40. Find the horizontal asymptote(s): $f(x) = \dfrac{x^2 - 4}{x^2 - 9}$

(a) $y = \pm 3$ **(b)** $x = \pm 3$ **(c)** $y = 1$ **(d)** $y = 0$ **(e)** $x = \pm 2, \pm 3$

1—Ans: c

41. Sketch the graph of the rational function $f(x) = \dfrac{3x}{x^3 + x}$. Find intercept(s), vertical and horizontal asymptotes.

    2—Ans: Intercepts: None

          Vertical asymptote: None

          Horizontal asymptote: $y = 0$

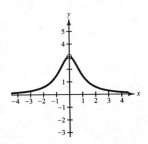

42. Sketch the graph of the rational function $f(x) = \dfrac{x}{x^2 - 2x}$. Find intercept(s), vertical and horizontal asymptotes.

    2—Ans: Intercepts: None

          Vertical asymptote: $x = 2$

          Horizontal asymptote: $y = 0$

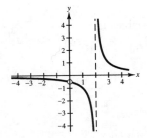

43. Sketch the graph of the rational function $f(x) = \dfrac{3x}{x^2 + 1}$. Find intercept(s), vertical and horizontal asymptotes.

    2—Ans: Intercepts: $(0, 0)$

          Vertical asymptote: None

          Horizontal asymptote: $y = 0$

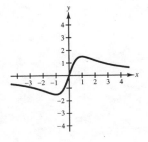

Section 8.6   Variation

1. Which statement is not consistent with the others?

    (a) y varies directly as x.

    (b) y varies inversely as x.

    (c) y is directly proportional to x.

    (d) $y = kx$ for some constant k.

    (e) x varies directly as y.

    1—Ans: b

2. The mathematical model for the statement "y varies directly as x" is:

    (a) $y = \dfrac{k}{x}$

    (b) $y = k + x$

    (c) $y = kx$

    (d) $y = ax + b$

    (e) None of these

    1—Ans: c

3. Write a mathematical model for the statement "y varies directly as t."

    1—Ans: $y = kt$, where k is the constant of proportionality.

4. Write a mathematical model for the statement "S varies directly as T."

    1—Ans: $S = kT$, where k is the constant of proportionality.

5. S varies directly as t; and $S = 10$ when $t = \frac{1}{2}$. The equation relating the variables is:

    (a) $S = \frac{1}{2}t$

    (b) $S = 20t$

    (c) $S = 10\left(\frac{1}{2}t\right)$

    (d) $10S = \frac{1}{2}t$

    (e) None of these

    1—Ans: b

6. R varies directly as V; and $R = \frac{5}{2}$ when $V = \frac{1}{3}$. The equation relating the variables is:

    (a) $R = \frac{5}{6}V$

    (b) $R = \frac{6}{5}V$

    (c) $R = \frac{2}{15}V$

    (d) $R = \frac{15}{2}V$

    (e) None of these

    1—Ans: d

7. W varies directly as r; and $W = \frac{7}{3}$ when $r = \frac{3}{5}$. The equation relating the variables is:

    (a) $W = \frac{35}{9}r$

    (b) $W = \frac{7}{5}$

    (c) $W = \frac{3}{5}r$

    (d) $W = \frac{44}{15}r$

    (e) None of these

    1—Ans: a

8. Y varies directly as x; and $Y = \frac{5}{9}$ when $x = \frac{10}{3}$. The equation relating the variables is:

(a) $Y = \frac{50}{27}x$ (b) $Y = \frac{35}{9}x$ (c) $Y = \frac{1}{6}x$

(d) $Y = 6x$ (e) None of these

1—**Ans:** c

9. P varies directly as x; and $P = \frac{50}{3}$ when $x = \frac{25}{12}$. Write the equation relating the variables.

1—**Ans:** $P = 8x$

10. Q varies directly as p; and $Q = \frac{18}{5}$ when $p = \frac{27}{25}$. Write the equation relating the variables.

1—**Ans:** $Q = \frac{10}{3}p$

11. $z = kxy$ is best described as an example of:

(a) Joint variation   (b) Inverse variation   (c) Joint and inverse variation

(d) Direct variation as a power   (e) None of these

1—**Ans:** a

12. $x = \dfrac{k}{y}$ is best described as an example of:

(a) Joint variation   (b) Inverse variation   (c) Joint and inverse variation

(d) Direct variation as a power   (e) None of these

1—**Ans:** b

13. Write a mathematical model (equation) for the given statement, using k as the constant of proportionality.

"W varies directly as u and inversely as v."

1—**Ans:** $W = k\dfrac{u}{v}$

14. Write a mathematical model (equation) for the given statement, using k as the constant of proportionality.

"F varies inversely as the square of r."

1—**Ans:** $F = \dfrac{k}{r^2}$

15. Write a mathematical model (equation) for the given statement, using k as the constant of proportionality.

"M varies directly as p and q."

1—**Ans:** $M = kpq$

16. Write a mathematical model (equation) for the given statement, using k as the constant of proportionality.

"R varies inversely as the cube of t."

1—Ans: $R = kt^3$

17. R is directly proportional to the square root of p. R is equal to $\dfrac{17}{5}$ when $p = 25$. The equation relating the variables is:

(a) $R = \dfrac{25}{17}\sqrt{p}$ (b) $R = \dfrac{17}{25}p^2$ (c) $R = \dfrac{17}{25}\sqrt{p}$ (d) $R = \dfrac{17}{\sqrt{p}}$ (e) None of these

1—Ans: c

18. W is directly proportional to the cube of x. W is equal to $\dfrac{15}{8}$ when $x = \dfrac{3}{4}$. The equation relating the variables is:

(a) $W = \dfrac{40}{9}x^3$ (b) $W = \dfrac{40}{9x^3}$ (c) $W = \dfrac{5}{2}\sqrt[3]{x}$ (d) $W = \dfrac{9}{40}x^3$ (e) None of these

1—Ans: a

19. M is directly proportional to the 4th power of S. When S is equal to 2, M is equal to $\frac{32}{25}$. Give the equation relating the variables.

1—Ans: $M = \frac{2}{25}S^4$

20. P is directly proportional to the cube root of x. When x is equals 64, P is equal to $\frac{7}{8}$. Give the equation relating the variables.

1—Ans: $P = \frac{7}{32}\sqrt[3]{x}$

21. F is inversely proportional to t. When $t = \dfrac{5}{2}$, F equals $\dfrac{7}{4}$. The equation relating the variables is:

(a) $F = \dfrac{7}{10t}$ (b) $F = \dfrac{10}{7t}$ (c) $F = \dfrac{35}{8t}$ (d) $F = \dfrac{7}{10}t$ (e) None of these

1—Ans: c

22. G is inversely proportional to the square root of t. G is equal to $\dfrac{5}{8}$ when t is equal to 49. The equation relating the variables is:

(a) $G = \dfrac{5}{56}\sqrt{t}$ (b) $G = \dfrac{35}{8\sqrt{t}}$ (c) $G = \dfrac{56}{5\sqrt{t}}$ (d) $G = \dfrac{35}{8}t$ (e) None of these

1—Ans: b

23. y is inversely proportional to x. y is equal to $\frac{3}{4}$ when x is equal to $\frac{2}{3}$. Find the value of y when $x = 4$.

   1—Ans: $y = \frac{1}{8}$

24. y is inversely proportional to x. y is equal to $\frac{4}{3}$ when x is equal to $\frac{21}{10}$. Find the value of y when $x = \frac{7}{15}$.

   1—Ans: $y = 6$

25. F varies jointly as x and y. F equals $\frac{1}{6}$ when $x = \frac{3}{8}$ and $y = \frac{5}{12}$. When $x = \frac{3}{4}$ and $y = \frac{5}{8}$ the value of F is:

   (a) 2   **(b)** $\frac{8}{9}$ **(c)** $\frac{9}{8}$ **(d)** $\frac{1}{2}$ **(e)** None of these

   2—Form: 8A—Ans: d

26. G varies jointly as x and y. G equals $\frac{2}{3}$ when $x = \frac{1}{2}$ and $y = \frac{1}{3}$. When $x = \frac{3}{2}$ and $y = \frac{1}{4}$ the value of G is:

   (a) $\frac{4}{9}$ **(b)** $\frac{2}{3}$ **(c)** $\frac{3}{2}$ **(d)** $\frac{3}{32}$ **(e)** None of these

   2—Form: 8B—Ans: c

27. I varies jointly as P and t. $I = 52.5$ when $P = 1000$ and $t = \frac{3}{4}$. Find the value of I when $P = 2500$ and $t = \frac{1}{2}$.

   2—Ans: 87.5

28. I varies jointly as P and t. $I = 90$ when $P = 2000$ and $t = \frac{5}{6}$. Find the value of I when $P = 3000$ and $t = \frac{1}{3}$.

   2—Ans: 54

29. I varies jointly as P and t. $I = 22.5$ when $P = 1500$ and $t = \frac{1}{4}$. Find the value of I when $P = 3000$ and $t = \frac{5}{12}$.

   2—Form: 8C—Ans: 75

30. I varies jointly as P and t. $I = 63$ when $P = 1500$ and $t = \frac{2}{3}$. Find the value of I when $P = 2000$ and $t = \frac{1}{2}$.

   2—Ans: 63

31. Q varies directly as x and inversely as y^2. Q is equal to 40 when x is 16 and y is 12. The equation relating the variables is:

   (a) $Q = \dfrac{40x^2}{9y}$ **(b)** $Q = \dfrac{5}{24}xy^2$ **(c)** $Q = \dfrac{360x}{y^2}$

   (d) $Q = \dfrac{160x}{3y}$ **(e)** None of these

   2—Ans: c

32. Q varies directly as x^2 and inversely as y. Q is equal to 30 when x is 12 and y is 20. The equation relating the variables is:

(a) $Q = 50\dfrac{x}{y}$ (b) $Q = \dfrac{25x^2}{6y}$ (c) $Q = \dfrac{6}{25}\dfrac{x^2}{y}$

(d) $Q = 18xy$ (e) None of these

2—Ans: b

33. P varies directly as T and inversely as V. P is equal to 0.8 when $T = 300$ and $V = 500$. Find the value of P when $T = 360$ and $V = 400$.

2—Ans: 1.2

34. F varies directly as M and inversely as R^2. F is equal to 10 when $M = 20$ and $R = 4$. Find the value of F when $M = 50$ and $R = 5$.

2—Ans: 16

35. According to Hook's Law the force F in pounds, required to stretch a spring x inches is directly proportional to x. If 20 pounds of force stretches a spring three inches, find the force required to stretch it five inches.

(a) $33\frac{2}{3}$ lbs   (b) 12 lbs   (c) 60 lbs   (d) 100 lbs   (e) None of these

1—Ans: a

36. The simple interest I earned by a principal of P dollars is jointly proportional to the time, t, and the principal, P. $50 is earned in three months by a principal of $2500. Find the amount of interest earned by $4500 in eight months.

(a) $90   (b) $200   (c) $360   (d) $240   (e) None of these

1—Ans: d

37. Neglecting air resistance, the distance d that an object falls varies directly as the square of the time t it has been falling. If the object falls 64 feet in two seconds, find how far it will have fallen after five seconds.

(a) 160 feet   (b) 400 feet   (c) 240 feet   (d) 320 feet   (e) None of these

1—Ans: b

38. The power P generated by a wind turbine varies directly as the cube of the wind speed w. The turbine generates 810 watts of power in a 30 miles-per-hour wind. Find the power it will generate in a 50 miles-per-hour wind.

(a) 1350 watts   (b) 2250 watts   (c) 3750 watts   (d) 4050 watts   (e) None of these

1—Ans: c

39. According to Hook's Law the force F in pounds, required to stretch a spring x inches is directly proportional to x. If 25 pounds of force stretches a spring four inches, find the force required to stretch the spring ten inches.

1—Ans: $\frac{250}{4}$ or 62.5 lbs

40. The simple interest I earned by a principal of P dollars is jointly proportional to the time t and the principal P. \$50 is earned in three months by a principal of \$2500. Find the amount of interest earned by \$6000 in nine months.

    2—Ans: \$360

41. Write a mathematical model for the statement "A varies jointly with x and the square of y."

    (a) $A = k(x + y^2)$ **(b)** $A = kxy^2$ **(c)** $A = kx\sqrt{y}$

    (d) $A = \dfrac{kx}{y^2}$ **(e)** None of these

    1—Form: 8A—Ans: b

42. Write a mathematical model for the statement "W varies directly with the square root of x."

    (a) $W = k\sqrt{x}$ **(b)** $W = kx^2$ **(c)** $W = k + x^2$

    (d) $W = \dfrac{k}{\sqrt{x}}$ **(e)** None of these

    1—Form: 8B—Ans: a

43. Find the value of the constant of proportionality for a mathematical model that relates S and t if S varies inversely as t and $S = 12$ when $t = \frac{3}{2}$.

    (a) 18   **(b)** 8   **(c)** $\frac{1}{8}$ **(d)** $\frac{1}{18}$ **(e)** None of these

    1—Form: 8A—Ans: a

44. Find the value of the constant of proportionality for a mathematical model that relates S and t if S varies inversely as the square t and $S = 12$ when $t = \frac{3}{2}$.

    (a) 18   **(b)** 27   **(c)** $\frac{16}{3}$ **(d)** $\frac{1}{18}$ **(e)** None of these

    1—Form: 8B—Ans: b

45. Write a mathematical model for the statement "A varies jointly as x and y and inversely as z."

    2—Ans: $A = \dfrac{kxy}{z}$

46. Write a mathematical model for the statement "A is inversely proportional to the square root of x."

    1—Form: 8C—Ans: $A = \dfrac{k}{\sqrt{x}}$

47. The demand D for a certain product varies inversely with the price p.

    a.   Write a mathematical model for this statement.

    b.   Find the constant of proportionality if $D = 600$ when $p = \$60$.

    c.   Find the demand when the price is \$90.

    d.   What price should be charged in order for the demand to be 1000?

    2—Ans: a. $D = \dfrac{k}{p}$ **b.** 36,000 **c.** 400 **d.** \$36

48. The power P generated by a wind turbine varies directly as the cube of the wind speed w.

    a.   Write a mathematical model for this statement.

    b.   Find the constant of proportionality if $P = 800$ watts when $w = 20$ miles-per-hour.

    c.   Find the power when the wind speed is 30 miles-per-hour.

    d.   Find the wind speed when the power is 12.5 watts.

    2—Form: 8C—Ans: a. $P = kw^3$ **b.** $\frac{1}{10}$ **c.** 2700 **d.** 5mph

49. Determine whether the variation model is of the form $y = kx$ or $y = \dfrac{k}{x}$ and find k.

x	10	20	30	40	50
y	2.5	5	7.5	10	12.5

    2—Ans: $y = kx$ and $k = \dfrac{1}{4}$

50. Determine whether the variation model is of the form $y = kx$ or $y = \dfrac{k}{x}$ and find k.

x	10	20	30	40	50
y	-0.06	-0.03	-0.02	-0.015	-0.012

    2—Ans: $y = \dfrac{k}{x}$ and $k = -0.6$

51. y is directly proportional to x and $y = 35$ when $x = 5$. Find the constant of proportionality.

    (a) $\frac{1}{7}$ **(b)** 7   **(c)** 175   **(d)** $\frac{1}{175}$ **(e)** None of these

    1—Ans: b

52. y is directly proportional to x and $y = 14$ when $x = 49$. Find the constant of proportionality.

    (a) 3   **(b)** 686   **(c)** $\frac{7}{2}$ **(d)** $\frac{2}{7}$ **(e)** None of these

    1—Ans: d

53. *x* is directly proportional to *y* and $x = 3$ when $y = 10$. Find the linear model that relates *x* and *y*.

    (a) $3x = 10y$ **(b)** $10x = 3y$ **(c)** $xy = 30$ **(d)** $\dfrac{x}{y} = 30$ **(e)** None of these

    1—Ans: b

54. *y* is directly proportional to *x* and $y = 2.4$ when $x = 15$. Find the linear model that relates *y* and *x*.

    (a) $y = 0.16x$ **(b)** $y = 0.625x$ **(c)** $y = 6.25$ **(d)** $y = 1.6x$ **(e)** None of these

    1—Ans: a

CHAPTER 9
Radicals and Complex Numbers

Section 9.1   Radicals and Rational Exponents

1. Choose the statement which is not valid.

    (a) -6 is a square root of 36.   (b) 2 is a sixth root of 64.   (c) -4 is a cube root of 64.

    (d) -3 is a fourth root of 81.   (e) -8 is a square root of 64.

    1—Ans: c

2. Choose the statement which is not valid.

    (a) -2 is a fifth root of 32.   (b) -4 is a cube root of -64.   (c) -5 is a square root of 25.

    (d) 3 is a fourth root of 81.   (e) -2 is a sixth root of 64.

    1—Ans: a

3. Fill in the blank space with the appropriate real number or words.

    Because $13^3 = 2197$, 13 is called the ▨▨▨▨▨▨ of 2197.

    1—Ans: Cube root

4. Fill in the blank space with the appropriate real number or words.

    Because $(-2)^6 = 64$, -2 is called a ▨▨▨▨▨▨ of 64.

    1—Ans: Sixth root

5. Which of the following square roots is not a real number?

    (a) $\sqrt{-2^3}$ (b) $\sqrt{(-7)^2}$ (c) $\sqrt{\frac{9}{16}}$ (d) $\sqrt{60}$ (e) None of these

    1—Ans: a

6. Which of the following square roots is not a real number?

    (a) $\sqrt{17}$ (b) $\sqrt{-64}$ (c) $\sqrt{(-5)^2}$ (d) $\sqrt{\frac{4}{25}}$ (e) None of these

    1—Ans: b

7. Find the principal cube root of -64.

    1—Ans: -4

8. Find the principal fourth root of $(-9)^2$.

    1—Ans: 3

9. Choose the statement which is not correct.

(a) $\sqrt{0} = 0$ (b) $\sqrt[3]{-64} = -4$ (c) $\sqrt[5]{32} = 2$ (d) $\sqrt{\frac{4}{25}} = \frac{2}{5}$ (e) $\sqrt{16} = -4$

1—Ans: e

10. Choose the statement which is not correct.

(a) $\sqrt{\frac{100}{49}} = \frac{10}{7}$ (b) $\sqrt{-16} = -4$ (c) $\sqrt[3]{0} = 0$

(d) $\sqrt[6]{64} = 2$ (e) $\sqrt{-4}$ is not a real number.

1—Ans: b

11. Evaluate $\sqrt{0.16}$ without using a calculator.

1—Ans: 0.4

12. Evaluate $\sqrt[3]{-\frac{27}{64}}$ without using a calculator.

1—Ans: $-\frac{3}{4}$

13. Find the value of $-\sqrt[4]{\frac{1}{625}}$.

(a) $\frac{1}{5}$ (b) -5 (c) $-\frac{1}{5}$ (d) 5 (e) 0.5

1—Ans: c

14. Find the value of $\dfrac{-1}{\sqrt[3]{-125}}$.

(a) $\frac{1}{5}$ (b) 5 (c) $-\frac{1}{5}$ (d) -5 (e) 0.5

1—Ans: a

15. Find the value of $\dfrac{1}{\sqrt[6]{64}}$.

(a) $\frac{1}{5}$ (b) 5 (c) $-\frac{1}{5}$ (d) -5 (e) 0.5

1—Ans: e

16. Find the value of $\sqrt{0.04}$.

(a) -5 (b) $\frac{1}{5}$ (c) $-\frac{1}{5}$ (d) 5 (e) 0.5

1—Ans: b

17. Find $\sqrt[3]{-0.027}$ without using a calculator.

1—Ans: -0.3

18. Find $\sqrt[3]{0.125}$ without using a calculator.

1—Ans: 0.5

19. Which of the following square roots is a rational number?

(a) $\sqrt{\frac{9}{4}}$ (b) $\sqrt{\frac{9}{14}}$ (c) $\sqrt{3^3}$ (d) $\sqrt{200}$ (e) $\sqrt{\frac{49}{27}}$

1—Ans: a

20. Which of the following square roots is an irrational number?

(a) $\sqrt{\frac{16}{49}}$ (b) $\sqrt{(4^3)}$ (c) $-\sqrt{0.25}$ (d) $\sqrt{200}$ (e) $\sqrt{0.09}$

1—Ans: d

21. Determine whether $\sqrt[3]{0.008}$ is a rational or an irrational number and state the reason.

1—Ans: Rational, $0.2 = \frac{1}{5}$ is the cube root of 0.008.

22. Determine whether $\sqrt{900}$ is a rational or an irrational number and state the reason.

1—Ans: Rational, 900 is a perfect square.

23. $(16)^{-3/4} =$

(a) 12   (b) $\frac{1}{12}$ (c) -12 (d) 8   (e) $\frac{1}{8}$

2—Ans: e

24. $(-8)^{-2/3} =$

(a) $\frac{16}{3}$ (b) $-\frac{3}{16}$ (c) $\frac{1}{4}$ (d) $-\frac{1}{4}$ (e) 4

2—Ans: c

25. $(25)^{-3/2} =$

(a) $\frac{1}{125}$ (b) 125   (c) $-\frac{75}{2}$ (d) -125 (e) $-\frac{1}{125}$

2—Ans: a

26. $\left(\frac{64}{27}\right)^{-2/3} =$

(a) $-\frac{128}{81}$ (b) $\frac{9}{16}$ (c) $\frac{81}{128}$ (d) $\frac{16}{9}$ (e) $-\frac{9}{16}$

2—Ans: b

27. Evaluate $\left(\frac{125}{27}\right)^{-2/3}$ without using a calculator.

2—Ans: $\frac{9}{25}$

28. Evaluate $\left(\frac{9}{100}\right)^{-3/2}$ without using a calculator.

2—Ans: $\frac{1000}{27}$

29. Evaluate $\left(\frac{81}{16}\right)^{-3/4}$ without using a calculator.

2—Ans: $\frac{8}{27}$

30. Evaluate $\left(-\frac{27}{8}\right)^{-4/3}$ without using a calculator.

2—Ans: $\frac{16}{81}$

31. Use a calculator to approximate $\sqrt[3]{719}$ to four decimal places.

(a) 9.2482   **(b)** 9.7153   **(c)** 9.9024   **(d)** 8.9587   **(e)** Not a real number

1—T—Ans: d

32. Use a calculator to approximate $\sqrt[3]{791}$ to four decimal places.

(a) 9.2482   **(b)** 9.7153   **(c)** 9.9024   **(d)** 8.9587   **(e)** Not a real number

1—T—Ans: a

33. Approximate $\sqrt[3]{-847}$ to four decimal places using a calculator. (If not possible, state the reason.)

1—T—Ans: -9.4615

34. Approximate $\sqrt[4]{-847}$ to four decimal places using a calculator. (If not possible, state the reason.)

1—T—Ans: Not possible, answer is not a real number.

35. Approximate $\sqrt[4]{847}$ to four decimal places using a calculator. (If not possible, state the reason.)

1—T—Ans: 5.3947

36. Approximate $\sqrt[3]{748}$ to four decimal places using a calculator. (If not possible, state the reason.)

1—T—Ans: 9.0775

37. Simplify $\left(\dfrac{y^{1/3}}{x}\right)^2 \cdot \dfrac{x^{4/3}}{y^{-1/3}}$.

(a) $\dfrac{1}{x^2 y^{8/3}}$ **(b)** $\dfrac{y}{x^{2/3}}$ **(c)** $\dfrac{x^2}{y^{4/3}}$ **(d)** $x^{4/3}y^2$ **(e)** None of these

1—Ans: b

38. Simplify $\left(\dfrac{y^{1/3}}{x^{-1/3}}\right)^2 \cdot \dfrac{x^{2/3}}{y^{-4/3}}$.

(a) $\dfrac{1}{x^2 y^{8/3}}$ **(b)** $\dfrac{y}{x^{2/3}}$ **(c)** $\dfrac{x^2}{y^{4/3}}$ **(d)** $x^{4/3}y^2$ **(e)** None of these

1—Ans: d

39. Simplify $\left(\dfrac{z^{-1/2}y^{3/2}}{x^{2/3}}\right)^6 \cdot \left(\dfrac{x^{-2}y^2}{z^4}\right)^{1/2}$. Express the answer in positive exponents only.

   2—Ans: $\dfrac{y^{10}}{x^5 z^5}$

40. Simplify $\left(\dfrac{z^{-1/3}y^{2/3}}{x^{3/2}}\right)^6 \cdot \left(\dfrac{x^{-1/2}y^{3/2}}{z^{-1/2}}\right)^2$. Express the answer in positive exponents only.

   2—Ans: $\dfrac{y^7}{x^{10}z}$

41. Evaluate without using a calculator: $81^{-3/4}$.

   (a) -27 **(b)** $\dfrac{1}{27}$ **(c)** $-\dfrac{243}{4}$ **(d)** $\dfrac{4}{\sqrt[3]{81}}$ **(e)** None of these

   1—Form: 9A—Ans: b

42. Evaluate without using a calculator: $64^{-2/3}$.

   (a) -16 **(b)** $-\frac{1}{16}$ **(c)** $-\frac{128}{3}$ **(d)** $\frac{1}{16}$ **(e)** None of these

   1—Form: 9B—Ans: d

43. Simplify $\left(\dfrac{x^{2/3}}{x^{1/2}}\right)^2$.

   (a) $x^{1/36}$ **(b)** $x^{7/36}$ **(c)** $x^{8/3}$ **(d)** $x^{1/3}$ **(e)** None of these

   2—Ans: d

44. Simplify $\left(\dfrac{x^{1/2}}{x^{1/3}}\right)^2$.

   (a) $x^{5/36}$ **(b)** $x^{1/3}$ **(c)** $x^{9/4}$ **(d)** x^3 **(e)** None of these

   2—Ans: b

45. Use a calculator to evaluate $\sqrt[3]{-17}$. Round your answer to three decimal places.

   (a) 4.123 **(b)** -4.123 **(c)** -2.571 **(d)** -5.667 **(e)** None of these

   1—T—Ans: c

46. Use your calculator to evaluate $\sqrt[3]{-29}$. Round your answer to three decimal places.

   (a) -3.072 **(b)** -5.385 **(c)** -9.667 **(d)** 3.072 **(e)** None of these

   1—T—Ans: a

47. Simplify: $x^{1/2} \cdot x^{1/3}$

(a) $x^{1/6}$ (b) x^6 (c) $x^{5/6}$ (d) $x^{1/5}$ (e) None of these

1—Form: 9A—Ans: c

48. Simplify: $x^{2/3} \cdot x^{3/4}$

(a) $x^{1/2}$ (b) $\dfrac{1}{x^{1/12}}$ (c) $x^{5/7}$ (d) $x^{17/12}$ (e) None of these

1—Form: 9B—Ans: d

49. Evaluate without using a calculator: $25^{-3/2}$.

1—Ans: $\dfrac{1}{125}$

50. Evaluate without using a calculator: $(-27)^{5/3}$.

1—Form: 9C—Ans: -243

51. Simplify $\left(\dfrac{x^{1/2}x^{1/3}}{x^{1/4}}\right)^2$.

2—Ans: $x^{7/6}$

52. Simplify $\left(\dfrac{x^{1/2}}{x^{1/3}x^{1/4}}\right)^2$.

2—Ans: $\dfrac{1}{x^{1/6}}$

53. Use a calculator to evaluate $\sqrt[3]{-25}$. Round your answer to three decimal places.

2—T—Ans: -2.924

54. Use a calculator to evaluate $-\sqrt[4]{729}$. Round your answer to three decimal places.

2—T—Ans: -5.196

55. Use a calculator to evaluate $246^{3/4}$. Round your answer to three decimal places.

1—T—Ans: 62.116

56. Use a calculator to evaluate $102^{4/5}$. Round your answer to three decimal places.

1—T—Ans: 40.446

57. Use a calculator to evaluate $513^{3/2}$. Round your answer to three decimal places.

(a) 64.083   (b) 11,619.195   (c) 87.723

(d) 8.606×10^{-5} (e) 67,502,848.5

1—T—Ans: b

58. Use a calculator to evaluate $392^{-4/3}$. Round your answer to three decimal places.

(a) 2868.896 (b) 88.098 (c) 0.011

(d) 1.412×10^{-11} (e) 3.486×10^{-4}

1—T—Ans: e

59. Evaluate without a calculator: $\sqrt{1 - 4(3)(-2)}$.

1—Form: 9C—Ans: 5

60. Evaluate without a calculator: $\sqrt{25 - 4(1)(6)}$.

1—Ans: 1

61. Evaluate without a calculator: $\sqrt{100 - 4(3)(-8)}$.

(a) 2 (b) 4 (c) 8.485 (d) 14 (e) 196

1—Form: 9A—Ans: d

62. Evaluate without a calculator: $\sqrt{1 - 4(2)(-21)}$.

(a) 12.124 (b) 169 (c) 13 (d) 11.225 (e) Not a real number

1—Form: 9B—Ans: c

63. Find the domain of $f(x) = \sqrt{2x - 3}$.

2—Ans: $x \geq \frac{3}{2}$

64. Find the domain of $f(x) = \sqrt{4x + 3}$.

2—Ans: $x \geq -\frac{3}{4}$

65. a. Use a graphing utility to graph $y = x^{2/3}$.
b. Explain why the range is $y \geq 0$.

2—T—Form: 9C—Ans:

a.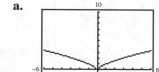

b. $y = x^{2/3} = \left(x^{1/3}\right)^2$
$y \geq 0$ because y is a squared quantity for any value of x.

66. Evaluate $\sqrt{\frac{81}{121}}$.

(a) $\frac{18}{121}$ (b) $\frac{6561}{14641}$ (c) $\frac{9}{13}$ (d) $\frac{9}{11}$ (e) None of these

1—Ans: d

67. Evaluate $\sqrt{9 + 16}$.

(a) 5   (b) 7   (c) 25   (d) 6   (e) None of these

1—Ans: a

68. Evaluate $(16)^{5/4}$.

(a) 20   (b) $\frac{1}{20}$ (c) 32   (d) $\frac{1}{32}$ (e) None of these

1—Ans: c

69. Evaluate $\left(\frac{27}{64}\right)^{-4/3}$.

(a) $-\frac{256}{81}$ (b) $\frac{9}{16}$ (c) $-\frac{9}{16}$ (d) $\frac{256}{81}$ (e) None of these

2—Ans: d

70. Simplify $\dfrac{7^{2/3}}{7^{3/4}}$.

(a) $\dfrac{1}{7^{1/12}}$ (b) $7^{1/12}$ (c) 7^{12} (d) $7^{1/2}$ (e) $7^{8/9}$

1—Ans: a

71. Evaluate $\dfrac{1}{81^{-1/2}}$.

(a) $\dfrac{1}{9}$ (b) 9   (c) $-\dfrac{1}{9}$ (d) -9 (e) None of these

2—Ans: b

72. Evaluate $\left(\frac{1}{64}\right)^{-2/3}$.

(a) -16 (b) $\frac{1}{16}$ (c) 16   (d) $\frac{128}{3}$ (e) 96

2—Ans: c

73. Simplify $(2x^{1/3})(4x^{1/2}y^{-3/5})$.

(a) $\dfrac{8x^{1/6}}{y^{3/5}}$ (b) $\dfrac{8x^{5/6}}{y^{3/5}}$ (c) $-8x^{5/6}y^{3/5}$

(d) $-8x^{1/6}y^{3/5}$ (e) $\dfrac{x^{5/6}}{2y^{3/5}}$

2—Ans: b

74. Simplify $\sqrt[3]{-625x^7y^5}$.

(a) $5xy\sqrt[3]{-5x^4y^2}$ (b) $-5xy\sqrt[3]{5x^4y^2}$ (c) $-125x^2y\sqrt[3]{5xy^2}$

(d) $-5x^2y\sqrt[3]{5xy^2}$ (e) Does not simplify

2—Ans: d

75. Simplify $\sqrt[3]{24x^4y^5}$.

(a) $3x^2y^2\sqrt[3]{6x^2y^3}$ (b) $8xy\sqrt[3]{3xy}$ (c) $2xy\sqrt[3]{6xy^2}$

(d) $2xy\sqrt[3]{3xy^2}$ (e) None of these

2—Ans: d

Section 9.2   Simplifying Radical Expressions

1. $\sqrt{3} \cdot \sqrt{10} =$

(a) $\sqrt{3 + 10}$ (b) $\sqrt{3^2 \cdot 10^2}$ (c) $\sqrt{3 \cdot 10}$ (d) $\sqrt{3\sqrt{10}}$ (e) None of these

1—Ans: c

2. $\sqrt{5} \cdot \sqrt{14} =$

(a) $\sqrt{5 + 14}$ (b) $\sqrt{5 \cdot 14}$ (c) $\sqrt{5^2 \cdot 14^2}$ (d) $\sqrt{5\sqrt{14}}$ (e) None of these

1—Ans: b

3. Write $\sqrt[3]{(9) \cdot (15)}$ as the product of two radicals and simplify.

2—Ans: $\sqrt[3]{27} \cdot \sqrt[3]{5} = 3\sqrt[3]{5}$

4. Write $\sqrt[4]{(4) \cdot (28)}$ as the product of two radicals and simplify.

2—Ans: $\sqrt[4]{16} \cdot \sqrt[4]{7} = 2\sqrt[4]{7}$

5. Simplify $\sqrt[3]{500}$.

(a) $5\sqrt[3]{4}$ (b) $10\sqrt[3]{5}$ (c) $10\sqrt{5}$ (d) $5\sqrt[3]{10}$ (e) None of these

1—Ans: a

6. Simplify $\sqrt{600}$.

(a) $2\sqrt{150}$ (b) $5\sqrt{24}$ (c) $10\sqrt{6}$ (d) $6\sqrt{10}$ (e) None of these

1—Ans: c

7. Simplify $\sqrt{900}$.

(a) $3\sqrt{10}$ (b) 30 (c) $10\sqrt{3}$ (d) $10\sqrt{9}$ (e) None of these

1—Ans: b

8. Simplify $\sqrt[4]{1200}$.

(a) $10\sqrt[4]{12}$ (b) $20\sqrt{3}$ (c) $8\sqrt[4]{75}$ (d) $2\sqrt[4]{75}$ (e) None of these

1—Ans: d

9. Simplify the radical $\sqrt{384}$.

    1—Ans: $8\sqrt{6}$

10. Simplify the radical $\sqrt[3]{720}$.

    1—Ans: $2\sqrt[3]{90}$

11. Simplify $\dfrac{\sqrt{243}}{\sqrt{45}}$.

    (a) $\sqrt{198}$ **(b)** $\sqrt{\dfrac{243}{45}}$ **(c)** $\dfrac{3\sqrt{15}}{5}$ **(d)** $\sqrt{\dfrac{81}{5}}$ **(e)** None of these

    1—Ans: c

12. Simplify $\dfrac{\sqrt{147}}{\sqrt{48}}$.

    (a) $\sqrt{99}$ **(b)** $\dfrac{\sqrt{147}}{48}$ **(c)** $\dfrac{7\sqrt{3}}{2\sqrt{12}}$ **(d)** $\dfrac{7}{4}$ **(e)** None of these

    1—Ans: d

13. Simplify the radical expression $\dfrac{\sqrt{135}}{\sqrt{48}}$.

    1—Ans: $\dfrac{3\sqrt{5}}{4}$

14. Simplify the radical expression $\dfrac{\sqrt{252}}{\sqrt{60}}$.

    1—Ans: $\dfrac{\sqrt{105}}{5}$

15. Simplify the radical expression $\dfrac{\sqrt[3]{16}}{\sqrt[3]{54}}$.

    1—Ans: $\dfrac{2}{3}$

16. Simplify the radical expression $\dfrac{\sqrt[4]{162}}{\sqrt[4]{32}}$.

    1—Ans: $\dfrac{3}{2}$

17. Simplify the radical $\sqrt[3]{250y^5z^4}$.

    (a) $5|yz|\sqrt[3]{2y^2z}$ **(b)** $5yz\sqrt[3]{2y^2z}$ **(c)** $5y^2z^2\sqrt{2y}$ **(d)** $5xy\sqrt{2y^2z}$ **(e)** None of these

    1—Ans: b.

18. Simplify the radical $\sqrt[4]{162u^5v^7}$.

   (a) $9u^2v^3\sqrt{2uv}$ (b) $3uv^2\sqrt{2uv}$ (c) $|3uv|\sqrt{2uv}$ (d) $3uv\sqrt[4]{2uv^3}$ (e) None of these

   1—Ans: d

19. Simplify the radical $\sqrt{300x^2y^5}$.

   1—Ans: $10|x|y^2\sqrt{3y}$

20. Simplify the radical $\sqrt{500x^4y^3}$.

   1—Ans: $10x^2y\sqrt{5y}$

21. Simplify the radical $\sqrt{\dfrac{12x^3}{y^4}}$.

   (a) $2|x|y^2\sqrt{3x}$

   (b) $\dfrac{2x}{y^2}\sqrt{3x}$

   (c) $2xy^2\sqrt{3x}$

   (d) $\dfrac{2x^2\sqrt{3x}}{y^2}$

   (e) None of these

   2—Ans: b

22. Simplify the radical $\sqrt[4]{\dfrac{81x^5}{32y^3}}$.

   (a) $\dfrac{3x}{4y}\sqrt[4]{8xy}$

   (b) $\dfrac{3}{4}xy\sqrt[4]{8xy}$

   (c) $\dfrac{3x^2}{4y^2}\sqrt[4]{8xy}$

   (d) $\dfrac{9}{4}\dfrac{x^2}{y^2}\sqrt{2xy}$

   (e) None of these

   2—Ans: a

23. Simplify the radical $\sqrt{44.1 \times 10^7}$.

   1—Ans: 2.1×10^4 or 21,000

24. Simplify the radical $\sqrt{14.4 \times 10^7}$.

   1—Ans: 1.2×10^4 or 12,000

25. Simplify the radical $\sqrt[3]{270 \times 10^{-4}}$.

   1—Ans: 3×10^{-1} or 0.3

26. Simplify the radical $\sqrt[4]{160 \times 10^{-5}}$.

   1—Ans: 0.2

27. Rationalize the denominator and simplify $\dfrac{2x}{\sqrt{14}}$.

  (a) $\dfrac{x}{7}$ **(b)** $\dfrac{\sqrt{14x}}{7}$ **(c)** $\dfrac{\sqrt{14x}}{7}$ **(d)** $\dfrac{\sqrt{7x}}{7}$ **(e)** None of these

  1—Ans: c

28. Rationalize the denominator and simplify $\sqrt{\dfrac{5}{2x}}$.

  (a) $\dfrac{\sqrt{10x}}{(2x)^2}$ **(b)** $\dfrac{\sqrt{10}}{2x}$ **(c)** $\dfrac{\sqrt{10}}{2|x|}$ **(d)** $\dfrac{\sqrt{10x}}{2x}$ **(e)** None of these

  1—Ans: d

29. Rationalize the denominator and simplify $\sqrt[3]{\dfrac{27x^3y^2}{32xy^4}}$.

  2—Ans: $\dfrac{3}{4y}\sqrt[3]{2x^2y}$

30. Rationalize the denominator and simplify $\sqrt[3]{\dfrac{56x}{28x^2y^2}}$.

  1—Ans: $\dfrac{1}{xy}\sqrt[3]{2x^2y}$

31. Simplify the expression $3\sqrt{5} + 7\sqrt{5}$.

  (a) $21\sqrt{25} = 105$ **(b)** $21\sqrt{5}$ **(c)** $10\sqrt{10}$

  (d) $10\sqrt{5}$ **(e)** None of these

  1—Ans: d

32. Simplify the expression $6\sqrt{7} + 3\sqrt{7}$.

  (a) $18\sqrt{49} = 126$ **(b)** $9\sqrt{14}$ **(c)** $9\sqrt{7}$

  (d) $18\sqrt{7}$ **(e)** None of these

  1—Ans: c

33. Combine the expression, $\sqrt[3]{x} - \sqrt[3]{8x} + \sqrt[3]{x^4}$, if possible.

  1—Ans: $(x - 1)\sqrt[3]{x}$

34. Combine the expression, $\sqrt[4]{81x} + \sqrt[4]{x} - \sqrt[4]{x^5}$, if possible.

  1—Ans: $(4 - x)\sqrt[4]{x}$

35. Combine the expression, $\sqrt[4]{16x^3} + 2\sqrt[4]{x^3} - \sqrt[4]{x^7}$, if possible.

  1—Ans: $(4 - x)\sqrt[4]{x^3}$

36. Combine the expression, $\sqrt[3]{27x} + \sqrt[3]{8x} - 2\sqrt[3]{x^4}$, if possible.

  1—Ans: $(5 - 2x)\sqrt[3]{x}$

37. Perform the indicated addition and simplify $\sqrt{40} + \dfrac{7}{\sqrt{10}}$.

  (a) $9\sqrt{10}$ **(b)** $\dfrac{7 + 2\sqrt{10}}{\sqrt{10}}$ **(c)** $\dfrac{9\sqrt{10}}{10}$ **(d)** $\dfrac{27\sqrt{10}}{10}$ **(e)** None of these

  1—Ans: d

38. Perform the indicated subtraction and simplify $\sqrt{18} - \dfrac{1}{\sqrt{2}}$.

  (a) $\dfrac{5\sqrt{2}}{2}$ **(b)** $\dfrac{\sqrt{18} - 1}{\sqrt{2}}$ **(c)** $\dfrac{6 - \sqrt{2}}{\sqrt{2}}$ **(d)** $5\sqrt{2}$ **(e)** None of these

  1—Ans: a

39. Perform the indicated addition and simplify your answer. $\dfrac{x}{\sqrt{2x}} + \sqrt{8x}$

  1—Ans: $\dfrac{5}{2}\sqrt{2x}$

40. Perform the indicated operation and simplify your answer. $\sqrt{8x} - \dfrac{x}{\sqrt{2x}}$

  1—Ans: $\dfrac{3}{2}\sqrt{2x}$

41. Simplify $\sqrt{48}$.

  (a) $16\sqrt{3}$ **(b)** $4\sqrt{3}$ **(c)** $4\sqrt{2}$ **(d)** 7   **(e)** None of these

  1—Ans: b

42. Simplify $\sqrt{125}$.

  (a) $25\sqrt{5}$ **(b)** $5\sqrt{3}$ **(c)** $5\sqrt{5}$ **(d)** 11   **(e)** None of these

  1—Ans: c

43. Simplify $\sqrt[5]{\dfrac{x^{10}}{32y^5}}$.

  (a) $\dfrac{x^5}{2}$ **(b)** $\dfrac{x^{10}}{32}$ **(c)** $\dfrac{x^2}{2\sqrt{2y}}$ **(d)** $\dfrac{x^2}{2y}$ **(e)** None of these

  1—Form: 9A—Ans: d

44. Simplify $\sqrt{\dfrac{81x^3}{y^6}}$.

(a) $\dfrac{9x^2}{y^3}$ (b) $\dfrac{9x^2}{y^4}$ (c) $\dfrac{9x\sqrt{x}}{y^3}$ (d) $\dfrac{9x}{y^3}$ (e) None of these

1—Form: **9B**—**Ans:** c

45. Simplify $\sqrt{8} + \sqrt{18}$.

(a) $\sqrt{26}$ (b) 12   (c) 10   (d) $5\sqrt{2}$ (e) None of these

2—**Ans:** d

46. Simplify $\sqrt{75} - \sqrt{12}$.

(a) $\sqrt{63}$ (b) 8   (c) $3\sqrt{7}$ (d) $3\sqrt{3}$ (e) None of these

2—**Ans:** d

47. Rationalize the denominator and simplify $\dfrac{6}{\sqrt{12}}$.

(a) $\sqrt{3}$ (b) $\dfrac{1}{\sqrt{2}}$ (c) $\dfrac{\sqrt{3}}{2}$ (d) 1   (e) None of these

2—Form: **9A**—**Ans:** a

48. Rationalize the denominator and simplify $\dfrac{8}{\sqrt{18}}$.

(a) $\dfrac{2}{3}$ (b) $\dfrac{4\sqrt{2}}{3}$ (c) $\sqrt{2}$ (d) $\dfrac{4}{3}$ (e) None of these

2—Form: **9B**—**Ans:** b

49. Simplify $\sqrt{18}$.

1—**Ans:** $3\sqrt{2}$

50. Simplify $\sqrt{24}$.

1—**Ans:** $2\sqrt{6}$

51. Simplify $\sqrt[3]{\dfrac{x^6}{8y^3}}$.

1—**Ans:** $\dfrac{x^2}{2y}$

52. Simplify $\sqrt{\dfrac{4x^2}{y^4}}$.

1—**Ans:** $\dfrac{2|x|}{y^2}$

53. Simplify $\sqrt{48} - \sqrt{12}$.

  2—Ans: $2\sqrt{3}$

54. Simplify $\sqrt{32} - \sqrt{50}$.

  2—Form: 9C—Ans: $-\sqrt{2}$

55. Rationalize the denominator and simplify $\dfrac{4x^3}{\sqrt{2x}}$.

  2—Ans: $2x^2\sqrt{2x}$

56. Rationalize the denominator and simplify $\dfrac{9x^6}{\sqrt{3x}}$.

  1—Form: 9C—Ans: $3x^5\sqrt{3x}$

57. Rationalize the denominator and simplify $\dfrac{3}{\sqrt{6}}$.

  1—Ans: $\dfrac{\sqrt{6}}{2}$

58. Rationalize the denominator and simplify $\dfrac{20}{\sqrt{5}}$.

  1—Ans: $4\sqrt{5}$

59. Rationalize the denominator and simplify $\dfrac{12}{\sqrt[3]{9}}$.

  1—Ans: $4\sqrt[3]{3}$

60. Rationalize the denominator and simplify $\dfrac{6}{\sqrt[5]{16}}$.

  1—Ans: $3\sqrt[5]{2}$

61. Rationalize the denominator and simplify $\sqrt{\dfrac{9}{x}}$.

  1—Ans: $\dfrac{3\sqrt{x}}{x}$

62. Rationalize the denominator and simplify $\dfrac{10x^3}{\sqrt{5x^3}}$.

  1—Ans: $2x\sqrt{5x}$

63. Find the length of the hypotenuse of the right triangle.

(a) 8   (b) $2\sqrt{13}$

(c) $5\sqrt{2}$ (d) 52

(e) 7

1—Form: 9A—Ans: b

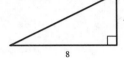

64. Find the length of the hypotenuse of the right triangle.

(a) $4\sqrt{5}$ (b) 80

(c) 12   (d) 10

(e) 9

1—Form: 9B—Ans: a

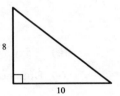

65. Find the length of the hypotenuse of the right triangle.

1—Ans: $2\sqrt{41}$

66. Find the length of the hypotenuse of the right triangle.

1—Form: 9C—Ans: $4\sqrt{10}$

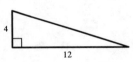

67. Simplify $\sqrt{100x^{36}}$.

(a) $10x^6$ (b) $10x^{36}$ (c) $10x^{18}$ (d) $100x^6$ (e) None of these

1—Ans: c

68. Simplify $\sqrt[3]{-24x^4}$.

(a) $2x\sqrt[3]{3x}$ (b) $2x^2\sqrt{6}$ (c) $-2x\sqrt[3]{3x}$ (d) $-2x\sqrt[3]{3x^2}$ (e) None of these

2—Ans: c

69. Rationalize the denominator and simplify $\dfrac{10}{3\sqrt{5}}$.

(a) $\dfrac{20}{9}$ (b) $\dfrac{2\sqrt{5}}{3}$ (c) $\dfrac{2}{3}$ (d) $\dfrac{10\sqrt{5}}{3}$ (e) None of these

1—Ans: b

70. Rationalize the denominator $\dfrac{1}{\sqrt[3]{x}}$.

(a) $\dfrac{\sqrt[3]{x^2}}{x}$ (b) $\dfrac{1}{x}$ (c) $\dfrac{\sqrt{x}}{x}$ (d) $\sqrt[3]{x}$ (e) None of these

2—Ans: a

71. Simplify $\sqrt{8} + \sqrt{50}$.

    (a) $\sqrt{58}$ **(b)** 14   **(c)** $7\sqrt{2}$ **(d)** $29\sqrt{2}$ **(e)** None of these

    1—Ans: c

72. Simplify $\sqrt{x^2y^3} - xy\sqrt{4y} + x\sqrt{9y^3}$.

    (a) $\sqrt{x^2y^3 - 4xy^2 + 9xy^3}$ **(b)** $\sqrt{6x^2y^4}$ **(c)** $2xy\sqrt{y}$

    (d) $6xy\sqrt{y}$ **(e)** None of these

    2—Ans: c

73. Simplify $\sqrt[3]{\sqrt{27}}$.

    (a) $\sqrt[5]{27}$ **(b)** 27   **(c)** $\sqrt[3]{3\sqrt{3}}$ **(d)** $\sqrt{3}$ **(e)** None of these

    2—Ans: d

74. Simplify $\sqrt[3]{-625x^7y^5}$.

    (a) $5xy\sqrt[3]{-5x^4y^2}$ **(b)** $-5xy\sqrt[3]{5x^4y^2}$ **(c)** $-125x^2y\sqrt[3]{5xy^2}$

    (d) $-5x^2y\sqrt[3]{5xy^2}$ **(e)** Does not simplify

    2—Ans: d

75. Simplify $\sqrt[3]{24x^4y^5}$.

    (a) $3x^3y^2\sqrt[3]{6x^2y^3}$ **(b)** $8xy\sqrt[3]{3xy}$ **(c)** $2xy\sqrt[3]{6xy^2}$

    (d) $2xy\sqrt[3]{3xy^2}$ **(e)** None of these

    2—Ans: d

76. Rationalize the denominator and simplify $\dfrac{2}{\sqrt[3]{2x}}$.

    (a) $\dfrac{\sqrt[3]{2x}}{x}$ **(b)** $\dfrac{\sqrt[3]{4x^2}}{x}$ **(c)** $\dfrac{2\sqrt[3]{2x}}{2x}$ **(d)** $\sqrt[3]{4x}$ **(e)** None of these

    2—Ans: b

77. Write as a single radical: $\sqrt[3]{\sqrt{2x}}$.

    (a) $\sqrt[6]{2x}$ **(b)** $\sqrt[5]{2x}$ **(c)** $\sqrt[3]{2x}$ **(d)** $\sqrt[3]{4x^2}$ **(e)** None of these

    2—Ans: a

78. Simplify $4\sqrt{9x} - 2\sqrt{4x} + 7$.

    (a) $8x + 7$ **(b)** $8\sqrt{x} + 7$ **(c)** $2\sqrt{5x} + 7$

    (d) Does not simplify   **(e)** None of these

    2—Ans: b

79. Write $\sqrt[3]{2x^2}$ in exponential form.

(a) $2x^{3/2}$ (b) $2x^{2/3}$ (c) $(2x)^{2/3}$ (d) $(2x^2)^{1/3}$ (e) None of these

2—Ans: d

80. The period T, in seconds, of a pendulum is $T = 2\pi\sqrt{\dfrac{L}{32}}$ where L is the length of the pendulum in feet. Find the period of a pendulum whose length is $\frac{1}{2}$ foot.

(a) π (b) $\dfrac{\pi}{2}$ (c) $\dfrac{\pi}{4}$ (d) $\dfrac{\pi}{8}$ (e) None of these

2—Ans: c

Section 9.3   Multiplying and Dividing Radical Expressions

1. Multiply and simplify: $\sqrt{5}\left(\sqrt{2} + \sqrt{3}\right)$.

(a) $\sqrt{7} + \sqrt{8}$ (b) $10 + 15 = 25$ (c) $\sqrt{10} + \sqrt{15}$

(d) 5 (e) None of these

1—Ans: c

2. Multiply and simplify: $\sqrt{2}\left(\sqrt{5} - \sqrt{3}\right)$.

(a) $10 - 6 = 4$ (b) $\sqrt{10} - \sqrt{6}$ (c) $\sqrt{7} - \sqrt{5}$

(d) 2 (e) None of these

1—Ans: b

3. Multiply $\sqrt{10}\left(\sqrt{18} - 3\sqrt{6}\right)$ and simplify the result.

1—Ans: $6\sqrt{5} - 6\sqrt{15}$

4. Multiply $\sqrt{6}\left(\sqrt{24} - 2\sqrt{27}\right)$ and simplify the result.

1—Ans: $12 - 18\sqrt{2}$

5. Multiply $\left(2\sqrt{3} - 1\right)\left(3\sqrt{3} - 1\right)$ and simplify the result.

(a) $6\sqrt{3} + 1$ (b) $17 - 5\sqrt{3}$ (c) $16 - 5\sqrt{3}$

(d) $19 - 5\sqrt{3}$ (e) None of these

1—Ans: d

6. Multiply $\left(2\sqrt{7} - \sqrt{2}\right)\left(\sqrt{7} + \sqrt{2}\right)$ and simplify the result.

(a) $12 + \sqrt{14}$ (b) $12 - \sqrt{14}$ (c) 12

(d) $16 + \sqrt{14}$ (e) None of these

1—Ans: a

7. Multiply $\left(2\sqrt{11} - \sqrt{2}\right)\left(\sqrt{11} + \sqrt{2}\right)$ and simplify the result.

1—Ans: $20 + \sqrt{22}$

8. Multiply $\left(3\sqrt{5} - \sqrt{6}\right)\left(\sqrt{5} + 2\sqrt{6}\right)$ and simplify the result.

1—Ans: $3 + 5\sqrt{30}$

9. Multiply $\left(5\sqrt{6} + \sqrt{10}\right)\left(2\sqrt{10} - \sqrt{6}\right)$ and simplify the result.

1—Ans: $-10 + 18\sqrt{15}$

10. Multiply $\left(\sqrt{15} + 3\sqrt{5}\right)\left(\sqrt{15} - \sqrt{5}\right)$ and simplify the result.

1—Ans: $10\sqrt{3}$

11. Multiply $\left(5 - \sqrt{x}\right)\left(2 + \sqrt{x}\right)$ and simplify the result.

  (a) $10 - x + 3\sqrt{x}$ **(b)** $10 - x$ **(c)** 7

  (d) $10 + 3\sqrt{x}$ **(e)** None of these

  1—Ans: a

12. Multiply $\left(4 + \sqrt{x}\right)\left(3 - 2\sqrt{x}\right)$ and simplify the result.

  (a) $12 - 2x$ **(b)** $12 - 2x - 5\sqrt{x}$ **(c)** $12 - 5\sqrt{x}$

  (d) $7 - \sqrt{x}$ **(e)** None of these

  1—Ans: b

13. Multiply $\left(4 - \sqrt{x}\right)\left(3 + 2\sqrt{x}\right)$ and simplify the result.

  (a) $12 - 2x$ **(b)** $12 + 5\sqrt{x}$ **(c)** $12 - 2x + 5\sqrt{x}$

  (d) $7 + \sqrt{x}$ **(e)** None of these

  1—Ans: c

14. Multiply $\left(5 + \sqrt{x}\right)\left(2 - \sqrt{x}\right)$ and simplify the result.

  (a) $10 - x$ **(b)** $10 - 3\sqrt{x}$ **(c)** 7

  (d) $10 - x - 3\sqrt{x}$ **(e)** None of these

  1—Ans: d

15. Multiply $\left(7 - 2\sqrt{x}\right)\left(4 + \sqrt{x}\right)$ and simplify the result.

  1—Ans: $28 - 2x - \sqrt{x}$

16. Multiply $\left(2 + 7\sqrt{x}\right)\left(1 - 4\sqrt{x}\right)$ and simplify the result.

  1—Ans: $2 - 28x - \sqrt{x}$

17. Multiply $\sqrt[3]{9}\left(\sqrt[3]{3} - 5\right)$ and simplify the result.

    (a) $3\sqrt[3]{3} - 5\sqrt[3]{9}$ **(b)** $-2\sqrt[3]{9}$ **(c)** $\sqrt[3]{12} - 5\sqrt[3]{9}$

    (d) $3 - 5\sqrt[3]{9}$ **(e)** None of these

    1—Ans: d

18. Multiply $\sqrt[3]{3}\left(\sqrt[3]{9} - 4\right)$ and simplify the result.

    (a) $\sqrt[3]{12} - 4\sqrt[3]{3}$ **(b)** $3\sqrt[3]{3} - 4$ **(c)** $3 - 4\sqrt[3]{3}$

    (d) $5\sqrt[3]{3}$ **(e)** None of these

    1—Ans: c

19. Multiply $\left(\sqrt[3]{4} + \sqrt[3]{2}\right)\left(\sqrt[3]{4} - \sqrt[3]{2}\right)$ and simplify the result.

    2—Ans: $2\sqrt[3]{2} - \sqrt[3]{4}$

20. Multiply $\left(\sqrt[3]{9} + \sqrt[3]{3}\right)\left(\sqrt[3]{9} - \sqrt[3]{3}\right)$ and simplify the result.

    2—Ans: $3\sqrt[3]{3} - \sqrt[3]{9}$

21. Multiply and simplify: $\left(2\sqrt{3} - \sqrt{7}\right)\left(5\sqrt{3} + 2\sqrt{7}\right)$.

    (a) 16 **(b)** $-\sqrt{21}$ **(c)** 70 **(d)** $16 - \sqrt{21}$ **(e)** None of these

    1—Ans: d

22. Multiply and simplify: $\left(2\sqrt{5} + \sqrt{3}\right)\left(3\sqrt{5} - 2\sqrt{3}\right)$.

    (a) 24 **(b)** $24 - \sqrt{15}$ **(c)** $36 + 5\sqrt{15}$ **(d)** $24 + 5\sqrt{15}$ **(e)** None of these

    1—Ans: b

23. Multiply and simplify: $\left(2\sqrt{11} - 3\sqrt{5}\right)\left(4\sqrt{11} + \sqrt{5}\right)$.

    (a) $73 - 10\sqrt{55}$ **(b)** 73 **(c)** $103 - 14\sqrt{55}$

    (d) $88 - 12\sqrt{55}$ **(e)** None of these

    1—Ans: a

24. Multiply and simplify: $\left(2\sqrt{12} + \sqrt{8}\right)\left(3\sqrt{3} - \sqrt{2}\right)$.

    (a) 32 **(b)** $\sqrt{24}$ **(c)** $32 + 2\sqrt{6}$ **(d)** $36 + 6\sqrt{3}$ **(e)** None of these

    1—Ans: c

25. Multiply $\left(2\sqrt{15} - \sqrt{14}\right)\left(\sqrt{10} + \sqrt{21}\right)$ and simplify your answer.
(Do not use a calculator.)

    2—Ans: $3\sqrt{6} + 4\sqrt{35}$

26. Multiply $\left(2\sqrt{18} - 3\sqrt{15}\right)\left(\sqrt{10} + \sqrt{12}\right)$ and simplify your answer.
(Do not use a calculator.)

2—Ans: $-6\sqrt{5} - 3\sqrt{6}$

27. Find the conjugate of the expression $\left(\sqrt{7} - \sqrt{5}\right)$.

(a) $(7 - 5)$ **(b)** $\sqrt{7} + \sqrt{5}$ **(c)** $\dfrac{1}{\sqrt{7} - \sqrt{5}}$ **(d)** $\dfrac{1}{\sqrt{7} + \sqrt{5}}$ **(e)** None of these

1—Ans: b

28. Find the conjugate of the expression $\left(\sqrt{11} + \sqrt{6}\right)$.

(a) $11 - 6$ **(b)** $\dfrac{1}{\sqrt{11} - \sqrt{6}}$ **(c)** $\sqrt{11} - \sqrt{6}$ **(d)** $\dfrac{1}{\sqrt{11} + \sqrt{6}}$ **(e)** None of these

1—Ans: c

29. For the expression $\left(\sqrt{17} - 3\right)$, write
a. its conjugate
b. the product of the expression and its conjugate.

1—Ans: a. $\sqrt{17} + 3$;   **b.** $\left(\sqrt{17} - 3\right)\left(\sqrt{17} + 3\right) = 17 - 9 = 8$

30. For the expression $\left(3 - \sqrt{11}\right)$, write
a. its conjugate
b. the product of the expression and its conjugate.

1—Ans: a. $3 + \sqrt{11}$;   **b.** $\left(3 - \sqrt{11}\right)\left(3 + \sqrt{11}\right) = 9 - 11 = -2$

31. Rationalize the denominator: $\dfrac{5}{\sqrt{11} - 3}$.

(a) $5\left(\sqrt{11} - 3\right)$ **(b)** $\dfrac{5}{\sqrt{11} - 3}$ **(c)** $\dfrac{\sqrt{11} + 3}{5}$

(d) $\dfrac{5\left(\sqrt{11} + 3\right)}{2}$ **(e)** None of these

1—Ans: d

32. Rationalize the denominator: $\dfrac{4}{\sqrt{5} - \sqrt{3}}$.

(a) $2\left(\sqrt{5} + \sqrt{3}\right)$ **(b)** $\dfrac{\sqrt{5} + \sqrt{3}}{4}$ **(c)** $\dfrac{\sqrt{5} - \sqrt{3}}{4}$

(d) $\dfrac{4}{\sqrt{5} + \sqrt{3}}$ **(e)** None of these

1—Ans: a

33. Rationalize the denominator and simplify: $\dfrac{5}{\sqrt{21} - 4}$.

1—Ans: $\sqrt{21} + 4$

34. Rationalize the denominator and simplify: $\dfrac{8}{\sqrt{13} - \sqrt{11}}$.

1—Ans: $4\left(\sqrt{13} + \sqrt{11}\right)$

35. Divide and simplify: $\left(\sqrt{3} - 1\right) \div \left(1 + \sqrt{3}\right)$.

   (a) $2 - 2\sqrt{3}$ **(b)** $2 - \sqrt{3}$ **(c)** $\dfrac{\sqrt{3} + 1}{2}$ **(d)** $\dfrac{1 + \sqrt{3}}{1 - \sqrt{3}}$ **(e)** None of these

2—Ans: b

36. Divide and simplify: $\left(\sqrt{5} + 2\right) \div \left(3 - \sqrt{5}\right)$.

   (a) $\dfrac{11 + 5\sqrt{5}}{4}$ **(b)** $\dfrac{11 - 5\sqrt{5}}{4}$ **(c)** $\dfrac{\sqrt{5} - 2}{3 + \sqrt{5}}$ **(d)** $\dfrac{2 - \sqrt{5}}{2}$ **(e)** None of these

2—Ans: a

37. Divide and simplify: $(2x - 2) \div \left(\sqrt{x} - 1\right)$.

   2—Ans: $2\left(\sqrt{x} + 1\right)$

38. Divide and simplify: $(2x - 4) \div \left(\sqrt{x} - \sqrt{2}\right)$.

   2—Ans: $2\left(\sqrt{x} + \sqrt{2}\right)$

39. Divide and simplify: $(2x - 8) \div \left(\sqrt{x} - 2\right)$.

   2—Ans: $2\left(\sqrt{x} + 2\right)$

40. Divide and simplify: $(9x - 3) \div \left(\sqrt{3x} - 1\right)$.

   2—Ans: $3\left(\sqrt{3x} + 1\right)$

41. Multiply and simplify: $\left(\sqrt{3} - 1\right)\left(\sqrt{3} + 2\right)$.

   (a) $7 + \sqrt{3}$ **(b)** 1 **(c)** $1 - \sqrt{3}$ **(d)** $1 + \sqrt{3}$ **(e)** None of these

1—Ans: d

42. Multiply and simplify: $\left(2 - \sqrt{3}\right)\left(5 + \sqrt{3}\right)$.

   (a) $7 - 3\sqrt{3}$ **(b)** $4 - 3\sqrt{3}$ **(c)** $7 + \sqrt{3}$ **(d)** 7 **(e)** None of these

1—Ans: a

43. Multiply and simplify: $\left(2 - \sqrt{x}\right)^2$.

    (a) $4 - x$ **(b)** $4 + x$ **(c)** $4 - 2\sqrt{x} + x$

    (d) $4 - 4\sqrt{x} + x$ **(e)** None of these

    1—Form: 9A—Ans: d

44. Multiply and simplify: $\left(\sqrt{x} + 2\right)^2$.

    (a) $x + 4$ **(b)** $x + 2\sqrt{x} + 4$ **(c)** $4x$

    (d) $x + 4\sqrt{x} + 4$ **(e)** None of these

    1—Form: 9B—Ans: d

45. Rationalize the denominator and simplify: $\dfrac{1}{1 + \sqrt{2}}$.

    (a) $\sqrt{2} - 1$ **(b)** $\dfrac{1}{3}$ **(c)** $\dfrac{1}{3 + 2\sqrt{2}}$ **(d)** $\dfrac{1 + \sqrt{2}}{3 + 2\sqrt{2}}$ **(e)** None of these

    1—Form: 9A—Ans: a

46. Rationalize the denominator and simplify: $\dfrac{2}{1 - \sqrt{3}}$.

    (a) -2 **(b)** $-1 + \sqrt{3}$ **(c)** $\dfrac{2}{2 - \sqrt{3}}$ **(d)** $-1 - \sqrt{3}$ **(e)** None of these

    1—Form: 9B—Ans: d

47. Multiply and simplify: $\sqrt{3}\left(4 - \sqrt{12}\right)$.

    1—Ans: $4\sqrt{3} - 6$

48. Multiply and simplify: $\sqrt{2}\left(3 - \sqrt{8}\right)$.

    1—Ans: $3\sqrt{2} - 4$

49. Multiply and simplify: $\left(\sqrt{x} - 3\right)\left(\sqrt{x} + 1\right)$.

    1—Ans: $x - 2\sqrt{x} - 3$

50. Multiply and simplify: $\left(2 - \sqrt{x}\right)\left(5 - \sqrt{x}\right)$.

    1—Ans: $10 - 7\sqrt{x} + x$

51. Rationalize the denominator and simplify: $\dfrac{\sqrt{3}}{\sqrt{2} - 1}$.

    1—Form: 9C—Ans: $\sqrt{3}\left(\sqrt{2} + 1\right)$

52. Rationalize the denominator and simplify: $\dfrac{\sqrt{2}}{1 - \sqrt{2}}$.

   1—Ans: $-2 - \sqrt{2}$

53. Divide and simplify: $\left(\sqrt{x} + 3\right) \div \left(\sqrt{x} + 2\right)$.

   2—Ans: $\dfrac{x + \sqrt{x} - 6}{x - 4}$

54. Divide and simplify: $\left(\sqrt{x} - 1\right) \div \left(\sqrt{x} + 1\right)$.

   2—Ans: $\dfrac{x - 2\sqrt{x} + 1}{x - 1}$

55. Rationalize the denominator: $\dfrac{1}{\sqrt{x + h + 1} - \sqrt{x + 1}}$.

   2—Form: 9C—Ans: $\dfrac{\sqrt{x + h + 1} + \sqrt{x + 1}}{h}$

56. Rationalize the denominator: $\dfrac{1}{\sqrt{x + h + 2} - \sqrt{x + 2}}$.

   2—Ans: $\dfrac{\sqrt{x + h + 2} + \sqrt{x + 2}}{h}$

57. Find $f\left(2 + \sqrt{3}\right)$ for the function $f(x) = x^2 - 2x - 1$.

   (a) $1 + \sqrt{3}$ **(b)** $4\sqrt{3}$ **(c)** $2 + 2\sqrt{3}$ **(d)** $12 + 6\sqrt{3}$ **(e)** $2 + 4\sqrt{3}$

   2—Form: 9A—Ans: c

58. Find $f\left(1 - \sqrt{2}\right)$ for the function $f(x) = 1 - x^2$.

   (a) $-2 + 2\sqrt{2}$ **(b)** 2 **(c)** $4 + 2\sqrt{2}$

   (d) $6\sqrt{2}$ **(e)** $2 - 2\sqrt{2}$

   2—Form: 9B—Ans: a

59. Find $f\left(5 + \sqrt{2}\right)$ for the function $f(x) = x^2 - 3x - 4$.

   2—Form: 9C—Ans: $8 + 7\sqrt{2}$

60. Find $f\left(-4 + \sqrt{3}\right)$ for the function $f(x) = x^2 + 6x - 11$.

   2—Ans: $-16 - 2\sqrt{3}$

61. Use a graphing utility to graph $y_1 = \dfrac{\sqrt{x}}{3 - \sqrt{x}}$. Then graph each of the choices for y_2 and determine which is equivalent to y_1.

(a) $y_2 = 3 + \sqrt{x}$ (b) $y_2 = \dfrac{3 + \sqrt{x}}{3 - \sqrt{x}}$ (c) $y_2 = \dfrac{1 + \sqrt{x}}{3 - x}$

(d) $y_2 = \dfrac{3\sqrt{x} + x}{9 - x}$ (e) $y_2 = \dfrac{3 + \sqrt{x}}{9 - x}$

1—T—Form: 9A—Ans: d

62. Use a graphing utility to graph $y_1 = \dfrac{\sqrt{x}}{1 + \sqrt{x}}$. Then graph each of the choices for y_2 and determine which is equivalent to y_1.

(a) $y_2 = \dfrac{-\sqrt{x}}{1 - x}$ (b) $y_2 = \dfrac{\sqrt{x}}{x - 1}$ (c) $y_2 = \dfrac{\sqrt{x} - x}{1 - x}$

(d) $y_2 = \dfrac{2\sqrt{x}}{1 - x}$ (e) $y_2 = \dfrac{\sqrt{x} + x}{1 - x}$

1—T—Form: 9B—Ans: c

63. Use a graphing utility to determine whether y_1 and y_2 are equivalent.

$$y_1 = \frac{4 - x}{2 + \sqrt{x}}, \quad y_2 = 2 - \sqrt{x}$$

1—T—Form: 9C—Ans: $y_1 = y_2$

64. Use a graphing utility to determine whether y_1 and y_2 are equivalent.

$$y_1 = 3 + 2\sqrt{x}, \quad y_2 = \frac{9 - 4x}{3 - 2\sqrt{x}}$$

1—T—Ans: $y_1 = y_2$

65. Rationalize the denominator: $\dfrac{12}{\sqrt{7} + 1}$.

1—Ans: $2\sqrt{7} - 2$

66. Rationalize the denominator: $\dfrac{21}{\sqrt{11} + 2}$.

1—Ans: $3\sqrt{11} - 6$

Section 9.4   Solving Radical Equations

1. Find a solution to the equation $\sqrt{x} - 8 = 0$.

    (a) 8   **(b)** -8 **(c)** 64   **(d)** -64 **(e)** None of these

    1—Ans: c

2. Find a solution to the equation $3 - \sqrt{-x} = 0$.

    (a) -3 **(b)** -9 **(c)** 3   **(d)** 9   **(e)** None of these

    1—Ans: b

3. Find a solution to the equation $10 - \sqrt{2x} = 0$.

    (a) 50   **(b)** -50 **(c)** 5   **(d)** -5 **(e)** None of these

    1—Ans: a

4. Find a solution to the equation $\sqrt{x} + 10 = 0$.

    (a) 100   **(b)** -100 **(c)** 10   **(d)** -10 **(e)** None of these

    1—Ans: e

5. Solve the equation $11 - \sqrt{-x} = 2$ for x.

    1—Ans: $x = -81$

6. Solve the equation $14 - \sqrt{2x} = 2$ for x.

    1—Ans: $x = 72$

7. Which of the following equations has no solution?

    (a) $\sqrt{-x} = 4$ **(b)** $\sqrt{x} = 4$ **(c)** $\sqrt{x} = -4$ **(d)** $\sqrt{x^2} = 4$ **(e)** None of these

    1—Ans: c

8. Which of the following equations has no solution?

    (a) $\sqrt{-x} = 5$ **(b)** $\sqrt{x} = 5$ **(c)** $\sqrt{x^2} = 5$ **(d)** $\sqrt{x} = -5$ **(e)** None of these

    1—Ans: d

9. Solve the equation $\sqrt{1 - 2x} - 2 = 3$.

    1—Ans: $x = -12$

10. Solve the equation $2 - \sqrt{2x - 1} = -5$.

    1—Ans: $x = 25$

11. Solve the equation $3\sqrt{x + 5} = 2\sqrt{7 - 2x}$.

    (a) 4   **(b)** 3   **(c)** -1 **(d)** -9 **(e)** None of these

    1—Ans: c

12. Solve the equation $\sqrt{x + 4} = \sqrt{14 - x}$.

    (a) -2 **(b)** 5   **(c)** 10   **(d)** -11 **(e)** None of these

    1—Ans: b

13. Solve the equation for x: $\sqrt{2x - 1} = 2\sqrt{1 - x}$.

    1—Ans: $x = \frac{5}{6}$

14. Solve the equation for x: $\sqrt{3x + 2} = 2\sqrt{3 - x}$.

    1—Ans: $x = \frac{10}{7}$

15. Solve the equation for x: $2\sqrt{4x - 3} = \sqrt{x + 1}$.

    1—Ans: $x = \frac{13}{15}$

16. Solve the equation for x: $\sqrt{3x - 2} = 2\sqrt{4 - x}$.

    1—Ans: $x = \frac{18}{7}$

17. Solve the equation $2x - 1 = 2\sqrt{2x - 2}$.

    (a) $x = 1$ **(b)** $x = \frac{3}{2}$ **(c)** $x = \frac{1}{2}$ **(d)** $x = -\frac{3}{2}$ **(e)** None of these

    2—Ans: b

18. Solve the equation $2x + 1 = 3\sqrt{x}$.

    (a) $x = \frac{1}{4}$ **(b)** $x = \frac{1}{2}$ **(c)** $x = \frac{9}{4}$ **(d)** $x = -1$ **(e)** None of these

    2—Ans: a

19. Solve the equation and check each solution.

$$3 - x = \sqrt{x} + 1$$

    2—Ans: $x = 1$

20. Solve the equation and check each solution.

$$2x + 2 = 5\sqrt{x}$$

    2—Ans: $x = \frac{1}{4}$ and $x = 4$

21. Solve the equation $\sqrt{5 - x} = 2 + \sqrt{9 + 2x}$.

    (a) $x = 1$ **(b)** $x = 8$ **(c)** $x = -4$ **(d)** $x = 4$ **(e)** None of these

    2—Ans: c

22. Solve the equation $\sqrt{9-x} + 2 = \sqrt{25 + 3x}$.

   (a) $x = 5$ **(b)** $x = -7$ **(c)** $x = 8$ **(d)** $x = 0$ **(e)** None of these

   2—Ans: d

23. Solve the equation $\sqrt{9-x} - 2 = \sqrt{25 + 3x}$.

   (a) $x = 5$ **(b)** $x = -7$ **(c)** $x = 8$ **(d)** $x = 0$ **(e)** None of these

   2—Ans: b

24. Solve the equation $\sqrt{9-x} + 6 = \sqrt{25 + 3x}$.

   (a) $x = 8$ **(b)** $x = -7$ **(c)** $x = 0$ **(d)** $x = 5$ **(e)** None of these

   2—Ans: a

25. Solve the equation for x. $\sqrt{2-x} + 1 = \sqrt{11 + x}$

   2—Ans: $x = -2$

26. Solve the equation for x. $\sqrt{10 + x} = 1 + \sqrt{15 - x}$

   2—Ans: $x = 6$

27. For the right triangle shown, the length of the hypotenuse, x, is:

   (a) $\sqrt{40}$ **(b)** $\sqrt{10}$

   (c) 58   **(d)** $\sqrt{58}$

   (e) None of these

   1—Ans: d

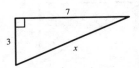

28. For the right triangle shown, the length of the hypotenuse, x, is:

   (a) 449   **(b)** $\sqrt{351}$

   (c) $\sqrt{449}$ **(d)** $\sqrt{27}$

   (e) None of these

   1—Ans: c

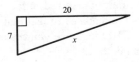

29. Use your calculator to find the length of x in the right triangle shown. (Round your answer to two decimal places.)

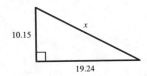

   1—T—Ans: 21.75

30. Use your calculator to find the length of x in the right triangle shown.
(Round your answer to two decimal places.)

1—T—Ans: 15.10

31. Use your calculator to find the length of x in the right triangle shown.
(Round your answer to two decimal places.)

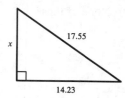

1—T—Ans: 10.27

32. Use your calculator to find the length of x in the right triangle shown.
(Round your answer to two decimal places.)

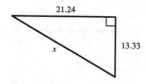

1—T—Ans: 25.08

33. The velocity of a freely-falling object is given by the formula $v = \sqrt{2gh}$, where v is the velocity measured in feet per second, $g = 32$ feet per second per second, and h is the distance in feet that the object has fallen. If a rock is dropped from a height of 100 feet, use your calculator to find the velocity when the object hits the ground.

(a) 100 feet per second   **(b)** 64 feet per second   **(c)** 80 feet per second

(d) 800 feet per second   **(e)** None of these

1—T—Ans: c

34. The velocity of a freely-falling object is given by the formula $v = \sqrt{2gh}$, where v is the velocity measured in feet per second, $g = 32$ feet per second per second, and h is the distance in feet that the object has fallen. If a rock is dropped from a height of 144 feet, use your calculator to find the velocity when the object hits the ground.

(a) 144 feet per second   **(b)** 80 feet per second   **(c)** 960 feet per second

(d) 96 feet per second   **(e)** None of these

1—T—Ans: d

35. The velocity of a freely-falling object is given by the formula $v = \sqrt{2gh}$, where v is the velocity measured in feet per second, $g = 32$ feet per second per second, and h is the distance in feet that the object has fallen. If a rock strikes the ground with a velocity of 80 feet per second, use your calculator to find the height from which it was dropped.

   (a) 100 feet   **(b)** 80 feet   **(c)** 144 feet   **(d)** 64 feet   **(e)** None of these

   1—T—Ans: a

36. The velocity of a freely-falling object is given by the formula $v = \sqrt{2gh}$, where v is the velocity measured in feet per second, $g = 32$ feet per second per second, and h is the distance in feet that the object has fallen. If a rock strikes the ground with a velocity of 96 feet per second, use your calculator to find the height from which it was dropped.

   (a) 96 feet   **(b)** 144 feet   **(c)** 80 feet   **(d)** 64 feet   **(e)** None of these

   1—T—Ans: b

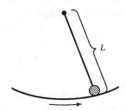

ILLUSTRATION FOR 37–38

37. The time, t, in seconds, for a pendulum of length L in feet, to move through one complete cycle (its *period*) is given by $t = 2\pi\sqrt{\dfrac{L}{32}}$.

   Use your calculator to find the length of the pendulum of a clock that has a period of 0.85 seconds.

   1—T—Ans: 0.586 foot or 7.03 inches

38. The time, t, in seconds, for a pendulum of length L in feet, to move through one complete cycle (its *period*) is given by $t = 2\pi\sqrt{\dfrac{L}{32}}$.

   Use your calculator to find the length of the pendulum of a clock that has a period of 1.05 seconds.

   1—T—Ans: 0.894 foot or 10.72 inches

39. The demand equation for a certain product is given by $p = 51 - \sqrt{2x - 1}$, where x is the number of units demanded per day and p is the price per unit. Use your calculator to find the demand when the price is $36.89.

   (a) $x = 120$ **(b)** $x = 100$ **(c)** $x = 80$ **(d)** $x = 150$ **(e)** None of these

   1—T—Ans: b

40. The demand equation for a certain product is given by $p = 51 - \sqrt{2x - 1}$, where x is the number of units demanded per day and p is the price per unit. Use your calculator to find the demand when the price is $35.54.

(a) $x = 120$ (b) $x = 100$ (c) $x = 80$ (d) $x = 150$ (e) None of these

1—T—Ans: a

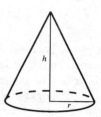

ILLUSTRATION FOR 41–42

41. The surface area of a circular cone is given by $S = \pi r\sqrt{r^2 + h^2}$, where h is the height and r is the base radius. Assume a teepee is in the shape of a circular cone. If a teepee with a base radius of 5 feet is made from 200 square feet of canvas, use your calculator to find the height of the teepee.

2—T—Ans: 11.7 feet

42. The surface area of a circular cone is given by $S = \pi r\sqrt{r^2 + h^2}$, where h is the height and r is the base radius. Assume a teepee is in the shape of a circular cone. If a teepee with a base radius of 6 feet is made from 200 square feet of canvas, use your calculator to find the height of the teepee.

2—T—Ans: 8.75 feet

43. Solve $\sqrt{4 + 3x} = 10$.

(a) 2   (b) 32   (c) $\frac{8}{3}$ (d) $\frac{64}{3}$ (e) None of these

1—Ans: b

44. Solve $\sqrt{2x + 1} = 7$.

(a) 3   (b) $\frac{13}{2}$ (c) 18   (d) 24   (e) None of these

1—Ans: d

45. Solve $\sqrt{x} + x = 2$.

(a) 1   (b) 1, 4   (c) 1, −4   (d) 2   (e) None of these

1—Ans: a

46. Solve $\sqrt{x} + 2 = x$.

(a) 1, 4   (b) 1   (c) 4   (d) 1, −4   (e) None of these

1—Ans: c

47. Find s when $t = 3$ in the equation $t = \dfrac{\sqrt{1350 - s}}{4}$.

    (a) 9175   **(b)** 1206   **(c)** 1494   **(d)** 1338   **(e)** None of these

    2—Form: 9A—Ans: b

48. Find x when $y = 4$ in the equation $\sqrt{2x} = \dfrac{y}{3}$.

    (a) $\dfrac{8}{9}$ **(b)** $\dfrac{2}{3}$ **(c)** $\dfrac{2\sqrt{2}}{3}$ **(d)** $\dfrac{8}{3}$ **(e)** None of these

    2—Form: 9B—Ans: a

49. Find the length of the unknown side of the right triangle in the accompanying figure.

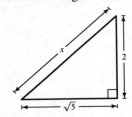

    (a) $2 + \sqrt{5}$ **(b)** $\sqrt{7}$ **(c)** 9   **(d)** 3   **(e)** None of these

    1—Ans: d

50. Find the length of the unknown side of the right triangle in the accompanying figure.

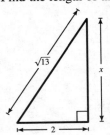

    (a) $\sqrt{11}$ **(b)** 3   **(c)** $\sqrt{13} - 2$ **(d)** $\sqrt{17}$ **(e)** None of these

    1—Ans: b

51. Solve $\sqrt{7 - 2x} = 2$.

    1—Ans: $\frac{3}{2}$

52. Solve $\sqrt{5x - 3} = 4$.

    1—Ans: $\frac{19}{5}$

53. Solve $\dfrac{2}{\sqrt{x - 1}} = 3$.

    2—Ans: $\frac{13}{9}$

54. Solve $\dfrac{3}{\sqrt{2-x}} = 4$.

   2—Form: 9C—Ans: $\dfrac{23}{16}$

55. Find c when $x = 3$ in the equation $x = \dfrac{2 + \sqrt{4 - 4c}}{2}$.

   2—Ans: -3

56. Find c when $x = 3$ in the equation $x = \dfrac{4 + \sqrt{16 - 4c}}{2}$.

   2—Form: 9C—Ans: 3

57. Find the length of the unknown side of the right triangle in the accompanying figure.

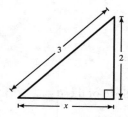

   1—Ans: $\sqrt{5}$

58. Find the length of the unknown side of the right triangle in the accompanying figure.

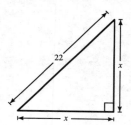

   1—Ans: $\sqrt{11}$

59. Solve $\sqrt{x + 4} + 2 = x$.

   (a) $\dfrac{-1 \pm \sqrt{33}}{2}$ **(b)** 5   **(c)** 0, 5

   (d) 0, 1   **(e)** None of these

   2—Form: 9A—Ans: b

60. Solve $3x + 5 = \sqrt{2 - 2x}$.

   (a) $-\frac{23}{9}, -1$ **(b)** $-\frac{23}{9}$ **(c)** 0, -1 **(d)** -1 **(e)** None of these

   2—Form: 9A—Ans: d

61. Solve $\sqrt[3]{4x - 1} = 3$.

(a) 7   (b) 1   (c) $\frac{1}{4}\left(1 - \sqrt[3]{3}\right)$ (d) $\frac{5}{2}$ (e) None of these

2—Ans: a

62. Solve $\sqrt{2 - 5x} = 5x$.

(a) $\frac{1}{5}$ (b) $-\frac{2}{5}$ (c) $\frac{1}{5}, -\frac{2}{5}$ (d) $\frac{1}{10}$ (e) None of these

2—Ans: a

63. Use a graphing utility to graph both sides of the equation $\sqrt[3]{6x - 4} - \sqrt[3]{2 - x} = 0$ on the same screen. Then use the graphs to determine the number of solutions and to approximate the solution(s). Check your approximations algebraically.

2—T—Ans: One solution; $\frac{6}{7}$

64. Use a graphing utility to graph both sides of the equation $\sqrt{x^2 + 11} - \sqrt{x^2 - 9} = 2$ on the same screen. Then use the graphs to determine the number of solutions and to approximate the solution(s). Check your approximations algebraically.

1—T—Form: 9C—Ans: Two solutions; -5 and 5

65. Use a graphing utility to graph both sides of the equation $\sqrt{x^2 + 9} + \sqrt{x^2 - 7} = 8$ on the same screen. Then use the graphs to determine the number of solutions.

(a) 0   (b) 1   (c) 2   (d) 3   (e) 4

1—T—Form: 9A—Ans: c

66. Use a graphing utility to graph both sides of the equation $\sqrt{5x - 4} = 2 - \sqrt{5x}$ on the same screen. Then use the graphs to determine the number of solutions.

(a) 0   (b) 1   (c) 2   (d) 3   (e) 4

1—T—Form: 9B—Ans: b

67. Solve $\sqrt{4x - 3} = 11$.

(a) $\frac{7}{2}$ (b) 2   (c) $\frac{11}{4}$ (d) 31   (e) None of these

1—Ans: d

68. Solve $\sqrt{5 + 2x} = 8$.

(a) $\frac{3}{2}$ (b) $\frac{59}{2}$ (c) $\frac{69}{2}$ (d) 4   (e) None of these

1—Ans: b

69. Solve $\sqrt[3]{2x - 3} = 4$.

(a) $\frac{7}{2}$ (b) $\frac{19}{2}$ (c) $\frac{67}{2}$ (d) $\frac{15}{2}$ (e) None of these

1—Ans: c

70. Solve $\sqrt{3 - 8x} = 4x$.

(a) 4 (b) $\frac{1}{4}, -\frac{3}{4}$ (c) $-\frac{3}{4}$ (d) $\frac{1}{4}$ (e) None of these

2—Ans: d

Section 9.5   Complex Numbers

1. Write the number in the *i*-form: $\sqrt{-\dfrac{29}{4}}$.

(a) $-\dfrac{29}{4}i$ (b) $-\dfrac{\sqrt{29}}{2}i$ (c) $\dfrac{29i}{2}$ (d) $\dfrac{\sqrt{29}}{2}i$ (e) None of these

1—Ans: d

2. Write the number in the *i*-form: $\sqrt{-\dfrac{31}{9}}$.

(a) $-\dfrac{\sqrt{31}}{3}i$ (b) $\dfrac{31i}{3}i$ (c) $\dfrac{\sqrt{31}}{3}i$ (d) $-\dfrac{31}{9}i$ (e) None of these

1—Ans: c

3. Write $\sqrt{-12}$ in *i*-form.

1—Ans: $2\sqrt{3}i$

4. Write $\sqrt{-68}$ in *i*-form.

1—Ans: $2\sqrt{17}i$

5. Add: $\sqrt{-108} + \sqrt{-75}$.

(a) $11\sqrt{3}i$ (b) $\sqrt{183}i$ (c) $3(\sqrt{6} + \sqrt{5})i$

(d) $11\sqrt{6}i$ (e) None of these

1—Ans: a

6. Subtract: $\sqrt{-125} - \sqrt{-20}$.

(a) $3\sqrt{10}i$ (b) $5(\sqrt{5} - \sqrt{2})i$ (c) $\sqrt{105}i$

(d) $3\sqrt{5}i$ (e) None of these

1—Ans: d

7. Add and write the answer in standard form.

$\sqrt{-98} + \sqrt{-32}$

1—Ans: $11\sqrt{2}i$

8. Add and write the answer in standard form.

$$\sqrt{-63} + \sqrt{-28}$$

1—Ans: $5\sqrt{7}i$

9. Simplify: $(i)^{26}$.

  (a) 1   **(b)** i **(c)** -1 **(d)** $-i$ **(e)** None of these

  1—Ans: c

10. Simplify: $(i)^{31}$.

  (a) 1   **(b)** i **(c)** -1 **(d)** $-i$ **(e)** None of these

  1—Ans: d

11. Simplify: $(i)^{44}$.

  (a) 1   **(b)** i **(c)** -1 **(d)** $-i$ **(e)** None of these

  1—Ans: a

12. Simplify: $(i)^{33}$.

  (a) 1   **(b)** i **(c)** -1 **(d)** $-i$ **(e)** None of these

  1—Ans: b

13. Multiply and simplify: $\sqrt{-40}\sqrt{-18}$.

  1—Ans: $-12\sqrt{5}$

14. Multiply and simplify: $\sqrt{-50}\sqrt{-54}$

  1—Ans: $-30\sqrt{3}$

15. Simplify: $\sqrt{-16} - \sqrt{32}$.

  (a) $-4\sqrt{2} - 4i$ **(b)** $-4\sqrt{2} + 4i$ **(c)** $4 + 4\sqrt{2}i$

  (d) $-4 - 4\sqrt{2}i$ **(e)** None of these

  1—Ans: b

16. Simplify: $-\left(\sqrt{-32} + \sqrt{16}\right)$.

  (a) $-4\sqrt{2} - 4i$ **(b)** $-4\sqrt{2} + 4i$ **(c)** $4 + 4\sqrt{2}i$

  (d) $-4 - 4\sqrt{2}i$ **(e)** None of these

  1—Ans: d

17. Determine the values of a and b so that $(a - 1) + bi = \sqrt{-16} - 4$.

  1—Ans: $a = -3, \quad b = 4$

18. Determine the values of a and b so that $(a - 2) - 2bi = 5 - \sqrt{-25}$.

   1—Ans: $a = 7, \quad b = \frac{5}{2}$

19. Perform the indicated operations and simplify: $\sqrt{-16} - (2 + 3i) + (1 - 4i)$.

   (a) $-1 - 11i$ **(b)** $3 - 5i$ **(c)** $-1 - 3i$ **(d)** $3 + 3i$ **(e)** None of these

   1—Ans: c

20. Perform the indicated operations and simplify: $(1 - 4i) - (2 + 3i) - \sqrt{-16}$.

   (a) $-1 - 11i$ **(b)** $3 - 5i$ **(c)** $-1 - 3i$ **(d)** $3 + 3i$ **(e)** None of these

   1—Ans: a

21. Perform the indicated operations and express the answer in standard form.

   $(3 - 5i) - \left(\sqrt{-25} + 2\right) - (4 - 2i)$

   1—Ans: $-3 - 8i$

22. Perform the indicated operations and express the answer in standard form.

   $\left(\sqrt{-25} - 2\right) - (3 - 5i) - (2i + 4)$

   1—Ans: $-9 + 8i$

23. Perform the multiplication and simplify: $(5 - 12i)(3 + 7i)$.

   (a) $99 + i$ **(b)** $99 - i$ **(c)** $-69 + 71i$ **(d)** $-69 - 71i$ **(e)** None of these

   1—Ans: b

24. Perform the multiplication and simplify: $(5 - 12i)(3 - 7i)$.

   (a) $99 + i$ **(b)** $99 - i$ **(c)** $-69 + 71i$ **(d)** $-69 - 71i$ **(e)** None of these

   1—Ans: d

25. Perform the multiplication and write your answer in standard form.

   $(5 - 7i)(-2 + 3i)$

   1—Ans: $11 + 29i$

26. Perform the multiplication and write your answer in standard form.

   $(-6i)(7 - 3i)$

   1—Ans: $-18 - 42i$

27. Perform the multiplication and write your answer in standard form.

   $(5 - 4i)^2$

   1—Ans: $9 - 40i$

28. Perform the multiplication and write your answer in standard form.

$$i(1 + i)^2$$

1—Ans: -2

29. The conjugate of $\sqrt{3} - \sqrt{2}i$ is:

(a) $\dfrac{1}{\sqrt{3} - \sqrt{2}i}$ (b) $\sqrt{2} - \sqrt{3}i$ (c) $\sqrt{2} + \sqrt{3}i$ (d) $3 + 2i$ (e) None of these

1—Ans: e

30. The conjugate of $5 + \sqrt{-7}$ is:

(a) $\dfrac{1}{5 + \sqrt{7}i}$ (b) $5 - 7i$ (c) $5 - \sqrt{7}i$ (d) $\sqrt{7} - 5i$ (e) None of these

1—Ans: c

31. Find the complex conjugate of i^3.

2—Ans: i

32. Find the complex conjugate of $(2 - i)^2$.

2—Ans: $3 + 4i$

33. Find the complex conjugate of $i(4 - 5i)$.

2—Ans: $5 - 4i$

34. Find the complex conjugate of $(1 + 2i)^2$.

2—Ans: $-3 - 4i$

35. Write $\dfrac{3 - 2i}{2 + 4i}$, in standard form.

(a) $\dfrac{1}{10} - \dfrac{4}{5}i$ (b) $-\dfrac{1}{10} + \dfrac{4}{5}i$ (c) $-\dfrac{1}{10} - \dfrac{4}{5}i$

(d) $\dfrac{1}{10} + \dfrac{4}{5}i$ (e) $\dfrac{3}{2} - \dfrac{1}{2}i$

2—Ans: c

36. Write $\dfrac{2 + 4i}{3 - 2i}$, in standard form.

(a) $-\dfrac{2}{13} - \dfrac{16}{13}i$ (b) $\dfrac{2}{13} - \dfrac{16}{13}i$ (c) $\dfrac{2}{13} + \dfrac{16}{13}i$

(d) $-\dfrac{2}{13} + \dfrac{16}{13}i$ (e) None of these

2—Ans: d

37. Perform the division, $\dfrac{3 + 7i}{3 - 7i}$, and write the answer in standard form.

    2—Ans: $-\dfrac{20}{29} + \dfrac{21}{29}i$

38. Perform the division, $\dfrac{3 - 7i}{3 + 7i}$, and write the answer in standard form.

    2—Ans: $-\dfrac{20}{29} - \dfrac{21}{29}i$

39. Perform the division, $\dfrac{1 + 4i}{4 - i}$, and write the answer in standard form.

    2—Ans: i

40. Perform the division, $\dfrac{4 - i}{1 + 4i}$, and write the answer in standard form.

    2—Ans: $-i$

41. Simplify: $(3 - 2i) + (-4 + 4i) - \left(1 + \sqrt{-4}\right)$.

    (a) $-2 + 4i$ **(b)** 0 **(c)** -2 **(d)** $4i$ **(e)** None of these

    1—Form: 9A—Ans: c

42. Simplify: $(5 - 3i) + (-2 - i) - \left(2 + \sqrt{-9}\right)$.

    (a) $1 - 7i$ **(b)** $1 - i$ **(c)** $5 - 7i$ **(d)** $1 + i$ **(e)** None of these

    1—Form: 9B—Ans: a

43. Multiply: $(3 + 4i)(2 - i)$.

    (a) $2 + 5i$ **(b)** $10 + 5i$ **(c)** $6 - 4i$ **(d)** $10 + 3i$ **(e)** None of these

    1—Ans: c

44. Multiply: $(2 - 4i)(3 + i)$.

    (a) $7 - 5i$ **(b)** $6 - 4i$ **(c)** $10 - 10i$ **(d)** $2 - 10i$ **(e)** None of these

    1—Ans: c

45. Divide: $(3 + 4i) \div (2 - i)$.

    (a) $\frac{3}{2} - 4i$ **(b)** $10 + 5i$ **(c)** $2 + i$ **(d)** $\frac{2}{5} + \frac{11}{5}i$ **(e)** None of these

    2—Form: 9A—Ans: d

46. Divide: $(3 + 4i) \div (2 + i)$.

    (a) $\frac{3}{2} + 4i$ **(b)** $2 + i$ **(c)** $\frac{2}{5} + i$ **(d)** $3 + 4i$ **(e)** None of these

    2—Form: 9B—Ans: b

47. Evaluate: $(2i)^2(i)(-i^2)$.

(a) $4i$ (b) 4 (c) $-4i$ (d) -4 (e) None of these

1—Ans: c

48. Evaluate: $(2i)^3(-i^2)(-i)$.

(a) -8 (b) $8i$ (c) $-8i$ (d) 8 (e) None of these

1—Ans: a

49. Perform the operations and write your answer in standard form.

$$(-2 - 3i) - (1 - i) - \left(-3 - \sqrt{-4}\right)$$

1—Ans: 0

50. Perform the operations and write your answer in standard form.

$$(-4 - 3i) + (2 + 5i) + \left(-2 - \sqrt{-9}\right)$$

1—Form: 9C—Ans: $4 - i$

51. Multiply $(4 - i)(3 - 2i)$ and write your answer in standard form.

1—Ans: $10 - 11i$

52. Multiply $(2 + 5i)(4 - i)$ and write your answer in standard form.

1—Form: 9C—Ans: $13 + 18i$

53. Divide $(4 - i) \div (3 - 2i)$ and write your answer in standard form.

2—Ans: $\frac{14}{13} + \frac{5}{13}i$

54. Divide $(2 + 5i) \div (4 - i)$ and write your answer in standard form.

2—Form: 9C—Ans: $\frac{3}{17} + \frac{22}{17}i$

55. Multiply the number $-2 + 5i$ by its conjugate.

(a) -21 (b) -29 (c) $-21 - 20i$ (d) $29 - 20i$ (e) 29

1—Form: 9A—Ans: e

56. Multiply the number $3 - 5i$ by its conjugate.

(a) -16 (b) 34 (c) -16 (d) $-16 - 30i$ (e) $25 - 15i$

1—Form: 9B—Ans: b

57. Multiply the number $6 - 3i$ by its conjugate.

1—Ans: 45

58. Multiply the number $-4 + 3i$ by its conjugate.

   1—Form: 9C—Ans: 25

59. Find the real number a so that $(a + 2i) + (3 - bi) = -5 + 6i$

   (a) -2 **(b)** -8 **(c)** 2 **(d)** -4 **(e)** None of these

   1—Ans: b

60. Find the real number b so that $(4 - bi) + (a + i) = 2 - 3i$

   (a) -2 **(b)** -4 **(c)** 4 **(d)** 0 **(e)** None of these

   1—Ans: c

61. Perform the indicated operation and write the result in standard form: $-2i(4 - 3i)$.

   (a) $-6 - 8i$ **(b)** $3 + 4i$ **(c)** $6 - 8i$ **(d)** $-6 - 4i$ **(e)** None of these

   1—Ans: a

62. Perform the indicated operation and write the result in standard form: $(2 + 5i)^2$.

   (a) $29 + 20i$ **(b)** $-21 + 10i$ **(c)** $-21 + 20i$ **(d)** $29 + 10i$ **(e)** None of these

   1—Ans: c

63. Perform the indicated operation and write the result in standard form: $\dfrac{2}{1 + i}$.

   (a) $2 + \dfrac{2}{i}$ **(b)** $1 - i$ **(c)** $2 + 2i$ **(d)** 1 **(e)** None of these

   2—Ans: b

64. Perform the indicated operation and write the result in standard form: $\dfrac{2 + 3i}{i}$.

   (a) $\dfrac{2}{i} + 3$ **(b)** $-3 - 2i$ **(c)** $3 - 2i$ **(d)** $-3 + 2i$ **(e)** None of these

   2—Ans: c

65. Perform the indicated operation and write the result in standard form: $\dfrac{2}{(3 - i)^2}$.

   (a) $\dfrac{4}{25} + \dfrac{3}{25}i$ **(b)** $\dfrac{1}{4 - 3i}$ **(c)** $8 - 6i$ **(d)** $\dfrac{1}{4} - \dfrac{1}{3}i$ **(e)** None of these

   2—Form: 9A—Ans: a

66. Perform the indicated operation and write the result in standard form: $\dfrac{(2 - i)(3 + 4i)}{2 + i}$.

   (a) $\dfrac{31}{5} - \dfrac{32}{5}t$ **(b)** 10 **(c)** $10 + 5i$ **(d)** 5 **(e)** None of these

   2—Form: 9B—Ans: d

CHAPTER 10
Quadratic Equations and Inequalities

Section 10.1   Factoring and Extracting Square Roots

1. Solve $9x^2 + 25x = 0$.

    (a) $x = 0$ and $x = \frac{25}{9}$ **(b)** $x = 0$ and $x = -\frac{9}{25}$ **(c)** $x = \frac{5}{3}$ and $x = -\frac{5}{3}$

    (d) $x = 0$ and $x = -\frac{25}{9}$ **(e)** None of these

    1—Ans: d

2. Solve $9x^2 - 16x = 0$.

    (a) $x = 0$ and $x = \frac{9}{16}$ **(b)** $x = \frac{4}{3}$ and $x = -\frac{4}{3}$ **(c)** $x = 0$ and $x = \frac{16}{9}$

    (d) $x = 0$ and $x = -\frac{16}{9}$ **(e)** None of these

    1—Ans: c

3. Solve the quadratic equation.

$$9x^2 + 6x + 1 = 0$$

    1—Ans: $x = -\frac{1}{3}$, repeated solution

4. Solve the quadratic equation.

$$4x^2 - 20x + 25 = 0$$

    1—Ans: $x = \frac{5}{2}$, repeated solution

5. Solve the quadratic equation $2x^2 - 11x + 12 = 0$.

    (a) $x = \frac{3}{2}$ and $x = -4$ **(b)** $x = \frac{3}{2}$ and $x = 4$ **(c)** $x = -\frac{3}{2}$ and $x = 4$

    (d) $x = -\frac{3}{2}$ and $x = -4$ **(e)** None of these

    1—Ans: b

6. Solve the quadratic equation $2x^2 + 5x - 12 = 0$.

    (a) $x = \frac{3}{2}$ and $x = -4$ **(b)** $x = \frac{3}{2}$ and $x = 4$ **(c)** $x = -\frac{3}{2}$ and $x = 4$

    (d) $x = -\frac{3}{2}$ and $x = -4$ **(e)** None of these

    1—Ans: a

7. Solve the quadratic equation $10x^2 + 21x - 10 = 0$.

    2—Ans: $x = \frac{2}{5}$ and $x = -\frac{5}{2}$

8. Solve the quadratic equation $10x^2 - 29x + 10 = 0$.

   2—Ans: $x = \frac{2}{5}$ and $x = \frac{5}{2}$

9. Solve the equation by factoring.

$$u(u - 10) + 4(u - 10) = 0$$

  (a) $u = 10$ and $u = -4$ **(b)** $u = 10$ and $u = 4$ **(c)** $u = -10$ and $u = -4$

  (d) $u = -10$ and $u = 4$ **(e)** None of these

   1—Ans: a

10. Solve the equation by factoring.

$$u(u + 10) - 4(u + 10) = 0$$

  (a) $u = 10$ and $u = -4$ **(b)** $u = 10$ and $u = 4$ **(c)** $u = -10$ and $u = -4$

  (d) $u = -10$ and $u = 4$ **(e)** None of these

   1—Ans: d

11. Solve the quadratic equation $2 + x^2 = 20 - x^2$.

   1—Ans: $x = 3$ and $x = -3$

12. Solve the quadratic equation $5 - 10x^2 = 6x^2 - 4$.

   1—Ans: $x = \frac{3}{4}$ and $x = -\frac{3}{4}$

13. Solve the quadratic equation $20(x^2 - 1) = 16 - 5x^2$.

   1—Ans: $x = \frac{6}{5}$ and $x = -\frac{6}{5}$

14. Solve the quadratic equation $3(x^2 - 3) = 16 - x^2$.

   1—Ans: $x = \frac{5}{2}$ and $x = -\frac{5}{2}$

15. Solve by extracting square roots $4(x + 2)^2 = 49$.

   1—Ans: $\frac{3}{2}, -\frac{11}{2}$

16. Solve by extracting square roots $9(z + 4)^2 = 64$.

   1—Ans: $-\frac{20}{3}, -\frac{4}{3}$

17. Solve $16(x + 1)^2 = 25$ by extracting square roots.

   1—Ans: $x = \frac{1}{4}$ and $x = -\frac{9}{4}$

18. Solve $9(x - 2)^2 = 49$ by extracting square roots.

   1—Ans: $x = -\frac{1}{3}$ and $x = \frac{13}{3}$

19. Solve $36(x - 3)^2 = 64$ by extracting square roots.

  1—Ans: $x = \frac{5}{3}$ and $x = \frac{13}{3}$

20. Solve $81(x + 4)^2 = 25$ by extracting square roots.

  1—Ans: $x = \dfrac{-31}{9}$ and $x = \dfrac{-41}{9}$

21. Which of the following has no real number solution?

  (a) $x^2 - 9 = 0$ **(b)** $x^2 - 9x = 0$ **(c)** $x^2 + 9 = 0$

  (d) $x^2 - 9x = 0$ **(e)** None of these

  1—Ans: c

22. Which of the following has no real number solution?

  (a) $4x^2 + 9 = 0$ **(b)** $4x^2 + 9x = 0$ **(c)** $4x^2 - 9x = 0$

  (d) $4x^2 - 9 = 0$ **(e)** None of these

  1—Ans: a

23. Solve $x^2 + 64 = 0$.

  1—Ans: $x = 8i$ and $x = -8i$

24. Solve $x^2 + 49 = 0$.

  1—Ans: $x = 7i$ and $x = -7i$

25. Solve by extracting square roots.

  $(x + 4)^2 = -5$

  (a) $x + 2 = \pm\sqrt{5}i$ **(b)** $x + 4 = 25$ **(c)** $x = -4 \pm \sqrt{5}i$

  (d) $x = -4 \pm \sqrt{5}$ **(e)** None of these

  2—Ans: c

26. Solve by extracting square roots.

  $(x - 9)^2 = -7$

  (a) $x = 3 \pm \sqrt{7}i$ **(b)** $x - 9 = 49$ **(c)** $x = 9 \pm \sqrt{7}$

  (d) $x = 9 \pm \sqrt{7}i$ **(e)** None of these

  2—Ans: d

27. Solve $(x - 10)^2 + 3 = 0$ by extracting square roots.

  2—Ans: $x = 10 \pm \sqrt{3}i$

28. Solve $(x + 5)^2 + 13 = 0$ by extracting square roots.

2—Ans: $x = -5 \pm \sqrt{13}i$

29. Solve $u - 6\sqrt{u} + 8 = 0$.

    (a) $u = 2$ and $u = 4$ **(b)** $u = 4$ only   **(c)** $u = 16$ only

    (d) $u = 4$ and $u = 16$ **(e)** All complex numbers

    2—Ans: d

30. Solve $u - 3\sqrt{u} + 2 = 0$.

    (a) $u = 2$ and $u = 1$ **(b)** $u = 2$ only   **(c)** $u = 4$ and $u = 1$

    (d) $u = 1$ only   **(e)** All complex numbers

    2—Ans: c

31. Find all real and complex solutions of $x^4 - 1 = 0$.

    2—Ans: $x = 1, x = -1, x = i, x = -i$

32. Find all real and complex solutions of $x^4 - 16 = 0$.

    2—Ans: $x = 2, x = -2, x = 2i, x = -2i$

33. Solve by factoring: $6x^2 - 7x = 20$.

    (a) $\frac{9}{2}, 20$ **(b)** $-\frac{4}{3}, \frac{5}{2}$ **(c)** $-\frac{5}{2}, 2$ **(d)** $-\frac{5}{2}, \frac{4}{3}$ **(e)** None of these

    1—Ans: b

34. Solve by factoring: $6x^2 - 25x = 9$.

    (a) $-\frac{1}{3}, \frac{9}{2}$ **(b)** $-\frac{1}{2}, 3$ **(c)** $\frac{9}{2}, \frac{22}{3}$ **(d)** $\frac{1}{2}, 3$ **(e)** None of these

    1—Ans: a

35. Solve by factoring: $3x^2 - 3x + 16 = 5x + 2x^2$.

    (a) $-4, 4$ **(b)** 4 **(c)** -4 **(d)** $-2, 8$ **(e)** None of these

    1—Ans: b

36. Solve by factoring: $3x^2 + 12x - 13 = 4x^2 + 2x + 12$.

    (a) -5 **(b)** $5, -5$ **(c)** 5 **(d)** $10, 15$ **(e)** None of these

    1—Ans: c

37. Solve by extracting square roots: $(2x + 30)^2 = 8100$.

    (a) 30 **(b)** $-465, 435$ **(c)** $30, 60$ **(d)** $-60, 30$ **(e)** None of these

    2—Ans: d

38. Solve by extracting square roots: $(3x + 10)^2 = 2500$.

    (a) $\frac{40}{3}$ **(b)** $-20, \frac{40}{3}$ **(c)** $\frac{490}{3}, 170$ **(d)** $-\frac{40}{3}, 20$ **(e)** None of these

    2—Ans: b

39. Solve by extracting square roots: $4(x - 1)^2 + 3 = 0$.

    (a) $1 + \frac{\sqrt{3}}{2}, 1 - \frac{\sqrt{3}}{2}$ **(b)** $\frac{1}{2} + \frac{\sqrt{3}}{2}i, -\frac{1}{2} + \frac{\sqrt{3}}{2}i$ **(c)** $1 + \frac{\sqrt{3}}{2}i, 1 - \frac{\sqrt{3}}{2}i$

    (d) $1 + \sqrt{7}i, 1 - \sqrt{7}i$ **(e)** None of these

    2—Form: 10A—Ans: c

40. Solve by extracting square roots: $9(x - 2)^2 + 1 = 0$.

    (a) $\frac{5}{3}, \frac{7}{3}$ **(b)** $2 - 2\sqrt{2}, 2 + 2\sqrt{2}$ **(c)** $2 - \sqrt{10}i, 2 + \sqrt{10}i$

    (d) $2 - \frac{i}{3}, 2 + \frac{i}{3}$ **(e)** None of these

    2—Form: 10B—Ans: d

41. Solve: $x^4 - 3x^2 - 4 = 0$.

    (a) $-1, 1, -2i, 2i$ **(b)** $-2, 2, -i, i$ **(c)** $-2, 2$

    (d) $2, i$ **(e)** None of these

    2—Ans: b

42. Solve: $x^4 - x^2 - 20 = 0$.

    (a) $-2, 2, -\sqrt{5}i, \sqrt{5}i$ **(b)** $\sqrt{5}, 2i$ **(c)** $-\sqrt{5}, \sqrt{5}$

    (d) $-\sqrt{5}, \sqrt{5}, -2i, 2i$ **(e)** None of these

    2—Ans: d

43. Solve by factoring: $6x^2 - x = 15$.

    1—Ans: $-\frac{3}{2}, \frac{5}{3}$

44. Solve by factoring: $4x^2 + 3x = 10$.

    1—Ans: $-2, \frac{5}{4}$

45. Solve by factoring: $20x^2 + 2x = 4x^2 + 10x - 1$.

    1—Ans: $\frac{1}{4}$

46. Solve by factoring: $18x^2 + 10x = 30x - 7x^2 - 4$.

    1—Ans: $\frac{2}{5}$

47. Solve by extracting square roots: $(3x + 60)^2 = 4500$.

   2—Ans: $-20 \pm 10\sqrt{5}$

48. Solve by extracting square roots: $(2x - 30)^2 = 4800$.

   2—Ans: $15 \pm 20\sqrt{3}$

49. Solve by extracting square roots: $4\left(x - \dfrac{1}{2}\right)^2 + 3 = 0$.

   2—Ans: $\dfrac{1}{2} \pm \dfrac{\sqrt{3}}{2}i$

50. Solve by extracting square roots: $9\left(x + \dfrac{1}{2}\right)^2 + 5 = 0$.

   2—Form: 10C—Ans: $-\dfrac{1}{2} \pm \dfrac{\sqrt{5}}{3}i$

51. Solve: $x^4 - 5x^2 - 36 = 0$.

   2—Ans: ± 3 and $\pm 2i$

52. Solve: $2x - 11\sqrt{x} + 14 = 0$.

   2—Ans: 4 and $\dfrac{49}{4}$

53. Use a graphing utility to approximate the solutions of the equation $(x + 3)^2 = 16$.

   2—T—Ans: -7 and 1

54. Use a graphing utility to approximate the solutions of the equation $(2x - 3)^2 = 4$.

   2—T—Form: 10C—Ans: $\dfrac{1}{2}$ and $\dfrac{5}{2}$

55. Use a graphing utility to approximate the solutions of the equation $(2x + 7)^2 = 4$.

   (a) -5 and -3 **(b)** $-\dfrac{9}{2}$ and $-\dfrac{5}{2}$ **(c)** $-\dfrac{7}{2}$ **(d)** $\dfrac{5}{2}$ and $\dfrac{9}{2}$ **(e)** There are none.

   2—T—Form: 10A—Ans: b

56. Use a graphing utility to approximate the solutions of the equation $(x - 5)^2 = 121$.

   (a) -6 **(b)** 5 **(c)** -5 **(d)** -16 and 6 **(e)** -6 and 16

   2—T—Form: 10B—Ans: e

57. Solve the equation $\left(\sqrt{x} + 1\right)^2 - \left(\sqrt{x} + 1\right) - 6 = 0$.

   2—Form: 10C—Ans: 4

58. Solve the equation $\frac{1}{x^2} + \frac{2}{x} - 15 = 0$.

2—Ans: $-\frac{1}{5}$ and $\frac{1}{3}$

59. Solve the equation $2\left(\frac{x+1}{x}\right)^2 - 5\left(\frac{x+1}{x}\right) - 12 = 0$.

(a) $-\frac{3}{2}$ and 4   (b) $-\frac{2}{5}$ and $\frac{1}{3}$ (c) $-\frac{2}{3}$ and $\frac{1}{4}$ (d) $-\frac{3}{5}$ and $-\frac{4}{3}$ (e) 2 and $-\frac{1}{3}$

2—Form: 10A—Ans: b

60. Solve the equation $2x^{2/3} - x^{1/3} - 6 = 0$.

(a) $-\frac{3}{2}$ and 2   (b) $\frac{9}{4}$ and 4   (c) $\frac{3}{2}$ and -2 (d) $-\frac{27}{8}$ and 8   (e) $\frac{27}{8}$ and -8

2—Form: 10B—Ans: d

61. Find a quadratic equation having $x = 3$ and $x = -\frac{1}{2}$ as solutions.

2—Ans: $2x^2 - 5x - 3 = 0$. The answer is not unique.

62. Find a quadratic equation having $x = 2 \pm 3i$ as solutions.

2—Ans: $x^2 - 4x + 13 = 0$. The answer is not unique.

63. Find a quadratic equation having $x = 3i$ and $x = -3i$ as solutions.

(a) $x^2 - 9 = 0$ (b) $x^4 - 10x^2 + 9 = 0$ (c) $x^2 + 9 = 0$

(d) $x^2 + 9x = 0$ (e) None of these

1—Ans: c

64. Find a quadratic equation having $x = 2 + \sqrt{3}$ and $x = 2 - \sqrt{3}$ as solutions.

(a) $x^2 - 4x + 7 = 0$ (b) $x^2 + 1 = 4x$ (c) $x^2 + 1 = 0$

(d) $x^2 + 4x + 1 = 0$ (e) None of these

2—Ans: b

65. Use a graphing utility to graph the function $y = x^4 + 5x^2 - 6$. Then use the graph to determine the number of real solutions for the equation $x^4 + 5x^2 - 6 = 0$.

(a) 0   (b) 1   (c) 2   (d) 3   (e) 4

1—T—Ans: c

66. Use a graphing utility to graph the function $y = x^4 - 13x^2 + 36$. Then use the graph to determine the number of real solutions for the equation $x^4 - 13x^2 + 36 = 0$.

(a) 0   (b) 1   (c) 2   (d) 3   (e) 4

1—T—Ans: e

67. Use a graphing utility to graph the function $y = 4x^2 - 4x + 4$. Then use the graph to determine the number of real solutions for the equation $4x^2 - 4x + 4 = 0$.

   (a) 0   **(b)** 1   **(c)** 2   **(d)** 3   **(e)** 4

   1—T—Ans: a

68. Use a graphing utility to graph the function $y = -2x^2 + 5x - 6$. Then use the graph to determine the number of real solutions for the equation $-2x^2 + 5x - 6 = 0$.

   1—T—Ans: 0

69. Use a graphing utility to graph the function $y = 9x^2 - 42x + 49$. Then use the graph to determine the number of real solutions for the equation $9x^2 - 42x + 49 = 0$.

   1—T—Ans: 1

70. Use a graphing utility to graph the function $y = 25x^2 + 110x + 121$. Then use the graph to determine the number of real solutions for the equation $25x^2 + 110x + 121 = 0$.

   (a) 0   **(b)** 1   **(c)** 2   **(d)** 3   **(e)** 4

   1—T—Ans: b

71. Find the radius of a circle if the area is 9 square inches.

   (a) 3 inches   **(b)** 1.69 inches   **(c)** 81π inches
   (d) 0.95 inches   **(e)** 3π inches

   1—Ans: b

72. Find the length of a side of a square if the area is 72 square inches.

   1—Ans: $6\sqrt{2}$ inches

Section 10.2   Completing the Square

1. What term should be added to $x^2 + 14x$ so that it becomes a perfect square trinomial?

   (a) 7   **(b)** 49   **(c)** -49 **(d)** 196   **(e)** None of these

   1—Ans: b

2. What term should be added to $x^2 + 13x$ so that it becomes a perfect square trinomial?

   (a) $\frac{169}{4}$ **(b)** $\frac{13}{2}$ **(c)** 169   **(d)** $-\frac{169}{4}$ **(e)** None of these

   1—Ans: a

3. Add a term to the expression so that it becomes a perfect square trinomial.

$$x^2 + 18x + \boxed{}$$

1—Ans: 81

4. Add a term to the expression so that it becomes a perfect square trinomial.

$$x^2 + 10x + \boxed{}$$

1—Ans: 25

5. Add a term to the expression so that it becomes a perfect square trinomial.

$$x^2 + \boxed{} + 81$$

(a) $18x$ **(b)** -18 **(c)** $-9x$ **(d)** 9   **(e)** None of these

1—Ans: a

6. Add a term to the expression so that it becomes a perfect square trinomial.

$$x^2 + \boxed{} + 64$$

(a) 16   **(b)** $-16x$ **(c)** -8 **(d)** $8x$ **(e)** None of these

1—Ans: b

7. Add a term to the expression so that it becomes a perfect square trinomial.

$$x^2 - \tfrac{5}{2}x + \boxed{}$$

1—Ans: $\frac{25}{16}$

8. Add a term to the expression so that it becomes a perfect square trinomial.

$$x^2 + \tfrac{8}{3} + \boxed{}$$

1—Ans: $\frac{16}{9}$

9. Which of the following is a perfect square trinomial?

(a) $x^2 + \frac{2}{5}x + \frac{4}{25}$ **(b)** $x^2 - x + 1$ **(c)** $x^2 - \frac{2}{3}x - \frac{1}{9}$

(d) $x^2 + \frac{1}{3}x + \frac{1}{36}$ **(e)** None of these

1—Ans: d

10. Which of the following is a perfect square trinomial?

(a) $x^2 + \frac{5}{4}x + \frac{25}{16}$ **(b)** $x^2 + \frac{5}{4}x + \frac{25}{64}$ **(c)** $x^2 + x + 1$

(d) $x^2 - \frac{5}{4}x - \frac{25}{64}$ **(e)** None of these

1—Ans: b

11. Fill in the missing terms in the parentheses.

$$x^2 - \tfrac{6}{7}x + \tfrac{9}{49} = (\quad)^2$$

1—Ans: $x - \frac{3}{7}$

12. Fill in the missing terms in the parentheses.

$$x^2 + \frac{14}{5}x + \frac{49}{25} = (\quad)^2$$

1—Ans: $x + \frac{7}{5}$

13. Complete the square: $x^2 - 8x - 1 = 0$.

(a) $(x - 4)^2 = 15$ **(b)** $(x - 8)^2 = 17$ **(c)** $(x - 8)^2 = 65$

(d) $(x - 4)^2 = 17$ **(e)** None of these

1—Ans: d

14. Complete the square: $x^2 - x - 4 = 0$.

(a) $\left(x - \frac{1}{2}\right)^2 = \frac{17}{4}$ **(b)** $\left(x - \frac{1}{4}\right)^2 = \frac{17}{4}$ **(c)** $\left(x + \frac{1}{2}\right)^2 = \frac{17}{4}$

(d) $\left(x - 1\right)^2 = 5$ **(e)** None of these

1—Ans: a

15. Complete the square: $x^2 + 7x + 11 = 0$.

(a) $\left(x - \frac{7}{2}\right)^2 = \frac{5}{4}$ **(b)** $\left(x + \frac{7}{2}\right)^2 = \frac{5}{4}$ **(c)** $(x + 7)^2 = 38$

(d) $\left(x + \frac{7}{4}\right)^2 = \frac{5}{4}$ **(e)** None of these

1—Ans: b

16. Complete the square: $x^2 - 5x + 5 = 0$.

(a) $(x - 5)^2 = 20$ **(b)** $\left(x + \frac{5}{2}\right)^2 = \frac{5}{2}$ **(c)** $\left(x - \frac{5}{2}\right)^2 = \frac{5}{4}$

(d) $\left(x - \frac{5}{4}\right)^2 = \frac{5}{4}$ **(e)** None of these

1—Ans: c

17. Complete the square: $x^2 - 3x - 1 = 0$.

1—Ans: $\left(x - \frac{3}{2}\right)^2 = \frac{13}{4}$

18. Complete the square: $x^2 + 7x + 9 = 0$.

1—Ans: $\left(x + \frac{7}{2}\right)^2 = \frac{13}{4}$

19. Solve $x^2 - 3x - 1 = 0$ by completing the square.

(a) $x = -\frac{3}{2} \pm \frac{\sqrt{13}}{2}$ **(b)** $x = \frac{3 \pm \sqrt{13}}{2}$ **(c)** $x = \frac{3 \pm \sqrt{5}}{2}$

(d) $x = \frac{-3 \pm \sqrt{5}}{2}$ **(e)** None of these

1—Ans: b

20. Solve $x^2 - x - 5 = 0$ by completing the square.

(a) $x = \dfrac{1 \pm \sqrt{21}}{2}$ (b) $x = \dfrac{-1 \pm \sqrt{21}}{2}$ (c) $x = \dfrac{1 \pm \sqrt{19}}{2}$

(d) $x = \dfrac{-1 \pm \sqrt{19}}{2}$ (e) None of these

1—Ans: a

21. Solve $x^2 - 4x - 2 = 0$ by completing the square.

1—Ans: $x = 2 \pm \sqrt{6}$

22. Solve $x^2 + 3x - 5 = 0$ by completing the square.

1—Ans: $x = \dfrac{-3 \pm \sqrt{29}}{2}$

23. Which of the quadratic equations has no real solution?

(a) $(x - 2)^2 - 41 = 0$ (b) $(x + 3)^2 - 11 = 0$ (c) $(x - 5)^2 + 14 = 0$

(d) $(x + 3)^2 - 21 = 0$ (e) None of these

1—Ans: c

24. Which of the quadratic equations has no real solution?

(a) $(x - 2)^2 + 41 = 0$ (b) $(x + 3)^2 - 11 = 0$ (c) $(x - 5)^2 - 14 = 0$

(d) $(x + 3)^2 - 21 = 0$ (e) None of these

1—Ans: a

25. Solve by completing the square: $x^2 + x + 3 = 0$.

2—Ans: $x = \dfrac{-1 \pm \sqrt{11}i}{2}$

26. Solve by completing the square: $x^2 - x + 5 = 0$.

2—Ans: $x = \dfrac{1 \pm \sqrt{19}i}{2}$

27. Solve $2x^2 - x - 4 = 0$ by completing the square.

(a) $x = \dfrac{-1 \pm \sqrt{33}}{4}$ (b) $x = \dfrac{1 \pm \sqrt{31}}{4}$ (c) $x = \dfrac{-1 \pm \sqrt{31}}{4}$

(d) $x = \dfrac{1 \pm \sqrt{33}}{4}$ (e) None of these

2—Ans: d

28. Solve $4x^2 - x + 2 = 0$ by completing the square.

(a) $x = \dfrac{-1 \pm \sqrt{31}}{8}$

(b) $x = \dfrac{1 \pm \sqrt{33}}{8}$

(c) $x = \dfrac{1 \pm \sqrt{31}i}{8}$

(d) $x = \dfrac{-1 \pm \sqrt{33}i}{8}$

(e) None of these

2—Ans: c

29. Solve $2x^2 + x - 2 = 0$ by completing the square.

2—Ans: $x = \dfrac{-1 \pm \sqrt{17}}{4}$

30. Solve $3x^2 + x - 1 = 0$ by completing the square.

2—Ans: $x = \dfrac{-1 \pm \sqrt{13}}{6}$

31. Solve $x - \dfrac{4}{x} = 2$.

(a) $x = 1 \pm \sqrt{5}$

(b) $x = 2 \pm \sqrt{3}$

(c) $x = 1 \pm \sqrt{5}i$

(d) $x = 2 \pm \sqrt{3}i$

(e) None of these

2—Ans: a

32. Solve $x - \dfrac{1}{x} = 4$.

(a) $x = 1 \pm \sqrt{5}$

(b) $x = 2 \pm \sqrt{5}$

(c) $x = 1 \pm \sqrt{5}i$

(d) $x = 2 \pm \sqrt{3}i$

(e) None of these

2—Ans: b

33. Solve $x + \dfrac{6}{x} = 2$.

(a) $x = 1 \pm \sqrt{5}$

(b) $x = 2 \pm \sqrt{3}$

(c) $x = 1 \pm \sqrt{5}i$

(d) $x = 2 \pm \sqrt{3}i$

(e) None of these

2—Ans: c

34. Solve $x + \dfrac{7}{x} = 4$.

(a) $x = 1 \pm \sqrt{5}$

(b) $x = 2 \pm \sqrt{3}$

(c) $x = 1 \pm \sqrt{5}i$

(d) $x = 2 \pm \sqrt{3}i$

(e) None of these

2—Ans: d

35. Find the positive solution of $0.1x^2 - 0.2x - 0.1 = 0$ to three decimal places.

1—T—Ans: 2.414

36. Find the negative solution of $0.1x^2 - 0.2x - 0.2 = 0$ to three decimal places.

1—T—Ans: -0.732

37. Find the real number c such that $x^2 - 10x + c$ is a perfect square trinomial.

(a) -25 (b) 100 (c) 25 (d) $25x^2$ (e) None of these

1—Ans: c

38. Find the real number c such that $x^2 - 12x + c$ is a perfect square trinomial.

(a) 144 (b) -36 (c) $36x^2$ (d) 36 (e) None of these

1—Ans: d

39. Solve by completing the square: $4x^2 + 20x + 9 = 0$.

(a) $-\frac{9}{2}, -\frac{1}{2}$ (b) $\frac{1}{2}, \frac{9}{2}$ (c) $-\frac{3}{4}, -3$

(d) $-5 + \frac{\sqrt{91}}{2}, -5 - \frac{\sqrt{91}}{2}$ (e) None of these

2—Form: 10A—Ans: a

40. Solve by completing the square: $4x^2 + 12x - 135 = 0$.

(a) $-\frac{9}{2}, \frac{15}{2}$ (b) $-\frac{5}{2}, \frac{3}{2}$ (c) $-\frac{15}{2}, \frac{9}{2}$

(d) $\frac{-3 - \sqrt{6}}{2}, \frac{-3 + \sqrt{6}}{2}$ (e) None of these

2—Form: 10B—Ans: c

41. Find the real number c such that $x^2 - 5x + c$ is a perfect square trinomial.

1—Form: 10B—Ans: $\frac{25}{4}$

42. Find the real number c such that $x^2 + 11x + c$ is a perfect square trinomial.

1—Ans: $\frac{121}{4}$

43. Solve by completing the square: $3x^2 - 12x - 6 = 0$.

2—Ans: $2 \pm \sqrt{6}$

44. Solve by completing the square: $3x^2 + 9x - 15 = 0$.

2—Ans: $-\frac{3}{2} \pm \frac{\sqrt{29}}{2}$

45. Find the real number c such that $x^2 - \frac{2}{3}x + c$ is a perfect square trinomial.

   (a) $\frac{4}{9}$ **(b)** 4 **(c)** $-\frac{4}{9}$ **(d)** $\frac{1}{9}$ **(e)** $\frac{1}{3}$

   1—Form: 10A—Ans: d

46. Find the real number c such that $x^2 + \frac{4}{5}x + c$ is a perfect square trinomial.

   (a) $\frac{4}{25}$ **(b)** $\frac{16}{25}$ **(c)** $\frac{2}{5}$ **(d)** $-\frac{16}{25}$ **(e)** $\frac{64}{25}$

   1—Form: 10B—Ans: a

47. Find the real number c such that $x^2 - \frac{8}{3}x + c$ is a perfect square trinomial.

   1—Form: 10C—Ans: $\frac{16}{9}$

48. Find the real number c such that $x^2 + \frac{10}{7}x + c$ is a perfect square trinomial.

   1—Ans: $\frac{25}{49}$

49. Use a calculator to find the real number c so that $u^2 - 2.3u + c$ is a perfect square trinomial. Write the trinomial as a binomial squared.

   2—T—Ans: 1.3225; $(u + 1.15)^2$

50. Use a calculator to find the real number c so that $t^2 + 0.7t + c$ is a perfect square trinomial. Write the trinomial as a binomial squared.

   2—T—Ans: 0.1225; $(t + 0.35)^2$

51. Use a calculator to find the real number c so that $s^2 - 1.7s + c$ is a perfect square trinomial. Then write the trinomial as a binomial squared.

   (a) $(s - 1.7)^2$ **(b)** $(s - 0.7225)^2$ **(c)** $(s - 0.85)^2$ **(d)** $(s + 0.85)^2$ **(e)** $(s - 1.3)^2$

   2—T—Ans: c

52. Use a calculator to find the real number c so that $y^2 - 4.9y + c$ is a perfect square trinomial. Then write the trinomial as a binomial squared.

   (a) $(y - 0.7)^2$ **(b)** $(y - 2.45)^2$ **(c)** $(y - 4.9)^2$ **(d)** $(y - 6.0025)^2$ **(e)** $(y + 0.7)^2$

   2—T—Ans: b

53. Solve the equation $3x^2 - 5x - 4 = 0$ by completing the square and use a calculator to estimate the solutions to two decimal places.

   2—T—Form: 10C—Ans: $\dfrac{5 + \sqrt{73}}{6} \approx 2.26$; $\dfrac{5 - \sqrt{73}}{6} \approx -0.59$

54. Solve the equation $2x^2 - 4x + 1 = 0$ by completing the square and use a calculator to estimate the solutions to two decimal places.

   2—T—Ans: $\dfrac{2 + \sqrt{2}}{2} \approx 1.71$; $\dfrac{2 - \sqrt{2}}{2} \approx 0.29$

55. Solve the equation $4x^2 + 5x - 2 = 0$ by completing the square and use a calculator to estimate the solutions to two decimal places.

(a) $-5.94, -4.06$ (b) $-6.27, 1.27$ (c) $-0.63 \pm 0.33i$

(d) $-1.57, 0.32$ (e) $-2.5 \pm 1.32i$

2—T—Form: 10A—Ans: d

56. Solve the equation $3x^2 - x - 3 = 0$ by completing the square and use a calculator to estimate the solutions to two decimal places.

(a) $-2.54, 3.54$ (b) $-2.04, 4.04$ (c) $-0.85, 1.18$

(d) $-0.01, 2.01$ (e) $0.16 \pm 0.99i$

2—T—Form: 10B—Ans: c

57. Solve the equation $x^2 + 6x - 2 = 0$ by completing the square.

1—Form: 10C—Ans: $-3 \pm \sqrt{11}$

58. Solve the equation $x^2 + 2x - 2 = 0$ by completing the square.

1—Ans: $-1 \pm \sqrt{3}$

59. Solve the equation $3x^2 - 2x - 12 = 0$ by completing the square.

2—Ans: $\dfrac{1 \pm \sqrt{37}}{3}$

60. Solve the equation $4x^2 + 2x - 15 = 0$ by completing the square.

2—Ans: $\dfrac{-1 \pm \sqrt{61}}{4}$

61. An open box with a rectangular base of x inches by $x + 6$ inches has a height of 10 inches. Find the dimensions of the base of the box if its volume is 270 cubic inches.

2—Ans: 3 inches by 9 inches

62. An open box with a rectangular base of x inches by $x + 8$ inches has a height of 6 inches. Find the dimensions of the base of the box if its volume is 918 cubic inches.

2—Ans: 9 inches by 17 inches

Section 10.3   The Quadratic Formula

1. Which of the quadratic equations is in standard form?

(a) $3 - 5x - 2x^2 = 0$ (b) $3x(x - 2) = 4$ (c) $(x - 3)(x + 2) = 0$

(d) $2x^2 - 7x - 2 = 0$ (e) None of these

1—Ans: d

2. Which of the quadratic equations is in standard form?

   (a) $0.02x^2 - 0.01x - 0.03 = 0$ **(b)** $(2x - 3)(3x - 2) = 0$ **(c)** $5x(x + 2) = 51$

   (d) $14 - 2x + 3x^2 = 0$ **(e)** None of these

   1—Ans: a

3. Write the quadratic equation $2(3 - 5x) = -5x^2$ in standard form.

   1—Ans: $5x^2 - 10x + 6 = 0$

4. Write the quadratic equation $2x(x - 3) = 5(x - 4)$ in standard form.

   1—Ans: $2x^2 - 11x + 20 = 0$

5. If the discriminate of a quadratic equation is positive and a perfect square, then the solutions of the equation are:

   (a) rational and equal   **(b)** irrational and unequal   **(c)** rational and unequal

   (d) complex numbers   **(e)** None of these

   2—Ans: c

6. If the discriminate of a quadratic equation is negative, then the solutions of the equation are:

   (a) rational and equal   **(b)** irrational and unequal   **(c)** rational and unequal

   (d) complex numbers   **(e)** None of these

   2—Ans: d

7. If the discriminate of a quadratic equation is positive but not a perfect square, then the solutions of the equation are:

   (a) rational and equal   **(b)** irrational and unequal   **(c)** rational and unequal

   (d) complex numbers   **(e)** None of these

   2—Ans: b

8. If the discriminate of a quadratic equation equals zero, then the solutions of the equation are:

   (a) rational and equal   **(b)** irrational and unequal   **(c)** rational and unequal

   (d) complex numbers   **(e)** None of these

   2—Ans: a

9. Use the discriminate of $3x^2 - 2x - 7 = 0$ to determine the number of real solutions of the equation.

   1—Ans: $b^2 - 4ac = 88$; two distinct irrational solutions

10. Use the discriminate of $4x^2 - 12x + 9 = 0$ to determine the number of real solutions of the equation.

    1—Ans: $b^2 - 4ac = 0$; one repeated solution.

11. Solve $49x^2 - 28x + 4 = 0$ using the Quadratic Formula.

    (a) $x = 0$ and $x = \frac{2}{7}$ **(b)** $x = \frac{2}{7}$ repeated   **(c)** $x = \frac{7}{2}$ and $x = \frac{2}{7}$

    (d) $x = -\frac{2}{7}$ repeated   **(e)** None of these

    1—Ans: b

12. Solve $25x^2 - 30x + 9 = 0$ using the Quadratic Formula.

    (a) $x = 0$ and $x = \frac{3}{5}$ **(b)** $x = \frac{5}{3}$ repeated   **(c)** $x = \frac{3}{5}$ and $x = \frac{5}{3}$

    (d) $x = \frac{3}{5}$ repeated   **(e)** None of these

    1—Ans: d

13. Use the Quadratic Formula to solve $25x^2 - 70x + 49 = 0$.

    1—Ans: $x = \frac{7}{5}$, repeated solution

14. Use the Quadratic Formula to solve $64x^2 - 80x + 25 = 0$.

    1—Ans: $x = \frac{5}{8}$, repeated solution

15. Use the Quadratic Formula to solve $6x^2 - x - 12 = 0$.

    (a) $x = \frac{2}{3}$ and $x = -\frac{3}{4}$ **(b)** $x = \frac{3}{2}$ and $x = -\frac{4}{3}$ **(c)** $x = -\frac{2}{3}$ and $x = \frac{3}{4}$

    (d) $x = -\frac{3}{2}$ and $x = \frac{4}{3}$ **(e)** None of these

    1—Ans: b

16. Use the Quadratic Formula to solve $12x^2 + x - 6 = 0$.

    (a) $x = \frac{2}{3}$ and $x = -\frac{3}{4}$ **(b)** $x = \frac{3}{2}$ and $x = -\frac{4}{3}$ **(c)** $x = -\frac{2}{3}$ and $x = \frac{3}{4}$

    (d) $x = -\frac{3}{2}$ and $x = \frac{4}{3}$ **(e)** None of these

    1—Ans: a

17. Use the Quadratic Formula to solve $6x^2 + 5x - 6 = 0$.

    1—Ans: $x = -\frac{3}{2}$ and $x = \frac{2}{3}$

18. Use the Quadratic Formula to solve $6x^2 - 5x - 6 = 0$.

    1—Ans: $x = \frac{3}{2}$ and $x = -\frac{2}{3}$

19. Use the Quadratic Formula to solve $5x^2 + 13x - 6 = 0$.

    1—Ans: $x = \frac{2}{5}$ and $x = -3$

20. Use the Quadratic Formula to solve $5x^2 - 13x - 6 = 0$.

    1—Ans: $x = -\frac{2}{5}$ and $x = 3$

21. Use the Quadratic Formula to solve $x^2 + x - 1 = 0$.

    (a) $x = \dfrac{-1 \pm \sqrt{5}}{2}$ **(b)** $x = \dfrac{1 + \pm \sqrt{5}}{2}$ **(c)** $x = \dfrac{-1 \pm \sqrt{3}}{2}$

    (d) $x = \dfrac{1 \pm \sqrt{3}}{2}$ **(e)** None of these

    1—Ans: a

22. Use the Quadratic Formula to solve $2x^2 + 2x - 1 = 0$.

    (a) $x = \dfrac{-1 \pm \sqrt{5}}{2}$ **(b)** $x = \dfrac{1 + \pm \sqrt{5}}{2}$ **(c)** $x = \dfrac{-1 \pm \sqrt{3}}{2}$

    (d) $x = \dfrac{1 \pm \sqrt{3}}{2}$ **(e)** None of these

    1—Ans: c

23. Use the Quadratic Formula to solve $x^2 + 2x - 1 = 0$.

    1—Ans: $x = -1 \pm \sqrt{2}$

24. Use the Quadratic Formula to solve $x^2 - 2x - 2 = 0$.

    1—Ans: $x = 1 \pm \sqrt{3}$

25. Which of the following quadratic equations has no real solution?

    (a) $2x^2 + x + 1 = 0$ **(b)** $3x^2 + 2x - 1 = 0$ **(c)** $2x^2 + 2x - 1 = 0$

    (d) $x^2 + 2x - 3 = 0$ **(e)** None of these

    1—Ans: a

26. Which of the following quadratic equations has no real solution?

    (a) $2x^2 + x - 1 = 0$ **(b)** $3x^2 + 2x - 1 = 0$ **(c)** $2x^2 + 2x - 1 = 0$

    (d) $x^2 + 2x + 3 = 0$ **(e)** None of these

    1—Ans: d

27. Use the Quadratic Formula to solve $3x^2 - 2x + 1 = 0$.

    1—Ans: $x = \dfrac{1 \pm \sqrt{2}\,i}{3}$

28. Use the Quadratic Formula to solve $2x^2 - 2x + 1 = 0$.

    1—Ans: $x = \dfrac{1 \pm i}{2}$

29. Use a calculator and the Quadratic Formula to find the solutions of $x^2 + x - 3 = 0$ to three decimal places.

(a) 1.303 and -2.303 (b) -1.303 and 2.303   (c) -2.158 and 1.158

(d) 2.158 and -1.158 (e) None of these

2—T—**Ans:** a

30. Use a calculator and the Quadratic Formula to find the solutions of $2x^2 - 2x - 5 = 0$ to three decimal places.

(a) 1.303 and -2.303 (b) -1.303 and 2.303   (c) -2.158 and 1.158

(d) 2.158 and -1.158 (e) None of these

2—T—**Ans:** d

31. Use a calculator and the Quadratic Formula to find the solutions of $2.08x^2 - 1.41x - 3.07 = 0$ to three decimal places.

2—T—**Ans:** $x \approx 1.600$ and $x \approx -0.922$

32. Use a calculator and the Quadratic Formula to find the solutions of $1.63x^2 + 2.71x - 2.53 = 0$ to three decimal places.

2—T—**Ans:** $x \approx -2.329$ and $x \approx 0.666$

33. The solutions to $3x - \dfrac{2}{x} = 1$ are:

(a) $x = -1$ and $x = \dfrac{2}{3}$ (b) $x = 1$ and $x = -\dfrac{2}{3}$ (c) $x = 1$ and $x = \dfrac{2}{3}$

(d) $x = -1$ and $x = -\dfrac{2}{3}$ (e) None of these

1—**Ans:** b

34. The solutions to $3x + \dfrac{2}{x} = -5$ are:

(a) $x = -1$ and $x = \dfrac{2}{3}$ (b) $x = 1$ and $-\dfrac{2}{3}$ (c) $x = 1$ and $x = \dfrac{2}{3}$

(d) $x = -1$ and $x = -\dfrac{2}{3}$ (e) None of these

1—**Ans:** d

35. Solve the equation and check your results.

$$\sqrt{3x + 2} = x - 2$$

2—**Ans:** $x = \dfrac{7 + \sqrt{41}}{2} \approx 6.702$

36. Solve the equation and check your results.

$$\sqrt{x + 2} = x + 1$$

2—Ans: $x = \dfrac{\sqrt{5} - 1}{2} \approx 0.618$

37. Solve the equation and check your results.

$$\sqrt{2 - x^2} = x + 1$$

2—Ans: $x = \dfrac{\sqrt{3} - 1}{2} \approx 0.366$

38. Solve the equation and check your results.

$$\sqrt{2 - x^2} = 1 - x$$

2—Ans: $x = \dfrac{1 - \sqrt{3}}{2} \approx -0.366$

39. Use the discriminant of the Quadratic Formula to determine which quadratic equation has one (repeated) real number solution.

(a) $3x^2 + 4x + 2 = 0$ (b) $x^2 - 5x - 4 = 0$ (c) $9x^2 - 6x + 1 = 0$

(d) $7x^2 + 2x - 1 = 0$ (e) None of these

1—Ans: c

40. Use the discriminant of the Quadratic Formula to determine which quadratic equation has no real number solutions.

(a) $x^2 + 4x + 2 = 0$ (b) $9x^2 - 6x + 1 = 0$ (c) $x^2 - 5x + 4 = 0$

(d) $7x^2 + 2x - 1 = 0$ (e) None of these

1—Ans: e

41. Solve by using the Quadratic Formula: $3x^2 - 6x + 2 = 0$.

(a) $\dfrac{3 - \sqrt{3}}{3}, \dfrac{3 + \sqrt{3}}{3}$ (b) $1 - \sqrt{3}, 1 + \sqrt{3}$ (c) $\dfrac{3 - \sqrt{15}}{3}, \dfrac{3 + \sqrt{15}}{3}$

(d) $\dfrac{1}{3}, 2$ (e) None of these

2—Form: 10A—Ans: a

42. Solve by using the Quadratic Formula: $x^2 + 4x + 2 = 0$.

(a) $-2 - 2\sqrt{2}, -2 + 2\sqrt{2}$ (b) $-2\sqrt{2}, -2 + \sqrt{2}$ (c) $-2 - \sqrt{6}, -2 + \sqrt{6}$

(d) $-4 - \sqrt{2}, -4 + \sqrt{2}$ (e) None of these

2—Form: 10B—Ans: b

43. Use a calculator to solve $2.5x^2 + 3.267x - 8.97 = 0$. Round your answer to three decimal places.

(a) $-6.643, 3.376$
(b) $-5.271, -1.263$
(c) $-8.276, 1.742$
(d) $2.657, 1.350$
(e) None of these

1—T—Form: 10A—Ans: d

44. Use a calculator to solve $1.37x^2 - 2.4x - 5.41 = 0$. Round your answer to three decimal places.

(a) $0.228, 4.572$
(b) $-1.296, 3.048$
(c) $-1.775, 4.175$
(d) $-5.720, 2.432$
(e) None of these

1—T—Form: 10B—Ans: b

45. Solve: $\dfrac{1}{x} - \dfrac{1}{x+1} = 1$

(a) $0, -1$
(b) $\dfrac{-1 - \sqrt{5}}{2}, \dfrac{-1 + \sqrt{5}}{2}$
(c) $-1 - \dfrac{\sqrt{5}}{2}, -1 + \dfrac{\sqrt{5}}{2}$
(d) $\dfrac{-1 - \sqrt{3}i}{2}, \dfrac{1 + \sqrt{3}i}{2}$
(e) None of these

2—Ans: b

46. Solve: $\dfrac{1}{x} - \dfrac{1}{x+2} = 1$

(a) $-1 - 2\sqrt{3}, -1 + 2\sqrt{3}$
(b) $0, -2$
(c) $-1 - \sqrt{3}, -1 + \sqrt{3}$
(d) $-1, 1$
(e) None of these

2—Ans: c

47. Use the discriminant to determine the number of real solutions of the equation $3x^2 + 3 = 6x$.

1—Ans: One (repeated)

48. Use the discriminant to determine the number of real solutions of the equation $x^2 - 1 = x$.

1—Ans: Two irrational

49. Solve by using the Quadratic Formula: $x^2 - 5x - 4 = 0$.

2—Ans: $\dfrac{5 \pm \sqrt{41}}{2}$

50. Solve by using the Quadratic Formula: $2x^2 - 2x - 1 = 0$.

2—Form: 10C—Ans: $\dfrac{1 \pm \sqrt{3}}{2}$

51. Use a calculator to solve the equation $3.27x^2 + 2.5x - 8.97 = 0$. Round your answer to three decimal places.

1—T—Ans: $-2.082, 1.318$

52. Use a calculator to solve the equation $1.36x^2 - 5.21x - 2.82 = 0$. Round your answer to three decimal places.

1—T—Form: 10C—Ans: $-0.481, 4.312$

53. Solve: $\sqrt{3x - 2} + 1 = x$.

2—Ans: $\dfrac{5 + \sqrt{13}}{2}$

54. Solve: $\dfrac{x}{5} - \dfrac{1}{x} = 2$.

2—Ans: $5 \pm \sqrt{30}$

55. Use a graphing utility to determine the type of solutions of the equation $4.6x^2 - 5.8x + 3.3 = 0$ by graphing the equation $y = 4.6x^2 - 5.8x + 3.3$.

(a) Two distinct real   **(b)** Two distinct complex   **(c)** One rational repeated

(d) No solutions

1—T—Form: 10A—Ans: b

56. Use a graphing utility to determine the type of solutions of the equation $-0.6x^2 + 2.9x + 2.1 = 0$ by graphing the equation $y = -0.6x^2 + 2.9x + 2.1$.

(a) Two distinct real   **(b)** Two distinct complex   **(c)** One rational repeated

(d) No solutions

1—T—Form: 10B—Ans: a

57. Use a graphing utility to determine the type of solutions of the equation $3.4x^2 + 27.2x + 54.4 = 0$ by graphing the equation $y = 3.4x^2 + 27.2x + 54.4$.

1—T—Form: 10C—Ans: One rational repeated

58. Use a graphing utility to determine the type of solutions of the equation $2.1x^2 - 6.3 = 0$ by graphing the equation $y = 2.1x^2 - 6.3$.

1—T—Ans: Two distinct real

59. Use the discriminant to determine the number of real solutions: $4x^2 - 2x - 7 = 0$.

(a) 0   **(b)** 1   **(c)** 2   **(d)** 3   **(e)** None of these

1—Ans: c

60. Use the discriminant to determine the number of real solutions: $7x^2 - 3x + 15 = 0$.

    (a) 0   **(b)** 1   **(c)** 2   **(d)** 3   **(e)** None of these

    1—Ans: a

61. Solve: $\dfrac{1}{x} - \dfrac{1}{x+1} = 1$

    (a) $-1, 0$ **(b)** $\dfrac{-1-\sqrt{5}}{2}, \dfrac{-1+\sqrt{5}}{2}$ **(c)** $-1-\dfrac{\sqrt{5}}{2}, -1+\dfrac{\sqrt{5}}{2}$

    (d) $-1, 1$ **(e)** None of these

    2—Ans: b

62. Solve: $\dfrac{1}{x-1} + \dfrac{x}{x+2} = 2$

    (a) $-2, 1$ **(b)** $-2, 0, 1$ **(c)** $-1 \pm \sqrt{7}$ **(d)** $-1 \pm \sqrt{3}$ **(e)** None of these

    2—Ans: c

Section 10.4   Graphs of Quadratic Functions

1. Which of the quadratic functions has a graph that opens upward?

    (a) $y = 2 - x - x^2$ **(b)** $y = x^2 + 2x - 2$ **(c)** $y = 4 - x^2$

    (d) $y = 9 - x - x^2$ **(e)** None of these

    1—Ans: b

2. Which of the quadratic functions has a graph that opens downward?

    (a) $y = x^2 + 16$ **(b)** $y = x^2 - 9$ **(c)** $y = 2x^2 - x - 2$

    (d) $y = 5 - x^2$ **(e)** None of these

    1—Ans: d

3. State any conditions on a so that the parabola $y = ax^2 + 7x - 2$ opens upward.

    1—Ans: $a > 0$

4. State any conditions on a so that the parabola $y = ax^2 + 7x - 2$ opens downward.

    1—Ans: $a < 0$

5. Find the x-intercepts for the parabola $y = 2x^2 - x - 1$.

    (a) $(0, -1)$ **(b)** $\left(-\frac{1}{2}, 0\right)$ and $(1, 0)$ **(c)** $\left(\frac{1}{2}, 0\right)$ and $(-1, 0)$

    (d) $(0, -1)$ and $(1, 0)$ **(e)** None of these

    1—Ans: b

6. Find the *x*-intercepts for the parabola $y = 1 - x - 2x^2$.

  (a) $(0, 1)$ **(b)** $\left(-\frac{1}{2}, 0\right)$ and $(-1, 0)$ **(c)** $(0, 1)$ and $(-1, 0)$

  (d) $\left(\frac{1}{2}, 0\right)$ and $(-1, 0)$ **(e)** None of these

  1—Ans: d

7. Find all intercepts of the parabola $y = x^2 - x - 6$.

  1—Ans: $(0, -6), (3, 0)$, and $(-2, 0)$

8. Find all intercepts of the parabola $y = 3x^2 - 2x - 5$.

  1—Ans: $(0, -5), (-1, 0)$, and $\left(\frac{5}{3}, 0\right)$

9. Find the vertex of the parabola $y = -x^2 + 4x - 2$.

  (a) $(-2, 10)$ **(b)** $(2, -2)$ **(c)** $(2, 2)$ **(d)** $(0, -2)$ **(e)** None of these

  1—Ans: c

10. Find the vertex of the parabola $y = 3x^2 - 6x + 2$.

  (a) $(1, -1)$ **(b)** $(-1, 11)$ **(c)** $(0, 2)$ **(d)** $(2, 2)$ **(e)** None of these

  1—Ans: a

11. Find the vertex of the parabola $y = x^2 - 6x + 9$.

  (a) $(-3, 36)$ **(b)** $(0, 9)$ **(c)** $(1, 4)$ **(d)** $(3, 0)$ **(e)** None of these

  1—Ans: d

12. Find the vertex of the parabola $y = -3x^2 + 18x - 20$.

  (a) $(0, -20)$ **(b)** $(3, 7)$ **(c)** $(1, -5)$ **(d)** $(-3, -101)$ **(e)** None of these

  1—Ans: b

13. Find the coordinates of the vertex of the parabola $y = -x^2 + 2x - 7$.

  1—Ans: $(1, -6)$

14. Find the coordinates of the vertex of the parabola $y = 2x^2 + 8x + 5$.

  1—Ans: $(-2, -3)$

15. Find the vertex of the parabola $y = -2x^2 + 5x - 7$.

  (a) $\left(\frac{5}{4}, -\frac{31}{8}\right)$ **(b)** $\left(-\frac{5}{4}, \frac{31}{8}\right)$ **(c)** $\left(-\frac{5}{4}, -\frac{31}{8}\right)$ **(d)** $\left(\frac{5}{4}, \frac{31}{8}\right)$ **(e)** None of these

  2—Ans: a

16. Find the vertex of the parabola $y = 2x^2 + 5x + 7$.

(a) $\left(\frac{5}{4}, -\frac{31}{8}\right)$ (b) $\left(-\frac{5}{4}, \frac{31}{8}\right)$ (c) $\left(-\frac{5}{4}, -\frac{31}{8}\right)$ (d) $\left(\frac{5}{4}, \frac{31}{8}\right)$ (e) None of these

  2—Ans: b

17. Find the coordinates of the vertex of the parabola $y = -x^2 + 3x - 5$.

  2—Ans: $\left(\frac{3}{2}, -\frac{11}{4}\right)$

18. Find the coordinates of the vertex of the parabola $y = x^2 + 3x + 5$.

  2—Ans: $\left(-\frac{3}{2}, \frac{11}{4}\right)$

19. Match the quadratic equation with its graph: $y = -\dfrac{x^2}{2} - x + 1$.

(a)

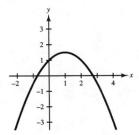

(b)

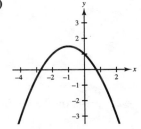

(c)

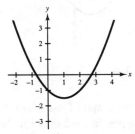

(d)

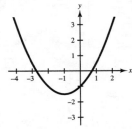

(e) None of these

  1—Ans: b

20. Match the quadratic equation with its graph: $y = \dfrac{x^2}{2} + x - 1$.

(a)

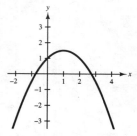

(b)

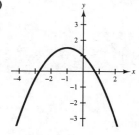

(c)

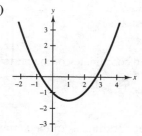

(d)

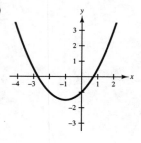

(e) None of these

1—Ans: d

21. Sketch the graph of the quadratic function $y = 2x^2 - 4x$ on the coordinate axes. List five points used in the table.

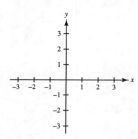

x					
y					

1—Ans: Points listed may vary.

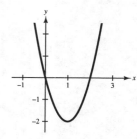

22. Sketch the graph of the quadratic function $y = -2x^2 - 4x$ on the coordinate axes. List five points used in the table.

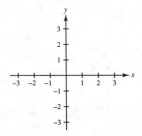

x					
y					

1—Ans: Points listed may vary.

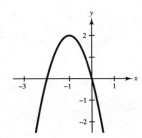

23. Match the quadratic function $y = \frac{1}{3}x^2 - 2x - 6$ with its graph.

(a)

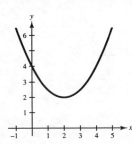

(b)

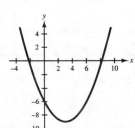

(c)

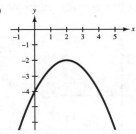

(d)

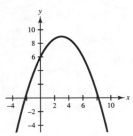

(e) None of these

1—Ans: b

24. Match the quadratic function $y = \frac{1}{2}x^2 - 2x + 4$ with its graph.

(a)

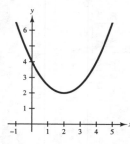

(b)

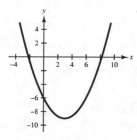

(c)

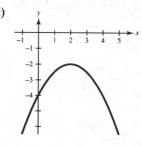

(d)

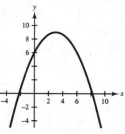

(e) None of these

1—Ans: a

25. Sketch the graph of the quadratic function $y = \dfrac{x^2}{4} - x - 3$ on the coordinate axes. List five points used in the table.

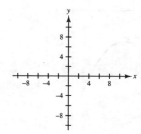

x					
y					

1—Ans: Points listed may vary.

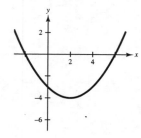

26. Sketch the graph of the quadratic function $y = \dfrac{x^2}{2} - 2x - 6$ on the coordinate axes. List five points used in the table.

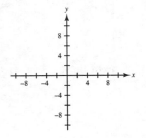

x				
y				

1—Ans: Points listed may vary.

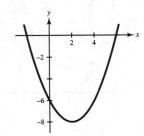

27. Write an equation of the parabola $y = a(x - h)^2 + k$ that has a vertex at $(1, -2)$ and $a = 3$.

   (a) $y = 3(x + 1)^2 + 2$ (b) $y = 2(x - 1)^2 + 3$ (c) $y = -3(x + 1)^2 - 2$

   (d) $y = 3(x - 1)^2 - 2$ (e) None of these

   1—Ans: d

28. Write an equation of the parabola $y = a(x - h)^2 + k$ that has a vertex at $(-1, -2)$ and $a = -3$.

   (a) $y = 3(x + 1)^2 + 2$ (b) $y = 2(x - 1)^2 + 3$ (c) $y = -3(x + 1)^2 - 2$

   (d) $y = 3(x - 1)^2 - 2$ (e) None of these

   1—Ans: c

29. Find the equation of the parabola with vertex at $(1, -4)$ and y-intercept $(0, -2)$.

   2—Ans: $y = 2x^2 - 4x - 2$

30. Find the equation of the parabola with vertex at $(2, -3)$ and y-intercept $(0, 3)$.

   2—Ans: $y = \frac{3}{2}x^2 - 6x + 3$

31. Find the equation of the parabola with vertex at $(-4, 2)$ and y-intercept $(0, 4)$.

   2—Ans: $y = \frac{1}{8}x^2 + x + 4$

32. Find the equation of the parabola with vertex at $(-3, 4)$ and y-intercept $(0, -5)$.

   2—Ans: $y = -x^2 - 6x - 5$

33. Find the vertex of the parabola $y = -x^2 - 6x + 2$.

   (a) $(3, -25)$ **(b)** $(-3, -25)$ **(c)** $(3, -7)$ **(d)** $(-3, 11)$ **(e)** None of these

   1—Form: 10A—Ans: d

34. Find the vertex of the parabola $y = 4x^2 - 16x + 3$.

   (a) $(-2, 51)$ **(b)** $(2, -13)$ **(c)** $(4, 3)$ **(d)** $(0, 3)$ **(e)** None of these

   1—Form: 10B—Ans: b

35. Determine the graph of the parabola $y = -2x^2 + 4x + 1$.

   (a)
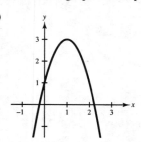

   (b)
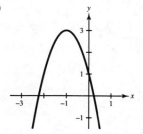

   (c)
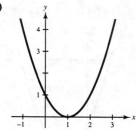

   (d)
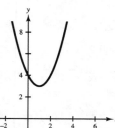

   (e) None of these

   1—Ans: a

36. Determine the graph of the parabola $y = x^2 - 2x + 4$.

   (a)
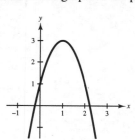

   (b)
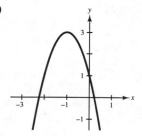

   (c)
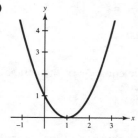

   (d)
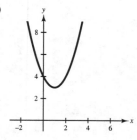

   (e) None of these

   1—Ans: d

37. Find the standard form of the equation of the parabola with vertex $(-1, 3)$ and passing through the point $(2, 1)$.

(a) $y = \frac{4}{9}(x + 1)^2 + 3$

(b) $y = -2x^2 - 4x - 2$

(c) $y = -2(x - 1)^2 + 3$

(d) $y = -\frac{2}{9}(x + 1)^2 + 3$

(e) None of these

2—Ans: d

38. Find the standard form of the equation of the parabola with vertex $(2, -1)$ and passing through the point $(0, 3)$.

(a) $y = (x - 2)^2 + 1$

(b) $y = (x - 2)^2 - 1$

(c) $y = (x - 2)^2 + 3$

(d) $y = \frac{1}{2}(x - 2)^2 - 1$

(e) None of these

2—Ans: b

39. The profit for a company is given by the equation

$$P = -\frac{1}{3}x^2 + 250x - 542$$

where x is the number of units produced. Use the graph of P to determine what production level will yield a maximum profit.

(a) 750   (b) 542   (c) 167   (d) 475   (e) None of these

2—Ans: b

40. The profit for a company is given by the equation

$$P = -0.0002x^2 + 140x - 250{,}000$$

where x is the number of units produced. Use the graph of P to determine what production level will yield a maximum profit.

(a) 700,000   (b) 350,000   (c) 893   (d) 350   (e) None of these

2—Ans: d

41. Consider the graph of the equation $y = -x^2 + 4x - 3$.

a. Does it open upward or downward?

b. Find the intercepts.

c. Find the vertex.

d. Sketch the graph.

2—Ans:

a. Downward

b. $(1, 0)$, $(3, 0)$, $(0, -3)$

c. $(2, 1)$

d.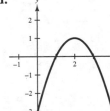

42. Consider the graph of the equation $y = x^2 - x - 2$.

   a. Does it open upward or downward?   **b.** Find the intercepts.

   c. Find the vertex.   **d.** Sketch the graph.

2—Ans:

   a. Upward   **b.** $(-1, 0), (2, 0), (0, -2)$

   c. $\left(\frac{1}{2}, -\frac{9}{4}\right)$ **d.**

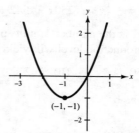

43. Find the equation of the parabola shown in the figure.

   (a) $y = x^2 - 1$ **(b)** $y = 2x - x^2$

   (c) $y = x^2 + 2x$ **(d)** $y = -x^2 - 1$

   (e) $y = x^2 + 2x + 2$

   2—Ans: c

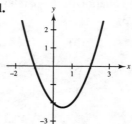

44. Find the equation of the parabola shown in the figure.

   (a) $y = -\frac{1}{2}x^2 + 2$ **(b)** $y = 2x^2 + 2$

   (c) $y = -2x^2 + 2$ **(d)** $y = \frac{1}{2}x^2 + 2$

   (e) $y = -\frac{1}{2}x^2 - 2$

   2—Ans: a

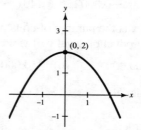

45. Write an equation of the parabola shown in the figure.

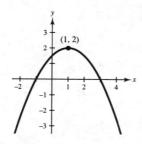

   2—Ans: $y = -\frac{1}{2}x^2 + x + \frac{3}{2}$

46. Write an equation of the parabola shown in the figure.

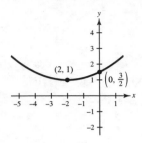

2—Ans: $y = \frac{1}{8}x^2 + \frac{1}{2}x + \frac{3}{2}$

47. Use a graphing utility to graph the two functions on the same screen. Use the graph to approximate any points of intersection.

$$y_1 = x^2 - 6x + 7 \quad \text{and} \quad y_2 = 2$$

1—T—Ans: $(1, 2)$ and $(5, 2)$

48. Use a graphing utility to graph the two functions on the same screen. Use the graph to approximate any points of intersection.

$$y_1 = x^2 - 3x + 2 \quad \text{and} \quad y_2 = 6$$

1—T—Ans: $(-1, 6)$ and $(4, 6)$

49. The graph of $h(x) = x^3 - 2$ can be obtained by shifting the graph of $f(x) = x^3$

   (a) two units upward.   **(b)** two units downward.   **(c)** two units to the right.

   (d) two units to the left.   **(e)** None of these.

   2—Ans: b

50. The graph of $h(x) = (x - 2)^3$ can be obtained by shifting the graph of $f(x) = x^3$

   (a) two units upward.   **(b)** two units downward.   **(c)** two units to the right.

   (d) two units to the left.   **(e)** None of these.

   2—Ans: c

51. If the graph of $f(x) = -x^2$ is shifted three units to the *left*, write its new equation.

   2—Ans: $h(x) = -(x + 3)^2$

52. If the graph of $f(x) = -x^2$ is shifted three units to the *right*, write its new equation.

   2—Ans: $h(x) = -(x - 3)^2$

53. If the graph of $f(x) = -x^2$ is shifted three units *upward*, write its new equation.

   2—Ans: $h(x) = -x^2 + 3$

54. If the graph of $f(x) = -x^2$ is shifted three units *downward*, write its new equation.

   2—Ans: $h(x) = -x^2 - 3$

55. The graph of $h(x) = 3 - x^2$ is obtained from the graph of $f(x) = x^2 - 3$ by:

   (a) a shift upward.   **(b)** a reflection in the *x*-axis.   **(c)** a shift to the left.

   (d) a shift downward.   **(e)** none of these

   2—Ans: b

56. The function $f(x) = x^4$ is reflected in the *x*-axis. Find the resulting function *g*.

   1—Ans: $g(x) = -x^4$

57. Use the graph of $y = x^2$ to write an equation to represent the transformation shown on the right.

   (a) $y = (x - 3)^2$ **(b)** $y = x^2 + 3$

   (c) $y = (x + 3)^2$ **(d)** $y = x^2 - 3$

   (e) None of these

   1—Ans: a

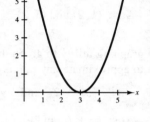

58. Use the graph of $y = x^2$ to write an equation to represent the transformation shown on the right.

   (a) $y = (x - 2)^2$ **(b)** $y = x^2 + 2$

   (c) $y = (x + 2)^2$ **(d)** $y = x^2 - 2$

   (e) None of these

   1—Ans: d

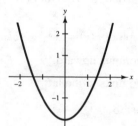

59. Use the graph of $y = x^2$ to sketch $y = (x + 1)^2$.

   1—Ans:

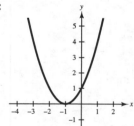

60. Use the graph of $y = x^2$ to sketch $y = -x^2$.

1—Ans:

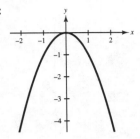

61. Use the graph of $y = \sqrt{x}$ to write an equation for the transformation shown.

(a) $x = \sqrt{y}$ **(b)** $y = -\sqrt{x}$

(c) $x = -\sqrt{y}$ **(d)** $y = \sqrt{x} - 1$

(e) $y = \sqrt{x} + 1$

1—Ans: b

62. Use the graph of $y = |x|$ to write an equation for the transformation shown.

(a) $y = |x - 2|$ **(b)** $y = |x| + 2$

(c) $y = |x + 2|$ **(d)** $y = |x| - 2$

(e) None of these

1—Ans: b

63. Use the graph of $y = x^2$ to find a formula for the function $y = f(x)$.

(a) $f(x) = (x - 2)^2 + 1$ **(b)** $f(x) = (x - 1)^2 + 2$

(c) $f(x) = (x + 2)^2 + 1$ **(d)** $f(x) = (x + 1)^2 - 2$

(e) None of these

2—Ans: a

64. Use the graph of $y = x^2$ to find a formula for the function $y = f(x)$.

(a) $y = (x + 1)^2 - 3$ **(b)** $y = -(x + 1)^2 - 3$

(c) $y = -x^2 - 3$ **(d)** $y = -(x - 1)^2 + 3$

(e) None of these

2—Ans: b

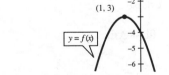

65. Identify the transformation of the graph of $f(x) = x^3$ and use a graphing utility to sketch the graph of h if $h(x) = x^3 - 3$.

1—T—Ans: 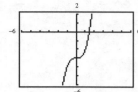 f is shifted 3 units down.

66. Identify the transformation of the graph of $f(x) = x^3$ and use a graphing utility to sketch the graph of h if $h(x) = (x - 3)^3$.

1—T—Ans: 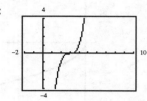 f is shifted 3 units to the right.

67. Write the equation of the parabola $y = -2x^2 + 4x$ in standard form and find the vertex.

   2—Form: 10C—Ans: $y = -2(x - 1)^2 + 2; (1, 2)$

68. If the graph of $f(x) = x^2$ is shifted two units to the left and one unit downward, write its new equation.

   2—Form: 10C—Ans: $y = (x - 2)^2 - 1$

69. Write a quadratic function for the parabola shown.

   (a) $y = (x - 3)^2 + 1$ **(b)** $y = -x^2 + 6x + 2$

   (c) $y = -(x - 3)^2 + 1$ **(d)** $y = -(x - 3)^2 + 2$

   (e) None of these

   2—Form: 10A—Ans: c

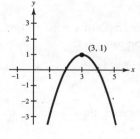

70. Write a quadratic function for the parabola shown.

   (a) $y = (x + 2)^2 - 2$ **(b)** $y = (x - 2)^2 - 2$

   (c) $y = -(x + 2)^2 + 2$ **(d)** $y = (x - 2)^2 + 2$

   (e) None of these

   2—Form: 10B—Ans: a

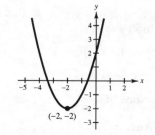

Section 10.5   Applications of Quadratic Equations

1. Find two consecutive odd numbers whose product is 483.

   1—Ans: 21 and 23

2. Find two consecutive even numbers whose product is 288.

   1—Ans: 16 and 18

3. Find a number if the sum of that number and its square is 272.

   (a) 16   **(b)** 19   **(c)** 17   **(d)** 21   **(e)** None of these

   1—Ans: a

4. Find a number if the sum of that number and its square is 380.

   (a) 16   **(b)** 19   **(c)** 17   **(d)** 21   **(e)** None of these

   1—Ans: b

5. Find two numbers which have the property that when each is added to its square, the result is 342.

   1—Ans: 18 and -19

6. Find two numbers which have the property that when each is added to its square, the result is 506.

   1—Ans: 22 and -23

7. Find the dimensions of a rectangle that is 5 feet longer than it is wide if its area is 374 square feet.

   (a) $17' \times 22'$ **(b)** $30' \times 35'$ **(c)** $40' \times 45'$ **(d)** $28' \times 33'$ **(e)** None of these

   1—Ans: a

8. Find the dimensions of a rectangle that is 5 feet longer than it is wide if its area is 924 square feet.

   (a) $17' \times 22'$ **(b)** $30' \times 35'$ **(c)** $40' \times 45'$ **(d)** $28' \times 33'$ **(e)** None of these

   1—Ans: d

9. The area of a rectangle is 56 square yards and its length is 2 yards more than three times its width. Find its dimensions.

   1—Ans: 4 yards by 14 yards

10. The area of a rectangle is 221 square feet and its perimeter is 60 feet. Find its dimensions.

   1—Ans: 17 feet by 13 feet

11. The area of a rectangle is 270 square feet and its perimeter is 66 feet. Find its dimensions.

    1—Ans: 18 feet by 15 feet

12. The area of a rectangle is 434 square yards and its length is 3 yards more than twice its length. Find its dimensions.

    1—Ans: 14 yards by 31 yards

13. The height of an object dropped from an initial height of 500 feet is given by $h = 500 - 16t^2$, where t is in seconds and h is in feet. How many seconds (to two decimal places) has the object been falling when its height is 200 feet?

    (a) 3.54 seconds   **(b)** 18.75 seconds   **(c)** 4.33 seconds

    (d) 5.59 seconds   **(e)** None of these

    1—Ans: c

14. The height of an object dropped from an initial height of 600 feet is given by $h = 600 - 16t^2$, where t is in seconds and h is in feet. How many seconds (to two decimal places) has the object been falling when its height is 100 feet?

    (a) 6.12 seconds   **(b)** 31.25 seconds   **(c)** 2.5 seconds

    (d) 5.59 seconds   **(e)** None of these

    1—Ans: d

15. The height of an object dropped from an initial height of 350 feet is given by $h = 350 - 16t^2$, where t is in seconds and h is in feet. How many seconds (to two decimal places) has the object been falling when it strikes the ground?

    1—Ans: 4.68 seconds

16. The height of an object dropped from an initial height of 450 feet is given by $h = 450 - 16t^2$, where t is in seconds and h is in feet. How many seconds (to two decimal places) has the object been falling when it strikes the ground?

    1—Ans: 5.30 seconds

17. The area of a triangle is given by $A = \frac{1}{2}bh$. The height of a triangle is $1\frac{1}{2}$ times the base and its area is 1323 square inches. Find its base and height.

    (a) $b = 63$ inches and $h = 94.5$ inches   **(b)** $b = 42$ inches and $h = 63$ inches

    (c) $b = 31.5$ inches and $h = 47.25$ inches   **(d)** $b = 63$ inches and $h = 72$ inches

    (e) None of these

    1—Ans: b

18. The area of a triangle is given by $A = \frac{1}{2}bh$. The height of a triangle is $1\frac{1}{2}$ times the base and its area is 768 square inches. Find its base and height.

   (a) $b = 48$ inches and $h = 32$ inches   **(b)** $b = 24$ inches and $h = 36$ inches

   (c) $b = 32$ inches and $h = 48$ inches   **(d)** $b = 48$ inches and $h = 72$ inches

   (e) None of these

   1—Ans: c

19. The area of a triangle is given by $A = \frac{1}{2}bh$. The height of a triangle is 2 inches longer than the base and its area is 18 square inches. Use a calculator to find the base (two decimal places).

   1—T—Ans: $b \approx 5.08$ inches

20. The area of a triangle is given by $A = \frac{1}{2}bh$. The height of a triangle is 3 inches shorter than the base and its area is 21 square inches. Use a calculator to find the base (two decimal places).

   1—T—Ans: $b \approx 8.15$ inches

21. A group of people could rent a social hall for $720. When 12 more people join the venture the cost per person is decreased by $10. Find the number of people in the larger group.

   (a) 24   **(b)** 30   **(c)** 36   **(d)** 18   **(e)** None of these

   1—Ans: c

22. A group of people could rent a social hall for $720. When 6 more people join the venture the cost per person is decreased by $6. Find the number of people in the larger group.

   (a) 30   **(b)** 36   **(c)** 18   **(d)** 24   **(e)** None of these

   1—Ans: a

23. A group of people could rent a social hall for $480. When 8 more people join the venture the cost per person is decreased by $10. How many people are in the larger group?

   1—Ans: 24

24. A group of people could rent a social hall for $480. When 14 more people join the venture the cost per person is decreased by $14. How many people are in the larger group?

   1—Ans: 30

25. A train makes a round trip between cities 200 miles apart. On the return half, the average speed is 20 mph faster than the average speed on the trip out and takes $\frac{1}{2}$ hour less time. Find the average speed on the trip out.

   (a) 120 mph   **(b)** 100 mph   **(c)** 60 mph   **(d)** 80 mph   **(e)** None of these

   1—Ans: d

26. A train makes a round trip between cities 200 miles apart. On the return half, the average speed is 20 mph faster than the average speed on the trip out and takes $\frac{1}{2}$ hour less time. Find the average speed on the return trip.

   (a) 120 mph   **(b)** 100 mph   **(c)** 60 mph   **(d)** 80 mph   **(e)** None of these

   1—Ans: b

27. A train makes a round trip between cities 200 miles apart. On the return half, the average speed is 20 mph faster than the average speed on the trip out and takes $\frac{1}{2}$ hour less time. Find the time required for the trip out.

   (a) 2 hours   **(b)** $1\frac{2}{3}$ hours   **(c)** $2\frac{1}{2}$ hours   **(d)** $2\frac{1}{6}$ hours   **(e)** None of these

   1—Ans: c

28. A train makes a round trip between cities 200 miles apart. On the return half, the average speed is 20 mph faster than the average speed on the trip out and takes $\frac{1}{2}$ hour less time. Find the time required for the return trip.

   (a) 2 hours   **(b)** $1\frac{2}{3}$ hours   **(c)** $2\frac{1}{2}$ hours   **(d)** $2\frac{1}{6}$ hours   **(e)** None of these

   1—Ans: a

29. A train makes a round trip between cities 300 miles apart. On the return half, the average speed is 25 mph faster than the average speed on the trip out and takes 1 hour less time. Find the average speed on the trip out.

   1—Ans: 75 miles per hour

30. A train makes a round trip between cities 300 miles apart. On the return half, the average speed is 25 mph faster than the average speed on the trip out and takes 1 hour less time. Find the time required on the return trip.

   1—Ans: 3 hours

31. Two machines, working together, can complete a job in 6 hours. The older machine would take 5 hours longer than the newer machine to complete the task if each did the job alone. How long would it take the older machine alone to do the job?

   (a) 10 hours   **(b)** 12 hours   **(c)** 15 hours   **(d)** 18 hours   **(e)** None of these

   2—Ans: c

32. Two machines, working together, can complete a job in 2 days. The older machine would take 3 days longer than the newer machine to complete the task if each did the job alone. How long would it take the newer machine alone to do the job?

(a) 4 days   (b) 3 days   (c) 5 days   (d) 6 days   (e) None of these

2—Ans: b

33. A man and a boy, working together, can mow a large lawn in $3\frac{3}{5}$ hours. Working alone, the man could complete the job 3 hours quicker than the boy could, working alone. How many hours would it take the boy to do the job alone?

2—Ans: 9 hours

34. A veteran employee and a trainee, working together, can conduct an inventory in 4 hours. Working alone, the veteran employee could complete the job 6 hours quicker than the trainee could, working alone. How many hours would it take the veteran employee to do the whole job alone?

2—Ans: 6 hours

35. The length of a room is four feet greater than its width and has an area of 236.25 square feet. Use a calculator to find the dimensions of the room.

(a) 12 ft by 19.69 ft   (b) 12.5 ft by 16.5 ft   (c) 13.5 ft by 17.5 ft

(d) 14 ft by 16.875 ft   (e) None of these

2—T—Ans: c

36. The width of a room is three feet less than its length and has an area of 378 square feet. Use a calculator to find the dimensions of the room.

(a) 17.5 ft by 20.5 ft   (b) 18 ft by 21 ft   (c) 14 ft by 17 ft

(d) 14 ft by 27 ft   (e) None of these

2—T—Ans: b

37. The daily cost in dollars C of producing x chairs is given by the quadratic equation

$$C = x^2 - 120x + 4200.$$

How many chairs are produced each day if the daily cost is \$600?

(a) 60   (b) 600   (c) 90   (d) 40   (e) None of these

2—Ans: a

38. Find the smaller of two consecutive positive numbers such that the one times twice the other equals 612.

(a) -18 (b) 12   (c) 18   (d) 17   (e) None of these

2—Ans: d

39. A picture frame has a total area of 147 square inches. The width of the frame is 0.62 times its length. Use a calculator to find the dimensions of the frame. Round your answer to two decimal places.

   2—T—Ans: 9.55 in. by 15.50 in.

40. A picture frame has a total area of 529 square inches. The length of the frame is 1.62 times its width. Use a calculator to find the dimensions of the frame. Round your answer to two decimal places.

   2—T—Ans: 18.07 in. by 29.27 in.

41. The daily profit P in dollars of producing x items is given by the quadratic equation

   $$P = x^2 - 300x + 23,500.$$

   Use a calculator to find how many items are produced if the daily profit is $1000.

   2—T—Ans: 150

42. The daily profit P in dollars of producing x items is given by the quadratic equation

   $$P = x^2 - 300x + 23,500.$$

   Use a calculator to find how many items are produced if the daily profit is $3025.

   2—T—Form: 10C—Ans: 195

43. Find the length of the hypotenuse of a right triangle if the two sides measure 39 centimeters and 52 centimeters.

   (a) 34.39 cm   **(b)** 9.54 cm   **(c)** 60 cm   **(d)** 65 cm   **(e)** None of these

   2—Form: 10A—Ans: d

44. Find the length of the leg of a right triangle if the hypotenuse measures 7 inches and the one leg measures 2 inches.

   (a) $\sqrt{53}$ **(b)** $3\sqrt{5}$ **(c)** 5   **(d)** $\sqrt{47}$ **(e)** None of these

   2—Form: 10B—Ans: b

45. Two airplanes leave simultaneously from the same airport, one flying due east, and the other flying due north. The eastbound plane is flying 50 miles per hour slower than the northbound one. If after 4 hours they are 1000 miles apart, how fast is the northbound plane traveling?

   (a) 150 mph   **(b)** 200 mph   **(c)** 100 mph   **(d)** 300 mph   **(e)** None of these

   2—Ans: b

46. Two airplanes leave simultaneously from the same airport, one flying due east, and the other flying due north. The eastbound plane is flying 50 miles per hour slower than the northbound one. If after 4 hours they are 1000 miles apart, how fast is the eastbound plane traveling?

(a) 150 mph   (b) 200 mph   (c) 100 mph   (d) 300 mph   (e) None of these

2—**Ans:** a

47. An open box is to be constructed from a square piece of material by cutting a 3-inch square from each corner. Use a calculator to find the dimensions of the square piece of material if the box is to have a volume of 363 cubic inches.

(a) 14″ by 14″   (b) 17″ by 17″   (c) 20″ by 20″   (d) 23″ by 23″   (e) 11″ by 11″

2—**T—Form: 10A—Ans:** b

48. An open box is to be constructed from a square piece of material by cutting a 4-inch square from each corner. Use a calculator to find the dimensions of the square piece of material if the box is to have a volume of 961 cubic inches.

(a) 23.5″ by 23.5″   (b) 31″ by 31″   (c) 19.5″ by 19.5″

(d) 15.5″ by 15.5″   (e) 17.5″ by 17.5″

2—**T—Form: 10B—Ans:** a

49. Find the smaller of two consecutive positive integers m and n such that $m^2 - n^2 = 27$.

1—**Ans:** 13

50. Find the larger of two consecutive positive integers m and n such that $m^2 - n^2 = 35$.

1—**Form: 10C—Ans:** 18

51. Use a calculator to find the interest rate r. Use the formula $A = P(l + r)^2$, where $A = \$1391.28$ is the amount after 2 years in an account earning an annual percent rate of r and $P = \$1250.00$ is the original investment.

2—**T—Form: 10C—Ans:** 5.5%

52. Use a calculator to find the interest rate r. Use the formula $A = P(l + r)^2$, where $A = \$5751.28$ is the amount after 2 years in an account earning an annual percent rate of r and $P = \$5000.00$ is the original investment.

2—**T—Ans:** 7.25%

53. Use a calculator to find the interest rate r. Use the formula $A = P(l + r)^2$, where $A = \$10,116.22$ is the amount after 2 years in an account earning an annual percent rate of r and $P = \$9000.00$ is the original investment.

(a) 7.5%   (b) 8.1%   (c) 5.75%   (d) 6.25%   (e) 6.02%

2—**T—Form: 10A—Ans:** e

54. Use a calculator to find the interest rate r. Use the formula $A = P(l + r)^2$, where $A = \$3291.77$ is the amount after 2 years in an account earning an annual percent rate of r and $P = \$3000.00$ is the original investment.

(a) 4.5%   **(b)** 5%   **(c)** 4.75%   **(d)** 7.25%   **(e)** 6.25%

2—T—Form: 10B—Ans: c

55. Find the larger of two consecutive even positive numbers such that the one number times triple the other equals 504.

(a) 12   **(b)** 25   **(c)** 16   **(d)** 14   **(e)** None of these

1—Ans: d

56. The daily cost in dollars, C of producing x tables is given by the quadratic equation

$$C = x^2 - 140x + 5700.$$

How many tables are produced each day if the daily cost is $800?

2—Ans: 70 tables

57. You plan to stabilize a T.V. antenna with two guy wires. The guy wires are attached to the antenna 30 feet from the base. How much wire will you need if each of the wires is secured 20 feet from the base of the antenna?

(a) $10\sqrt{13}$ ft   **(b)** $20\sqrt{5}$ ft   **(c)** $20\sqrt{13}$ ft   **(d)** $10\sqrt{5}$ ft   **(e)** None of these

2—Ans: c

58. Using data from the years 1970 to 1990, a mathematical model for the consumer price index is

$$0.05t^2 + 3.63t + 37.68$$

where $t = 0$ corresponds to 1970. When did the C.P.I. reach a value of 150?

2—Ans: 1993

59. The total revenue (in thousands) for selling x units (in thousands) is given by

$$R = x(60 - 0.4x).$$

How many units must be sold to produce a revenue of $1440 thousand?

2—Ans: 120 thousand

60. A triangular sign has a height that is equal to its base. The area of the sign is 8 square feet. Find the height of the sign.

2—Ans: 4 feet

61. A one-story building is 12 feet longer than it is wide. The building has 2080 square feet of floor space. What are the dimensions of the building?

2—Ans: 40 ft $\times$ 52 ft

62. Between 1970 and 1990, the average cost of a new car can be modeled by

$$\text{Cost} = 30.5t^2 + 4192, \quad t \geq 0$$

where $t = 0$ represents 1970. If the average cost of a new car continued to increase according to this model, when did the average cost reach \$22,000? (Source: Commerce Department American Autodatum)

2—Ans: 1994

Section 10.6   Quadratic and Rational Inequalities

1. Find the critical number of $3x - 5$.

(a) 3   (b) -5 (c) $\frac{3}{5}$ (d) $\frac{5}{3}$ (e) $-\frac{3}{5}$

1—Ans: d

2. Find the critical number of $6x + 5$.

(a) -5 (b) 6   (c) $\frac{5}{6}$ (d) $-\frac{6}{5}$ (e) $-\frac{5}{6}$

1—Ans: e

3. Find the critical number of $8x + 5$.

1—Ans: $x = -\frac{5}{8}$

4. Find the critical number of $16x - 11$.

1—Ans: $x = \frac{11}{16}$

5. Find the critical numbers of $2x^2 + 5x - 12$.

(a) $x = \frac{3}{2}$ and $x = 4$ (b) $x = 6$ and $x = 2$ (c) $x = 6$ and $x = -2$

(d) $x = -\frac{3}{2}$ and $x = 4$ (e) $x = \frac{3}{2}$ and $x = -4$

1—Ans: e

6. Find the critical numbers of $2x^2 + 11x - 6$.

(a) $x = -6$ and $x = \frac{1}{2}$ (b) $x = 6$ and $x = -\frac{1}{2}$ (c) $x = 3$ and $x = -1$

(d) $x = -3$ and $x = \frac{6}{11}$ (e) $x = 3$ and $x = -\frac{6}{11}$

1—Ans: a

7. Find the critical numbers of $10x^2 - x - 24$.

1—Ans: $x = -\frac{3}{2}$ and $x = \frac{8}{5}$

8. Find the critical numbers of $2x^2 + 7x - 15$.

1—Ans: $x = -5$ and $x = \frac{3}{2}$

9. Determine the graph of the interval on which $2x - 8$ is always positive.

(a) [number line with open bracket at 4 going right, marked 0 1 2 3 4 5]

(b) [number line with closed bracket at 4 going right, marked 0 1 2 3 4 5]

(c) [number line with open bracket at 4 going left, marked 0 1 2 3 4 5]

(d) [number line with closed bracket at 4 going left, marked 0 1 2 3 4 5]

(e) None of these

1—Ans: a

10. Determine the graph of the interval on which $2x + 8$ is always negative.

(a) [number line with closed bracket at −4 going left, marked −5 −4 −3 −2 −1 0]

(b) [number line with open bracket at −4 going left, marked −5 −4 −3 −2 −1 0]

(c) [number line with closed bracket at −4 going right, marked −5 −4 −3 −2 −1 0]

(d) [number line with open bracket at −4 going right, marked −5 −4 −3 −2 −1 0]

(e) None of these

1—Ans: b

11. Show graphically the interval on which $x^2 - x - 6$ is entirely positive.

1—Ans:

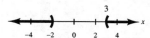

12. Show graphically the interval on which $x^2 + 2x - 8$ is entirely negative.

1—Ans: [number line with open interval from −4 to 2, marked −6 −4 −2 0 2 4]

13. Determine the solution to the quadratic inequality $5x(x + 3) \le 0$.

(a) $(-\infty, -3] \cup [0, \infty)$ (b) $(-\infty, -3) \cup (0, \infty)$ (c) $[-3, 0]$

(d) $(-3, 0)$ (e) None of these

1—Ans: c

14. Determine the solution to the quadratic inequality $5x(x + 3) > 0$.

(a) $(-\infty, -3] \cup [0, \infty)$ (b) $(-\infty, -3) \cup (0, \infty)$ (c) $[-3, 0]$

(d) $(-3, 0)$ (e) None of these

1—Ans: b

15. Solve the inequality $4z^2 - 9 \ge 0$ and sketch the graph of the solution on the real number line.

2—Ans: $\left(-\infty, -\tfrac{3}{2}\right] \cup \left[\tfrac{3}{2}, \infty\right)$

16. Solve the inequality $9z^2 - 4 < 0$ and sketch the graph of the solution on the real number line.

2—Ans: $\left(-\frac{2}{3}, \frac{2}{3}\right)$

17. Solve the inequality $9z^2 - 16 \leq 0$ and sketch the graph of the solution on the real number line.

2—Ans: $\left[-\frac{4}{3}, \frac{4}{3}\right]$

18. Solve the inequality $16z^2 - 9 > 0$ and sketch the graph of the solution on the real number line.

2—Ans: $\left(-\infty, -\frac{3}{4}\right) \cup \left(\frac{3}{4}, \infty\right)$

19. Determine the solution to the quadratic inequality $x^2 + x - 1 > 0$.

(a) $\left(-\infty, \dfrac{-1 - \sqrt{5}}{2}\right) \cup \left(\dfrac{-1 + \sqrt{5}}{2}, \infty\right)$

(b) $\left(\infty, \dfrac{-1 - \sqrt{5}}{2}\right] \cup \left[\dfrac{-1 + \sqrt{5}}{2}, \infty\right)$

(c) $\left[\dfrac{-1 - \sqrt{5}}{2}, \dfrac{-1 + \sqrt{5}}{2}\right]$

(d) $\left(\dfrac{-1 - \sqrt{5}}{2}, \dfrac{-1 + \sqrt{5}}{2}\right)$

(e) None of these

2—Ans: a

20. Determine the solution to the quadratic inequality $x^2 + x - 1 \leq 0$.

(a) $\left(-\infty, \dfrac{-1 - \sqrt{5}}{2}\right) \cup \left(\dfrac{-1 + \sqrt{5}}{2}, \infty\right)$

(b) $\left(\infty, \dfrac{-1 - \sqrt{5}}{2}\right] \cup \left[\dfrac{-1 + \sqrt{5}}{2}, \infty\right)$

(c) $\left[\dfrac{-1 - \sqrt{5}}{2}, \dfrac{-1 + \sqrt{5}}{2}\right]$

(d) $\left(\dfrac{-1 - \sqrt{5}}{2}, \dfrac{-1 + \sqrt{5}}{2}\right)$

(e) None of these

2—Ans: c

21. Solve the inequality $x^2 - 2x - 1 < 0$ and sketch the graph of the solution on the real number line.

    2—Ans: $\left(1 - \sqrt{2}, 1 + \sqrt{2}\right)$

22. Solve the inequality $x^2 - 2x - 1 \geq 0$ and sketch the graph of the solution on the real number line.

    2—Ans: $\left(-\infty, 1 - \sqrt{2}\right] \cup \left[1 + \sqrt{2}, \infty\right)$

23. Find the critical numbers of $\dfrac{3x}{x - 4}$.

    (a) $x = 0$ and $x = 4$ **(b)** $x = 0$ only   **(c)** $x = 4$ only

    (d) $x = 0$ and $x = -4$ **(e)** None of these

    1—Ans: a

24. Find the critical numbers of $\dfrac{x - 3}{5x}$.

    (a) $x = 0$ and $x = -3$ **(b)** $x = 0$ only   **(c)** $x = 0$ and $x = 3$

    (d) $x = 3$ only   **(e)** None of these

    1—Ans: c

25. Find the critical numbers of $\dfrac{x - 1}{2x - 6}$.

    (a) $x = 3$ and $x = -1$ **(b)** $x = 3$ only   **(c)** $x = 1$ only

    (d) $x = 1$ and $x = 3$ **(e)** None of these

    1—Ans: d

26. Find the critical numbers of $\dfrac{2x + 4}{2x - 4}$.

    (a) $x = -2$ and $x = 4$ **(b)** $x = 2$ and $x = -2$ **(c)** $x = 2$ only

    (d) $x = -2$ only   **(e)** None of these

    1—Ans: b

27. Determine the critical numbers of $\dfrac{3x}{x+2}$ and locate them on the real number line.

    1—Ans: $x = 0$ and $x = -2$;

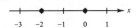

28. Determine the critical numbers of $\dfrac{x-1}{2(x+2)}$ and locate them on the real number line.

    1—Ans: $x = -2$ and $x = 1$;

29. Determine the solution to the rational inequality $\dfrac{-6}{x-2} < 0$.

    (a) $(-\infty, 2)$ **(b)** $(-\infty, -2]$ **(c)** $(2, \infty)$ **(d)** $[-2, 0)$ **(e)** None of these

    1—Ans: c

30. Determine the solution to the rational inequality $\dfrac{5}{2-x} > 0$.

    (a) $(-\infty, 2)$ **(b)** $(-\infty, -2]$ **(c)** $(2, \infty)$ **(d)** $[-2, 0)$ **(e)** None of these

    1—Ans: a

31. Solve the rational inequality $\dfrac{y-3}{2y+6} < 0$ and sketch the graph of the solution on the real number line.

    2—Ans: $(-3, 3)$;

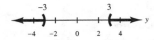

32. Solve the rational inequality $\dfrac{y-3}{2y+6} > 0$ and sketch the graph of the solution on the real number line.

    2—Ans: $(-\infty, -3) \cup (3, \infty)$;

33. Solve the rational inequality $\dfrac{4-2y}{y+1} < 0$ and sketch the graph of the solution on the real number line.

2—Ans: $(-\infty, -1) \cup (2, \infty)$;

34. Solve the rational inequality $\dfrac{4-2y}{y+1} > 0$ and sketch the graph of the solution on the real number line.

2—Ans: $(-1, 2)$;

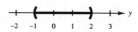

35. Determine the solution of the rational inequality $\dfrac{8}{x+3} \geq 2$.

    (a) $(-3, 1)$ **(b)** $(-3, 1]$ **(c)** $[-3, 1]$ **(d)** $[-3, 1)$ **(e)** None of these

    2—Ans: b

36. Determine the solution of the rational inequality $\dfrac{8}{x+3} > 2$.

    (a) $(-3, 1)$ **(b)** $(-3, 1]$ **(c)** $[-3, 1]$ **(d)** $[-3, 1)$ **(e)** None of these

    2—Ans: a

37. Determine the solution of the rational inequality $\dfrac{2}{1-x} > \dfrac{1}{2}$.

    (a) $[-3, 1]$ **(b)** $(-3, 1]$ **(c)** $(-3, 1)$ **(d)** $[-3, 1)$ **(e)** None of these

    2—Ans: c

38. Determine the solution of the rational inequality $\dfrac{2}{1-x} \geq \dfrac{1}{2}$.

    (a) $[-3, 1]$ **(b)** $(-3, 1]$ **(c)** $(-3, 1)$ **(d)** $[-3, 1)$ **(e)** None of these

    2—Ans: d

39. The height of a projectile fired straight up from ground level with an initial velocity of 80 feet per second is given by $h = -16t^2 + 80t$, where h is measured in feet and t is measured in seconds. For what interval of time will the height of the projectile exceed 96 feet?

    2—Ans: $(2, 3)$; between 2 and 3 seconds

40. The height of a projectile fired straight up from ground level with an initial velocity of 112 feet per second is given by $h = -16t^2 + 112t$, where h is measured in feet and t is measured in seconds. For what interval of time will the height of the projectile exceed 160 feet?

   2—Ans: $(2, 5)$; between 2 and 5 seconds

41. Solve the inequality $2x^2 + 3x \geq 5$.

   (a) $\left[-\frac{5}{2}, 1\right]$ **(b)** $\left[-\frac{5}{2}, \infty\right)$ **(c)** $\left(-\infty, -\frac{5}{2}\right] \cup [1, \infty)$

   (d) $\left(-\infty, -\frac{3}{2}\right] \cup [5, \infty)$ **(e)** None of these

   2—Ans: c

42. Solve the inequality $2x^2 + 3x < 9$.

   (a) $\left(-3, \frac{3}{2}\right)$ **(b)** $(-\infty, -3) \cup \left(\frac{3}{2}, \infty\right)$ **(c)** $\left[-3, \frac{3}{2}\right]$

   (d) $(-\infty, 3) \cup (9, \infty)$ **(e)** None of these

   2—Ans: a

43. Solve the inequality $\dfrac{2}{x - 1} < 5$.

   (a) $(-\infty, 1)$ **(b)** $\left(\frac{7}{5}, \infty\right)$ **(c)** $\left(-\infty, -\frac{3}{5}\right) \cup \left(\frac{7}{5}, \infty\right)$

   (d) $(-\infty, 1) \cup \left(\frac{7}{5}, \infty\right)$ **(e)** None of these

   2—Form: 10A—Ans: d

44. Solve the inequality $\dfrac{2}{x + 1} \geq 5$.

   (a) $(-\infty, -1) \cup \left[-\frac{3}{5}, \infty\right)$ **(b)** $\left(-\infty, -\frac{3}{5}\right]$ **(c)** $\left(-1, -\frac{3}{5}\right]$

   (d) $\left(-\infty, \frac{1}{5}\right]$ **(e)** None of these

   2—Form: 10B—Ans: c

45. Solve the inequality $2x^2 - 5x \geq 3$.

   2—Ans: $\left(-\infty, -\frac{1}{2}\right] \cup [3, \infty)$

46. Solve the inequality $3x^2 + 2x \leq 5$.

   2—Ans: $\left[-\frac{5}{3}, 1\right]$

47. Solve the inequality $\dfrac{3}{x - 2} > 2$ and graph the solution on the real number line.

   2—Ans: $\left(2, \frac{7}{2}\right)$

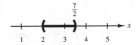

48. Solve the inequality $\dfrac{5}{x+3} \leq 1$ and graph the solution on the real number line.

2—Form: 10C—Ans: $(-\infty, -3) \cup [2, \infty)$

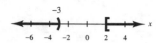

49. Use a graphing utility to solve the inequality $x^2 - x \leq 6$.

   (a) $[-2, 3]$ **(b)** $(-\infty, -2] \cup [3, \infty)$ **(c)** $[-3, 2]$

   (d) $(-\infty, 3]$ **(e)** $(-\infty, \infty)$

1—T—Form: 10A—Ans: a

50. Use a graphing utility to solve the inequality $x - x^2 < -12$.

   (a) $[-3, 4]$ **(b)** $(-\infty, -3) \cup (4, \infty)$ **(c)** $(-3, 4)$

   (d) $(-4, 3)$ **(e)** $(-\infty, \infty)$

1—T—Form: 10B—Ans: b

51. Use a graphing utility to solve the inequality $(x - 2)^2 \leq 9$.

1—T—Ans: $[-1, 5]$

52. Use a graphing utility to solve the inequality $(x + 4)^2 > 9$.

1—T—Ans: $(-\infty, -7) \cup (-1, \infty)$

53. Use a graphing utility to solve the inequality $x^2 + 1 \geq 0$.

1—T—Form: 10C—Ans: $(-\infty, \infty)$

54. Use a graphing utility to solve the inequality $(x - 5)^2 < -2$.

1—T—Ans: No solution

55. Use a graphing utility to solve the inequality $\dfrac{4}{x+1} \leq \dfrac{3}{x+2}$.

   (a) $(-\infty, -5] \cup (-2, -1)$ **(b)** $(-5, -2) \cup (-1, \infty)$ **(c)** $(-\infty, -5) \cup (-2, -1)$

   (d) $(-5, -2] \cup [-1, \infty)$ **(e)** $(-\infty, \infty)$

2—T—Ans: a

56. Use a graphing utility to solve the inequality $\dfrac{3x - 7}{x + 2} < 1$.

(a) $(-\infty, -2) \cup \left(\dfrac{9}{2}, \infty\right)$ (b) $\left(-2, \dfrac{9}{2}\right)$ (c) $\left(-2, \dfrac{5}{2}\right)$

(d) $\left[-2, \dfrac{9}{2}\right)$ (e) $(-\infty, \infty)$

2—T—Ans: b

57. Solve the inequality $x^2 + 4x + 2 \le 0$.

(a) $\left[-2 - \sqrt{2}, \infty\right)$ (b) $\left[-2 - \sqrt{2}, -2 + \sqrt{2}\right]$

(c) $\left(-\infty, -2 - \sqrt{2}\right] \cup \left(-2 + \sqrt{2}, \infty\right)$ (d) $[-2, 2]$

(e) $(-\infty, \infty)$

2—Ans: b

58. Solve the inequality $x^2 - 2x > 2$.

(a) $\left(1 - \sqrt{3}, \infty\right)$ (b) $\left(1 - \sqrt{3}, 1 + \sqrt{3}\right)$

(c) $\left(-\infty, 1 - \sqrt{3}\right] \cup \left(1 + \sqrt{3}, \infty\right)$ (d) No solution

(e) $(-\infty, \infty)$

2—Ans: c

59. Solve the inequality $\dfrac{x + 16}{3x + 2} \le 5$.

(a) $\left(-\infty, -\frac{2}{3}\right] \cup \left[\frac{3}{7}, \infty\right)$ (b) $\left[-\frac{2}{3}, \frac{3}{7}\right]$ (c) $\left(-\infty, -\frac{2}{3}\right) \cup \left[\frac{3}{7}, \infty\right)$

(d) $\left(-\frac{2}{3}, \frac{3}{7}\right]$ (e) $(-\infty, \infty)$

2—Ans: c

60. Solve the inequality $\dfrac{x + 7}{3x - 1} < 1$.

(a) $\left(\frac{1}{3}, 4\right)$ (b) $\left[\frac{1}{3}, 4\right]$ (c) $\left(-\infty, \frac{1}{3}\right] \cup (4, \infty)$

(d) $\left(-\infty, \frac{1}{3}\right) \cup (4, \infty)$ (e) $(-\infty, \infty)$

2—Ans: d

61. Find the domain of the function $f(x) = \sqrt{36 - x^2}$.

(a) $[-6, 6]$ (b) $(-\infty, -6] \cup [6, \infty)$ (c) $(-6, 6)$

(d) $(-\infty, -6) \cup (6, \infty)$ (e) $(-\infty, \infty)$

2—Form: 10A—Ans: a

62. Find the domain of the function $f(x) = \sqrt{9x^2 - 169}$.

    (a) $\left(-\frac{13}{3}, \frac{13}{3}\right)$ **(b)** $\left[-\frac{13}{3}, \frac{13}{3}\right]$ **(c)** $\left(-\infty, \frac{-13}{3}\right] \cup \left[\frac{13}{3}, \infty\right)$

    (d) $\left(-\infty, -\frac{13}{3}\right) \cup \left(\frac{13}{3}, \infty\right)$ **(e)** $(-\infty, \infty)$

    2—Form: 10B—Ans: c

63. Find the domain of the function $f(x) = \sqrt{x^2 - 7x - 8}$.

    2—Form: 10C—Ans: $(-\infty, -1] \cup [8, \infty)$

64. Find the domain of the function $f(x) = \sqrt{6 - x - x^2}$.

    2—Ans: $[-3, 2]$

CHAPTER 11
Exponential and Logarithmic Functions

Section 11.1 Exponential Functions

1. If $f(x) = 3^x$, find the value of $f(-2)$.

   (a) 9   **(b)** $\frac{1}{9}$ **(c)** -6 **(d)** -8 **(e)** None of these

   1—Ans: b

2. If $f(x) = 5^{-x}$, find the value of $f(-3)$.

   (a) 125   **(b)** 15   **(c)** $\frac{1}{125}$ **(d)** 243   **(e)** None of these

   1—Ans: a

3. For $g(x) = 2700\left(\frac{1}{3}\right)^{-x}$, evaluate $g(-3)$.

   1—Ans: 100

4. For $g(x) = 1250(5^{-x})$, evaluate $g(2)$.

   1—Ans: 50

5. Use your calculator to evaluate $G(5)$ to two decimal places for $G(t) = 500(1.06)^t$.

   (a) 373.63   **(b)** 514.78   **(c)** 669.11   **(d)** 485.64   **(e)** None of these

   1—T—Ans: c

6. Use your calculator to evaluate $G(-5)$ to two decimal places for $G(t) = 500(1.06)^t$.

   (a) 373.63   **(b)** 514.78   **(c)** 669.11   **(d)** 485.64   **(e)** None of these

   1—T—Ans: a

7. Use your calculator to evaluate $R(2)$ to two decimal places for $R(u) = \dfrac{1000}{(1.01)^{10u}}$.

   1—T—Ans: 819.54

8. Use your calculator to evaluate $R(-2)$ to two decimal places for $R(u) = \dfrac{1000}{(1.01)^{10u}}$.

   1—T—Ans: 1200.19

9. Use your calculator to evaluate $F(0.2)$ for $F(t) = e^{-t^2}$.

   (a) 11.023   **(b)** 2.003   **(c)** 1.041   **(d)** 0.961   **(e)** None of these

   1—T—Ans: d

10. Use your calculator to evaluate $F(0.2)$ for $F(t) = e^{(-t)2}$.

    (a) 11.023   **(b)** 2.003   **(c)** 1.041   **(d)** 0.961   **(e)** None of these

    1—T—Ans: c

11. $Y(t) = 400e^{0.02t}$. Use your calculator to evaluate $Y(45)$ to two decimal places.

    1—T—Ans: 983.84

12. $Y(t) = 400e^{0.02t}$. Use your calculator to evaluate $Y(-45)$ to two decimal places.

    1—T—Ans: 162.63

13. Match the graph shown with its equation.

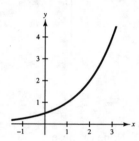

    (a) $f(x) = -2^x$ **(b)** $f(x) = 2^{-x}$ **(c)** $f(x) = 1 - 2^x$

    (d) $f(x) = 2^{x-1}$ **(e)** $f(x) = 2^{1-x}$

    1—Ans: d

14. Match the graph shown with its equation.

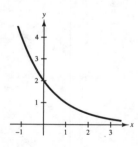

    (a) $f(x) = -2^x$ **(b)** $f(x) = 2^{-x}$ **(c)** $f(x) = 1 - 2^x$

    (d) $f(x) = 2^{x-1}$ **(e)** $f(x) = 2^{1-x}$

    1—Ans: e

15. Sketch the graph of $f(x) = 2^x - 2$.

    1—Ans:

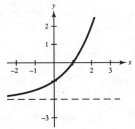

16. Sketch the graph of $f(x) = 3 - 2^x$.

    1—Ans:

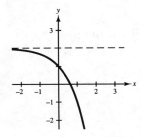

17. Match the graph shown with its equation.

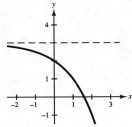

   (a) $f(x) = 2 - e^x$ **(b)** $f(x) = 2 - e^{-x}$ **(c)** $f(x) = 1 + e^x$

   (d) $f(x) = 2e^{-x} - 1$ **(e)** $f(x) = 1 + e^{-x}$

   2—Ans: a

18. Match the graph shown with its equation.

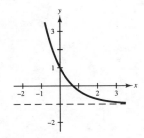

   (a) $f(x) = 2 - e^x$ **(b)** $f(x) = 2 - e^{-x}$ **(c)** $f(x) = 1 + e^x$

   (d) $f(x) = 2e^{-x} - 1$ **(e)** $f(x) = 1 + e^{-x}$

   2—Ans: d

19. $5000 is invested for five years at an annual interest rate of 8%. Use a calculator to find the final balance, if the compounding occurs quarterly.

    (a) $7459.12   **(b)** $7346.64   **(c)** $7429.74   **(d)** $7449.23   **(e)** None of these

    1—T—Ans: c

20. $5000 is invested for five years at an annual interest rate of 8%. Use a calculator to find the final balance, if the compounding occurs monthly.

    (a) $7459.12   **(b)** $7346.64   **(c)** $7429.74   **(d)** $7449.23   **(e)** None of these

    1—T—Ans: d

21. $8000 is invested for seven years in an account paying an interest rate of $7\frac{1}{2}$%. Find the final balance if the compounding occurs annually.

    1—T—Ans: $13,272.39

22. $8000 is invested for seven years in an account paying an interest rate of $7\frac{1}{2}$%. Find the final balance if the compounding occurs continuously.

    1—T—Ans: $13,523.67

23. Find the principal, P, that will yield a balance of $7500 when invested for five years at 8.5% annual interest rate compounded annually.

    (a) $4782.21   **(b)** $4987.84   **(c)** $4307.81   **(d)** $4648.27   **(e)** None of these

    1—T—Ans: b

24. Find the principal, P, that will yield a balance of $7500 when invested for six years at 7.5% annual interest rate compounded continuously.

    (a) $4782.21   **(b)** $4987.84   **(c)** $4307.81   **(d)** $4648.27   **(e)** None of these

    1—T—Ans: a

25. Find the principal, P, that will yield a balance of $10,000 when invested for five years at 8.2% annual interest rate compounded quarterly.

    1—T—Ans: $6664.07

26. Find the principal, P, that will yield a balance of $10,000 when invested for six years at 7.8% annual interest rate compounded monthly.

    1—T—Ans: $6272.03

27. The new price of an automobile was $12,000. After t years its value is given by $V = 12{,}000(0.72)^t$. Use a calculator to find its value, to the nearest dollar, after five years.

    (a) $2322   **(b)** $4320   **(c)** $5150   **(d)** $3272   **(e)** None of these

    1—T—Ans: a

28. The new price of an automobile was $12,000. After t years its value is given by $V = 12{,}000(0.72)^t$. Use a calculator to find its value, to the nearest dollar, after six years.

(a) $2322   ((b) $1672   (c) $3272   (d) $1275   (e) None of these

1—T—Ans: b

29. Assume an annual inflation rate of 5% for the next ten years. Find the expected selling price in ten years of an item that retails today for $62.50.

(a) $93.75   (b) $65.63   (c) $101.80   (d) $75.70   (e) None of these

2—T—Ans: c

30. Assume an annual inflation rate of 5% for the next ten years. Find the expected selling price in ten years of an item that retails today for $40.

(a) $42   (b) $60   (c) $52.25   (d) $65.15   (e) None of these

2—T—Ans: d

31. The new price of an automobile was $13,500. After t years its value is given by $V = 13{,}500(0.78)^t$. Find the value, to the nearest dollar, of the car after five years.

2—T—Ans: $3898

32. The new price of an automobile was $13,500. After t years its value is given by $V = 13{,}500(0.78)^t$. Find the value, to the nearest dollar, of the car after six years.

2—T—Ans: $3040

33. Assume an annual inflation rate of 4.5% for the next ten years. Find the expected selling price ten years from now of an item which retails today for $55.

2—T—Ans: $85.41

34. Assume an annual inflation rate of 4.5% for the next ten years. Find the expected selling price ten years from now of an item which retails today for $90.

2—T—Ans: $139.77

35. Find $f(-3)$ if $f(x) = 3^x$.

(a) -9 (b) -27 (c) $\frac{1}{27}$ (d) $-\frac{1}{27}$ (e) None of these

1—Ans: c

36. Find $f(-4)$ if $f(x) = 2^x$.

(a) -8 (b) $-\frac{1}{16}$ (c) -16 (d) $\frac{1}{16}$ (e) None of these

1—Ans: d

37. Find $g(4)$ if $g(x) = (1.14)^x$. Round your answer to four decimal places.

   (a) 4.5600   **(b)** 1.6890   **(c)** 1.6889   **(d)** 0.5921   **(e)** None of these

   1—T—Ans: b

38. Find $g(7)$ if $g(x) = (2.12)^x$. Round your answer to four decimal places.

   (a) 14.84   **(b)** 131.8257   **(c)** 192.4647   **(d)** 192.4646   **(e)** None of these

   1—T—Ans: c

39. Find the amount of an investment of $1000 invested at a rate of 9% for three years if the interest is compounded monthly.

   (a) $270   **(b)** $1270   **(c)** $1309.96   **(d)** $1308.65   **(e)** None of these

   1—T—Form: 11A—Ans: d

40. Find the amount of an investment of $1000 invested at a rate of 11% for two years if the interest is compounded quarterly.

   (a) $220   **(b)** $1242.38   **(c)** $1220   **(d)** $1246.08   **(e)** None of these

   1—T—Form: 11B—Ans: b

41. Let $f(x) = 3^{-x}$. Find:

   a. $f(2)$ **b.** $f(-3)$ **c.** $f(0)$

   1—Ans:
   a. $\frac{1}{9}$ **b.** 27   **c.** 1

42. Let $f(x) = 2^{-x}$. Find:

   a. $f(0)$ **b.** $f(-3)$ **c.** $f(5)$

   1—Form: 11C—Ans:
   a. 1   **b.** 8   **c.** $\frac{1}{32}$

43. Evaluate $100(1.05)^7$. Round your answer to four decimal places.

   1—T—Ans: 140.7100

44. Find the balance for $1000 invested at a rate of 9% for three years if the interest is compounded monthly.

   2—T—Ans: $1308.05

45. If $2000 is invested at $8\frac{1}{2}$% interest compounded daily, find the balance after 10 years. (Assume a non-leap year.)

   2—T—Form: 11C—Ans: $4678.83

46. A certain population decreases according to the equation $y = 300 - 5e^{0.2t}$. Find the population (to the nearest integer) when $t = 10$.

(a) 295   (b) 293   (c) 263   (d) 37   (e) None of these

2—T—Form: 11A—Ans: c

47. A certain population grows according to the equation $y = 40e^{0.025t}$. Find the population (to the nearest integer) when $t = 50$.

(a) 140   (b) 2051   (c) 45   (d) 50   (e) None of these

2—T—Form: 11B—Ans: a

48. Evaluate when $t = 12$: $200e^{-0.37t}$.

(a) 16954.9883   (b) 1.6436   (c) 2.3592   (d) -2413.8343 (e) None of these

1—T—Ans: c

49. Evaluate when $x = -15$: $14e^{-0.012x}$.

(a) -6.8501 (b) 6.8501   (c) 11.6938   (d) 16.7610   (e) None of these

1—T—Ans: d

50. Evaluate when $x = 55$: $300 - 4e^{0.003x}$.

(a) 304.7176   (b) 295.2824   (c) 296.6084   (d) 298.2059   (e) None of these

1—T—Ans: b

51. Evaluate when $t = 4$: $\dfrac{200}{1 + e^{-3t}}$.

(a) 200.1991   (b) 200.0000   (c) -6.3252 (d) 199.9988   (e) None of these

1—T—Ans: d

52. Match the graph with the correct function.

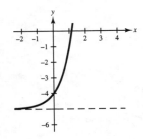

(a) $f(x) = 4^x - 5$ (b) $f(x) = 4^x + 5$ (c) $f(x) = 4^{-x} + 5$

(d) $f(x) = 4^{-x} + 5$ (e) None of these

1—Ans: a

53. Match the graph with the correct function.

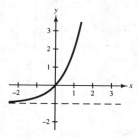

(a) $y = 3^{x-1}$ (b) $y = 3^x - 1$ (c) $y = 3^{1-x}$

(d) $y = 3^{-x} - 1$ (e) None of these

1—Ans: b

54. Match the graph with the correct function.

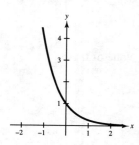

(a) $f(x) = \left(\frac{1}{2}\right)^x - 1$ (b) $f(x) = 3^{-x^2} - 1$ (c) $f(x) = 3^{x+1}$

(d) $f(x) = 4^{-x}$ (e) None of these

1—Ans: d

55. Sketch the graph: $f(x) = 3^x - 5$.

2—Ans:

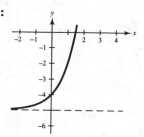

56. Sketch the graph: $f(x) = 2 - 3^x$.

2—Ans:

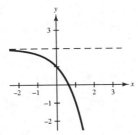

57. Find the balance for $2000 invested at a rate of 8% for three years if the interest is compounded monthly.

(a) $540 (b) $2540.47 (c) $2480 (d) $480 (e) None of these

2—T—Ans: b

58. Determine the balance after two years if $1250 is invested at $5\frac{1}{2}$% compounded continuously.

(a) $145.35 (b) $1387.50 (c) $2641.35 (d) $1395.35 (e) None of these

2—T—Ans: d

59. If $5000 is invested at $7\frac{1}{2}$% interest compounded daily, find the balance after eight years. (Assume a non-leap year.)

(a) $4110 (b) $43,115.03 (c) $9110.03 (d) $8000 (e) None of these

2—T—Ans: c

60. Determine the principal that must be invested at a rate of 8% compounded quarterly so that the balance in 40 years will be $200,000.

(a) $90,578.10 (b) $47,539.00 (c) $12,416.00

(d) $8414.00 (e) None of these

2—T—Ans: d

61. $1500 is invested at a rate of 8% compounded quarterly. What is the balance at the end of five years?

(a) $1624.67 (b) $2237.74 (c) $2228.92 (d) $2226.04 (e) None of these

2—T—Ans: c

62. $1500 is invested at a rate of 10% compounded monthly. What is the balance at the end of 12 years?

(a) $1657.70 (b) $3512.55 (c) $4955.47 (d) $4980.18 (e) None of these

2—T—Ans: c

63. $2100 is invested at a rate of 7% compounded monthly. What is the balance at the end of 10 years?

2—T—Ans: $4220.29

64. $3500 is invested at a rate of 9% compounded continuously. What is the balance at the end of 18 years?

(a) $68,932.98   **(b)** $17,685.82   **(c)** $17,493.53   **(d)** $8608.61   **(e)** None of these

2—T—Ans: b

65. $2000 is invested at a rate of $7\frac{1}{2}$% compounded continuously. What is the balance at the end of 20 years?

2—T—Ans: $8963.38

66. Determine the amount of money that should be invested at a rate of 8% compounded quarterly to produce a final balance of $20,000 in 10 years.

(a) $16,406.97   **(b)** $9057.81   **(c)** $18,463.80   **(d)** $9081.26   **(e)** None of these

2—T—Ans: b

67. Determine the amount of money that should be invested at a rate of $6\frac{1}{2}$% compounded monthly to produce a final balance of $15,000 in 20 years.

(a) $4101.34   **(b)** $5216.07   **(c)** $2458.83   **(d)** $14,056.14   **(e)** None of these

2—T—Ans: a

68. Determine the amount of money that should be invested at a rate of 7% compounded continuously to produce a final balance of $15,000 in 20 years.

2—T—Ans: $3698.95

69. A certain population increases according to the model $P(t) = 250e^{0.47t}$. Use the model to determine the population when $t = 5$. Round your answer to the nearest integer.

(a) 400   **(b)** 1597   **(c)** 1998   **(d)** 2621   **(e)** None of these

2—T—Ans: d

70. A certain population increases according to the model $P(t) = 250e^{0.47t}$. Use the model to determine the population when $t = 10$. Round your answer to the nearest integer.

(a) 400   **(b)** 4091   **(c)** 27,487   **(d)** 23,716   **(e)** None of these

2—T—Ans: c

71. Five pounds of plutonium (Pu^{230}) is released in a nuclear accident. The amount of plutonium that is present after t years is given by

$$P = 5e^{-0.00002845t}.$$

How much will remain after 50,000 years?

2—T—Ans: 1.2 pounds

72. One hundred grams of radium (Ra^{226}) is stored in a container. The amount of radium present after t years is given by

$$R = 100e^{-0.0004279t}.$$

How much of the 100 grams will remain after 5000 years?

2—T—Ans: 11.8 grams

73. The total number of shares of stock listed on the New York Stock Exchange between 1945 and 1992 can be approximated by the function

$$y = 12.051e^{0.099327t}, \quad 45 \leq t \leq 92$$

where y represents the number of listed shares (in millions) and $t = 45$ represents 1945. How many shares were listed in 1980? (Source: *New York Stock Exchange*)

2—T—Ans: 34,041 shares

Section 11.2   Inverse Functions

1. Given $f(x) = 2x - 3$ and $g(x) = 2 - x^2$. Find the value of $(g \circ f)(3)$.

   (a) 3   (b) -21 (c) -17 (d) -7 (e) None of these

   1—Ans: d

2. Given $f(x) = 2x - 3$ and $g(x) = 2 - x^2$. Find the value of $(f \circ g)(3)$.

   (a) 3   (b) -21 (c) -17 (d) -7 (e) None of these

   1—Ans: c

3. Given $f(x) = |x - 6|$ and $g(x) = |1 - 2x|$. Find the value of $(g \circ f)(-1)$.

   1—Ans: 13

4. Given $f(x) = |x - 6|$ and $g(x) = |1 - 2x|$. Find the value of $(f \circ g)(-1)$.

   1—Ans: 3

5. Given $f(x) = \sqrt{x + 1}$ and $g(x) = \dfrac{1}{x^2 - 1}$. Find the value of $(f \circ g)\left(\dfrac{5}{3}\right)$.

   (a) $\dfrac{4}{5}$ (b) $\dfrac{3}{5}$ (c) $\dfrac{5}{3}$ (d) $\dfrac{5}{4}$ (e) None of these

   1—Ans: d

6. Given $f(x) = \sqrt{x + 1}$ and $g(x) = \dfrac{1}{x^2 - 1}$. Find the value of $(g \circ f)\left(\dfrac{5}{3}\right)$.

(a) $\dfrac{4}{5}$ (b) $\dfrac{3}{5}$ (c) $\dfrac{5}{3}$ (d) $\dfrac{5}{4}$ (e) None of these

1—Ans: b

7. Given $f(x) = \sqrt{x - 4}$ and $g(x) = x^2 + 2$. Find the domain of $(f \circ g)(x)$.

(a) $x \geq 4$ (b) $-\sqrt{2} \leq x \leq \sqrt{2}$ (c) $x \geq \sqrt{2}$ and $x \leq -\sqrt{2}$

(d) All real values of x (e) None of these

2—Ans: c

8. Given $f(x) = \sqrt{x - 4}$ and $g(x) = x^2 + 2$. Find the domain of $(g \circ f)(x)$.

(a) $x \geq 4$ (b) $-\sqrt{2} \leq x \leq \sqrt{2}$ (c) $x \geq \sqrt{2}$ and $x \leq -\sqrt{2}$

(d) All real values of x (e) None of these

2—Ans: a

9. Given $f(x) = \sqrt{1 - x}$ and $g(x) = |2 - x|$. Find the domain of $(f \circ g)(x)$.

2—Ans: $1 \leq x \leq 3$

10. Given $f(x) = \sqrt{x - 1}$ and $g(x) = |x + 2|$. Find the domain of $(f \circ g)(x)$.

2—Ans: $x \leq -3$ and $x \geq -1$

11. Find the inverse of the function $f(x) = -7x$.

(a) $7x$ (b) $-\frac{1}{7}x$ (c) $\frac{1}{7}x$ (d) $-7x$ (e) None of these

1—Ans: b

12. Find the inverse of the function $f(x) = x + 7$.

(a) $\dfrac{x}{7}$ (b) $7 + x$ (c) $7 - x$ (d) $x - 7$ (e) None of these

1—Ans: d

13. Find the inverse of the function $f(x) = \frac{1}{5}x$.

(a) $5x$ (b) $-\frac{1}{5}x$ (c) $-5x$ (d) $x - 5$ (e) None of these

1—Ans: a

14. Find the inverse of the function $f(x) = x - 7$.

(a) $7 - x$ (b) $\dfrac{x}{7}$ (c) $x + 7$ (d) $\dfrac{1}{x - 7}$ (e) None of these

1—Ans: c

15. Verify algebraically that $f(x) = \frac{5}{3}x$ and $g(x) = \frac{3}{5}x$ are inverse functions.

1—Ans: $f(g(x)) = \frac{5}{3}(\frac{3}{5}x) = x$; $g(f(x)) = \frac{3}{5}(\frac{5}{3}x) = x$

16. Verify algebraically that $f(x) = -x + 2$ and $g(x) = -x + 2$ are inverse functions.

1—Ans: $f(g(x)) = -(-x + 2) + 2 = x$; $g(f(x)) = -(-x + 2) + 2 = x$

17. Find the inverse of the function $f(x) = -\frac{1}{2}x + 3$.

(a) $-2(x + 3)$　　　　(b) $f(x) = -2(x - 3)$　　　　(c) $2(x + 3)$

(d) $2(x - 3)$　　　　(e) None of these

1—Ans: b

18. Find the inverse of the function $f(x) = -\frac{1}{2}x - 3$.

(a) $-2(x + 3)$　　　　(b) $f(x) = -2(x - 3)$　　　　(c) $2(x + 3)$

(d) $2(x - 3)$　　　　(e) None of these

1—Ans: a

19. Find the inverse of the function $f(x) = \frac{1}{2}x - 3$.

(a) $-2(x + 3)$　　　　(b) $f(x) = -2(x - 3)$　　　　(c) $2(x + 3)$

(d) $2(x - 3)$　　　　(e) None of these

1—Ans: c

20. Find the inverse of the function $f(x) = \frac{1}{2}x + 3$.

(a) $-2(x + 3)$　　　　(b) $f(x) = -2(x - 3)$　　　　(c) $2(x + 3)$

(d) $2(x - 3)$　　　　(e) None of these

1—Ans: d

21. Verify algebraically that $f(x) = 3x - 1$ and $g(x) = \frac{1}{3}(x + 1)$ are inverse functions.

1—Ans: $f(g(x)) = 3[\frac{1}{3}(x + 1)] - 1 = x$ and $g(f(x)) = \frac{1}{3}[(3x - 1) + 1] = x$

22. Verify algebraically that $f(x) = -3x + 1$ and $g(x) = -\frac{1}{3}(x - 1)$ are inverse functions.

1—Ans: $f(g(x)) = -3[-\frac{1}{3}(x - 1)] + 1 = x$ and $g(f(x)) = -\frac{1}{3}[(-3x + 1) - 1] = x$

23. Find the inverse of the function $f(t) = t^3$.

(a) $3t^2$　　　(b) $\sqrt[3]{t}$　　　(c) $-t^3$　　　(d) $\frac{1}{t^3}$　　　(e) None of these

1—Ans: b

24. Find the inverse of the function $f(t) = \sqrt[5]{t}$.

  (a) $-\sqrt[5]{t}$　　(b) $-t^5$　　(c) $\dfrac{1}{\sqrt[5]{t}}$　　(d) t^5　　(e) None of these

  1—Ans: d

25. Find the inverse of the function $f(s) = \dfrac{3}{s-2}$.

  2—Ans: $f^{-1}(s) = \dfrac{2x+3}{s}$

26. Find the inverse of the function $f(t) = \dfrac{2}{t+1}$.

  2—Ans: $f^{-1}(t) = \dfrac{2-t}{t}$

27. Find the inverse of the function $g(x) = \dfrac{4}{2x-1}$.

  2—Ans: $g^{-1}(x) = \dfrac{x+4}{2x}$

28. Find the inverse of the function $h(r) = \dfrac{3}{r-4}$.

  2—Ans: $h^{-1}(r) = \dfrac{3+4r}{r}$

29. Find the inverse of the function $f(x) = (x-1)^2, \quad x \geq 1$.

  (a) $\sqrt{x}-1$　　(b) $\sqrt{x}+1$　　(c) $\sqrt{x+1}$　　(d) $\sqrt{x-1}$　　(e) None of these

  2—Ans: b

30. Find the inverse of the function $f(x) = \sqrt{x}-1$.

  (a) $(1-x)^2$　　　　　　(b) $\sqrt{1-x}$　　　　　　(c) $(1+x)^2, x \geq -1$

  (d) $\dfrac{1}{\sqrt{x}-1}$　　　　　(e) None of these

  2—Ans: c

31. Find the inverse of the function $f(x) = \sqrt{9-x}$.

  2—Ans: $f^{-1}(x) = 9-x^2, \quad x \geq 0$

32. Find the inverse of the function $f(x) = 9 - x^2, \quad x \geq 0$.

  2—Ans: $f^{-1}(x) = \sqrt{9-x}$

33. Find the inverse of the function $f(x) = x^2 - 4, \quad x \geq 0$.

    2—Ans: $f^{-1}(x) = \sqrt{x + 4}$

34. Find the inverse of the function $f(x) = \sqrt{x + 4}, \quad x \geq 0$.

    2—Ans: $f^{-1}(x) = x^2 - 4, \quad x \geq 2$

35. Use a graphing utility to choose the function which has no inverse.

    (a) $f(x) = x$ **(b)** $f(x) = 2x^2$ **(c)** $f(x) = x^3$

    (d) $f(x) = 2x + 1$ **(e)** None of these

    1—T—Ans: b

36. Use a graphing utility to choose the function which has no inverse.

    (a) $f(x) = x$ **(b)** $f(x) = 8x^3$ **(c)** $f(x) = 1 - 2x$

    (d) $f(x) = |x|$ **(e)** None of these

    1—T—Ans: d

37. Use a graphing utility to choose the function which has no inverse.

    (a) $f(x) = x^4$ **(b)** $f(x) = 8x^3$ **(c)** $f(x) = 3x$

    (d) $f(x) = 5 - 2x$ **(e)** None of these

    1—T—Ans: a

38. Use a graphing utility to choose the function which has no inverse.

    (a) $f(x) = 2x$ **(b)** $f(x) = 3 + x$ **(c)** $f(x) = |x - 1|$

    (d) $f(x) = 8x^3$ **(e)** None of these

    1—T—Ans: c

39. Use a graphing utility to determine if f has an inverse. If f has an inverse, find it. If f has no inverse, state why not.

    $f(x) = |x - 2|$

    1—T—Ans: No inverse; $f(x) = |x - 2|$ fails the horizontal line test.

40. Use a graphing utility to determine if $f(x)$ has an inverse. If $f(x)$ has an inverse, find it. If $f(x)$ has no inverse, state why not.

    $f(x) = 4x^2$

    1—T—Ans: No inverse; $f(x) = 4x^2$ fails the horizontal line test.

41. If $(4, -2)$ lies on the graph of $f(x)$, and if $f(x)$ has an inverse $f^{-1}(x)$, determine which point is on the graph of $f^{-1}(x)$.

    (a) $(-4, 2)$ **(b)** $(2, -4)$ **(c)** $(-2, 4)$ **(d)** $(4, 2)$ **(e)** None of these

    1—Ans: c

42. If $(3, -5)$ lies on the graph of $f(x)$, and if $f(x)$ has an inverse $f^{-1}(x)$, determine which point is on the graph of $f^{-1}(x)$.

    (a) $(-5, 3)$ **(b)** $(-3, 5)$ **(c)** $(5, -3)$ **(d)** $(-3, -5)$ **(e)** None of these

    1—Ans: a

43. $(-3, 4)$ lies on the graph of $f(x)$, which has an inverse $f^{-1}(x)$. Determine a point which must lie on the graph of $f^{-1}(x)$.

    1—Ans: $(4, -3)$

44. $(7, -2)$ lies on the graph of $f(x)$, which has an inverse $f^{-1}(x)$. Determine a point which must lie on the graph of $f^{-1}(x)$.

    1—Ans: $(-2, 7)$

45. Determine which function has an inverse.

    (a)
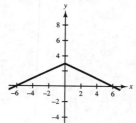
    (b)
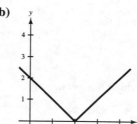
    (c)
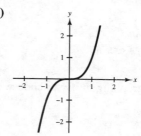

    (d)
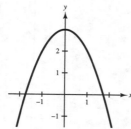
    (e)
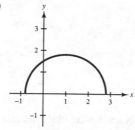

    1—Ans: c

46. Determine which function has an inverse.

(a)

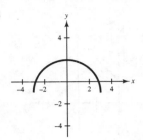

(b)

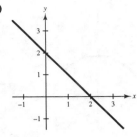

(c)

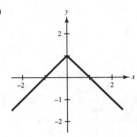

(d)

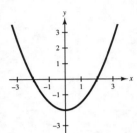

(e)

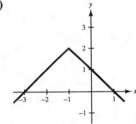

1—Ans: b

47. Determine which function has an inverse.

(a)

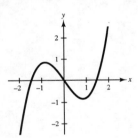

(b)

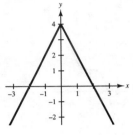

(c)

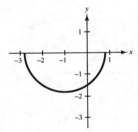

(d)

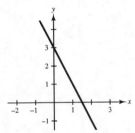

(e)

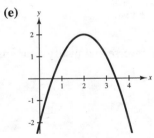

1—Ans: d

48. Determine which function has an inverse.

(a)
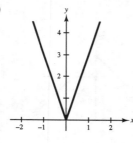

(b)
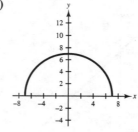

(c)
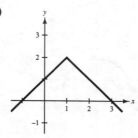

(d)
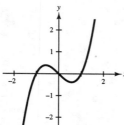

(e)
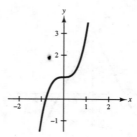

1—Ans: e

49. Determine whether or not the function has an inverse and justify your answer.

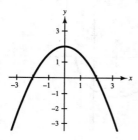

1—Ans: It does not. It fails the horizontal line test.

50. Determine whether or not the function has an inverse and justify your answer.

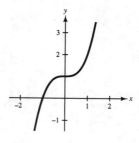

1—Ans: It has an inverse. It passes the horizontal line test.

51. Given $f(x) = \sqrt{x}$. $f^{-1}(x) = x^2$ is the inverse function if x is restricted to:

(a) $x \le 0$ (b) $x \ge 0$ (c) $x^2 > 0$ (d) $x \ge 1$ (e) None of these

1—Ans: b

52. Given $f(x) = \sqrt{x-1}$. $f^{-1}(x) = x^2 + 1$ is the inverse function if x is restricted to:

(a) $x \le 0$ (b) $x \ge 1$ (c) $x \ge 0$ (d) $x \le 1$ (e) None of these

1—Ans: c

53. Given $f(x) = \sqrt{x+1}$. $f^{-1}(x) = x^2 - 1$ is the inverse function if x is restricted to:

(a) $x \ge 0$ (b) $x \ge -1$ (c) $x \le 0$ (d) $x \le -1$ (e) None of these

1—Ans: a

54. Given $f(x) = \sqrt{x+2}$. $f^{-1}(x) = x^2 - 2$ is the inverse function if x is restricted to:

(a) $x \le 0$ (b) $x \ge -2$ (c) $x \le -2$ (d) $x \ge 0$ (e) None of these

1—Ans: d

55. Place a restriction on the domain of the function $f(x) = 16 - x^2$ so that the graph of the restricted function satisfies the horizontal line test for inverses.

1—Ans: $x \ge 0$ Answer is not unique.

56. Place a restriction on the domain of the function $f(x) = (x-4)^2$ so that the graph of the restricted function satisfies the horizontal line test for inverses.

1—Ans: $x \le 4$ or $x \ge 4$ Answer is not unique.

57. Let $f(x) = \dfrac{1}{\sqrt{x}}$ and $g(x) = 1 - x^2$. Find $(f \circ g)(x)$.

(a) $\dfrac{1 - x^2}{\sqrt{x}}$ (b) $\dfrac{1}{\sqrt{1 - x^2}}$ (c) $1 - \dfrac{1}{x}$ (d) $\dfrac{1}{\sqrt{x}} + 1 - x^2$ (e) None of these

1—Ans: b

58. Let $f(x) = \dfrac{1}{\sqrt{x}}$ and $g(x) = 1 - x^2$. Find $(g \circ f)(x)$.

(a) $\dfrac{1 - x^2}{\sqrt{x}}$ (b) $\dfrac{1}{\sqrt{1 - x^2}}$ (c) $1 - \dfrac{1}{x}$ (d) $\dfrac{1}{\sqrt{x}} + 1 - x^2$ (e) None of these

1—Ans: c

59. Let $f(x) = \sqrt{x-4}$ and $g(x) = 9 - 8x - x^2$. Find $g(f(4))$.

(a) $(9 - 8x - x^2)(\sqrt{x} + 4)$ (b) 0 (c) 9

(d) -9.1 (e) None of these

1—Form: 11A—Ans: c

60. Let $f(x) = \sqrt{x + 4}$ and $g(x) = 9 - 8x - x^2$. Find $f(g(1))$.

(a) $\sqrt{13 - 8x - x^2}$ (b) $4 - 8\sqrt{5}$ (c) $-2, 2$

(d) 2 (e) None of these

1—Form: 11B—Ans: d

61. Find the inverse of the function $f(x) = \sqrt{2 + x}$.

(a) $\dfrac{1}{\sqrt{2 + x}}$ (b) $\sqrt{2 - x}$ (c) $x^2 + 2$ (d) $x^2 - 2$ (e) None of these

2—Ans: d

62. Find the inverse of the function $f(x) = \dfrac{2}{3x + 1}$.

(a) $\dfrac{3x - 1}{2}$ (b) $\dfrac{2 - x}{3x}$ (c) $\dfrac{3x + 1}{2}$ (d) $\dfrac{1 - x}{3x}$ (e) None of these

2—Ans: b

63. Let $f(x) = x - 2$ and $g(x) = \dfrac{x + 5}{3}$. Find $(g \circ f)(x)$.

1—Ans: $\dfrac{x + 3}{3}$

64. Let $f(x) = x - 2$ and $g(x) = \dfrac{x + 5}{3}$. Find $(f \circ g)(x)$.

1—Form: 11C—Ans: $\dfrac{x - 1}{3}$

65. Given $f(x) = 3x^3 - 1$. Use a graphing utility to determine which function is f^{-1}.

(a) $\dfrac{1}{3x^3 - 1}$ (b) $3x^{-3} - 1$ (c) $3(x + 1)$ (d) $\sqrt[3]{\dfrac{x + 1}{3}}$ (e) None of these

2—T—Form: 11A—Ans: d

66. Given $f(x) = 2x^5$. Use a graphing utility to determine which function is f^{-1}.

(a) $\sqrt[5]{\dfrac{x}{2}}$ (b) $\dfrac{1}{2}\sqrt[5]{x}$ (c) $\dfrac{1}{2x^5}$ (d) $\dfrac{2}{x^5}$ (e) None of these

2—T—Form: 11B—Ans: a

67. Given $f(x) = x^2 + 1$ for $x \geq 0$. Use a graphing utility to determine which function is f^{-1}.

(a) $\dfrac{1}{x^2 + 1}$ (b) $\sqrt{x - 1}$ (c) $\sqrt{x} - 1$ (d) $1 - \sqrt{x}$ (e) None of these

2—T—Form: 11C—Ans: b

68. Given $f(x) = \sqrt{2 + x}$. Use a graphing utility to determine which function is f^{-1}.

   (a) $\dfrac{1}{\sqrt{2 + x}}$, $x \geq -2$ **(b)** $\sqrt{2 - x}$, $x \geq 0$ **(c)** $x^2 + 2$, $x \geq -2$

   (d) $x^2 - 2$, $x \geq 0$ **(e)** None of these

   2—T—Ans: d

69. Use a graphing utility to determine which of the functions does not have an inverse.

   (a) $f(x) = x^3$ **(b)** $g(x) = x^2 + 4$ **(c)** $h(x) = 2x + 5$

   (d) $p(x) = \dfrac{2}{x}$ **(e)** None of these

   2—T—Ans: b

70. Use a graphing utility to determine which of the functions has an inverse.

   (a) $f(x) = \dfrac{1}{x}$ **(b)** $g(x) = |x - 4|$ **(c)** $h(x) = 5$

   (d) $p(x) = \sqrt{9 - x^2}$ **(e)** None of these

   2—T—Ans: a

71. Find the inverse of the function: $f(x) = \dfrac{2}{3x + 1}$.

   (a) $\dfrac{3x - 1}{2}$ **(b)** $\dfrac{2 - x}{3x}$ **(c)** $\dfrac{3x + 1}{2}$ **(d)** $\dfrac{1 - x}{2}$ **(e)** None of these

   2—Form: 11A—Ans: b

72. Find the inverse of the function: $f(x) = \dfrac{7}{x + 2}$.

   (a) $f(x)$ has no inverse   **(b)** $\dfrac{x + 2}{7}$ **(c)** $\dfrac{7 - 2x}{x}$

   (d) $-\dfrac{7}{x + 2}$ **(e)** None of these

   2—Form: 11B—Ans: c

73. Let $f(x) = \dfrac{2}{\sqrt{x}}$ and $g(x) = 9x + 4$. Find $(f \circ g)(x)$.

   (a) $\dfrac{2}{3x + 2}$ **(b)** $\dfrac{18x + 8}{\sqrt{x}}$ **(c)** $\dfrac{18}{\sqrt{x}} + 4$

   (d) $\dfrac{2}{\sqrt{9x + 4}}$ **(e)** None of these

   2—Ans: d

74. Let $f(x) = \dfrac{1}{\sqrt{x}}$ and $g(x) = 4 - x^2$. Find $(g \circ f)(x)$.

(a) $4 - \dfrac{1}{x^2}$

(b) $4 - \dfrac{1}{x}$

(c) $\dfrac{1}{\sqrt{4 - x^2}}$

(d) $\dfrac{4 - x^2}{\sqrt{x}}$

(e) None of these

2—Ans: b

75. Let $f(x) = x - 4$ and $g(x) = \dfrac{x + 7}{2}$. Find $(g \circ f)(x)$.

(a) $\dfrac{x + 3}{2}$

(b) $\dfrac{x - 1}{2}$

(c) $\dfrac{x^2 + 3x - 28}{2}$

(d) $\dfrac{x + 5}{3(x - 2)}$

(e) None of these

2—Ans: a

76. Let $f(x) = \sqrt{x - 9}$ and $g(x) = 4 - 3x - x^2$. Find $(g \circ f)(25)$.

(a) -6

(b) -24

(c) 0

(d) -24 and 0

(e) None of these

2—Ans: b

77. Let $f(x) = \sqrt{x + 4}$ and $g(x) = 4 - 3x - x^2$. Find $(f \circ g)(1)$.

(a) $-3\sqrt{5} - 1$ (b) 2

(c) $-2, 2$

(d) 0

(e) None of these

2—Ans: b

78. Let $f(x) = \dfrac{1}{2\sqrt{x}}$ and $g(x) = 3x - 11$. Find $(f \circ g)(5)$.

(a) $\dfrac{1}{8}$

(b) $-\dfrac{3}{2\sqrt{5}} - 11$ (c) $\dfrac{1}{4}$

(d) $\pm\dfrac{1}{4}$

(e) None of these

2—Ans: c

79. Let $f(x) = \dfrac{1}{\sqrt{x}}$ and $g(x) = 4x - 5$. Find the domain of $(f \circ g)(x)$.

(a) $\left[\dfrac{5}{4}, \infty\right]$ (b) $\left(-\infty, \dfrac{5}{4}\right)$ (c) $\left(\dfrac{5}{4}, \infty\right)$ (d) $(0, \infty)$ (e) None of these

2—Ans: c

80. Find the inverse of the function $f(x) = \dfrac{2x}{7}$.

(a) $14x$ (b) $\dfrac{7x}{2}$ (c) $\dfrac{7}{2x}$ (d) $2x - 7$ (e) None of these

1—**Ans:** b

81. Find the inverse of the function $f(x) = 8 - 3x$.

(a) $\dfrac{1}{8 - 3x}$ (b) $3x + -8$ (c) $\dfrac{8}{3} - x$ (d) $\dfrac{8 - x}{3}$ (e) None of these

1—**Ans:** d

82. Find the inverse of the function $f(x) = \dfrac{x - 4}{5}$.

(a) $5x + 4$ (b) $5x - 4$ (c) $\dfrac{5}{x - 4}$ (d) $\dfrac{1}{5}x - 4$ (e) None of these

1—**Ans:** a

83. Find the inverse of the function $f(x) = \dfrac{3 + 8x}{9}$.

(a) $\dfrac{3 - 8x}{9}$ (b) $\dfrac{9}{3 + 8x}$ (c) $\dfrac{9x - 3}{8}$ (d) $\dfrac{3 - 9x}{8}$ (e) None of these

2—**Ans:** c

84. Find the inverse of the function $f(x) = \dfrac{1}{7x - 2}$.

(a) $7x - 2$ (b) $2 - 7x$ (c) $\dfrac{1}{7x} + 2$ (d) $\dfrac{1 + 2x}{7x}$ (e) None of these

2—**Ans:** d

85. Find the inverse of the function $f(x) = \dfrac{5}{x - 3}$.

(a) $f(x)$ has no inverse   (b) $\dfrac{5 + 3x}{x}$ (c) $\dfrac{x - 3}{5}$

(d) $-\dfrac{5}{x - 3}$ (e) None of these

2—**Ans:** b

86. Find the inverse of the function $f(x) = \dfrac{3}{x}$.

(a) $\dfrac{3}{x}$ (b) $\dfrac{x}{3}$ (c) x (d) $-\dfrac{3}{x}$ (e) None of these

2—**Ans:** a

87. Given $f(x) = 2x^3 - 3$, find $f^{-1}(x)$.

(a) $\dfrac{1}{2x^3 - 3}$

(b) $2x^{-3} - 3$

(c) $\sqrt[3]{\dfrac{x + 3}{2}}$

(d) $3 - 2x^3$

(e) None of these

2—**Ans:** c

88. Given $f(x) = 4x^7$, find $f^{-1}(x)$.

(a) $\dfrac{1}{4x^7}$

(b) $4\sqrt[7]{x}$

(c) $\dfrac{4}{x^7}$

(d) $\sqrt[7]{\dfrac{x}{4}}$

(e) None of these

2—**Ans:** d

89. Given $f(x) = x^2 + 4$ for $x \geq 0$, find $f^{-1}(x)$.

(a) $\dfrac{1}{x^2 + 4}$

(b) $\sqrt{x} - 4$

(c) $\sqrt{x - 4}$

(d) $\sqrt{x} - 2$

(e) None of these

2—**Ans:** c

90. Given $f(x) = \sqrt{3 - x}$. Find $f^{-1}(x)$.

(a) $\dfrac{1}{\sqrt{3 - x}}, \ x < 3$

(b) $3 - x^2, \ x \geq 0$

(c) $x^2 - 3, \ x \geq 3$

(d) $9 + x^2, \ x \geq 0$

(e) None of these

2—**Ans:** b

91. Given $f(x) = 9 - 3x^2$ for $x \geq 0$, find $f^{-1}(x)$.

(a) $\dfrac{1}{9 - 3x^2}$

(b) $\sqrt{\dfrac{9 - x}{3}}$

(c) $\sqrt{3 - x}$

(d) $3 - \sqrt{x}$

(e) None of these

2—**Ans:** b

92. Given $f(x) = \sqrt[3]{x + 7}$, find $f^{-1}(x)$.

(a) $x^3 + 343$

(b) $(x + 7)^3$

(c) $x^3 - 7$

(d) $\dfrac{1}{\sqrt[3]{x + 7}}$

(e) None of these

2—**Ans:** c

93. Given $f(x) = x^{2/5}$, find $f^{-1}(x)$.

(a) $\dfrac{5}{2}x$

(b) $\dfrac{1}{x^{2/5}}$

(c) $x^{-2/5}$

(d) $x^{5/2}$

(e) None of these

2—**Ans:** d

94. Given $f(x) = \sqrt{6x - 5}$, find $f^{-1}(x)$.

(a) $\sqrt{6y - 5}$, $y \geq \dfrac{5}{6}$ (b) $\dfrac{1}{6}(x^2 + 5)$, $x \geq 0$ (c) $\dfrac{1}{\sqrt{6x - 5}}$, $x \geq 0$

(d) $(6x - 5)^2$, $x \geq \dfrac{5}{6}$ (e) None of these

2—Ans: b

95. Determine which of the functions does not have an inverse.

(a) $f(x) = x^{1/5}$ (b) $g(x) = x^3 - 4$ (c) $h(x) = 4x - 3$

(d) $p(x) = 2x^2 - 1$ (e) None of these

2—Ans: d

96. Determine which of the functions has an inverse.

(a) $f(x) = 3$ (b) $g(x) = \dfrac{2}{3x}$ (c) $h(x) = |3 - x|$

(d) $p(x) = \sqrt{4 - x^2}$ (e) None of these

2—Ans: b

Section 11.3   Logarithmic Functions

1. Determine which of the following represent equivalent forms.

(a) $\log_2 8 = x$ and $x^2 = 8$ (b) $\log_3 N = 3$ and $N = 3(3)$ (c) $\log_2 M = 4$ and $M = 2^4$

(d) $\log_b 64 = 2$ and $2^b = 64$ (e) None of these

1—Ans: c

2. Determine which of the following represent equivalent forms.

(a) $\log_b 64 = 2$ and $64 = b^2$ (b) $\log_4 N = 3$ and $N = 4(3)$ (c) $\log_3 27 = x$ and $27 = x^3$

(d) $\log_b 32 = 5$ and $5^b = 32$ (e) None of these

1—Ans: a

3. Write $\log_2 M = 5$ in exponential form.

1—Ans: $M = 2^5$

4. Write $\log_{25} N = \frac{1}{2}$ in exponential form.

1—Ans: $N = 25^{1/2}$

5. Write $64 = 2^6$ in logarithmic form.

1—Ans: $\log_2 64 = 6$

6. Write $\frac{1}{81} = 3^{-4}$ in logarithmic form.

1—Ans: $\log_3 \frac{1}{81} = -4$

7. Evaluate $\log_4 \frac{1}{8}$.

(a) $\frac{3}{2}$ (b) $\frac{1}{2}$ (c) $-\frac{3}{2}$ (d) -2 (e) None of these

1—Ans: c

8. Evaluate $\log_{16} 32$.

(a) $\frac{4}{5}$ (b) 2   (c) $-\frac{4}{5}$ (d) $\frac{5}{4}$ (e) None of these

1—Ans: d

9. Evaluate $\log_3 \frac{1}{9}$.

(a) -2 (b) $\frac{1}{27}$ (c) 2   (d) -3 (e) None of these

1—Ans: a

10. Evaluate $\log_{25} 125$.

(a) 5   (b) $\frac{3}{2}$ (c) 3   (d) $-\frac{3}{2}$ (e) None of these

1—Ans: b

11. Evaluate $\log_8 32$ without a calculator.

1—Ans: $\frac{5}{3}$

12. Evaluate $\log_{1/2} 64$ without a calculator.

1—Ans: -6

13. Evaluate $\log_8 1$ without a calculator.

(a) 1   (b) 8   (c) Not defined   (d) 0   (e) None of these

1—Ans: d

14. Evaluate $\log_5 5$ without a calculator.

(a) 0   (b) 1   (c) 5   (d) $\frac{1}{5}$ (e) None of these

1—Ans: b

15. Evaluate $\log_{81} 27$ without a calculator.

1—Ans: $\frac{3}{4}$

16. Evaluate $\log_{64} 16$ without a calculator.

1—Ans: $\frac{2}{3}$

17. Evaluate $\log_{100} 10$ without a calculator.

1—Ans: $\frac{1}{2}$

18. Evaluate $\log_{100} 1000$ without a calculator.

1—Ans: $\frac{3}{2}$

19. Which of the following is not defined?

(a) $\log_2 1$ (b) $\log_1 2$ (c) $\log_2 2$ (d) $\log_2 \frac{1}{2}$ (e) None of these

1—Ans: b

20. Which of the following is not defined?

(a) $\log_3 3$ (b) $\log_3 1$ (c) $\log_3 \frac{1}{3}$ (d) $\log_3 (-3)$ (e) None of these

1—Ans: d

21. Evaluate ln 371.4 to three decimal places with the aid of a calculator.

1—T—Ans: 5.917

22. Evaluate ln 0.7154 to three decimal places with the aid of a calculator.

1—T—Ans: -0.335

23. Use your calculator to find the value of $\ln\left(1 + \dfrac{0.07}{12}\right)$ to four decimal places.

(a) -2.2341 (b) 0.0025   (c) 0.0058   (d) -5.144 (e) None of these

1—T—Ans: c

24. Use your calculator to find the value of $\ln\left(\dfrac{1 + \sqrt{5}}{2}\right)$ to four decimal places.

(a) 0.4812   (b) 0.2090   (c) 1.6180   (d) 0.7505   (e) None of these

1—T—Ans: a

25. Use your calculator to evaluate $\ln\left(\dfrac{\sqrt{37} + 9}{4}\right)$ to four decimal places.

1—T—Ans: 1.3273

26. Use your calculator to evaluate $\ln\left(\dfrac{16 + \sqrt{5}}{3}\right)$ to four decimal places.

1—T—Ans: 1.8048

27. Use your calculator to evaluate $\log_{10}\left(\dfrac{17 + \sqrt{41}}{5}\right)$ to four decimal places.

    1—T—Ans: 0.6703

28. Use your calculator to evaluate $\log_{10}\left(\dfrac{51 + \sqrt{47}}{7}\right)$ to four decimal places.

    1—T—Ans: 0.9172

29. Match the graph to the appropriate equation.

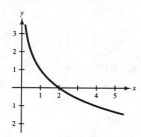

    (a) $y = \log_2(x + 2)$ **(b)** $y = 1 - \log_2(2 - x)$ **(c)** $y = 1 + \log_2(1 - x)$

    (d) $y = 1 - \log_2 x$ **(e)** None of these

    2—Ans: d

30. Match the graph to the appropriate equation.

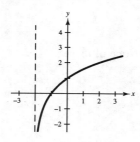

    (a) $y = \log_2(x + 2)$ **(b)** $y = 1 - \log_2(2 - x)$ **(c)** $y = 1 + \log_2(1 - x)$

    (d) $y = 1 - \log_2 x$ **(e)** None of these

    2—Ans: a

31. Sketch the graph of $y = 1 + \ln(-x)$.

    2—Ans:

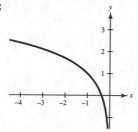

32. Sketch the graph of $y = 1 - \ln x$.

2—Ans:

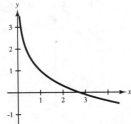

33. Use the change of base formula to determine the value for $\log_7 1084$. Round your answer to three decimal places.

(a) 3.591   **(b)** 6.988   **(c)** 1.946   **(d)** 3.035   **(e)** None of these

2—T—Ans: a

34. Use the change of base formula to determine the value for $\log_5 971$. Round your answer to three decimal places.

(a) 2.987   **(b)** 4.274   **(c)** 6.878   **(d)** 1.609   **(e)** None of these

2—T—Ans: b

35. Use the change of base formula to evaluate $\log_3 \sqrt{37}$ to three decimal places.

2—T—Ans: 1.643

36. Use the change of base formula to evaluate $\log_5 0.641$ to three decimal places.

2—T—Ans: -0.276

37. Use the change of base formula to evaluate $\log_2\left(\frac{49}{27}\right)$ to three decimal places.

2—T—Ans: 0.860

38. Use the change of base formula to evaluate $\log_4\left(7 - \sqrt{3}\right)$ to three decimal places.

2—T—Ans: 1.199

39. Find the domain of the function $f(x) = \ln(x - 1)$.

(a) $x \geq 1$ **(b)** $x > 1$ **(c)** $x < 1$
(d) All real numbers   **(e)** None of these

1—Ans: b

40. Find the domain of the function $f(x) = \ln(x + 1)$.

(a) $x \geq -1$ **(b)** $x < -1$ **(c)** All real numbers
(d) $x > -1$ **(e)** None of these

1—Ans: d

41. Use your calculator to evaluate $\ln \frac{2}{3}$. Round your answer to four decimal places.

    (a) 0.2310   **(b)** 0.1003   **(c)** -0.1761 **(d)** -0.4055 **(e)** None of these

    1—T—Ans: d

42. Use your calculator to evaluate $\ln \frac{3}{2}$. Round your answer to four decimal places.

    (a) 0.5493   **(b)** 0.1761   **(c)** 0.4055   **(d)** 1.5850   **(e)** None of these

    1—T—Ans: c

43. Evaluate $\log_{27} 3$ without the use of a calculator.

    (a) 9   **(b)** $\frac{1}{9}$ **(c)** 3   **(d)** $\frac{1}{3}$ **(e)** None of these

    1—Form: 11A—Ans: d

44. Evaluate $\log_2 \frac{1}{16}$ without the use of a calculator.

    (a) -4 **(b)** $\frac{1}{4}$ **(c)** 8   **(d)** $\frac{1}{8}$ **(e)** None of these

    1—Form: 11B—Ans: a

45. Evaluate $\log_{1/16} 4$ without the use of a calculator.

    1—Ans: $-\frac{1}{2}$

46. Evaluate $\log_2 \frac{1}{16}$ without the use of a calculator.

    1—Form: 11C—Ans: -4

47. Use a calculator to evaluate $\ln \frac{3}{4}$. Round your answer to 4 decimal places.

    1—T—Form: 11C—Ans: -0.2877

48. Use a calculator to evaluate $\ln \frac{4}{3}$. Round your answer to 4 decimal places.

    1—T—Ans: 0.2877

49. Evaluate $\ln e^4$ without the use of a calculator.

    (a) $\frac{1}{4}$ **(b)** e^{-4} **(c)** 4   **(d)** -4 **(e)** $-\frac{1}{4}$

    1—Form: 11A—Ans: c

50. Evaluate $\ln \dfrac{1}{e^2}$ without the use of a calculator.

    (a) e^{-2} **(b)** 2   **(c)** $\dfrac{1}{2}$ **(d)** -2 **(e)** $-\dfrac{1}{2}$

    1—Form: 11B—Ans: d

51. Evaluate $\ln \dfrac{1}{e^{\sqrt{2}}}$ without the use of a calculator.

1—Form: 11C—Ans: $-\sqrt{2}$

52. Evaluate $\ln \dfrac{e^4}{e^5}$ without the use of a calculator.

1—Ans: -1

53. Use a calculator to evaluate $\dfrac{15 \ln 23}{\ln 7 - \ln 2}$.

   (a) 37.5429   **(b)** 23.4767   **(c)** 34.8698   **(d)** 4.5908   **(e)** None of these

   2—T—Ans: a

54. Use a calculator to evaluate $\dfrac{3 \ln 5}{7 \ln 6 - 2 \ln 7}$.

   (a) -3.8222 **(b)** -2.6559 **(c)** 0.5582   **(d)** -11.6058 **(e)** None of these

   2—T—Ans: c

55. Write in exponential form: $\log_x 81 = 4$.

   (a) $4^x = 81$ **(b)** $x^4 = 81$ **(c)** $81^x = 4$ **(d)** $81^4 = x$ **(e)** None of these

   1—Ans: b

56. Write in exponential form: $\ln x = \sqrt{2}$.

   (a) $x = \sqrt{2}$ **(b)** $e^{\sqrt{2}} = x$ **(c)** $\left(\sqrt{2}\right)^x = y$ **(d)** $e^x = \sqrt{2}$ **(e)** None of these

   2—Ans: b

57. Find the vertical asymptote of the function: $f(x) = \ln(x + 7)$

   (a) $x = 7$ **(b)** $x = -7$ **(c)** $x = -6$ **(d)** $(-7, 0)$ **(e)** None of these

   1—Ans: b

58. Match the graph with the correct function.

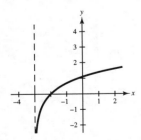

   (a) $f(x) = -3 + \ln x$ **(b)** $f(x) = 3 + \ln x$ **(c)** $f(x) = \ln(x - 3)$

   (d) $f(x) = \ln(x + 3)$ **(e)** None of these

   2—Ans: d

59. Match the graph with the correct function.

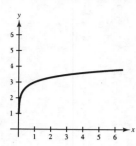

(a) $f(x) = 3 + \log_{10} x$ **(b)** $f(x) = \log_{10}(x + 3)$ **(c)** $f(x) = \frac{1}{3} \log_{10} x$

(d) $f(x) = 3\log_{10} x$ **(e)** None of these

2—Ans: a

60. Match the graph with the correct function.

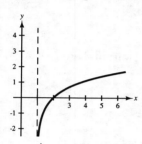

(a) $f(x) = e^x$ **(b)** $f(x) = e^{x-1}$ **(c)** $f(x) = \ln x$

(d) $f(x) = \ln(x - 1)$ **(e)** None of these

2—Ans: d

61. Sketch the graph: $f(x) = 1 + \ln x$

    2—Ans:

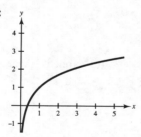

62. Find the vertical asymptote: $f(x) = 2 + \ln x$

(a) $x = 2$ **(b)** $y = 2$ **(c)** $x = 0$ **(d)** $x = -2$ **(e)** None of these

2—Ans: c

63. Students in an algebra class were given an exam and then tested monthly with an equivalent exam. The average score for the class was given by the human memory model

$$f(t) = 85 - 16\log_{10}(t + 1), \quad 0 \le t \le 12$$

where t is the time in months. What is the average score after 3 months?

(a) 77   (b) 67   (c) 75   (d) 63   (e) None of these

2—T—Ans: c

64. A principal P invested at $7\frac{1}{2}\%$ interest compounded continuously increases to an amount K times the original principal after t years, where t is given by

$$t = \frac{\ln K}{0.075}.$$

Determine the number of years necessary to triple the investment (Hint: $K = 3$).

(a) 6.4   (b) 14.6   (c) 12.8   (d) 8.2   (e) None of these

2—T—Ans: b ·

65. Students in a seventh-grade class were given an exam. During the next 2 years, the same students were retested several times. The average score was given by the model

$$f(t) = 90 - 15\log_{10}(t + 1), \quad 0 \le t \le 24$$

where t is the time in months. What was the average score after 10 months?

2—T—Ans: 74

Section 11.4   Properties of Logarithms

1. Without using a calculator find the value of $\log_5 75 - \log_5 3$.

(a) 2   (b) $\frac{1}{2}$ (c) 25   (d) 5   (e) None of these

1—Ans: a

2. Without using a calculator find the value of $\log_6 4 + \log_6 9$.

(a) $\log_6 13$ (b) $\frac{1}{2}$ (c) 6   (d) 2   (e) None of these

1—Ans: d

3. Evaluate $\log_3 81$ without a calculator.

1—Ans: 4

4. Evaluate $\log_5\left(\frac{1}{125}\right)$ without a calculator.

1—Ans: -3

5. Evaluate $\log_7 \sqrt[3]{7}$ without a calculator.

    1—Ans: $\frac{1}{3}$

6. Evaluate $\log_4 64$ without a calculator.

    1—Ans: 3

7. Find the expression equivalent to $\log_7 5x$.

    (a) $\ln 7 + \ln 5x$ **(b)** $\log_7 5 + \log_7 x$ **(c)** $(\log_7 5) + (\log_7 x)$

    (d) $7 \ln 5x$ **(e)** None of these

    1—Ans: b

8. Find the expression equivalent to $\log_3 9x^2$. (Assume $x > 0$.)

    (a) $2\log_3 x$ **(b)** $\ln 3 + 4\ln x$ **(c)** $4x$

    (d) $2 + 2\log_3 x$ **(e)** None of these

    1—Ans: d

9. Find the expression equivalent to $\log_{10}\left(100\sqrt[3]{x^2 + 1}\right)$.

    (a) $10 \log_{10} \sqrt[3]{x^2 + 1}$ **(b)** $\frac{10}{3} \log_{10}(x^2 + 1)$ **(c)** $2 + \frac{1}{3} \log_{10}(x^2 + 1)$

    (d) $3 + 10 \log_{10}(x^2 + 1)$ **(e)** None of these

    1—Ans: c

10. Find the expression equivalent to $\ln \dfrac{x^2}{\sqrt{x + 1}}$. (Assume $x > 0$.)

    (a) $2 \ln x - \frac{1}{2} \ln(x + 1)$ **(b)** $(\ln x)(\ln(x + 1))$ **(c)** $\dfrac{4 \ln x}{\ln(x + 1)}$

    (d) $\left(x + \sqrt{x + 1}\right)\ln 2$ **(e)** None of these

    1—Ans: a

11. Use the properties of logarithms to expand $\log_4 \sqrt[4]{x^4 + 1}$ as a sum, difference, or multiple of logarithms.

    1—Ans: $\frac{1}{4} \log_4(x^4 + 1)$

12. Use the properties of logarithms to expand $\sqrt[3]{\dfrac{x^2}{y}}$ as a sum, difference, or multiple of logarithms. (Assume $x > 0$.)

    1—Ans: $\dfrac{2}{3} \log_5 x - \dfrac{1}{3} \log_5 y$

13. Condense the expression $2 + 3 \log_3 x$.

  (a) $2 \log_3(x^3)$ **(b)** $(\log_3 8)(\log_3 x^3)$ **(c)** $\log_3(2x)^3$

  (d) $\log_3(9x^3)$ **(e)** None of these

  2—Ans: d

14. Condense the expression $3 \log_2 y + 2 \log_2 x - 3$.

  (a) $\log_2\left(\dfrac{x^2 y^3}{8}\right)$ **(b)** $\log_2(y^3 + x^2) - 3$ **(c)** $\log_2(8x^2 y^3)$

  (d) $\log_2\left(\dfrac{3xy}{4}\right)$ **(e)** None of these

  2—Ans: a

15. Use the properties of logarithms to condense $4 \log_3 x - 3 \log_3 y + \log_3 z$ to a single logarithm.

  2—Ans: $\log_3 \dfrac{x^4 z}{y^3}$

16. Use the properties of logarithms to condense $2 - \dfrac{1}{2} \log_{10}(x + 1)$ to a single logarithm.

  2—Ans: $\log_{10} \dfrac{100}{\sqrt{x + 1}}$

17. Use the properties of logarithms to condense $4(\ln x - 3 \ln y)$ to a single logarithm.

  2—Ans: $\ln \dfrac{x^4}{y^{12}}$

18. Use the properties of logarithms to condense $1 - \frac{1}{2} \log_3 5x$ to a single logarithm.

  2—Ans: $\log_3 \dfrac{3}{\sqrt{5x}}$

19. Condense the expression $\log_4 5x + \log_4 2y$.

  (a) $(\log_4 5x)(\log_4 2y)$ **(b)** $\log_8 10xy$ **(c)** $\log_4 10xy$

  (d) $(5x)^4(2y^4)$ **(e)** None of these

  1—Ans: c

20. Condense the expression $\log_4 5x - \log_4 2y$.

     (a) $\dfrac{\log_4 5x}{\log_4 2y}$ **(b)** $\log_4 \dfrac{5x}{2y}$ **(c)** $\log_0 \dfrac{5x}{2y}$

     (d) $\dfrac{(5x)^4}{(2y)^4}$ **(e)** None of these

     1—Ans: b

21. Condense the expression $-3 \log_2 x + \log_2 3$.

     (a) $\log_2 \dfrac{3}{x^3}$ **(b)** $\dfrac{\log_2 3}{\log_2 x^3}$ **(c)** $\log_2(-3x) \cdot \log_2 3$

     (d) $\dfrac{3}{x^3}$ **(e)** None of these

     1—Ans: a

22. Condense the expression $\ln x - 2 \ln y + 3 \ln z$.

     (a) $(\ln x)(\ln - 2)(\ln 3z)$ **(b)** $\dfrac{\ln x \ln z^3}{\ln y^2}$ **(c)** $\dfrac{xz^3}{y^2}$

     (d) $\ln\left(\dfrac{xz^3}{y^2}\right)$ **(e)** None of these

     1—Ans: d

23. Use the properties of logarithms to condense $2[\log_{10} x - \log_{10} (x + 1)]$ to a single logarithm.

     1—Ans: $\log_{10} \dfrac{x^2}{(x + 1)^2}$

24. Use the properties of logarithms to condense $\log_5 3x + \log_5 5x$ to a single logarithm.

     1—Ans: $\log_5 15x^2$

25. Choose the equation which is valid.

     (a) $\ln e^{2x} = e^{2x}$ **(b)** $\ln e^{-2x} = \dfrac{1}{2x}$ **(c)** $\ln e^{2x} = 2x$

     (d) $\ln e^x = 1$ **(e)** None of these

     1—Ans: c

26. Choose the equation which is valid.

     (a) $\log_3 32 - \log_3 4 = 8$ **(b)** $\log_3 32 - \log_3 4 = \dfrac{\log_3 32}{\log_3 4}$ **(c)** $4 \log_3 4 = 16$

     (d) $\log_3 32 - \log_3 4 = 2$ **(e)** None of these

     1—Ans: d

27. Determine if the given equation is true or false. If it is false, rewrite it by correcting the right member.

$$\log_5 x - \log_5 y = \frac{\log_5 x}{\log_5 y}$$

1—Ans: False. $\log_5 x - \log_5 y = \log_5 \left(\dfrac{x}{y}\right)$

28. Determine if the given equation is true or false. If it is false, rewrite it by correcting the right member.

$$\log_{10} (uv) = \log_{10} u \cdot \log_{10} v$$

1—Ans: False. $\log_{10} (uv) = \log_{10} u + \log_{10} v$

29. Determine if the given equation is true or false. If it is false, rewrite it by correcting the right member.

$$\log_2 5x = \log_2 5 \cdot \log_2 x$$

1—Ans: False. $\log_2 5x = \log_2 5 + \log_2 x$

30. Determine if the given equation is true or false. If it is false, rewrite it by correcting the right member.

$$5 \ln (2x) = \ln [5(2x)]$$

1—Ans: False. $5 \ln (2x) = \ln (2x)^5$

31. Given $\log_b 2 \approx 0.3562$ and $\log_b 3 \approx 0.5646$. Find the value of $\log_b 18$.

   (a) -0.1478 **(b)** -0.7730 **(c)** 1.2770 **(d)** 1.4854 **(e)** None of these

   1—Ans: d

32. Given $\log_b 2 \approx 0.3562$ and $\log_b 3 \approx 0.5646$. Find the value of $\log_b 12$.

   (a) -0.1478 **(b)** -0.7730 **(c)** 1.2770 **(d)** 1.4854 **(e)** None of these

   1—Ans: c

33. Given $\log_b 2 \approx 0.3562$ and $\log_b 3 \approx 0.5646$. Find the value of $\log_b \frac{2}{9}$.

   (a) -0.1478 **(b)** -0.7730 **(c)** 1.2770 **(d)** 1.4854 **(e)** None of these

   1—Ans: b

34. Given $\log_b 2 \approx 0.3562$ and $\log_b 3 \approx 0.5646$. Find the value of $\log_b \frac{3}{4}$.

   (a) -0.1478 **(b)** -0.7730 **(c)** 1.2770 **(d)** 1.4854 **(e)** None of these

   1—Ans: a

35. Given $\log_b 2 = 0.28906$, $\log_b 3 = 0.45816$, and $\log_b 5 = 0.67119$. Find $\log_b 48$.

   2—Ans: 1.61440

36. Given $\log_b 2 = 0.28906$, $\log_b 3 = 0.45816$, and $\log_b 5 = 0.67119$. Find $\log_b \frac{6}{25}$.

   2—Ans: -0.59516

37. Find the expression equivalent to $\log_6 \frac{36}{x}$.

   (a) $2 + 2\log_6(11x)$ **(b)** $\frac{1}{2} + \frac{1}{2}\log_6(10x)$ **(c)** $2 + \log_6 x$

   (d) $2 - \log_6 x$ **(e)** None of these

   1—Ans: d

38. Find the expression equivalent to $\log_6(6^2 x)$.

   (a) $2 + 2\log_6(11x)$ **(b)** $\frac{1}{2} + \frac{1}{2}\log_6(10x)$ **(c)** $2 + \log_6 x$

   (d) $2 - \log_6 x$ **(e)** None of these

   1—Ans: c

39. Simplify the expression $\ln(5e^3)$ by expanding using the rules of logarithms.

   1—Ans: $3 + \ln 5$

40. Simplify the expression $\ln\left(\frac{6}{e^7}\right)$ by expanding using the rules of logarithms.

   1—Ans: $\ln 6 - 7$

41. Simplify the expression $\log_{10}\left(\frac{10^4}{x^2}\right)$ by expanding using the rules of logarithms. (Assume $x > 0$.)

   1—Ans: $4 - 2\log_{10} x$

42. Simplify the expression $\log_{10} \sqrt{9 \cdot 10^6}$ by expanding using the rules of logarithms.

   1—Ans: $3 + \log_{10} 3$

43. Given $\log_b 10 = 0.8977$ and $\log_b 3 = 0.4283$, match $\log_b \sqrt{810}$ with the appropriate decimal approximation.

   (a) 1.9890   **(b)** 1.3055   **(c)** 3.0803   **(d)** 2.6520   **(e)** None of these

   2—Ans: b

44. Given $\log_b 10 = 0.8977$ and $\log_b 3 = 0.4283$, match $\log_b \sqrt{27,000}$ with the appropriate decimal approximation.

   (a) 1.9890   **(b)** 1.3055   **(c)** 3.0803   **(d)** 2.6520   **(e)** None of these

   2—Ans: a

45. Given $\log_b 2 \approx 0.2702$ and $\log_b 10 \approx 0.8977$ evaluate to four decimal places $\log_b \sqrt[3]{4000}$.

2—Ans: 1.0778

46. Given $\log_b 2 \approx 0.2702$ and $\log_b 10 \approx 0.8977$ evaluate to four decimal places $\log_b \left(\dfrac{100}{\sqrt{8}}\right)$.

2—Ans: 1.3901

47. Use the properties of logarithms to expand $\log_{10}\left(\dfrac{2x\sqrt{y}}{z^2}\right)$ as a sum, difference, or multiple of logarithms.

(a) $\log_{10} 2x + \log_{10} \sqrt{y} + \log_{10} z^2$

(b) $\log_{10} 2 + \log_{10} x + \dfrac{1}{2}\log_{10} y + 2\log_{10} z$

(c) $\log_{10} 2 + \log_{10} x + \dfrac{1}{2}\log_{10} y - 2\log_{10} z$

(d) $(\log_{10} 2)(\log_{10} x)\left(\dfrac{1}{2}\log_{10} y\right)/(2\log_{10} z)$

(e) None of these

2—Form: 11A—Ans: c

48. Use the properties of logarithms to expand $\ln\left(\dfrac{x^2 y}{2\sqrt{z}}\right)$ as a sum, difference, or multiple of logarithms.

(a) $2\ln x + \ln y - \ln 2 + \dfrac{1}{2}\ln z$

(b) $2\ln x + \ln y - \ln 2 - \dfrac{1}{3}\ln z$

(c) $(2\ln x)(\ln y)/(\ln 2)\left(\dfrac{1}{2}\ln z\right)$

(d) $2\ln x + 2\ln y - \ln 2 - \dfrac{1}{2}\ln z$

(e) None of these

2—Form: 11B—Ans: b

49. Use the properties of logarithms to condense $\ln(x + 1) + 4\ln x$ into a logarithm of a single quantity.

(a) $\ln(x + 1 + x^4)$

(b) $\ln[x^4(x + 1)]$

(c) $\ln(5x + 1)$

(d) $\ln\left(\dfrac{x + 1}{x^4}\right)$

(e) None of these

1—Form: 11A—Ans: b

50. Use the properties of logarithms to condense $2 \log_{10} x - \dfrac{1}{2} \log_{10} z$ into a logarithm of a single quantity.

    (a) $\log_{10}\left(x^2 - \sqrt{z}\right)$ **(b)** $\log_{10}\left(\dfrac{x}{z}\right)$ **(c)** $\log_{10} \dfrac{x^2}{\sqrt{z}}$

    (d) $\log_{10}\left(\dfrac{4x}{z}\right)$ **(e)** None of these

    1—Form: 11B—Ans: c

51. Simplify $\ln\left(e^{x^2+1}\right)$.

    (a) $x^2 + 1$ **(b)** $\ln e^{x^2} + \ln e$ **(c)** $(\ln e^{x^2})(\ln e)$

    (d) $\ln e^{x^2}$ **(e)** None of these

    1—Form: 11A—Ans: a

52. Simplify $e^{\ln(x^2+1)}$.

    (a) $e^{\ln x^2} + e^{\ln 1}$ **(b)** $x^2 + 1$ **(c)** $(e^{\ln x^2})(e^{\ln 1})$

    (d) $\dfrac{1}{x^2 + 1}$ **(e)** None of these

    1—Form: 11B—Ans: b

53. Use the properties of logarithms to expand $\log_{10}\left(\dfrac{xy^2z}{3}\right)$.

    2—Ans: $\log_{10} x + 2 \log_{10} y + \log_{10} z - \log_{10} 3$

54. Use the properties of logarithms to expand $\ln \dfrac{x}{yz}$.

    2—Form: 11C—Ans: $\ln x - \ln y - \ln z$

55. Use the properties of logarithms to condense $2 \log_{10} x - \dfrac{1}{2} \log_{10} z$.

    2—Ans: $\log_{10} \dfrac{x^2}{\sqrt{z}}$

56. Use the properties of logarithms to condense $\ln x - \dfrac{1}{2} \ln y - \ln z$.

    2—Ans: $\ln \dfrac{x}{\sqrt{y}z}$

57. Simplify: $\ln\left(\dfrac{e^{x^2+1}}{e}\right)$

    2—Form: 11C—Ans: x^2

58. Simplify: $\log_{10}\left(\dfrac{10^{x^2+1}}{100}\right)$

   2—Ans: $x^2 - 1$

59. Use the properties of logarithms to expand and simplify $\log_{10}\sqrt{\dfrac{10}{t}}$.

   2—Form: 11C—Ans: $\dfrac{1}{2} - \dfrac{1}{2}\log_{10}t$

60. Use the properties of logarithms to expand and simplify $\ln\left(\dfrac{x-1}{e}\right)^3$.

   2—Ans: $3\ln(x-1) - 3$

61. Use the properties of logarithms to expand and simplify $\ln 5e^3$.

   1—Ans: $3 + \ln 5$

62. Use the properties of logarithms to expand and simplify $\log_{10} 300$.

   1—Ans: $2 + \log_{10} 3$

63. Find the value of $\log_6 3 + \log_6 12$ without a calculator.

   1—Ans: 2

64. Find the value of $\log_3 54 - \log_3 2$ without a calculator.

   1—Ans: 3

65. Find the value of $\log_2 48 - \log_2 3$ without a calculator.

   (a) 45   **(b)** 4   **(c)** 3   **(d)** 2   **(e)** $\frac{1}{2}$

   1—Ans: b

Section 11.5   Solving Exponential and Logarithmic Equations

1. Solve for x if $3^{x+4} = 3^{8-x}$ without using a calculator.

   (a) $x = 4$ **(b)** $x = 0$ **(c)** $x = 2$ **(d)** $x = -4$ **(e)** None of these

   1—Ans: c

2. Solve for x if $2^{1-x} = 2^{2x}$ without using a calculator.

   (a) $x = \frac{1}{2}$ **(b)** $x = -1$ **(c)** $x = 3$ **(d)** $x = \frac{1}{3}$ **(e)** None of these

   1—Ans: d

3. Solve for x without using a calculator.

$$8^x = 4^{2-x}$$

1—Ans: $x = \frac{4}{5}$

4. Solve for x without using a calculator.

$$3^{2-x} = 27^{1-x}$$

1—Ans: $x = \frac{1}{2}$

5. Solve for x without using a calculator.

$$8^{2-x} = 32^{-x}$$

1—Ans: $x = -3$

6. Solve for x without using a calculator.

$$25^{1-x} = 125^{2x}$$

1—Ans: $x = \frac{1}{4}$

7. Solve for x if $\log_2 (1 - 3x) = 3$ without using a calculator.

(a) $x = -\frac{8}{3}$ **(b)** $x = \frac{1}{3}$ **(c)** $x = -\frac{7}{3}$ **(d)** $x = 0$ **(e)** None of these

1—Ans: c

8. Solve for x if $\log_{10} 5x = \log_{10}(x + 8)$ without using a calculator.

(a) $x = 43$ **(b)** $x = -2$ **(c)** $x = -\frac{4}{3}$ **(d)** $x = 2$ **(e)** None of these

1—Ans: d

9. Solve for x without using a calculator.

$$\log_4 2x = 3$$

1—Ans: $x = 32$

10. Solve for x without using a calculator.

$$\log_{10} (3x - 2) = 2$$

1—Ans: $x = 34$

11. Simplify $\ln e^{5x-2}$.

(a) $\dfrac{1}{5x - 2}$ **(b)** $5x - 2$ **(c)** $2 - 5x$ **(d)** $\ln (5x - 2)$ **(e)** None of these

1—Ans: b

12. Simplify $e^{\ln(1+4x)}$

(a) $\dfrac{1}{1+4x}$

(b) $e^{2(1+4x)}$

(c) $-(1+4x), \quad x < -\frac{1}{4}$

(d) $1+4x, \quad x > -\frac{1}{4}$

(e) None of these

1—Ans: d

13. Simplify $\ln e^{5x-2}$ using the properties of exponents and logarithms.

1—Ans: $5x - 2$

14. Simplify $\log_5 5x^{2+1}$ using the properties of exponents and logarithms.

1—Ans: $x^2 + 1$

15. Use a calculator to solve for x to three decimal places: $10^{3x} = 48$.

(a) $x = 0.560$ (b) $x = 1.600$ (c) $x = 1.290$ (d) $x = 5.043$ (e) None of these

2—T—Ans: a

16. Use a calculator to solve for x to three decimal places: $7^{x/3} = 39$.

(a) $x = 4.773$ (b) $x = 10.991$ (c) $x = 2.238$ (d) $x = 5.648$ (e) None of these

2—T—Ans: d

17. Use a calculator to solve for x: $20^{x-1} = 40$. (Round to three decimal places.)

2—T—Ans: $x = 2.231$

18. Use a calculator to solve for x: $1000^{0.28x} = 100$. (Round to three decimal places.)

2—T—Ans: $x = 2.381$

19. Use a calculator to solve for x: $(35)^{1-x} = 16$. (Round to three decimal places.)

2—T—Ans: $x = 0.220$

20. Use a calculator to solve for x: $(64)^{2x} = 95$. (Round to three decimal places.)

2—T—Ans: $x = 0.547$

21. Use a calculator to solve for x to three decimal places: $1500(1.02)^x = 2100$.

(a) $x = 1.372$

(b) $x = 16.991$

(c) $x = 3.322$

(d) $x = 1.327$

(e) None of these

2—T—Ans: b

22. Use a calculator to solve for x to three decimal places: $2150(1.03)^x = 2800$.

    (a) $x = 1.264$ **(b)** $x = 0.111$ **(c)** $x = 8.936$

    (d) $x = 6.288$ **(e)** None of these

    2—T—Ans: c

23. Use a calculator to solve for x to three decimal places: $3000(1.09)^x = 5000$.

    (a) $x = 0.469$ **(b)** $x = 0.557$ **(c)** $x = 3.028$

    (d) $x = 5.928$ **(e)** None of these

    2—T—Ans: d

24. Use a calculator to solve for x to three decimal places: $1850(1.05)^x = 2000$.

    (a) $x = 1.598$ **(b)** $x = 1.281$ **(c)** $x = 47.682$

    (d) $x = 5.200$ **(e)** None of these

    2—T—Ans: a

25. Use a calculator to solve for x : $2700(1.035)^{2x} = 4000$.
(Round answer to three decimal places.)

    2—T—Ans: 5.713

26. Use a calculator to solve for x : $3050(1.021)^{4x} = 4500$.
(Round answer to three decimal places.)

    2—T—Ans: 4.679

27. Use a calculator to solve for x to three decimal places: $\ln x = 0.200$.

    (a) 1.020   **(b)** 1.221   **(c)** 7.389   **(d)** 10.000   **(e)** None of these

    1—T—Ans: b

28. Use a calculator to solve for x to three decimal places: $\ln x = 0.020$.

    (a) 1.020   **(b)** 1.221   **(c)** 7.389   **(d)** 10.000   **(e)** None of these

    1—T—Ans: a

29. Use a calculator to solve for x : $\frac{3}{2}\ln(x + 2) = 1.5$.
(Round to three decimal places.)

    1—T—Ans: 0.718

30. Use a calculator to solve for x : $7\ln(x - 1) = 0.5$.
(Round to three decimal places.)

    1—T—Ans: 2.074

31. Use a calculator to solve for x : $5 \ln (x + 3) = 2.4$.
(Round to three decimal places.)

    1—T—Ans: 1.384

32. Use a calculator to solve for x : $35 \ln (x - 3) = 78$.
(Round to three decimal places.)

    1—T—Ans: 12.287

33. Use a calculator to solve for x to two decimal places: $9.24 \log_{10}(2x - 1) = 7.15$.

    (a) 18.00   **(b)** 11.83   **(c)** 3.47   **(d)** 34.30   **(e)** None of these

    2—T—Ans: c

34. Use a calculator to solve for x to two decimal places: $4.82 \log_{10}(3x) = 9.70$.

    (a) 18.00   **(b)** 11.83   **(c)** 3.47   **(d)** 34.30   **(e)** None of these

    2—T—Ans: d

35. Solve for x: $\log_{10}[x(2x - 1)] = 1$.

    1—Ans: $x = -2$ and $x = \frac{5}{2}$

36. Solve for x: $\log_{10}[15(3x - 1)] = 2$.

    1—Ans: $x = -\frac{4}{3}$ and $x = \frac{5}{3}$

37. Solve for x: $\log_2[x(x - 2)] = 3$.

    1—Ans: $x = 4$ and $x = -2$

38. Solve for x: $\log_3[x(2x + 3)] = 2$.

    1—Ans: $x = \frac{3}{2}$ and $x = -3$

39. Solve without using a calculator: $\log_3 x = 2$.

    (a) 8   **(b)** 9   **(c)** 6   **(d)** $\frac{2}{3}$ **(e)** None of these

    1—Ans: b

40. Solve without using a calculator: $\log_3 x = 4$.

    (a) 64   **(b)** 12   **(c)** $\frac{4}{3}$ **(d)** 81   **(e)** None of these

    1—Ans: d

41. Solve without using a calculator: $\log_{10}(2x + 5) = 0$.

    (a) 1   **(b)** $-\frac{5}{2}$ **(c)** -2 **(d)** -2.3219 **(e)** None of these

    1—Form: 11A—Ans: c

42. Solve without using a calculator: $\log_{10}(2x + 5) = 1$.

    (a) $\frac{5}{2}$ **(b)** -2 **(c)** $\frac{15}{2}$ **(d)** 10   **(e)** None of these

    1—Form: 11B—Ans: a

43. Solve: $10^{y/2} = 76$. Use a calculator and round your answer to four decimal places.

    (a) 15.2   **(b)** 8.6615   **(c)** 577.2   **(d)** 3.7616   **(e)** None of these

    1—T—Form: 11A—Ans: d

44. Solve: $10^{y/3} = 29$. Use a calculator and round your answer to four decimal places.

    (a) 8.7   **(b)** 4.3872   **(c)** 10.1019   **(d)** 0.4875   **(e)** None of these

    1—T—Form: 11B—Ans: b

45. Solve: $100e^{0.06t} = 152$. Use a calculator and round your answer to four decimal places.

    (a) 1.4315   **(b)** 7.8373   **(c)** 3.2321   **(d)** 6.9785   **(e)** None of these

    2—T—Form: 11A—Ans: d

46. Solve: $100e^{0.07t} = 152$. Use a calculator and round your answer to four decimal places.

    (a) 3.0780   **(b)** 7.9832   **(c)** 5.9816   **(d)** -0.1575 **(e)** None of these

    2—T—Form: 11B—Ans: c

47. Solve: $3 \ln x = 7$. Use a calculator and round your answer to four decimal places.

    (a) 10.3123   **(b)** 365.5444   **(c)** 0.8473   **(d)** 0.6486   **(e)** None of these

    2—T—Ans: a

48. Solve: $2 \ln x = 7$. Use a calculator and round your answer to four decimal places.

    (a) 10.0989   **(b)** 1089.2441   **(c)** 2.8074   **(d)** 33.1155   **(e)** None of these

    2—T—Ans: d

49. Use a calculator to solve $\left(1 + \dfrac{0.06}{4}\right)^{4t} = 1.52$. Round your answer to two decimal places.

    2—T—Ans: 7.03

50. Use a calculator to solve $\left(1 + \dfrac{0.07}{4}\right)^{4t} = 3$. Round your answer to two decimal places.

    2—T—Form: 11C—Ans: 15.83

51. Solve: $\ln x^4 = 7$.

    2—Ans: $\pm e^{7/4}$

52. Solve: $\ln \sqrt{3 - x} = 1$.

    2—Form: 11C—Ans: $3 - e^2$

53. Solve without using a calculator: $\log_{10} x - \log_{10} (x + 1) = -1$.

    2—Ans: $\frac{1}{9}$

54. Solve without using a calculator: $\ln x - \ln (x + 1) = 1$.

    2—Form: 11C—Ans: $\dfrac{e}{1 - e}$

55. Find the number of years required for a $3000 investment to double at a 7% interest rate compounded continuously. Round your answer to one decimal place.

    2—T—Ans: 9.9 years

56. Find the number of years required for a $2000 investment to triple at a 8% interest rate compounded continuously. Round your answer to one decimal place.

    2—T—Ans: 13.7 years

57. Find the number of years required for a $2000 investment to triple at a $9\frac{1}{2}$% interest rate compounded continuously.

    (a) 12.6   **(b)** 13.7   **(c)** 11.6   **(d)** 15.1   **(e)** None of these

    2—T—Ans: c

58. The variety of suburban non-domesticated wildlife is approximated by the model $V = 15 \cdot 10^{0.02x}$, $0 \le x \le 36$ where x is the number of months since the development was completed. Use this model to approximate the number of months since the develpment was completed if $V = 24$.

    2—T—Ans: 10 months

59. A savings account had a balance of $4000 four years ago and has a balance of $5384.46 today. Find the annual percentage rate if the interest is compounded quarterly.

    (a) 8.7%   **(b)** 6.50%   **(c)** 7.5%   **(d)** 7.0%   **(e)** None of these

    2—T—Ans: c

60. A savings account had a balance of $2000 five years ago and has a balance of $2814.19 today. Find the annual percentage rate if the interest is compounded monthly.

    (a) 5.85%   **(b)** 8.35%   **(c)** 7.00%   **(d)** 6.85%   **(e)** None of these

    2—T—Ans: d

61. A deposit of $5000 is placed in a savings account at an annual rate of 8%, compounded continuously. Find the time required for the balance in the account to be $8000. (Round your answer to two decimal places.)

   2—T—Ans: 5.87 years

62. A deposit of $5000 is placed in a savings account at an annual rate of 8%, compounded continuously. Find the time required for the balance in the account to be $15,000. (Round your answer to two decimal places.)

   2—T—Ans: 13.73 years

Section 11.6   Applications

1. Find the annual interest rate if $500 grows to $541.64 in two years and the interest is compounded continuously.

   (a) 6%   **(b)** 4%   **(c)** 12%   **(d)** 10%   **(e)** None of these

   1—T—Ans: b

2. Find the annual interest rate if $500 grows to $563.75 in two years and the interest is compounded continuously.

   (a) 6%   **(b)** 4%   **(c)** 12%   **(d)** 10%   **(e)** None of these

   1—T—Ans: a

3. Find the interest rate used if $500 grows to $585.83 in two years and the interest is compounded quarterly.

   2—T—Ans: 8%

4. Find the interest rate used if $500 grows to $563.58 in two years and the interest is compounded monthly.

   2—T—Ans: 6%

5. Find the interest rate used if $500 grows to $577.81 in two years and the interest is compounded yearly.

   2—T—Ans: 7.5%

6. Find the interest rate used if $500 grows to $609.20 in two years and the interest is compounded quarterly.

   2—T—Ans: 10%

7. Approximate the time required for an investment to double in value when invested at 8% annual interest rate, compounded annually.

   (a) 8.69 years   **(b)** 8.75 years   **(c)** 8.84 years   **(d)** 9.01 years   **(e)** None of these

   1—T—Ans: d

8. Approximate the time required for an investment to double in value when invested at 8% annual interest rate, compounded every six months.

  (a) 8.69 years   **(b)** 8.75 years   **(c)** 8.84 years   **(d)** 9.01 years   **(e)** None of these

  1—T—Ans: c

9. Approximate the time required for an investment to double in value if the interest is compounded continuously with an annual rate of 6%. (Round your answer to two decimal places.)

  1—T—Ans: 11.55 years

10. Approximate the time required for an investment to double in value if the interest is compounded continuously with an annual rate of 7%. (Round your answer to two decimal places.)

  1—T—Ans: 9.90 years

11. Determine the type of compounding used given that an initial investment of $1000 grows to $1485.95 when invested at an annual rate of 8% for five years.

  (a) Monthly   **(b)** Quarterly   **(c)** Annually

  (d) Continuously   **(e)** None of these

  2—T—Ans: b

12. Determine the type of compounding used given that an initial investment of $1000 grows to $1469.33 when invested at an annual rate of 8% for five years.

  (a) Monthly   **(b)** Quarterly   **(c)** Annually

  (d) Continuously   **(e)** None of these

  2—T—Ans: c

13. An initial investment of $1000 grows to $2112.06 in ten years when invested at an annual rate of 7.5%. Determine the type of compounding used. (Choose from $n = 1, n = 4, n = 12$ or continuous.)

  2—T—Ans: Monthly, $n = 12$

14. An initial investment of $1000 grows to $2117.00 in ten years when invested at an annual rate of 7.5%. Determine the type of compounding used. (Choose from $n = 1, n = 4, n = 12$ or continuous.)

  2—T—Ans: Continuous

15. A bank offers 7.5% interest compounded quarterly. Find the effective annual yield.

  (a) 7.79%   **(b)** 7.76%   **(c)** 7.71%   **(d)** 7.64%   **(e)** None of these

  1—T—Ans: c

16. A bank offers 8.2% interest compounded quarterly. Find the effective annual yield.

    (a) 8.45%   **(b)** 8.51%   **(c)** 8.37%   **(d)** 8.54%   **(e)** None of these

    1—T—Ans: a

17. A bank offers 7.8% interest compounded monthly. Find the effective annual yield.

    (a) 8.11%   **(b)** 8.08%   **(c)** 7.95%   **(d)** 8.03%   **(e)** None of these

    1—T—Ans: b

18. A bank offers 7.2% interest compounded continuously. Find the effective annual yield.

    (a) 7.33%   **(b)** 7.44%   **(c)** 7.40%   **(d)** 7.46%   **(e)** None of these

    1—T—Ans: d

19. A bank offers 8% interest compounded quarterly. Find the effective annual percentage rate (to two decimal places).

    1—T—Ans: 8.24%

20. A bank offers 8% interest compounded monthly. Find the effective annual percentage rate (to two decimal places).

    1—T—Ans: 8.30%

21. Determine how much principal P must be deposited at 8% annual rate, compounded quarterly, to produce a balance of $5000 in ten years.

    (a) $2315.97   **(b)** $2252.62   **(c)** $2246.64   **(d)** $2264.45   **(e)** None of these

    1—T—Ans: d

22. Determine how much principal P must be deposited at 8% annual rate, compounded annually, to produce a balance of $5000 in ten years.

    (a) $2315.97   **(b)** $2252.62   **(c)** $2246.64   **(d)** $2264.45   **(e)** None of these

    1—T—Ans: a

23. Determine how much principal P must be deposited at 8.5% annual interest rate, compounded quarterly, to produce a balance of $8000 in five years.

    1—T—Ans: $5253.50

24. Determine how much principal P must be deposited at 8.5% annual interest rate, compounded annually, to produce a balance of $8000 in five years.

    1—T—Ans: $5320.36

25. Determine how much principal P must be deposited at 8.5% annual interest rate, compounded monthly, to produce a balance of $8000 in five years.

    1—T—Ans: $5238.00

26. Determine how much principal P must be deposited at 8.5% annual interest rate, compounded continuously, to produce a balance of $8000 in five years.

1—T—Ans: $5230.16

27. $2500 is invested in an account paying 7.3% annual interest rate, compounded monthly. Find the balance after three years.

  (a) $3088.44   **(b)** $3112.08   **(c)** $3110.01   **(d)** $3105.94   **(e)** None of these

  1—T—Ans: c

28. $2500 is invested in an account paying 7.3% annual interest rate, compounded annually. Find the balance after three years.

  (a) $3088.44   **(b)** $3112.08   **(c)** $3110.01   **(d)** $3105.94   **(e)** None of these

  1—T—Ans: a

29. $2500 is invested in an account paying 7.3% annual interest rate, compounded monthly. Find the balance after three years.

  (a) $3088.44   **(b)** $3112.08   **(c)** $3110.01   **(d)** $3105.94   **(e)** None of these

  1—T—Ans: d

30. $2500 is invested in an account paying 7.3% annual interest rate, compounded continuously. Find the balance after three years.

  (a) $3088.44   **(b)** $3112.08   **(c)** $3110.01   **(d)** $3105.94   **(e)** None of these

  1—T—Ans: b

31. $500 is invested in an account paying 8.1% annual rate, compounded quarterly. Find the balance after 20 years.

  1—T—Ans: $2485.98

32. $500 is invested in an account paying 8.1% annual rate, compounded annually. Find the balance after 20 years.

  1—T—Ans: $2374.02

33. The population of a city was 80,000 in 1985 and increased 10% by 1995. Predict the population of the city in 2005.

  (a) 96,800   **(b)** 81,600   **(c)** 100,000   **(d)** 96,000   **(e)** None of these

  1—Ans: a

34. The population of a city was 210,000 in 1985 and increased 10% by 1995. Predict the population of the city in 2005.

  (a) 252,000   **(b)** 276,000   **(c)** 214,200   **(d)** 254,100   **(e)** None of these

  1—Ans: d

35. Determine which is the better investment: $500 for five years at 7.5% compound continuously, or $500 for five years at 7.7% compounded annually.

2—T—Ans: The 7.5% rate produces $727.50, slightly better than $724.52 at the 7.7% rate.

36. Determine which is the better investment: an 8.3% annual rate compounded quarterly, or an 8.5% annual rate compounded yearly.

2—T—Ans: The effective rate of the 8.3% investment is 8.56%, slightly higher than the 8.5% actual annual rate.

37. Determine which is the better effective annual rate: an 8.6% annual rate compounded continuously, or an 9.0% annual rate compounded yearly.

2—T—Ans: The 8.6% rate has an effective rate of 8.98%, slightly lower than the 9.0% actual annual rate.

38. Determine which is the better investment: $500 for ten years at 6.9% annual rate compounded continuously, or $500 for ten years at 7.3% compounded quarterly.

2—T—Ans: The 7.3% rate produces $1,030.73, while the 6.9% rate only produces $996.86

39. The half-life of a radioactive substance is 5.0 years. Find the time required for 90% of the sample to decay. (Round your answer to the nearest tenth.)

(a) 14.2 years   **(b)** 16.6 years   **(c)** 23.4 years   **(d)** 9 years   **(e)** None of these

2—Ans: b

40. The half-life of a radioactive substance is 10.0 years. Find the time required for 75% of the sample to decay. (Round your answer to the nearest tenth.)

(a) 15.0 years   **(b)** 25.3 years   **(c)** 18.9 years   **(d)** 20.0 years   **(e)** None of these

2—Ans: d

41. The half-life of radioactive radium is 1620 years. Find how much is left of a one-gram sample after 100 years. (Round your answer to three decimal places.)

2—T—Ans: 0.958 grams

42. The half-life of radioactive radium is 1620 years. Find how many years it takes for a one-gram sample to reduce by 10%.

2—T—Ans: 246 years

43. The half-life of radioactive radium is 1620 years. Find what percent of a sample is left after 200 years. (Round your answer to the nearest tenth.)

2—T—Ans: 91.8%

44. The half-life of radioactive radium is 1620 years. Find what percent of a sample is left after 500 years. (Round your answer to the nearest tenth.)

2—T—Ans: 80.7%

45. A savings account had a balance of $2000 five years ago and has a balance of $2760.84 today. Find the annual percentage rate if the interest is compounded quarterly.

(a) 5.83%   (b) 6.50%   (c) 6.27%   (d) 6.63%   (e) None of these

2—T—Form: 11A—Ans: b

46. A savings account had a balance of $2000 five years ago and has a balance of $2835.25 today. Find the annual percentage rate if the interest is compounded quarterly.

(a) 5.83%   (b) 8.35%   (c) 7.00%   (d) 6.85%   (e) None of these

2—T—Form: 11B—Ans: c

47. The number of bacteria N in a culture is given by the model $N = 100e^{kt}$ where t is the time in hours. When $t = 5$, $N = 300$. Find the number of hours it takes for the population to double its size ($N = 200$). Round your answer to four decimal places.

(a) 1.6667   (b) 3.1546   (c) 10   (d) 2.3671   (e) None of these

2—T—Ans: b

48. The number of bacteria N in a culture is given by the model $N = 250e^{kt}$ where t is the time in hours. When $t = 10$, $N = 300$. Find the number of hours it takes for the population to double its size ($N = 500$). Round your answer to four decimal places.

(a) 4.6977   (b) 19.3426   (c) 3.1546   (d) 38.0178   (e) None of these

2—T—Ans: d

49. The population P in a certain town is given by the model $P = 50,000e^{kt}$ where t is the time in years. When $t = 2$, $P = 60,000$. Find the number in years it will take for the population to double its size ($P = 100,000$). Round your answer to four decimal places.

2—T—Ans: 7.6036

50. The pH of a solution is determined by pH $= -\log_{10}[H^+]$ when pH is a measure of the hydrogen ion concentration $[H^+]$, measured in moles per liter. Find the pH of a solution for which $[H^+] = 7.61 \times 10^{-6}$.

1—T—Ans: 5.12

51. A savings account with a balance of $10,000 ten years ago has a balance of $22,255.41 today. Find the annual percentage rate if the interest is compounded continuously.

2—T—Ans: 8%

52. A deposit of $2000 is made into a fund with an annual interest rate of $8\frac{1}{2}\%$. Find the time necessary for the investment to amount to $10,000 if the interest is compounded quarterly. Round your answer to two decimal places.

2—T—Ans: 19.14 years

53. A deposit of $1000 is made into a fund with an annual interest rate of 10%. Find the time necessary for the investment to double if the interest is compounded continuously. Round your answer to two decimal places.

(a) 10 years   **(b)** 7.23 years   **(c)** 6.93 years   **(d)** 20 years   **(e)** None of these

2—T—Form: 11A—Ans: c

54. A deposit of $6000 is made into a fund with an annual interest rate of 10%. Find the time necessary for the investment to triple if the interest is compounded continuously. Round your answer to two decimal places.

(a) 30 years   **(b)** 15 years   **(c)** 10.99 years   **(d)** 11.12 years   **(e)** None of these

2—T—Form: 11B—Ans: c

55. The demand equation for a certain product is given by $p = 450 - 0.4e^{0.007x}$. Find the demand x if the price charged is $300.

2—T—Ans: 847

56. The demand equation for a certain product is given by $p = 450 - 0.4e^{0.007x}$. Find the demand x if the price charged is $315.

2—T—Ans: 832

57. Find the constant k so that the exponential function $y = 3e^{kt}$ passes through the points given on the graph.

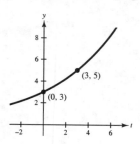

2—T—Ans: $k = \frac{1}{3} \ln \frac{5}{3} \approx 0.1703$

58. Find the constant k so that the exponential function $y = 2e^{kt}$ passes through the points given on the graph.

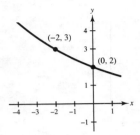

2—T—Form: 11C—Ans: $k = -\frac{1}{2} \ln \frac{3}{2} \approx -0.2027$

59. On the Richter Scale, the magnitude R of an earthquake intensity I is given by $R = \log_{10} I$. Find the intensity per unit of area for the earthquake in Yugoslavia in 1979 which measured $R = 7.2$.

2—T—Form: 11C—Ans: 15,848,931.92

60. On the Richter Scale, the magnitude R of an earthquake intensity I is given by $R = \log_{10} I$. Find the magnitude R of an earthquake of intensity $I = 100,000,000$.

(a) 8   **(b)** 9   **(c)** 10   **(d)** 18.42   **(e)** None of these

1—Ans: a

C H A P T E R   1 2
Sequences, Series, and Probability

Section 12.1   Sequences and Series

1. 1, 3, 7, 15, 31 are the first five terms of which sequence? (Begin with $n = 1$.)

   (a) $a_n = 2 - \dfrac{1}{n}$

   (b) $a_n = 2 - \dfrac{1}{2^n}$

   (c) $a_n = 2^n - 1$

   (d) $a_n = 2 - \left(\dfrac{1}{3}\right)^n$

   (e) None of these

   1—Ans: c

2. $\dfrac{3}{2}, \dfrac{7}{4}, \dfrac{15}{8}, \dfrac{31}{16}, \dfrac{63}{32}$ are the first five terms of which sequence? (Begin with $n = 1$.)

   (a) $a_n = 2 - \dfrac{1}{n}$

   (b) $a_n = 2 - \dfrac{1}{2^n}$

   (c) $a_n = 2^n - 1$

   (d) $a_n = 2 - \left(\dfrac{1}{3}\right)^n$

   (e) None of these

   1—Ans: b

3. Write the first five terms of the sequence $a_n = (-1)^n 2n$. (Begin with $n = 1$.)

   1—Ans: $-2, 4, -6, 8, -16$

4. Write the first five terms of the sequence $a_n = 2 + \left(-\frac{1}{2}\right)^n$. (Begin with $n = 1$.)

   1—Ans: $\frac{3}{2}, \frac{9}{4}, \frac{15}{8}, \frac{33}{16}, \frac{63}{32}$

5. $-\dfrac{1}{2}, \dfrac{1}{3}, \dfrac{1}{4}, -\dfrac{1}{5}, \dfrac{1}{6}$ are the first five terms of which sequence?

   (a) $a_n = \dfrac{(-1)^{n+1}}{n}$

   (b) $a_n = \dfrac{(-1)^n}{2^{n-1}}$

   (c) $a_n = \dfrac{(-1)^{n+1}}{2^n}$

   (d) $a_n = \dfrac{(-1)^n}{n+1}$

   (e) None of these

   1—Ans: d

6. $1, -\dfrac{1}{2}, \dfrac{1}{3}, -\dfrac{1}{4}, \dfrac{1}{5}$ are the first five terms of which sequence?

(a) $a_n = \dfrac{(-1)^{n+1}}{n}$

(b) $a_n = \dfrac{(-1)^n}{2^{n-1}}$

(c) $a_n = \dfrac{(-1)^{n+1}}{2^n}$

(d) $a_n = \dfrac{(-1)^n}{n+1}$

(e) None of these

1—**Ans:** a

7. $-1, \dfrac{1}{2}, -\dfrac{1}{4}, \dfrac{1}{8}, -\dfrac{1}{16}$ are the first five terms of which sequence?

(a) $a_n = \dfrac{(-1)^{n+1}}{n}$

(b) $a_n = \dfrac{(-1)^n}{2^{n-1}}$

(c) $a_n = \dfrac{(-1)^{n+1}}{2^n}$

(d) $a_n = \dfrac{(-1)^n}{n+1}$

(e) None of these

1—**Ans:** b

8. $\dfrac{1}{2}, -\dfrac{1}{4}, \dfrac{1}{8}, -\dfrac{1}{16}, \dfrac{1}{32}$ are the first five terms of which sequence?

(a) $a_n = \dfrac{(-1)^{n+1}}{n}$

(b) $a_n = \dfrac{(-1)^n}{2^{n-1}}$

(c) $a_n = \dfrac{(-1)^{n+1}}{2^n}$

(d) $a_n = \dfrac{(-1)^n}{n+1}$

(e) None of these

1—**Ans:** c

9. Write the first five terms of the sequence $a_n = \dfrac{(-1)^n}{n^2+1}$. (Begin with $n = 1$.)

1—**Ans:** $-\dfrac{1}{2}, \dfrac{1}{5}, -\dfrac{1}{10}, \dfrac{1}{17}, -\dfrac{1}{26}$

10. Write the first five terms of the sequence $a_n = \dfrac{(-1)^{n+1}}{n^2+n}$. (Begin with $n = 1$.)

1—**Ans:** $\dfrac{1}{2}, -\dfrac{1}{6}, \dfrac{1}{12}, -\dfrac{1}{20}, \dfrac{1}{30}$

11. $2, 1, \dfrac{36}{43}, \dfrac{10}{13}, \dfrac{30}{41}$ are the first five terms of which sequence?

(a) $a_n = \dfrac{2n-1}{2n+1}$

(b) $a_n = \dfrac{3n(n+1)}{5n^2-2}$

(c) $a_n = \dfrac{2n}{n^2+1}$

(d) $a_n = \dfrac{2n}{3n-2}$

(e) None of these

1—**Ans:** b

12. $1, \dfrac{4}{5}, \dfrac{3}{5}, \dfrac{8}{17}, \dfrac{5}{13}$ are the first five terms of which sequence?

(a) $a_n = \dfrac{2n-1}{2n+1}$ **(b)** $a_n = \dfrac{3n(n+1)}{5n^2-2}$ **(c)** $a_n = \dfrac{2n}{n^2+1}$

(d) $a_n = \dfrac{2n}{3n-2}$ **(e)** None of these

1—Ans: c

13. Write the first five terms of the sequence $a_n = \dfrac{2n-1}{n^2+1}$. (Begin with $n = 1$.)

1—Ans: $\dfrac{1}{2}, \dfrac{3}{5}, \dfrac{1}{2}, \dfrac{7}{17}, \dfrac{9}{26}$

14. Write the first five terms of the sequence $a_n = \dfrac{n^2+1}{2n-1}$. (Begin with $n = 1$.)

1—Ans: $2, \dfrac{5}{3}, 2, \dfrac{17}{7}, \dfrac{26}{9}$

15. $1, 1, \dfrac{2}{3}, \dfrac{1}{3}, \dfrac{2}{15}$ are the first five terms of which sequence?

(a) $a_n = \dfrac{2^n}{n!}$ **(b)** $a_n = \dfrac{n^2}{n!}$ **(c)** $a_n = \dfrac{n!}{(n+1)!}$

(d) $a_n = \dfrac{2^{n-1}}{n!}$ **(e)** None of these

1—Ans: d

16. $2, 2, \dfrac{4}{3}, \dfrac{2}{3}, \dfrac{4}{15}$ are the first five terms of which sequence?

(a) $a_n = \dfrac{2^n}{n!}$ **(b)** $a_n = \dfrac{n^2}{n!}$ **(c)** $a_n = \dfrac{n!}{(n+1)!}$

(d) $a_n = \dfrac{2^{n-1}}{n!}$ **(e)** None of these

1—Ans: a

17. $\dfrac{1}{2}, \dfrac{1}{3}, \dfrac{1}{4}, \dfrac{1}{5}, \dfrac{1}{6}$ are the first five terms of which sequence?

(a) $a_n = \dfrac{2^n}{n!}$ **(b)** $a_n = \dfrac{n^2}{n!}$ **(c)** $a_n = \dfrac{n!}{(n+1)!}$

(d) $a_n = \dfrac{2^{n-1}}{n!}$ **(e)** None of these

1—Ans: c

18. $1, 2, \dfrac{3}{2}, \dfrac{2}{3}, \dfrac{5}{24}$ are the first five terms of which sequence?

(a) $a_n = \dfrac{2^n}{n!}$ (b) $a_n = \dfrac{n^2}{n!}$ (c) $a_n = \dfrac{n!}{(n+1)!}$

(d) $a_n = \dfrac{2^{n-1}}{n!}$ (e) None of these

1—**Ans:** b

19. Write the first five terms of the sequence $a_n = \dfrac{3^n}{n!}$. (Begin with $n = 1$.)

1—**Ans:** $3, \dfrac{9}{2}, \dfrac{9}{2}, \dfrac{27}{8}, \dfrac{81}{40}$

20. Write the first five terms of the sequence $a_n = \dfrac{(n-1)!}{n!}$. (Begin with $n = 1$.)

1—**Ans:** $1, \dfrac{1}{2}, \dfrac{1}{3}, \dfrac{1}{4}, \dfrac{1}{5}$

21. Choose the term nth term that generates the sequence $1, 0, 1, 0, 1, 0, \ldots$.

(a) $a_n = \dfrac{1 - (-1)^n}{2}$ (b) $a_n = (-1)^{(n-1)n/2}$ (c) $a_n = (-1)^{n(n+1)/2}$

(d) $a_n = \dfrac{(-1)^n - 1}{2}$ (e) None of these

2—**Ans:** a

22. Choose the term nth term that generates the sequence $-1, 0, -1, 0, -1, 0, \ldots$.

(a) $a_n = \dfrac{1 - (-1)^n}{2}$ (b) $a_n = (-1)^{(n-1)n/2}$ (c) $a_n = (-1)^{n(n+1)/2}$

(d) $a_n = \dfrac{(-1)^n - 1}{2}$ (e) None of these

2—**Ans:** d

23. Write the first six terms of the sequence whose nth term is $a_n = (-1)^{n+1}$.

1—**Ans:** $1, -1, 1, -1, 1, -1$

24. Write the first six terms of the sequence whose nth term is $a_n = (-1)^n$.

1—**Ans:** $-1, 1, -1, 1, -1, 1$

25. Simplify $\dfrac{14!}{13!}$.

(a) 182 (b) $2! = 2$ (c) $13!$ (d) 14 (e) None of these

1—**Ans:** d

26. Simplify $\dfrac{14!}{12!}$.

    (a) 182   (b) $2! = 2$ (c) $12!$ (d) 14   (e) None of these

    1—Ans: a

27. Simplify $\dfrac{6!}{3!}$.

    (a) $2! = 2$ (b) 6   (c) 120   (d) $3! = 6$ (e) None of these

    1—Ans: c

28. Simplify $\dfrac{8!}{4!}$.

    (a) $4! = 24$ (b) 1680   (c) $2! = 2$ (d) 56   (e) None of these

    1—Ans: b

29. Simplify $\dfrac{8!}{5!}$.

    1—Ans: 336

30. Simplify $\dfrac{20!}{18!}$.

    1—Ans: 380

31. Choose the sigma notation for $1 + 3 + 5 + 7 + 9$.

    (a) $\displaystyle\sum_{n=1}^{\infty} 2n + 1$ (b) $\displaystyle\sum_{n=0}^{9} 2n + 1$ (c) $\displaystyle\sum_{n=1}^{5} 2n - 1$

    (d) $\displaystyle\sum_{n=0}^{4} 2n - 1$ (e) None of these

    1—Ans: c

32. Choose the sigma notation for $1 - 1 + \dfrac{1}{2} - \dfrac{1}{6} + \dfrac{1}{24} - \dfrac{1}{120}$.

    (a) $\displaystyle\sum_{n=0}^{5} \dfrac{1}{n!}$ (b) $\displaystyle\sum_{n=0}^{5} \dfrac{(-1)^n}{n!}$ (c) $\displaystyle\sum_{n=1}^{5} \dfrac{1}{n!}$

    (d) $\displaystyle\sum_{n=1}^{5} \dfrac{(-1)^n}{n!}$ (e) None of these

    1—Ans: b

33. Write the sum $1 + \dfrac{1}{1 \cdot 2} + \dfrac{1}{1 \cdot 2 \cdot 3} + \dfrac{1}{1 \cdot 2 \cdot 3 \cdot 4} + \dfrac{1}{1 \cdot 2 \cdot 3 \cdot 4 \cdot 5}$ in sigma notation.

1—Ans: $\displaystyle\sum_{n=1}^{5} \dfrac{1}{n!}$

34. Write the sum $\dfrac{2}{1} + \dfrac{3}{2} + \dfrac{4}{3} + \dfrac{5}{4} + \dfrac{6}{5} + \dfrac{7}{6}$ in sigma notation.

1—Ans: $\displaystyle\sum_{n=1}^{6} \dfrac{n+1}{n}$

35. Find the value of $\displaystyle\sum_{i=1}^{7} \left(\dfrac{1}{2i-1} - \dfrac{1}{2i+1} \right)$.

(a) $\dfrac{14}{15}$ **(b)** $\dfrac{19}{15}$ **(c)** $\dfrac{8}{15}$ **(d)** $\dfrac{27}{15}$ **(e)** None of these

2—Ans: a

36. Find the value of $\displaystyle\sum_{n=3}^{10} \left(\dfrac{1}{n} - \dfrac{1}{n+1} \right)$.

(a) $\dfrac{7}{99}$ **(b)** $\dfrac{8}{33}$ **(c)** $\dfrac{19}{11}$ **(d)** $\dfrac{8}{11}$ **(e)** None of these

2—Ans: b

37. Use a graphing utility to find the value of $\displaystyle\sum_{n=1}^{6} \left(\dfrac{1}{2^n} \right)$.

(a) 0.328125   **(b)** 0.9375   **(c)** 0.984375   **(d)** 0.96875   **(e)** None of these

2—T—Ans: c

38. Use a graphing utility to find the value of $\displaystyle\sum_{n=0}^{6} \dfrac{(-1)^n}{2^n}$.

(a) $0.666\overline{6}$ **(b)** 1.984375   **(c)** 0.890625   **(d)** 0.671875   **(e)** None of these

2—T—Ans: d

39. Use a graphing utility to find the sum of $\displaystyle\sum_{n=0}^{4} \left(-\dfrac{1}{3} \right)^n$.

2—T—Ans: $\dfrac{61}{81} \approx 0.75309$

40. Use a graphing utility to find the sum of $\displaystyle\sum_{n=0}^{5} (-1)^n n^2$.

2—T—Ans: -15

41. Find the fifth term of the sequence whose nth term is given by $a_n = 2(3^{n-1})$. (Begin with $n = 1$.)

    (a) 486   **(b)** -486 **(c)** $\frac{1}{162}$ **(d)** 162   **(e)** None of these

    1—Form: 12A—Ans: d

42. Find the tenth term of the sequence whose nth term is given by
$a_n = \dfrac{2n + 1}{5 + 3(n - 1)}$. (Begin with $n = 1$.)

    (a) $\frac{21}{32}$ **(b)** $\frac{21}{72}$ **(c)** $\frac{22}{32}$ **(d)** $\frac{19}{29}$ **(e)** None of these

    1—Form: 12B—Ans: a

43. Find the third term of the sequence whose nth term is given by $a_n = \dfrac{(-1)^{n+1}}{n}$. (Begin with $n = 1$.)

    (a) $\frac{1}{3}$ **(b)** $\frac{1}{81}$ **(c)** $-\frac{1}{3}$ **(d)** $\frac{1}{27}$ **(e)** None of these

    1—Ans: a

44. Find the third term of the sequence whose nth term is given by $a_n = \dfrac{(-1)^n}{n + 1}$. (Begin with $n = 1$.)

    (a) $\frac{1}{3}$ **(b)** $\frac{1}{4}$ **(c)** $-\frac{1}{4}$ **(d)** $-\frac{3}{4}$ **(e)** None of these

    1—Ans: c

45. Evaluate $\dfrac{6!}{4!2!}$.

    (a) $\frac{3}{4}$ **(b)** $\frac{1}{8}$ **(c)** 15   **(d)** 30   **(e)** None of these

    1—Ans: c

46. Evaluate $\dfrac{7!}{4!3!}$.

    (a) $\frac{7}{12}$ **(b)** 35   **(c)** $\frac{7}{24}$ **(d)** 210   **(e)** None of these

    1—Ans: b

47. Use a graphing utility to evaluate $\displaystyle\sum_{i=1}^{4}(1 - i)$.

    (a) -3 **(b)** -6 **(c)** 6 **(d)** -5 **(e)** None of these

    1—T—Form: 12A—Ans: b

48. Use a graphing utility to evaluate $\displaystyle\sum_{i=1}^{4}(2i - 1)$.

    (a) $8i - 2$ **(b)** 16 **(c)** 7 **(d)** 6 **(e)** None of these

    1—T—Form: 12B—Ans: b

49. Use sigma notation to write the sum $\dfrac{2}{1} + \dfrac{3}{2} + \dfrac{4}{3} + \cdots + \dfrac{7}{6}$.

    (a) $\displaystyle\sum_{n=1}^{7}\dfrac{n}{n - 1}$ **(b)** $\displaystyle\sum_{n=1}^{6}\dfrac{n + 1}{n}$ **(c)** $\displaystyle\sum_{n=1}^{7}\dfrac{n}{n + 1}$

    (d) $\displaystyle\sum_{n=2}^{n}\dfrac{n}{n + 1}$ **(e)** None of these

    2—Form: 12A—Ans: b

50. Use sigma notation to write the sum $\dfrac{3}{1} + \dfrac{3}{4} + \dfrac{3}{9} + \dfrac{3}{16} + \dfrac{3}{25}$.

    (a) $\displaystyle\sum_{i=1}^{5}\dfrac{1}{i^2}$ **(b)** $\displaystyle\sum_{i=1}^{5}\dfrac{3}{4i}$ **(c)** $\displaystyle\sum_{i=1}^{6}\dfrac{3}{i^2}$

    (d) $\displaystyle\sum_{i=1}^{5}\dfrac{3}{i^2}$ **(e)** None of these

    2—Form: 12B—Ans: d

51. Write the first five terms of the sequence whose nth term is $a_n = \dfrac{(-1)^n}{n!}$. (Assume that n begins with 1.)

    2—Ans: $-1, \dfrac{1}{2}, -\dfrac{1}{6}, \dfrac{1}{24}, -\dfrac{1}{120}$

52. Write the first five terms of the sequence whose nth term is $a_n = \dfrac{n!}{(n + 2)!}$. (Assume that n begins with 0.)

    2—Form: 12C—Ans: $\dfrac{1}{2}, \dfrac{1}{6}, \dfrac{1}{12}, \dfrac{1}{20}, \dfrac{1}{30}$

53. Use a graphing utility to find the sum $\displaystyle\sum_{i=1}^{10}(3i + 1)$.

    1—T—Ans: 175

54. Use a graphing utility to find the sum $\sum_{i=0}^{8} i!$.

2—T—Form: 12C—Ans: 46,234

55. Use sigma notation to write the sum $1 + \dfrac{1}{2} + \dfrac{1}{3} + \dfrac{1}{4} + \dfrac{1}{5} + \dfrac{1}{6} + \dfrac{1}{7}$.

2—Ans: $\sum_{n=1}^{7} \dfrac{1}{n}$

56. Use sigma notation to write the sum $\dfrac{1}{2} + \dfrac{2}{6} + \dfrac{3}{24} + \dfrac{4}{120} + \dfrac{5}{720}$.

2—T—Form: 12C—Ans: $\sum_{n=1}^{5} \dfrac{n}{(n+1)!}$

57. Find the partial sum S_3 for the sequence whose nth term is $a_n = 2n + 1$. (Assume n begins with 1.)

1—Ans: 15

58. Find the partial sum S_4 for the sequence whose nth term is $a_n = (-1)^{n+1}n$. (Assume n begins with 1.)

1—Form: 12C—Ans: -2

59. Find the partial sum S_5 for the sequence whose nth term is $a_n = n^2 - 1$. (Assume n begins with 1.)

(a) 10   **(b)** 50   **(c)** 25   **(d)** 40   **(e)** 52

1—Form: 12A—Ans: b

60. Find the partial sum S_3 for the sequence whose nth term is $a_n = \dfrac{(-1)^n}{n}$. (Assume n begins with 1.)

(a) $-\dfrac{1}{3}$ **(b)** $-\dfrac{1}{6}$ **(c)** $-\dfrac{2}{3}$ **(d)** $-\dfrac{5}{6}$ **(e)** $\dfrac{5}{6}$

1—Form: 12B—Ans: d

Section 12.2 Arithmetic Sequences

1. Find the common difference of the arithmetic sequence $-4, -1, 2, 5, 8, 11, \ldots$.

(a) -3 **(b)** -4 **(c)** 3   **(d)** 11   **(e)** None of these

1—Ans: c

2. Find the common difference of the arithmetic sequence $3, \frac{3}{2}, 0, -\frac{3}{2}, -3, -\frac{9}{2}, \ldots$.

    (a) $\frac{3}{2}$ **(b)** $-\frac{3}{2}$ **(c)** 3 **(d)** 0 **(e)** None of these

    1—Ans: b

3. Find the common difference of the arithmetic sequence $10, \frac{37}{4}, \frac{17}{2}, \frac{31}{4}, \ldots$.

    1—Ans: $-\frac{3}{4}$

4. Find the common difference of the arithmetic sequence $5, \frac{13}{2}, 8, \frac{19}{2}, \ldots$.

    1—Ans: $\frac{3}{2}$

5. Determine which sequence is arithmetic.

    (a) $1, 2, 4, 7, 11, \ldots$ **(b)** $\ln 2, \ln 3, \ln 4, \ln 5, \ldots$ **(c)** $-3, 0, 3, 6, 9, \ldots$

    (d) $\frac{1}{1}, \frac{1}{2}, \frac{1}{3}, \frac{1}{4}, \frac{1}{5}, \ldots$ **(e)** None of these

    1—Ans: c

6. Determine which sequence is arithmetic.

    (a) $-\frac{1}{2}, -\frac{1}{3}, -\frac{1}{4}, -\frac{1}{5}, \ldots$ **(b)** $-3, -2, 0, 3, 7, \ldots$ **(c)** $e, e^2, e^3, e^4, e^5, \ldots$

    (d) $-\frac{1}{3}, -\frac{4}{3}, -\frac{7}{3}, -\frac{10}{3}, \ldots$ **(e)** None of these

    1—Ans: d

7. Determine if the sequence $2, \frac{10}{3}, \frac{14}{3}, 6, \frac{22}{3}, \ldots$ is arithmetic. If so, give the common difference.

    1—Ans: It is arithmetic. $\frac{4}{3}$ is the common difference.

8. Determine if the sequence $1, \frac{1}{4}, \frac{1}{7}, \frac{1}{10}, \ldots$ is arithmetic. If so, give the common difference.

    1—Ans: It is not arithmetic.

9. $-2, 3, 8, 13, 18$ are the first five terms of which arithmetic sequence? (Begin with $n = 1$.)

    (a) $a_n = 3n - 2$ **(b)** $a_n = 5n - 7$ **(c)** $a_n = 3 - 5n$

    (d) $a_n = 3n - 5$ **(e)** None of these

    1—Ans: b

10. $-2, -7, -12, -17, -22$ are the first five terms of which arithmetic sequence? (Begin with $n = 1$.)

    (a) $a_n = 3n - 2$ **(b)** $a_n = 5n - 7$ **(c)** $a_n = 3 - 5n$

    (d) $a_n = 3n - 5$ **(e)** None of these

    1—Ans: c

11. 1, 4, 7, 10, 13 are the first five terms of which arithmetic sequence?
(Begin with $n = 1$.)

(a) $a_n = 3n - 2$ (b) $a_n = 5n - 7$ (c) $a_n = 3 - 5n$

(d) $a_n = 3n - 5$ (e) None of these

1—Ans: a

12. $-2, 1, 4, 7, 10$ are the first five terms of which arithmetic sequence?
(Begin with $n = 1$.)

(a) $a_n = 3n - 2$ (b) $a_n = 5n - 7$ (c) $a_n = 3 - 5n$

(d) $a_n = 3n - 5$ (e) None of these

1—Ans: d

13. Write the first five terms of the arithmetic sequence $a_n = 2 - \frac{2}{3}n$.
(Begin with $n = 1$.)

1—Ans: $\frac{4}{2}, \frac{2}{3}, 0, -\frac{2}{3}, -\frac{4}{3}$

14. Write the first five terms of the arithmetic sequence $a_n = \frac{2}{3}n - 2$.
(Begin with $n = 1$.)

1—Ans: $-\frac{4}{3}, -\frac{2}{3}, 0, \frac{2}{3}, \frac{4}{3}$

15. Find the formula for nth term of the arithmetic sequence with $a_1 = 3$ and $d = -\frac{1}{2}$.
(Begin with $n = 1$.)

(a) $a_n = 3 - \frac{1}{2}n$ (b) $a_n = 3n - \frac{1}{2}$ (c) $a_n = -\frac{1}{2}n + \frac{7}{2}$

(d) $a_n = \frac{7}{2}n - \frac{1}{2}$ (e) None of these

1—Ans: c

16. Find the formula for nth term of the arithmetic sequence with $a_1 = \frac{5}{2}$ and $d = -\frac{1}{2}$.
(Begin with $n = 1$.)

(a) $a_n = 3 - \frac{1}{2}n$ (b) $a_n = 3n - \frac{1}{2}$ (c) $a_n = -\frac{1}{2}n + \frac{7}{2}$

(d) $a_n = \frac{7}{2}n - \frac{1}{2}$ (e) None of these

1—Ans: a

17. Find the formula for nth term of the arithmetic sequence with $a_1 = 6$ and $d = -\frac{3}{2}$.
(Begin with $n = 1$.)

1—Ans: $a_n = \frac{15}{2} - \frac{3}{2}n$

18. Find the formula for nth term of the arithmetic sequence with $a_1 = -2$ and $d = 1.2$.
(Begin with $n = 1$.)

1—Ans: $a_n = -3.2 + 1.2n$

19. Write the first five terms of the arithmetic sequence with $a_1 = 5$ and $d = 3$.

   (a) $2, 5, 8, 11, 14$ **(b)** $3, 8, 13, 18, 23$ **(c)** $5, 8, 11, 14, 17$

   (d) $-2, 3, 8, 13, 18$ **(e)** None of these

   1—Ans: c

20. Write the first five terms of the arithmetic sequence with $a_1 = 3$ and $d = 5$.

   (a) $2, 5, 8, 11, 14$ **(b)** $3, 8, 13, 18, 23$ **(c)** $5, 8, 11, 14, 17$

   (d) $-2, 3, 8, 13, 18$ **(e)** None of these

   1—Ans: b

21. Write the first five terms of the arithmetic sequence with $a_1 = 2$ and $d = 3$.

   (a) $2, 5, 8, 11, 14$ **(b)** $3, 8, 13, 18, 23$ **(c)** $5, 8, 11, 14, 17$

   (d) $-2, 3, 8, 13, 18$ **(e)** None of these

   1—Ans: a

22. Write the first five terms of the arithmetic sequence with $a_1 = -2$ and $d = 5$.

   (a) $2, 5, 8, 11, 14$ **(b)** $3, 8, 13, 18, 23$ **(c)** $5, 8, 11, 14, 17$

   (d) $-2, 3, 8, 13, 18$ **(e)** None of these

   1—Ans: d

23. Write the first five terms of the arithmetic sequence with $a_1 = 0.08$ and $d = -0.001$.

   1—Ans: $0.08, 0.079, 0.078, 0.077, 0.076$

24. Write the first five terms of the arithmetic sequence with $a_1 = 4$ and $d = \frac{5}{8}$.

   1—Ans: $4, \frac{37}{8}, \frac{21}{4}, \frac{47}{8}, \frac{13}{2}$

25. Find the formula for the nth term of the arithmetic sequence for which $a_3 = 7$ and $a_6 = 13$.

   (a) $a_n = -2n + 19$ **(b)** $a_n = 7n - 28$ **(c)** $a_n = 2n + 1$

   (d) $a_n = 7n - 35$ **(e)** None of these

   2—Ans: c

26. Find the formula for the nth term of the arithmetic sequence for which $a_3 = -14$ and $a_6 = 7$.

   (a) $a_n = -2n + 19$ **(b)** $a_n = 7n - 28$ **(c)** $a_n = 2n + 1$

   (d) $a_n = 7n - 35$ **(e)** None of these

   2—Ans: d

27. Find a formula for the *n*th term of the arithmetic sequence for which
    $a_4 = 0.48$ and $a_8 = 0.84$.

    2—Ans: $a_n = 0.09n + 0.12$

28. Find a formula for the *n*th term of the arithmetic sequence for which
    $a_3 = \frac{17}{6}$ and $a_{10} = \frac{19}{3}$.

    2—Ans: $a_n = \frac{1}{2}n + \frac{4}{3}$

29. Find the partial sum $\displaystyle\sum_{n=1}^{50}(2.4 + 0.2n)$.

    (a) 750   **(b)** 167.5   **(c)** 3070   **(d)** 375   **(e)** None of these

    2—Ans: d

30. Find the partial sum $\displaystyle\sum_{n=1}^{30}\left(\frac{4}{3}n + \frac{1}{3}\right)$.

    (a) 315   **(b)** 1260   **(c)** 630   **(d)** 195   **(e)** None of these

    2—Ans: c

31. Find the partial sum $\displaystyle\sum_{n=10}^{20}(7 + 0.2n)$.

    2—Ans: 110

32. Find the partial sum $\displaystyle\sum_{n=1}^{30}\left(\frac{1}{3} - \frac{2}{3}n\right)$.

    2—Ans: -300

33. Find the partial sum $\displaystyle\sum_{n=11}^{30}(12 + 3n)$.

    2—Ans: 1470

34. Find the partial sum $\displaystyle\sum_{n=10}^{30}(2.4 + 0.03n)$.

    2—Ans: 63

35. Determine which is the *n*th partial sum of the arithmetic sequence
    3, 10, 17, 24, 31, . . . , $n = 15$.

    (a) 235   **(b)** 780   **(c)** 4950   **(d)** 1824   **(e)** None of these

    2—Ans: b

36. Determine which is the *n*th partial sum of the arithmetic sequence
150, 144, 138, 132, 126, . . . ,   *n* = 19.

    (a) 235   **(b)** 780   **(c)** 4950   **(d)** 1824   **(e)** None of these

    2—Ans: d

37. Find the sum of the positive integers from 1 through 80.

    2—Ans: 3240

38. Find the sum of the positive integers from 51 through 100.

    2—Ans: 3775

39. Find the sum of the even integers from 32 to 90 inclusive.

    2—Ans: 1830

40. Find the sum of the odd integers from 31 to 89 inclusive.

    2—Ans: 1800

41. Find the ninth term of the arithmetic sequence with the first term $a_1 = 4$ and common difference $d = 10$.

    (a) 94   **(b)** 84   **(c)** 46   **(d)** 49   **(e)** None of these

    2—Form: 12A—Ans: b

42. Find the eighth term of the arithmetic sequence with the first term $a_1 = 5$ and common difference $d = 8$.

    (a) 69   **(b)** 48   **(c)** 61   **(d)** 104   **(e)** None of these

    2—Form: 12B—Ans: c

43. Find a formula for the *n*th term of the arithmetic sequence with the common difference $d = -2$ and the third term $a_3 = 15$. (Begin with *n* = 1.)

    (a) $a_n = -2n + 9$ **(b)** $a_n = -2n + 19$ **(c)** $a_n = -2n + 21$

    (d) $a_n = -2n + 15$ **(e)** None of these

    1—Ans: c

44. Find a formula for the *n*th term of the arithmetic sequence with the common difference $d = -3$ and the second term $a_2 = 12$. (Begin with *n* = 1.)

    (a) $a_n = -3n + 18$ **(b)** $a_n = -3n + 15$ **(c)** $a_n = -3n + 12$

    (d) $a_n = 12n - 3$ **(e)** None of these

    1—Ans: a

45. Find the sum of the first 18 terms of the arithmetic sequence whose nth term is $a_n = 3n - 1$.

    (a) 495   **(b)** 53   **(c)** 459   **(d)** 445   **(e)** None of these

    2—Form: 12A—Ans: a

46. Find the sum of the first 20 terms of the arithmetic sequence whose nth term is $a_n = 3n - 1$.

    (a) 570   **(b)** 610   **(c)** 59   **(d)** 551   **(e)** None of these

    2—Form: 12B—Ans: b

47. Find the 17th term of the arithmetic sequence with first term $a_1 = 2$ and common difference $d = 7$.

    2—Ans: 114

48. Find the 30th term of the arithmetic sequence with first term $a_1 = -5$ and common difference $d = \frac{1}{3}$. (Begin with $n = 1$.)

    2—Ans: $\frac{14}{3}$

49. Find a formula for the nth term of the arithmetic sequence with common difference $d = -\frac{3}{2}$ and the second term $a_2 = 15$. (Begin with $n = 1$.)

    2—Ans: $-\frac{3}{2}n + 18$

50. Find a formula for a_n for the arithmetic sequence with $a_2 = 15$ and $d = \frac{3}{2}$. (Begin with $n = 1$.)

    2—Form: 12C—Ans: $a_n = \frac{3}{2}n + 12$

51. Find the sum of the first 50 positive integers that are multiples of 3.

    2—Form: 12C—Ans: 3825

52. Find the sum of the first 30 terms of the sequence: $\sqrt{2}, 2\sqrt{2}, 3\sqrt{2}, 4\sqrt{2}, 5\sqrt{2}, \ldots$

    2—Ans: $465\sqrt{2}$

53. Write the first five terms of the arithmetic sequence defined recursively.

$$a_1 = 21$$
$$a_{k+1} = a_k - 4$$

    1—Form: 12C—Ans: 21, 17, 13, 9, 5

54. Write the first five terms of the arithmetic sequence defined recursively.

$$a_1 = 5$$
$$a_{k+1} = a_k + 7$$

1—Ans: 5, 12, 19, 26, 33

55. Write the first five terms of the arithmetic sequence defined recursively.

$$a_1 = -3$$
$$a_{k+1} = a_k + 5$$

(a) $-3, -2, -1, 0, 1$ (b) $-3, -1, 1, 3, 5$ (c) $-3, 0, 3, 6, 9$

(d) $-3, 2, 7, 12, 17$ (e) $5, 10, 15, 20, 25$

1—Form: 12A—Ans: d

56. Write the first five terms of the arithmetic sequence defined recursively.

$$a_1 = 42$$
$$a_{k+1} = a_k - 6$$

(a) $42, 48, 54, 60, 66$ (b) $-6, 0, 6, 12, 18$ (c) $42, 41, 40, 39, 38$

(d) $42, 43, 44, 45, 46$ (e) $42, 36, 30, 24, 18$

1—Form: 12B—Ans: e

Section 12.3   Geometric Sequences and Series

1. Find the common ratio of this geometric sequence $2, \frac{3}{2}, \frac{9}{8}, \frac{27}{32}, \frac{81}{128}, \cdots$

(a) $\frac{4}{3}$ (b) $-\frac{2}{3}$ (c) $\frac{3}{2}$ (d) $\frac{3}{4}$ (e) None of these

1—Ans: d

2. Find the common ratio of this geometric sequence $9, -6, 4, -\frac{8}{3}, \frac{16}{9}, \cdots$

(a) $\frac{4}{3}$ (b) $-\frac{2}{3}$ (c) $\frac{3}{2}$ (d) $\frac{3}{4}$ (e) None of these

1—Ans: b

3. Find the common ratio of the geometric sequence $5, -\frac{15}{4}, \frac{45}{16}, -\frac{135}{64}, \frac{405}{256}, \cdots$

1—Ans: $-\frac{3}{4}$

4. Find the common ratio of the geometric sequence $\frac{8}{9}, \frac{4}{3}, 2, 3, \frac{9}{2}, \cdots$

1—Ans: $\frac{3}{2}$

5. Choose the sequence which is geometric.

  (a) $1, -1, 2, -2, 3, -3, \ldots$ (b) $2, 4, 6, 8, 10, \ldots$ (c) $2, -1, \frac{1}{2}, -\frac{1}{4}, \frac{1}{8}, \ldots$

  (d) $1, 2, -4, -8, 16, 32, \ldots$ (e) None of these

  1—Ans: c

6. Choose the sequence which is geometric.

  (a) $1, 2, -4, -8, 16, 32, \ldots$ (b) $4, -1, \frac{1}{4}, -\frac{1}{16}, \frac{1}{64}, \ldots$ (c) $1, -3, 5, -7, 9, \ldots$

  (d) $4, 2, 0, -2, -4, \ldots$ (e) None of these

  1—Ans: b

7. Determine whether the sequence $20, -10, 5, -\frac{5}{2}, \frac{5}{4}, \ldots$ is geometric. If so, find the common ratio.

  1—Ans: It is geometric. The common ratio is $-\frac{1}{2}$.

8. Determine whether the sequence $20, 15, 10, 5, 0, \ldots$ is geometric. If so, find the common ratio.

  1—Ans: It is not geometric.

9. Write the first five terms of the geometric sequence that has $a_1 = -3$ and $r = -\frac{1}{2}$.

  (a) $3, -\frac{3}{2}, \frac{3}{4}, -\frac{3}{8}, \frac{3}{16}$ (b) $-\frac{1}{2}, \frac{3}{2}, -\frac{9}{2}, \frac{27}{2}, -\frac{81}{2}$ (c) $\frac{1}{2}, -\frac{3}{2}, \frac{9}{2}, -\frac{27}{2}, \frac{81}{2}$

  (d) $-3, \frac{3}{2}, -\frac{3}{4}, \frac{3}{8}, -\frac{3}{16}$ (e) None of these

  1—Ans: d

10. Write the first five terms of the geometric sequence that has $a_1 = 3$ and $r = -\frac{1}{2}$.

  (a) $3, -\frac{3}{2}, \frac{3}{4}, -\frac{3}{8}, \frac{3}{16}$ (b) $-\frac{1}{2}, \frac{3}{2}, -\frac{9}{2}, \frac{27}{2}, -\frac{81}{2}$ (c) $\frac{1}{2}, -\frac{3}{2}, \frac{9}{2}, -\frac{27}{2}, \frac{81}{2}$

  (d) $-3, \frac{3}{2}, -\frac{3}{4}, \frac{3}{8}, -\frac{3}{16}$ (e) None of these

  1—Ans: a

11. Write the first five terms of the geometric sequence that has $a_1 = \frac{1}{2}$ and $r = -3$.

  (a) $3, -\frac{3}{2}, \frac{3}{4}, -\frac{3}{8}, \frac{3}{16}$ (b) $-\frac{1}{2}, \frac{3}{2}, -\frac{9}{2}, \frac{27}{2}, -\frac{81}{2}$ (c) $\frac{1}{2}, -\frac{3}{2}, \frac{9}{2}, -\frac{27}{2}, \frac{81}{2}$

  (d) $-3, \frac{3}{2}, -\frac{3}{4}, \frac{3}{8}, -\frac{3}{16}$ (e) None of these

  1—Ans: c

12. Write the first five terms of the geometric sequence that has $a_1 = -\frac{1}{2}$ and $r = -3$.

  (a) $3, -\frac{3}{2}, \frac{3}{4}, -\frac{3}{8}, \frac{3}{16}$ (b) $-\frac{1}{2}, \frac{3}{2}, -\frac{9}{2}, \frac{27}{2}, -\frac{81}{2}$ (c) $\frac{1}{2}, -\frac{3}{2}, \frac{9}{2}, -\frac{27}{2}, \frac{81}{2}$

  (d) $-3, \frac{3}{2}, -\frac{3}{4}, \frac{3}{8}, -\frac{3}{16}$ (e) None of these

  1—Ans: b

13. Write the first five terms of the geometric sequence that has $a_1 = \frac{3}{4}$ and $r = \frac{2}{3}$.

1—Ans: $\frac{3}{4}, \frac{1}{2}, \frac{1}{3}, \frac{2}{9}, \frac{4}{27}$

14. Write the first five terms of the geometric sequence that has $a_1 = -\frac{3}{2}$ and $r = -\frac{2}{3}$.

1—Ans: $-\frac{3}{2}, 1, -\frac{2}{3}, \frac{4}{9}, -\frac{8}{27}$

15. A geometric sequence has $a_1 = -\frac{1}{3}$ and $r = 7$. Find the formula for its nth term. (Assume n begins with 1.)

(a) $a_n = 7\left(\frac{1}{3}\right)^n$ (b) $a_n = 7\left(-\frac{1}{3}\right)^{n-1}$ (c) $a_n = -\frac{1}{3}(7)^n$

(d) $a_n = -\frac{1}{3}(7)^{n-1}$ (e) None of these

1—Ans: d

16. A geometric sequence has $a_1 = -\frac{1}{7}$ and $r = 3$. Find the formula for its nth term. (Assume n begins with 1.)

(a) $a_n = \frac{3}{7}(-1)^n$ (b) $a_n = 3\left(-\frac{1}{7}\right)^{n-1}$ (c) $a_n = -\frac{1}{7}(3)^{n-1}$

(d) $a_n = -\frac{1}{7}(3)^n$ (e) None of these

1—Ans: c

17. Assuming n begins with 1, write the formula for the nth term of the geometric sequence for which $a_1 = \frac{3}{8}$ and $r = \frac{2}{7}$.

1—Ans: $a_n = \frac{3}{8}\left(\frac{2}{7}\right)^{n-1}$

18. Assuming n begins with 1, write the formula for the nth term of the geometric sequence for which $a_1 = 19$ and $r = -\frac{3}{4}$.

1—Ans: $a_n = 19\left(-\frac{3}{4}\right)^{n-1}$

19. Given that $a_1 = 8$ and $r = -\frac{1}{2}$ for a geometric sequence, find the value of a_8.

(a) -4 (b) $\frac{1}{8}$ (c) $\frac{1}{16}$ (d) $\frac{1}{32}$ (e) None of these

1—Ans: e, $a_8 = -\frac{1}{16}$

20. Given that $a_1 = -24$ and $r = -\frac{1}{\sqrt{2}}$ for a geometric sequence, find the value of a_9.

(a) $\frac{3}{2}$ (b) $-3\sqrt{2}$ (c) -3 (d) $-\frac{3}{2}$ (e) None of these

1—Ans: d

21. Given that $a_1 = \frac{3}{64}$ and $r = \frac{2}{3}$ for a geometric sequence, find the value of a_{10}.

(a) $\frac{16}{13,122}$ (b) $\frac{8}{6561}$ (c) $\frac{4}{2178}$ (d) $\frac{4}{6561}$ (e) None of these

1—Ans: b

22. Given that $a_1 = 18$ and $r = -\frac{1}{3}$ for a geometric sequence, find the value of a_7.

   (a) $\frac{2}{81}$ **(b)** $-\frac{2}{27}$ **(c)** $-\frac{2}{162}$ **(d)** $\frac{2}{27}$ **(e)** None of these

   1—Ans: a

23. For a geometric sequence, given that $a_3 = \frac{\sqrt{2}}{9}$ and $a_6 = \frac{4}{243}$, find a_{10}.

   2—Ans: $a_{10} = \frac{16}{19{,}683}$

24. For a geometric sequence, given that $a_2 = 3.600$ and $a_4 = 5.184$, use a calculator to find a_{10}, correct to three decimal places.

   2—T—Ans: $a_{10} = 15.479$

25. Use a calculator to find $\displaystyle\sum_{i=1}^{5} 3^{i-1}$.

   (a) 121   **(b)** 242   **(c)** 81   **(d)** 364   **(e)** None of these

   2—T—Ans: a

26. Use a calculator to find $\displaystyle\sum_{i=1}^{8} 4(2^{i-1})$.

   (a) 514   **(b)** 1026   **(c)** 511   **(d)** 1020   **(e)** None of these

   2—T—Ans: d

27. Use a calculator to find $\displaystyle\sum_{i=1}^{6} 3\left(\frac{2}{3}\right)^{i-1}$.

   (a) $\frac{65}{9} \approx 7.222$ **(b)** $\frac{211}{27} \approx 7.815$ **(c)** $\frac{665}{81} \approx 8.209$
   (d) $\frac{2059}{243} \approx 8.473$ **(e)** None of these

   2—T—Ans: c

28. Use a calculator to find $\displaystyle\sum_{i=1}^{5} 8\left(\frac{2}{3}\right)^{i-1}$.

   (a) $\frac{520}{27} \approx 19.259$ **(b)** $\frac{1688}{81} \approx 20.840$ **(c)** $\frac{256}{243} \approx 1.053$
   (d) $\frac{5320}{243} \approx 21.893$ **(e)** None of these

   2—T—Ans: b

29. Use a calculator to find the sum $\displaystyle\sum_{i=1}^{20} 100(1.01)^{i-1}$ to three decimal places.

   2—T—Ans: 2201.900

30. Use a calculator to find the sum $\sum_{i=1}^{20} 50(1.02)^{i-1}$ to three decimal places.

2—T—Ans: 1214.868

31. Use a calculator to find nth partial sum of the geometric sequence
$1, -\frac{1}{3}, \frac{1}{9}, -\frac{1}{27}, \ldots, \quad n = 8$.

(a) 1.499   (b) 0.750   (c) 0.664   (d) 1.333   (e) None of these

2—T—Ans: b

32. Use a calculator to find nth partial sum of the geometric sequence
$1, \frac{1}{3}, \frac{1}{9}, \frac{1}{27}, \ldots, \quad n = 7$.

(a) 1.499   (b) 0.750   (c) 0.664   (d) 1.333   (e) None of these

2—T—Ans: a

33. Use a calculator to find nth partial sum of the geometric sequence
$1, -\frac{1}{2}, \frac{1}{4}, -\frac{1}{8}, \ldots, \quad n = 8$.

(a) 1.499   (b) 0.750   (c) 0.664   (d) 1.333   (e) None of these

2—T—Ans: c

34. Use a calculator to find nth partial sum of the geometric sequence
$1, \frac{1}{4}, \frac{1}{16}, \frac{1}{64}, \ldots, \quad n = 7$.

(a) 1.499   (b) 0.750   (c) 0.664   (d) 1.333   (e) None of these

2—T—Ans: d

35. Use a calculator to find nth partial sum of the geometric sequence
$1, \frac{1}{\sqrt{2}}, \frac{1}{2}, \frac{1}{2\sqrt{2}}, \ldots, \quad n = 10$ to four decimal places.

2—T—Ans: 3.3075

36. Use a calculator to find nth partial sum of the geometric sequence
$1, -\frac{1}{\sqrt{2}}, \frac{1}{2}, -\frac{1}{2\sqrt{2}}, \frac{1}{4}, \ldots, \quad n = 10$ to four decimal places.

2—T—Ans: 0.5675

37. \$1000 is deposited each year into an account paying 6% interest, compounded yearly. At the beginning of the 21st year the account contains
$\$1000 + \$1000(1.06) + \$1000(1.06)^2 + \cdots + \$1000(1.06)^{20}$.
Find the total in the account.

(a) \$44,865.18   (b) \$47, 552.53   (c) \$42,348.95

(d) \$39,992.73   (e) None of these

2—T—Ans: d

38. $1000 is deposited each year into an account paying 6.5% interest, compounded yearly. At the beginning of the 21st year the account contains
$1000 + $1000(1.065) + $1000(1.065)^2 + \cdots + $1000(1.065)^{20}.
Find the total in the account.

(a) $44,865.18

(b) $47, 552.53

(c) $42,348.95

(d) $39,992.73

(e) None of these

2—T—Ans: c

39. $100 is deposited each month into an account paying 6% interest compounded monthly. At the beginning of the 11th year, the account contains
$100 + $100(1.005) + $100(1.005)^2 + \cdots + 100(1.005)^{120}.
Find the total in the account.

2—T—Ans: $16,569.87

40. $100 is deposited each month into an account paying 6% interest compounded monthly. At the beginning of the 15th year, the account contains
$100 + $100(1.005) + $100(1.005)^2 + \cdots + 100(1.005)^{180}.
Find the total in the account.

2—T—Ans: $26,461.63

41. Find the common ratio of the geometric sequence: $3, \frac{3}{2}, \frac{3}{4}, \frac{3}{8}, \frac{3}{16}, \ldots$

(a) -2 (b) $\frac{3}{2}$ (c) $\frac{3}{4}$ (d) $\frac{1}{2}$ (e) None of these

1—Ans: d

42. Find the common ratio of the geometric sequence: $4, 6, 9, \frac{27}{2}, \frac{81}{4}, \ldots$

(a) $\frac{2}{3}$ (b) 2 (c) $\frac{3}{2}$ (d) 3 (e) None of these

1—Ans: c

43. Find a formula for the *n*th term of the geometric sequence with first term $a_1 = 2$ and common ratio $r = -\frac{1}{3}$. (Begin with $n = 1$.)

(a) $a_n = \left(-\frac{2}{3}\right)^n$ (b) $a_n = 2 - \frac{1}{3}n$ (c) $a_n = 2\left(-\frac{1}{3}\right)^{n-1}$

(d) $a_n = 2\left(-\frac{1}{3}\right)^n$ (e) None of these

1—Ans: c

44. Find a formula for the *n*th term of the geometric sequence with first term $a_1 = 3$ and common ratio $r = -\frac{1}{2}$. (Begin with $n = 1$.)

(a) $a_n = 3\left(-\frac{1}{2}\right)^{n-1}$ (b) $a_n = \left(-\frac{3}{2}\right)^{n-1}$ (c) $a_n = 3 - \frac{1}{2}n$

(d) $a_n = 3\left(-\frac{1}{2}\right)^n$ (e) None of these

1—Ans: a

45. Find the sum of the first six terms of the geometric sequence for which
$a_1 = 2$ and $a_2 = -4$.

(a) -42 (b) $\frac{130}{3}$ (c) 42 (d) $-\frac{62}{3}$ (e) None of these

2—**Ans:** a

46. Find the sum of the first six terms of the geometric sequence for which
$a_1 = 4$ and $a_2 = 12$.

(a) 288 (b) 484 (c) 1465 (d) 1456 (e) None of these

2—**Ans:** d

47. A person buys a \$100,000 term life insurance policy. During the next five years the value of the policy will depreciate at the rate of 4% per year. (That is, at the end of each year, the depreciated value is 96% of what it was at the beginning of the year.) Find the depreciated value of the policy at the end of five full years.

(a) \$88,000   (b) \$84,934.66   (c) \$81,537.27

(d) \$78,275.78   (e) None of these

2—T—**Form: 12A—Ans:** c

48. A person buys a \$100,000 term life insurance policy. During the next five years the value of the policy will depreciate at the rate of 3% per year. (That is, at the end of each year, the depreciated value is 97% of what it was at the beginning of the year.) Find the depreciated value of the policy at the end of five full years.

(a) \$88,529.28   (b) \$85,873.40   (c) \$83,297.20

(d) \$85,000   (e) None of these

2—T—**Form: 12B—Ans:** b

49. Find the common ratio of the geometric sequence: $-4, 3, -\frac{9}{4}, \frac{27}{16}, -\frac{81}{64}, \ldots$.

1—**Ans:** $-\frac{3}{4}$

50. Determine whether the sequence $-2, \frac{4}{3}, -\frac{8}{9}, \frac{16}{27}, \ldots$ is geometric. If it is, find its common ratio.

1—**Form: 12C—Ans:** Yes, $r = -\frac{2}{3}$.

51. Find the 20th term of the geometric sequence with $a_1 = 5$ and $r = 1.1$.

(a) 1.1665 (b) 37.0012 (c) 33.6375 (d) 30.5795 (e) None of these

2—**Form: 12A—Ans:** d

52. Find the 23rd term of the geometric sequence with $a_1 = -23$ and $r = \sqrt{2}$.

(a) $-47,104\sqrt{2}$ (b) $-2048\sqrt{2}$ (c) -2048

(d) $-47,104$ (e) None of these

2—**Form: 12B—Ans:** d

53. Use a calculator to find the sum $\sum_{n=0}^{10} 2\left(\frac{3}{5}\right)^n$. Round your answer to four decimal places.

   (a) 4.9690   **(b)** 5.0000   **(c)** 4.9819   **(d)** 55.0000   **(e)** None of these

   2—T—Form: 12A—Ans: c

54. Use a calculator to find the sum $\sum_{j=0}^{40} 3(1.05)^j$. Round your answer to two decimal places.

   (a) 383.52   **(b)** 362.40   **(c)** 984   **(d)** 22.18   **(e)** None of these

   2—T—Form: 12B—Ans: a

55. Find a formula for the *n*th term of the geometric sequence with first term $a_1 = 5$ and common ratio $r = \frac{2}{3}$. (Begin with $n = 1$.)

   1—Form: 12C—Ans: $5\left(\frac{2}{3}\right)^{n-1}$

56. Find the first five terms of the geometric sequence with $a_1 = 3$ and $r = \frac{3}{2}$.

   1—T—Form: 12C—Ans: $3, \frac{3}{2}, \frac{27}{4}, \frac{81}{8}, \frac{243}{16}$

57. Find the sum $\sum_{n=0}^{\infty} \left(-\frac{1}{2}\right)^n$.

   (a) $-\frac{1}{3}$ **(b)** 2   **(c)** $\frac{2}{3}$ **(d)** 1   **(e)** $-\frac{1}{4}$

   1—Ans: c

58. Find the sum $\sum_{n=0}^{\infty} \left(\frac{3}{4}\right)^n$.

   (a) 4   **(b)** 3   **(c)** $\frac{3}{7}$ **(d)** 1   **(e)** $\frac{4}{3}$

   1—Ans: a

59. Find the sum $\sum_{n=0}^{\infty} 5\left(-\frac{2}{3}\right)^n$.

   (a) -2 **(b)** $\frac{3}{5}$ **(c)** 3   **(d)** $\frac{10}{3}$ **(e)** $-\frac{10}{3}$

   2—Form: 12A—Ans: c

60. Find the sum $\sum_{n=0}^{\infty} 3\left(-\frac{3}{4}\right)^n$.

   (a) $\frac{4}{7}$ **(b)** $-\frac{3}{7}$ **(c)** $-\frac{9}{7}$ **(d)** 12   **(e)** $\frac{12}{7}$

   2—Form: 12B—Ans: e

61. Find the sum $\sum_{n=0}^{\infty} 2\left(-\frac{2}{5}\right)^n$.

   2—Form: 12C—Ans: $\frac{10}{5}$

62. Find the sum $\sum_{n=0}^{\infty} 4\left(\frac{1}{6}\right)^n$.

2—Ans: $\frac{24}{5}$

Section 12.4 The Binomial Theorem

1. Evaluate $_8C_3$.

   (a) 65   **(b)** 24   **(c)** 336   **(d)** 56   **(e)** None of these

   1—Ans: d

2. Evaluate $_{10}C_7$.

   (a) 70   **(b)** 210   **(c)** 120   **(d)** 45   **(e)** None of these

   1—Ans: c

3. Evaluate $_{15}C_{12}$.

   (a) 180   **(b)** 455   **(c)** 1365   **(d)** 105   **(e)** None of these

   1—Ans: b

4. Evaluate $_9C_5$.

   (a) 126   **(b)** 84   **(c)** 45   **(d)** 36   **(e)** None of these

   1—Ans: a

5. Evaluate $_9C_3$.

   1—Ans: 84

6. Evaluate $_{11}C_3$.

   1—Ans: 165

7. Evaluate $_{20}C_{18}$.

   (a) 153   **(b)** 190   **(c)** 816   **(d)** 1140   **(e)** None of these

   1—Ans: b

8. Evaluate $_{18}C_{16}$.

   (a) 153   **(b)** 190   **(c)** 816   **(d)** 1140   **(e)** None of these

   1—Ans: a

9. Evaluate $_{15}C_{10}$.

   1—Ans: 3003

10. Evaluate $_{20}C_{14}$.

 1—Ans: 38,760

11. Evaluate $_{14}C_7$.

 1—Ans: 3432

12. Evaluate $_{13}C_6$.

 1—Ans: 1716

13. Choose the quantity equal to $_{13}C_5$.

 (a) $_{13}C_9$ **(b)** $_{13}C_8$ **(c)** $_{13}C_6$ **(d)** $_{13}C_7$ **(e)** None of these

 1—Ans: b

14. Choose the quantity equal to $_{13}C_6$.

 (a) $_{13}C_9$ **(b)** $_{13}C_8$ **(c)** $_{13}C_5$ **(d)** $_{13}C_7$ **(e)** None of these

 1—Ans: d

15. Choose the coefficient equal to $_{20}C_3$.

 1—Ans: $_{20}C_{17}$

16. Choose the coefficient equal to $_{19}C_8$.

 1—Ans: $_{19}C_{11}$

17. Which row of Pascal's Triangle is represented by 1, 5, 10, 10, 5, 1?

 (a) Fourth row   **(b)** Third row   **(c)** Fifth row   **(d)** Tenth row   **(e)** None of these

 1—Ans: c

18. Which row of Pascal's Triangle is represented by 1, 4, 6, 4, 1?

 (a) Fourth row   **(b)** Third row   **(c)** Fifth row   **(d)** Tenth row   **(e)** None of these

 1—Ans: a

19. Write the fourth row of Pascal's Triangle.

 1—Ans: 1, 4, 6, 4, 1

20. Write the seventh row of Pascal's Triangle.

 1—Ans: 1, 7, 21, 35, 35, 21, 7, 1

21. Find the coefficient of the term x^4y^2 if $(x + y)^6$ is expanded.

    (a) 35   **(b)** 20   **(c)** 10   **(d)** 15   **(e)** None of these

    2—Ans: d

22. Find the coefficient of the term x^3y^4 if $(x + y)^7$ is expanded.

    (a) 35   **(b)** 20   **(c)** 10   **(d)** 15   **(e)** None of these

    2—Ans: a

23. Write the expansion for $(x + y)^5$.

    2—Ans: $x^5 + 5x^4y + 10x^3y^2 + 10x^2y^3 + 5xy^4 + y^5$

24. Write the expansion for $(x + y)^6$.

    2—Ans: $x^6 + 6x^5y + 15x^4y^2 + 20x^3y^3 + 15x^2y^4 + 6xy^5 + y^6$

25. Write the expansion for $(x + y)^4$.

    2—Ans: $x^4 + 4x^3y + 6x^2y^2 + 4xy^3 + y^4$

26. Write the expansion for $(x + y)^7$.

    2—Ans: $x^7 + 7x^6y + 21x^5y^2 + 35x^4y^3 + 35x^3y^4 + 21x^2y^5 + 7xy^6 + y^7$

27. Find the coefficient of the term x^3y^{15} in expanding $(x + y)^{18}$.

    (a) 816   **(b)** 1140   **(c)** 1001   **(d)** 12,650   **(e)** None of these

    2—Ans: a

28. Find the coefficient of the term x^3y^{17} in expanding $(x + y)^{20}$.

    (a) 816   **(b)** 1140   **(c)** 1001   **(d)** 12,650   **(e)** None of these

    2—Ans: b

29. Find the coefficient of the term x^6y^{12} in expanding $(x + y)^{18}$.

    2—Ans: 18,564

30. Find the coefficient of the term $x^{14}y^6$ in expanding $(x + y)^{20}$.

    2—Ans: 38,760

31. Find the coefficient of the term x^8 in expanding $(x + 2)^{10}$.

    (a) 120   **(b)** 45   **(c)** 180   **(d)** 90   **(e)** None of these

    1—Ans: c

32. Find the coefficient of the term x^5 in expanding $(x + 2)^{10}$.

   (a) 252   **(b)** 3360   **(c)** 210   **(d)** 8064   **(e)** None of these

   1—Ans: d

33. Write the expansion for $(3x - 2y)^4$.

   2—Ans: $81x^4 - 216x^3y + 216x^2y^2 - 96xy^3 + 16y^4$

34. Write the expansion for $(2x - 3y)^4$.

   2—Ans: $16x^2 - 96x^3y + 216x^2y^2 - 216xy^3 + 81y^4$

35. Write the expansion for $(4x - y)^4$.

   2—Ans: $256x^4 - 256x^3y + 96x^2y^2 - 16xy^3 + y^4$

36. Write the expansion for $(4x + 3y)^4$.

   2—Ans: $256x^4 + 768x^3y + 864x^2y^2 + 432xy^3 + 81y^4$

37. Use the binomial expansion to approximate
   $(1.01)^{10} = 1 + 10(0.01) + 45(0.01)^2 + \cdots$ to three decimal places.

   (a) 1.146   **(b)** 1.101   **(c)** 1.105   **(d)** 1.015   **(e)** None of these

   2—T—Ans: c

38. Use the binomial expansion to approximate $(1.03)^8 = 1 + 8(0.03) + 28(0.03)^2 + \cdots$
   to three decimal places.

   (a) 1.027   **(b)** 1.667   **(c)** 1.167   **(d)** 1.267   **(e)** None of these

   2—T—Ans: d

39. Use the binomial expansion to approximate $(1.02)^9 = 1 + 9(0.02) + 36(0.02)^2 + \cdots$
   to three decimal places.

   2—T—Ans: 1.195

40. Use the binomial expansion to approximate
   $(0.98)^9 = (1 - 0.02)^9 = 1 - 9(0.02) + 36(0.02)^2 + \cdots$ to three decimal places.

   2—T—Ans: 0.834

41. Evaluate $_{10}C_7$.

   (a) 720   **(b)** $\frac{10}{7}$ **(c)** 60   **(d)** 120   **(e)** None of these

   1—Ans: d

42. Evaluate $_8C_4$.

(a) 1680   (b) 70   (c) $\frac{1}{12}$ (d) 24   (e) None of these

1—Ans: b

43. Use Pascal's Triangle to expand $(2a - b)^3$.

(a) $8a^3 - 4a^2b + 2ab^2 - b^3$ (b) $8a^3 + 12a^2b + 6ab^2 + b^3$ (c) $8a^3 - 12a^2b + 6ab^2 - b^3$

(d) $8a^3 - b^3$ (e) None of these

2—Ans: c

44. Use Pascal's Triangle to expand $(3x - y)^3$.

(a) $27x^3 - 9x^2y + 3xy^2 - y^3$ (b) $27x^3 + 27x^2y + 9xy^2 + y^3$ (c) $27x^3 - y^3$

(d) $27x^3 - 27x^2y + 9xy^2 - y^3$ (e) None of these

2—Ans: d

45. Use the Binomial Theorem to find the x^4 term in the expansion of $(x + 2y)^7$.

(a) $35x^4y^3$ (b) $8x^4y^3$ (c) $1680x^4y^3$

(d) $280x^4y^3$ (e) None of these

1—Form: 12A—Ans: d

46. Use the Binomial Theorem to find the x^4 term in the expansion of $(2x + y)^7$.

(a) $35x^4y^3$ (b) $560x^4y^3$ (c) $16x^4y^3$

(d) $280x^4y^3$ (e) None of these

1—Form: 12B—Ans: b

47. Find the coefficient of x^3y^5 in the expansion of $(3x + 2y)^8$.

2—Form: 12C—Ans: 48,384

48. Find the coefficient of x^2y^7 in the expansion of $(3x - 2y)^9$.

2—Ans: $-41,472$

49. Use Pascal's Triangle to evaluate the complex number $(2 - i)^4$.

(a) 17   (b) $-7 - 24i$ (c) $13 + 6i$ (d) 15   (e) None of these

2—Form: 12A—Ans: b

50. Use Pascal's Triangle to evaluate the complex number $(2 + i)^4$.

(a) $-7 - 24i$ (b) $7 - 24i$ (c) $13 + 6i$ (d) $-7 + 24i$ (e) 17

2—Form: 12B—Ans: d

51. Use Pascal's Triangle to evaluate the complex number $(3 - i)^3$.

   2—Form: 12C—Ans: $18 - 26i$

52. Use Pascal's Triangle to evaluate the complex number $(3 + 2i)^3$.

   2—Ans: $-9 + 26i$

53. Use a graphing utility to evaluate $_{25}C_{17}$.

   (a) 1,081,575   **(b)** 2,042,975   **(c)** 0   **(d)** 480,700   **(e)** 3.85×10^{20}

   1—T—Form: 12A—Ans: a

54. Use a graphing utility to evaluate $_{18}C_{12}$.

   (a) 8568   **(b)** 0   **(c)** 18,564   **(d)** 125,970   **(e)** 6.03×10^{13}

   1—T—Form: 12B—Ans: c

55. Use a graphing utility to evaluate $_{99}C_{45}$.

   1—T—Ans: 3.38×10^{28}

56. Use a graphing utility to evaluate $_{81}C_{59}$.

   1—T—Form: 12C—Ans: 3.72×10^{19}

Section 12.5   Counting Principles

1. A jar contains fifty marbles numbered from 1 through 50. One marble is to be drawn from the jar at random. In how many ways is it possible that the digit 5 will appear at least once on the marble selected?

   (a) 4   **(b)** 5   **(c)** 6   **(d)** 14   **(e)** None of these

   1—Ans: c

2. A jar contains fifty marbles numbered from 1 through 50. One marble is to be drawn from the jar at random. In how many ways is it possible that the digit 1 will appear at least once on the marble selected?

   (a) 4   **(b)** 5   **(c)** 6   **(d)** 14   **(e)** None of these

   1—Ans: d

3. A jar contains fifty marbles numbered from 1 through 50. One marble is to be drawn from the jar at random. In how many ways is it possible to obtain a marble whose number is divisible by 3?

   1—Ans: 16

4. A jar contains fifty marbles numbered from 1 through 50. One marble is to be drawn from the jar at random. In how many ways is it possible to obtain a marble whose number is divisible by 7?

1—Ans: 7

5. A jar contains fifty marbles numbered from 1 through 50. Two marbles are drawn from the jar without replacement. In how many ways could the sum of the numbers total 10?

(a) 9   **(b)** 10   **(c)** 4   **(d)** 5   **(e)** None of these

1—Ans: c

6. A jar contains fifty marbles numbered from 1 through 50. Two marbles are drawn from the jar without replacement. In how many ways could the sum of the numbers total 21?

(a) 9   **(b)** 10   **(c)** 4   **(d)** 5   **(e)** None of these

1—Ans: b

7. A jar contains fifty marbles numbered from 1 through 50. Two marbles are drawn from the jar without replacement. In how many ways could both numbers drawn be odd numbers?

1—Ans: 300

8. A jar contains fifty marbles numbered from 1 through 50. Two marbles are drawn from the jar without replacement. In how many ways could the sum of the numbers be less than or equal to 8? Assume the order of the draw is not important.

1—Ans: 12

9. A jar contains fifty marbles numbered 1 through 50. A marble is withdrawn from the jar, its number recorded, and it is returned to the jar. A second marble is then drawn from the jar and its number is recorded also. Without regard to the order in which the numbers are drawn, in how many different ways could the sum of the numbers total 20?

(a) 9   **(b)** 10   **(c)** 5   **(d)** 6   **(e)** None of these

1—Ans: b

10. A jar contains fifty marbles numbered 1 through 50. A marble is withdrawn from the jar, its number recorded, and it is returned to the jar. A second marble is then drawn from the jar and its number is recorded also. Without regard to the order in which the numbers are drawn, in how many different ways could the sum of the numbers total 19?

(a) 9   **(b)** 10   **(c)** 5   **(d)** 6   **(e)** None of these

1—Ans: a

11. A jar contains fifty marbles numbered 1 through 50. A marble is withdrawn from the jar, its number recorded, and it is returned to the jar. A second marble is then drawn from the jar and its number is recorded also. Assuming the order in which the numbers are drawn is not important, in how many different ways could the sum of the numbers be 50?

    1—Ans: 25

12. A jar contains fifty marbles numbered 1 through 50. A marble is withdrawn from the jar, its number recorded, and it is returned to the jar. A second marble is then drawn from the jar and its number is recorded also. Assuming the order in which the numbers are drawn is not important, in how many different ways could the sum of the numbers be an odd number?

    1—Ans: 625

13. How many combinations are possible from a wardrobe which can supply seven different sport coats and twelve distinctly different pairs of slacks?

    (a) 7^{12} **(b)** $7 + 12 = 19$ **(c)** $7 \cdot 12 = 84$

    (d) $12 - 7 = 5$ **(e)** None of these

    1—Ans: c

14. A restaurant offers a choice of three appetizers, two salads, five main courses, and three desserts. How many different dinners are possible?

    (a) 13   **(b)** 21   **(c)** 45   **(d)** 90   **(e)** None of these

    1—Ans: d

15. For a serial number, a three-letter code is followed by a four-digit number. Twelve alphabet letters are available but each can be used only once in each serial number. Zero is never used as the first digit in the four-digit sequence. How many different letter-number combinations are available?

    2—Ans: 11,880,000

16. A code consists of three letters, followed by three numerals, followed by another letter. The first three letters are chosen from A, B, C, D, E, F, G, H each of which may be used for any of the three leading letters. 0 through 9 may serve for each of the three numerals and the trailing letter must be A, B, or C. How many different codes are possible?

    2—Ans: 1,536,000

17. An identification tag contains two letters (each chosen from any of the 26 letters of the alphabet) and a three-digit number. How many different such tags are possible?

    2—Ans: 676,000

18. An identification tag contains three letters (each chosen from any of the 26 letters of the alphabet) and a three-digit number. How many different such tags are possible?

    2—Ans: 17,576,000

19. How many three-digit numbers can be formed if 0's and 1's are not used?

    (a) 810   **(b)** 270   **(c)** 720   **(d)** 512   **(e)** None of these

    2—Ans: d

20. How many three-digit numbers can be formed if adjacent digits are never the same numeral? (Example: 858 is accepted but 885 is not.)

    (a) 810   **(b)** 270   **(c)** 720   **(d)** 512   **(e)** None of these

    2—Ans: a

21. How many three-digit numbers can be formed with two (but not three) digits being the same numeral?

    (a) 810   **(b)** 270   **(c)** 720   **(d)** 512   **(e)** None of these

    2—Ans: b

22. How many three-digit numbers can be formed if all three digits are different?

    (a) 810   **(b)** 270   **(c)** 720   **(d)** 512   **(e)** None of these

    2—Ans: c

23. How many four-digit numbers can be formed using only odd digits?

    2—Ans: 625

24. How many four-digit numbers can be formed without using the digits 5 or 7?

    2—Ans: 4096

25. How many different ways can eight people be seated in a row of eight seats?

    (a) $\dfrac{7!}{2}$ **(b)** $2 \cdot 4!4!$ **(c)** $2 \cdot 3!3!$ **(d)** $8!$ **(e)** None of these

    1—Ans: d

26. In how many different ways can eight people be seated around a round table?

    (a) $\dfrac{7!}{2}$ **(b)** $2 \cdot 4!4!$ **(c)** $2 \cdot 3!3!$ **(d)** $8!$ **(e)** None of these

    1—Ans: a

27. In how many different ways can four men and four women be seated in a row of eight seats if the men and the women alternate in the seating?

    (a) $\dfrac{7!}{2}$ **(b)** $2 \cdot 4!4!$ **(c)** $2 \cdot 3!3!$ **(d)** $8!$ **(e)** None of these

    1—Ans: b

28. In how many different ways can four men and four women be seated in a row of eight seats if there is a "Couple of Honor" (one man and one woman) who occupy the center seats and the men and women are alternated in the overall seating?

(a) $\dfrac{7!}{2}$ (b) $2 \cdot 4!4!$ (c) $2 \cdot 3!3!$ (d) $8!$ (e) None of these

2—Ans: c

29. Twelve contestants are vying for three spots on the national Olympic team. How many possible outcomes are there?

1—Ans: 220

30. In how many different ways can a group of fourteen people be sub-divided into a group of nine people and a group of five people?

1—Ans: 2002 ways

31. In how many ways can a student select five essay questions to answer from a list of nine questions on a final exam?

(a) 24   (b) 126   (c) 210   (d) 252   (e) None of these

1—Ans: b

32. In how many ways can a student select four essay questions to answer from a list of ten questions on a final exam?

(a) 24   (b) 126   (c) 210   (d) 252   (e) None of these

1—Ans: c

33. Ten points are located in the coordinate plane so that no three are collinear. How many triangles can be formed by choosing their vertices from the ten points?

1—Ans: 120 triangles

34. Fifteen points are located in the coordinate plane so that no three are collinear. How many triangles can be formed by choosing their vertices from the fifteen points?

1—Ans: 455 triangles

35. There are seven people and four numbered seats. In how many different ways can people be assigned to fill the seats?

1—Ans: 840 ways

36. There are eight people and four numbered seats. In how many different ways can people be assigned to fill the seats?

1—Ans: 1680 ways

37. In how many ways can a three-card combination be drawn from a standard deck of 52 playing cards if all the cards drawn must be red?

    (a) 286   (b) 1144   (c) 2600   (d) 22,100   (e) None of these

    1—Ans: c

38. In how many ways can a three-card combination be drawn from a standard deck of 52 playing cards if all the cards drawn must belong to the same suit?

    (a) 286   (b) 1144   (c) 2600   (d) 22,100   (e) None of these

    1—Ans: b

39. In how many ways can a three-card combination be drawn from a standard deck of 52 playing cards if all the cards drawn cannot be face cards?

    1—Ans: 9880

40. In how many ways can a three-card combination be drawn from a standard deck of 52 playing cards if all the cards drawn must be hearts?

    1—Ans: 286

41. An auto license plate is made using two letters followed by three digits. Find the number of plates possible.

    (a) 676,000   (b) 468,000   (c) 492,804

    (d) 1,757,600   (e) None of these

    1—Form: 12A—Ans: a

42. Determine the number of possible five digit zip codes.

    (a) 120   (b) 90,000   (c) 3,628,800

    (d) 100,000   (e) None of these

    1—Form: 12B—Ans: d

43. Determine the number of three digit numbers that can be formed from the ten digits 0, 1, 2, 3, 4, 5, 6, 7, 8, 9 under the condition that the first digit be 8 or 4.

    (a) 1000   (b) 200   (c) 100   (d) 180   (e) None of these

    1—Ans: b

44. Determine the number of three digit character codes that can be formed from the letters of the alphabet under the condition that the first letter be b or d.

    (a) 17,576   (b) 16,224   (c) 1300   (d) 1352   (e) None of these

    1—Ans: d

45. A five character license plate is made using a letter followed by three digits and then another letter. How many license plates are possible?

   1—Ans: 676,000

46. A small college needs four additional faculty members: a mathematician, two chemists, and an engineer. In how many ways can these positions be filled if there are two applicants for mathematics, six applicants for chemistry, and three applicants for engineering?

   2—Ans: 90

47. A random number generator selects an integer from 1 to 20. Find the number of ways in which a number that is a multiple of three can be selected.

   (a) 6   **(b)** 720   **(c)** 5   **(d)** 120   **(e)** None of these

   1—Form: 12A—Ans: a

48. A random number generator selects two integers from 1 to 20. Find the number of ways that the sum of these two integers is 8.

   (a) 4   **(b)** 7   **(c)** 9   **(d)** 6   **(e)** None of these

   2—Form: 12B—Ans: b

49. An organization consisting of 54 members is going to elect four officers. No person may hold more than one office. How many different oucomes are possible?

   (a) 354,294   **(b)** 8,503,056   **(c)** 316,251   **(d)** 7,590,024   **(e)** None of these

   2—Form: 12A—Ans: d

50. A class of 9 students line up single file for lunch. How many different ways can this occur if the 6 boys in the class must line up first?

   (a) 18   **(b)** 60,480   **(c)** 4320   **(d)** 504   **(e)** None of these

   2—Form: 12B—Ans: c

51. How many ways can 4 girls be picked from a group of 30 girls?

   1—Form: 12C—Ans: 27,405

52. A group of 6 students are seated in a single row at a football game. In how many different orders can they be seated?

   1—Ans: 720

53. In how many ways can 5 people be seated in a row of 5 chairs?

   1—Ans: $5! = 120$

54. In how many ways can 7 people be seated in a row of 7 chairs?

   1—Form: 12C—Ans: $7! = 5040$

55. Use a graphing utility to evaluate $_{15}C_7$.

    1—T—Ans: 6435

56. Use a graphing utility to evaluate $_{24}C_{19}$.

    1—T—Form: 12C—Ans: 42,504

Section 12.6   Probability

1. One can play Game A or Game B and in either case win (W), lose (L), or draw (D). Determine the sample space.

    (a) {A, B, W, L, D}

    (b) {AW, AL, AD, BW, BL, BD}

    (c) {AB, WLD}

    (d) {AW, BL, D}

    (e) None of these

    1—Ans: b

2. One can play Game A, Game B or Game C and in each case win (W) or lose (L). Determine the sample space.

    (a) {AW, BW, CW, AL, BL, CL}

    (b) {A, B, C, W, L}

    (c) {ABC, WL}

    (d) {AW, BL, C}

    (e) None of these

    1—Ans: a

3. A restaurant special offers a choice of three sandwiches (#1, #2, and #3) and a choice of two beverages (H or C). Determine the sample space.

    (a) {#1, #2, #3, H, C}

    (b) {#1H, #2C, #3}

    (c) {#123, HC}

    (d) {#1H, #2H, #3H, #1C, #2C, #3C}

    (e) None of these

    1—Ans: d

4. A restaurant special offers a choice of two sandwiches (#1 or #2) and a choice of two beverages (H or C). Determine the sample space.

    (a) {#1, #2, H, C}

    (b) {#1H, #2C}

    (c) {#1H, #1C, #2H, #2C}

    (d) {#12, HC}

    (e) None of these

    1—Ans: c

5. One can play Game A, Game B, or Game C and in each event can win (W), lose (L), or draw (D). Determine the sample space of possible events.

    1—Ans: AW, AL, AD, BW, BL, BD, CW, CL, CD

6. A single six-sided die and a coin are tossed together. Determine the sample space of events for possible outcomes.

    1—Ans: 1H, 2H, 3H, 4H, 5H, 6H, 1T, 2T, 3T, 4T, 5T, 6T

7. A coin is tossed three times. Find the probability of getting two heads and one tail.

    (a) $\frac{1}{8}$ **(b)** $\frac{1}{2}$ **(c)** $\frac{3}{8}$ **(d)** $\frac{1}{4}$ **(e)** None of these

    1—Ans: c

8. A coin is tossed three times. Find the probability of getting one head and two tails.

    (a) $\frac{1}{2}$ **(b)** $\frac{3}{8}$ **(c)** $\frac{1}{4}$ **(d)** $\frac{1}{8}$ **(e)** None of these

    1—Ans: b

9. Four coins are tossed. Find the probability that no heads will occur.

    1—Ans: $\frac{1}{16}$

10. Four coins are tossed. Find the probability that one head and three tails is the event obtained.

    1—Ans: $\frac{1}{4}$

11. A pair of six-sided dice is tossed. Find the probability of getting a total of eight.

    (a) $\frac{7}{36}$ **(b)** $\frac{5}{36}$ **(c)** $\frac{1}{6}$ **(d)** $\frac{1}{9}$ **(e)** None of these

    1—Ans: b

12. A pair of six-sided dice is tossed. Find the probability of getting a total of five.

    (a) $\frac{7}{36}$ **(b)** $\frac{5}{36}$ **(c)** $\frac{1}{6}$ **(d)** $\frac{1}{9}$ **(e)** None of these

    1—Ans: d

13. Find the probability of getting a nine when a pair of six-sided dice is tossed.

    1—Ans: $\frac{1}{9}$

14. Find the probability of getting a ten when a pair of six-sided dice is tossed.

    1—Ans: $\frac{1}{12}$

15. A card is drawn from a standard deck of playing cards. Find the probability of getting a card numbered from five to ten.

    (a) $\frac{2}{13}$ **(b)** $\frac{3}{26}$ **(c)** $\frac{3}{13}$ **(d)** $\frac{6}{13}$ **(e)** None of these

    1—Ans: d

16. A card is drawn from a standard deck of playing cards. Find the probability of getting a 2, 3, or 4.

    (a) $\frac{2}{13}$ (b) $\frac{3}{26}$ (c) $\frac{3}{13}$ (d) $\frac{6}{13}$ (e) None of these

    1—Ans: c

17. A card is drawn from a standard deck of playing cards. Find the probability that the card is an ace or a heart.

    2—Ans: $\frac{4}{13}$

18. A card is drawn from a standard deck of playing cards. Find the probability that the card is neither a face card nor an ace.

    2—Ans: $\frac{9}{13}$

19. A number from 000 to 999 is chosen at random. Find the probability that none of its three digits are 0 or 1.

    (a) 0.810   (b) 0.270   (c) 0.720   (d) 0.512   (e) None of these

    2—Ans: d

20. A number from 000 to 999 is chosen at random. Find the probability that the three digits are all different numerals.

    (a) 0.810   (b) 0.270   (c) 0.720   (d) 0.512   (e) None of these

    2—Ans: c

21. A number from 0000 to 9999 is chosen at random. Find the probability that it is formed entirely of odd digits.

    2—Ans: 0.0625

22. A number from 0000 to 9999 is chosen at random. Find the probability that the adjacent digits are never the same numeral. (Example: 8616 is accepted but 8661 is not.)

    2—Ans: 0.729

23. Jim, Mary, and six other people are seated by random selection around a round table. Find the probability that Jim and Mary will occupy adjacent seats.

    (a) $\frac{1}{4}$ (b) $\frac{6}{7}$ (c) $\frac{2}{7}$ (d) $\frac{1}{28}$ (e) None of these

    2—Ans: c

24. Jim, Mary, and six other people are seated by random selection around a round table. Find the probability that Jim and Mary are not seated across from each other.

    (a) $\frac{1}{4}$ (b) $\frac{6}{7}$ (c) $\frac{2}{7}$ (d) $\frac{1}{28}$ (e) None of these

    2—Ans: b

25. In a "Race of Champions" there are twelve nearly identical racing cars and twelve invited champions of motor racing. Find the probability that a given driver will finish no worse than third.

    2—Ans: $\frac{1}{4}$

26. In a hundred yard dash there are seven entrants of nearly equal ability. Find the probability that a given runner will finish first or second in two successive races.

    2—Ans: $\frac{4}{49}$

27. In a group of fifteen high school seniors, eight have expressed an interest in attending college. If two are selected at random, find the probability that both are in the college aspiring group.

    2—Ans: $\frac{4}{15}$

28. In a group of fifteen high school seniors, eight have expressed an interest in attending college. If two are selected at random, find the probability that one is interested in college and the other is not.

    2—Ans: $\frac{8}{15}$

29. A student is well prepared in five of nine possible topics to be covered on a final exam. The test asks essay questions on four of the nine topics. Find the probability that the student is prepared for all four questions.

    (a) $\frac{1}{126}$ **(b)** $\frac{20}{63}$ **(c)** $\frac{5}{126}$ **(d)** $\frac{10}{63}$ **(e)** None of these

    2—Ans: c

30. A student is well prepared in five of nine possible topics to be covered on a final exam. The test asks essay questions on four of the nine topics. Find the probability that the student is not well prepared for any of the questions.

    (a) $\frac{1}{126}$ **(b)** $\frac{20}{63}$ **(c)** $\frac{5}{126}$ **(d)** $\frac{10}{63}$ **(e)** None of these

    2—Ans: a

31. A student takes a multiple choice test in which there are six choices for each question. Find the probability that the question is answered correctly if the student can eliminate two of the choices and guesses from the remaining choices.

    1—Ans: $\frac{1}{4}$

32. A student takes a multiple choice test in which there are six choices for each question. Find the probability that the question is answered correctly if the student can eliminate three of the choices and guesses from the remaining choices.

    1—Ans: $\frac{1}{3}$

33. A person is to be transferred to one of three possible locations. The probability that it will be location A is 0.27. The probability that it will be location B is 0.32. Find the probability that it will be location C.

1—Ans: 0.41

34. A person is to be transferred to one of three possible locations. The probability that it will be location A is 0.15. The probability that it will be location B is 0.39. Find the probability that it will be location C.

1—Ans: 0.46

35. A standard deck of playing cards has 52 different cards. If three cards are drawn from the deck, find the probability that exactly one ace is included among the three cards.

   (a) 0.783   **(b)** 0.118   **(c)** 0.013   **(d)** 0.204   **(e)** None of these

1—T—Ans: d

36. A standard deck of playing cards has 52 different cards. If three cards are drawn from the deck, find the probability that exactly two aces are included among the three cards.

   (a) 0.783   **(b)** 0.118   **(c)** 0.013   **(d)** 0.204   **(e)** None of these

1—T—Ans: c

37. A standard deck of playing cards has 52 different cards. If three cards are drawn from the deck, find the probability that exactly no aces are included among the three cards.

   (a) 0.783   **(b)** 0.118   **(c)** 0.013   **(d)** 0.204   **(e)** None of these

1—T—Ans: a

38. A standard deck of playing cards has 52 different cards. If three cards are drawn from the deck, find the probability that all three cards are red cards.

   (a) 0.783   **(b)** 0.118   **(c)** 0.013   **(d)** 0.204   **(e)** None of these

1—T—Ans: b

39. A standard deck of playing cards has 52 different cards. If three cards are drawn from the deck, find the probability that all three cards belong to the same suit. (Round your answer to three decimal places.)

2—T—Ans: 0.052

40. A standard deck of playing cards has 52 different cards. If three cards are drawn from the deck, find the probability that all three cards are from three different suits. (Round your answer to two decimal places.)

2—T—Ans: 0.40

41. Find the probability of choosing an E when selecting a letter at random from those in the word COLLEGE.

   (a) $\frac{2}{7}$ **(b)** $\frac{1}{5}$ **(c)** $\frac{2}{5}$ **(d)** $\frac{1}{7}$ **(e)** None of these

   1—Form: 12A—Ans: a

42. Find the probability of choosing an A, B, or N when selecting a letter at random from those in the word BANANA.

   (a) $\frac{1}{26}$ **(b)** 0   **(c)** 1   **(d)** $\frac{3}{7}$ **(e)** None of these

   1—Form: 12B—Ans: c

43. A multiple choice test question has five possible choices. Find the probability of randomly selecting the correct answer.

   (a) $\frac{1}{4}$ **(b)** $\frac{1}{2}$ **(c)** $\frac{1}{5}$ **(d)** $\frac{4}{5}$ **(e)** None of these

   1—Ans: c

44. A multiple choice test question has four possible choices. Find the probability of randomly selecting the correct answer.

   (a) $\frac{1}{4}$ **(b)** $\frac{1}{3}$ **(c)** $\frac{3}{4}$ **(d)** $\frac{1}{2}$ **(e)** None of these

   1—Ans: a

45. A card is drawn at random from a standard deck of playing cards. Find the probability that it is not an ace.

   (a) $\frac{1}{13}$ **(b)** $\frac{4}{52}$ **(c)** $\frac{3}{4}$ **(d)** $\frac{12}{13}$ **(e)** None of these

   1—Ans: d

46. A card is drawn at random from a standard deck of playing cards. Find the probability that it is not a spade.

   (a) $\frac{1}{4}$ **(b)** $\frac{12}{13}$ **(c)** $\frac{3}{4}$ **(d)** $\frac{1}{13}$ **(e)** None of these

   1—Ans: c

47. In a group of ten children, three have blond hair and seven have brown hair. If a child is chosen at random, what is the probability that child will have brown hair?

   1—Ans: $\frac{7}{10}$

48. In an experiment in which 2 six-sided dice are tossed, what is the probability of not getting a sum of 10?

   2—Form: 12C—Ans: $\frac{11}{12}$

49. Each of 20 questions on a multiple choice test has five possible choices. If a student randomly selected his answer for each of the 20 questions, what is the probability that he will get the test completely correct?

2—Ans: $\frac{1}{5^{20}}$

50. A die is tossed 3 times. What is the probability that a 2 will come up all three times?

2—Form: 12C—Ans: $\frac{1}{216}$

51. If the probability of getting a rotten apple in a basket of apples if 12%, what is the probability of getting 3 good apples choosing from each of three different baskets? Round your answer to four decimal places.

(a) 0.9983   (b) 0.0017   (c) 0.8800   (d) 0.6815   (e) None of these

2—T—Form: 12A—Ans: d

52. Two integers from 0 to 9 inclusive are chosen by a random number generator. What is the probability of choosing the number 2 both times?

(a) $\frac{1}{10}$ (b) $\frac{1}{100}$ (c) $\frac{1}{50}$ (d) $\frac{4}{5}$ (e) None of these

2—Form: 12B—Ans: b

53. If the probability that an event will occur is $\frac{6}{11}$, find the probability that the event will not occur.

(a) 0   (b) 1   (c) $\frac{6}{11}$ (d) $\frac{5}{11}$ (e) 5

1—Form: 12A—Ans: d

54. If the probability that an event will occur is 0.47, find the probability that the event will not occur.

(a) 0.63   (b) 1   (c) 0   (d) 0.47   (e) 0.53

1—Form: 12B—Ans: e

55. If the probability that an event will occur is $\frac{13}{17}$, find the probability that the event will not occur.

1—Form: 12C—Ans: $\frac{4}{17}$

56. If the probability that an event will occur is $\frac{1}{7}$, find the probability that the event will not occur.

1—Ans: $\frac{6}{7}$

Test Form A

Chapter 1

Name _____ Date _____

Class _____ Section _____

1. Determine which numbers in the following set are rational numbers: $\left\{-2, -\frac{1}{2}, 0, 1, 3\right\}$.

   (a) $\left\{-\frac{1}{2}\right\}$

   (b) $\left\{-2, -\frac{1}{2}, 1, 3\right\}$

   (c) $\left\{-2, -\frac{1}{2}, 0, 1, 3\right\}$

   (c) $\{1, 3\}$

   (e) None of these

2. Which of the following statements is *true*?

   (a) $-2.3 > 2.1$

   (b) $2.3 < 2.1$

   (c) $2.1 > 2.3$

   (d) $-2.3 < -2.1$

   (e) None of these

3. Which of the following statements is *true*?

   (a) $-\frac{3}{2} > -\frac{1}{2}$

   (b) $-\frac{1}{2} > \frac{1}{3}$

   (c) $\frac{1}{2} < -\frac{3}{2}$

   (d) $\frac{1}{2} > \frac{1}{3}$

   (e) None of these

4. Which of the following statements is *true*?

   (a) The sum of 8 and -3 is 11.

   (b) The sum of 8 and -3 is -11.

   (c) The sum of 8 and -3 is 5.

   (d) The sum of 8 and -3 is -5.

   (e) None of these

5. Which of the following statements is *false*?

   (a) $7(-2) = -14$

   (b) $(-9)5 = -45$

   (c) $3(-4) = -12$

   (d) $8(-6) = 48$

   (e) None of these

6. Which of the following statements is *true*?

   (a) $(-7)(-8) = 56$

   (b) $(-4)5 = 20$

   (c) $(-7)(-8) = -56$

   (d) $(-4)(-5) = -20$

   (e) None of these

7. Which of the following statements is *true*?

   (a) $-144 \div -12 = -12$

   (b) $-144 \div -8 = 18$

   (c) $-144 \div 12 = 12$

   (d) $-144 \div 8 = 18$

   (e) None of these

8. Which of the following statements is *true*?

   (a) $\left|-\frac{32}{4}\right| = 8$

   (b) $\left|-\frac{32}{4}\right| = -2$

   (c) $\left|-\frac{32}{4}\right| = -8$

   (d) $\left|-\frac{32}{8}\right| = -4$

   (e) None of these

9. Which of the following statements is *true*?

   (a) The least common multiple of 15 and 6 is 60.   (b) The least common multiple of 16 and 6 is 24.

   (c) The least common multiple of 15 and 6 is 30.   (d) The least common multiple of 16 and 6 is 96.

   (e) None of these

10. Which of the following fractions is in simplest form?

   (a) $\frac{5}{10}$ (b) $\frac{5}{7}$ (c) $\frac{5}{15}$ (d) $\frac{5}{20}$ (e) $\frac{5}{25}$

11. Which of the following statements is *true*?

   (a) $\frac{1}{2} + \left(-\frac{1}{3}\right) = -\frac{1}{6}$ (b) $\frac{1}{2} + \left(-\frac{1}{3}\right) = \frac{0}{5}$ (c) $\frac{1}{2} + \left(-\frac{1}{3}\right) = \frac{1}{6}$

   (d) $\frac{1}{2} + \left(-\frac{1}{3}\right) = \frac{0}{6}$ (e) None of these

12. Which of the following statements is *true*?

   (a) $2\frac{1}{6} \div 1\frac{3}{4} = \frac{24}{91}$ (b) $2\frac{1}{6} \div 1\frac{3}{4} = \frac{21}{26}$ (c) $2\frac{1}{6} \div 1\frac{3}{4} = \frac{91}{24}$

   (d) $2\frac{1}{6} \div 1\frac{3}{4} = \frac{26}{21}$ (e) None of these

13. Which of the following statements is *false*?

   (a) $(-2)^4 = 16$ (b) $-2^4 = 16$ (c) $(-2)^3 = -8$

   (d) $(-2)^5 = -32$ (e) None of these

14. Evaluate the expression: $96 \div 4 \div 4 \cdot 2$.

   (a) 48   (b) 12   (c) 192   (d) 3   (e) None of these

15. Choose the *property* of real numbers that justifies the statement
    $(-6 \cdot 5)4 = -6(5 \cdot 4)$.

   (a) Distributive Property   (b) Commutative Property of Multiplication

   (c) Associative Property of Multiplication   (d) Multiplicative Identity Property

   (e) Multiplicative Inverse Property

16. Choose the *property* of real numbers that justifies the statement
    $(3x + 8) + (-3x - 8) = 0$.

   (a) Additive Inverse Property   (b) Additive Identity Property

   (c) Multiplicative Inverse Property   (d) Multiplicative Identity Property

   (e) Distributive Property

Test Form B

Chapter 1

Name _____   Date _____

Class _____   Section _____

1. Determine which numbers in the following set are whole numbers:
   $\left\{-2, -\frac{1}{2}, 0, 1, 3\right\}$.

   (a) $\left\{-\frac{1}{2}\right\}$ **(b)** $\left\{-2, -\frac{1}{2}, 1, 3\right\}$ **(c)** $\left\{-2, -\frac{1}{2}, 0, 1, 3\right\}$

   (d) $\{0, 1, 3\}$ **(e)** None of these

2. Which of the following statements is *false*?

   (a) $-2 < -4$ **(b)** $3 > -1$ **(c)** $-2 < 3$

   (d) $-1 > -3$ **(e)** None of these

3. Which of the following statements is *true*?

   (a) $-3.4 < -3.2$ **(b)** $3.4 < 3.2$ **(c)** $3.2 > 3.4$

   (d) $-3.4 > 3.2$ **(e)** None of these

4. Which of the following statements is *true*?

   (a) $\frac{1}{3} < \frac{1}{2}$ **(b)** $-\frac{3}{2} > \frac{1}{2}$ **(c)** $-\frac{1}{2} > \frac{1}{2}$

   (d) $-\frac{1}{2} < -\frac{3}{2}$ **(e)** None of these

5. Which of the following statements is *false*?

   (a) $-36 + 12 = -24$ **(b)** $-14 + 6 = 8$ **(c)** $-12 + (-6) = -18$

   (d) $43 + (-21) = 22$ **(e)** None of these

6. Which of the following statements is *false*?

   (a) $5(-7) = -35$ **(b)** $(-10)3 = -30$ **(c)** $4(-8) = 32$

   (d) $(-4)(6) = -24$ **(e)** None of these

7. Which of the following statements is *true*?

   (a) $(-2)(5) = 10$ **(b)** $(-9)(-6) = 54$ **(c)** $(-2)(-5) = -10$

   (d) $(-9)(-6) = -54$ **(e)** None of these

8. Determine which operation is undefined and state why.

   (a) $\dfrac{0}{10}$ **(b)** $0 \div 8$ **(c)** 0×8 **(d)** $\dfrac{-7}{-5}$ **(e)** $7 \div 0$

9. Which of the following fractions is in simplest form?

   (a) $\frac{6}{9}$ **(b)** $\frac{6}{10}$ **(c)** $\frac{6}{11}$ **(d)** $\frac{6}{12}$ **(e)** $\frac{6}{15}$

10. Which of the following statements is *true*?

(a) $-2\frac{1}{3} - 4\frac{1}{4} = -6\frac{2}{7}$

(b) $-2\frac{1}{3} - 4\frac{1}{4} = -6\frac{7}{12}$

(c) $-2\frac{1}{3} - 4\frac{1}{4} = \frac{24}{12}$

(d) $-2\frac{1}{3} - 4\frac{1}{4} = -\frac{24}{12}$

(e) None of these

11. Which of the following statements is *true*?

(a) $\left(-\frac{4}{5}\right)\left(-\frac{5}{8}\right) = -\frac{9}{13}$

(b) $\left(-\frac{4}{5}\right)\left(-\frac{5}{8}\right) = \frac{1}{2}$

(c) $\left(-\frac{4}{5}\right)\left(-\frac{5}{8}\right) = \frac{20}{13}$

(d) $\left(-\frac{4}{5}\right)\left(-\frac{5}{8}\right) = -\frac{9}{40}$

(e) None of these

12. Which of the following statements is *true*?

(a) $\frac{7}{12} \div \frac{2}{3} = \frac{8}{7}$

(b) $\frac{7}{12} \div \frac{2}{3} = \frac{14}{36}$

(c) $\frac{7}{12} \div \frac{2}{3} = \frac{7}{8}$

(d) $\frac{7}{12} \div \frac{2}{3} = \frac{36}{14}$

(e) None of these

13. Which of the following statements is *true*?

(a) $-(-6)^2 = -36$

(b) $-(-6)^2 = 36$

(c) $-(-6)^2 = 12$

(d) $-(-6)^2 = -12$

(e) None of these

14. Which of the following statements is *true*?

(a) $5^2 \cdot 4^3 = 10 \cdot 12$

(b) $5^2 \cdot 4^3 = 20^5$

(c) $5^2 \cdot 4^3 = 100^3$

(d) $5^2 \cdot 4^3 = 25 \cdot 64$

(e) None of these

15. Evaluate the expression: $128 \div 4 \div 4 \cdot 2$.

(a) 256

(b) 4

(c) 64

(d) 16

(e) None of these

16. Choose the *property* of real numbers that justifies the statement
$\frac{1}{3a} + 0 = \frac{1}{3a}(3a \neq 0)$.

(a) Additive Inverse Property

(b) Additive Identity Property

(c) Multiplicative Inverse Property

(d) Multiplicative Identity Property

(e) Distributive Property

Test Form C
Chapter 1

Name _____ Date _____

Class _____ Section _____

1. Identify the real number that corresponds to the point plotted on the number line.

   $$\xleftarrow{\hspace{0.3cm}}\underset{-3}{+}\;\underset{-2}{+}\;\underset{-1}{\bullet}\;\underset{0}{+}\;\underset{1}{+}\;\underset{2}{+}\;\underset{3}{+}\xrightarrow{\hspace{0.3cm}} x$$

2. Place the correct inequality symbol ($<$ or $>$) between the two numbers.

   $-0.68 \rule{0.8cm}{0.25cm} -0.86$

3. Find the sum: $(-3) + (-2) + (-4)$.

4. Find the difference: $76 - (-52)$.

5. Find the product: $7(-2)(-3)$.

6. Evaluate the expression: $\dfrac{10(-24)}{-16}$.

7. Find the prime factorization of 48.

8. Find the greatest common factor of 24 and 36.

9. Find the least common multiple of 12 and 21.

10. Write the fraction $\frac{30}{64}$ in simplest form.

11. Evaluate the expression $\frac{3}{8} - \frac{1}{12} - \frac{5}{6}$. Write the result in simplest form.

12. Evaluate the expression $\left(2\frac{3}{8}\right)\left(\frac{4}{9}\right)$. Write the result in simplest form.

13. Rewrite in exponential form: $3 \cdot 3 \cdot 3 \cdot 3 \cdot 3$.

14. Evaluate: $24 - [2(3 - 8) + 2^3]$.

15. Use a calculator to evaluate $200\left(1 + \frac{0.05}{12}\right)^{24}$. Round the result to two decimal places.

16. Use the Commutative Property of Multiplication to rewrite: $(-15 + x)4$.

Test Form A

Chapter 2

Name _____   Date _____

Class _____   Section _____

1. Identify the coefficient of the term $-7x$.

   (a) 7   **(b)** -7 **(c)** $7x$ **(d)** $-7x$ **(e)** x

2. Evaluate $-xy + x^2$ when $x = -1$ and $y = 2$.

   (a) -1 **(b)** 3   **(c)** 1   **(d)** -4 **(e)** None of these

3. Evaluate $-a^2 + a$ when $a = -2$.

   (a) 6   **(b)** -2 **(c)** 2   **(d)** -6 **(e)** None of these

4. Which of the following statements is *false*?

   (a) $(a + 3)^4 = (a + 3)(a + 3)(a + 3)(a + 3)$ **(b)** $(a + 3)^4 = a^4 + 3^4$

   (c) $(a + 3)^4 = (a + 3)^2(a + 3)^2$ **(d)** $(a + 3)^4 = (a + 3)(a + 3)^3$

   (e) $(a + 3)^4 = (a + 3)^3(a + 3)$

5. Simplify $(-8a^3)(-3a^2)$.

   (a) $-16a^5$ **(b)** $16a^6$ **(c)** $16a^5$ **(d)** $-16a^6$ **(e)** None of these

6. Simplify $[(x + 1)^3]^2$.

   (a) $[(x^3 + 1)]^2$ **(b)** $(x + 1)^5$ **(c)** $(x + 1)^6$

   (d) $(x + 1)^9$ **(e)** None of these

7. Identify the rule of algebra which justifies the statement $14\left(\frac{1}{14}\right) = 1$.

   (a) Additive Identity Property   **(b)** Multiplicative Identity Property

   (c) Additive Inverse Property   **(d)** Multiplicative Inverse Property

   (e) Distributive Property

8. Which of the following pairs of terms are *like* terms?

   (a) $4xy$ and $5x^2y$ **(b)** $9x^2$ and $7x^2$ **(c)** $2x^2y$ and $4xy^2$

   (d) $3x^3$ and $4y^3$ **(e)** None of these

9. Which of the following statements is *true*?

   (a) $4x(x + 3) = 4x^2 + 3$ **(b)** $-(x^3 + 2) = -x^3 + 2$

   (c) $-4(x^3 + 6) = -4x^3 + 24$ **(d)** $-4(x^3 + 6) = -4x^3 - 24$

   (e) None of these

10. Simplify $4x - 3[x + 2(x - 1)]$.

(a) $-5x + 3$ (b) $-5x - 2$ (c) $-5x - 6$

(d) $-5x + 6$ (e) None of these

11. Let x represent a number. A variable expression in x representing 4 added to the product of 3 and x, all divided by 7 is given by:

(a) $\frac{3}{7}x + 4$ (b) $\frac{3x + 4}{7}$ (c) $3x + \frac{4}{7}$

(d) $\frac{3(x + 4)}{7}$ (e) None of these

12. Choose the appropriate verbal description of the following: $5x - 4$.

(a) Five times x, subtracted from four. (b) Four subtracted from x, multiplied by five.

(c) Four subtracted from the product of x and five. (d) Four subtracted from five, multiplied by x.

(e) None of these

13. Determine whether the value of x is a solution to the equation $x^2 - 2x = x + 4$.

(a) $x = 0$ (b) $x = 1$ (c) $x = 4$

(d) $x = -2$ (e) $x = -4$

14. (-1) is a solution of:

(a) $-x^2 = x$ (b) $(-x)^2 = x$ (c) $x = x^2$

(d) $(-x)^2 - x = 0$ (e) None of these

15. Describe the step used in transforming the given equation into the equivalent equation.

$\frac{3}{4}x + 1 = \frac{3}{2}x - 2$ into $3x + 4 = 6x - 8$

(a) Reduce fractions on one or both sides of the equation.

(b) Multiply both sides of the equation by the same nonzero quantity.

(c) Divide both sides of the equation by the same nonzero quantity.

(d) Combine like terms.

(e) Subtract the same quantity from both sides of the equation.

16. Match the verbal statement with the correct equation.

Three times the sum of a number and 5 is 75.

(a) $3(x + 5) = 75$ (b) $x + 5 = 3(75)$ (c) $x + 5(3) = 75$

(d) $3x + 5 = 75$ (e) None of these

Test Form B

Chapter 2

Name _____ Date _____

Class _____ Section _____

1. Identify the coefficient of the term $3y^2$.

  (a) y **(b)** $3y^2$ **(c)** 3 **(d)** y^2 **(e)** 2

2. Evaluate $x^2 - xy$ when $x = -2$ and $y = 1$.

  (a) 2 **(b)** -6 **(c)** 6 **(d)** -2 **(e)** None of these

3. Evaluate $a - a^2$ when $a = -3$.

  (a) -12 **(b)** 6 **(c)** -6 **(d)** 12 **(e)** None of these

4. Which of the following statements is *false*?

  (a) $(b + 3)^4 = (b + 3)(b + 3)(b + 3)(b + 3)$ **(b)** $(b + 3)^4 = (b + 3)^3(b + 3)$

  (c) $(b + 3)^4 = (b + 3)^2(b + 3)^2$ **(d)** $(b + 3)^4 = (b + 3)(b + 3)^3$

  (e) $(b + 3)^4 = b^4 + 3^4$

5. Simplify $[(y + 2)^2]^3$.

  (a) $(y + 2)^8$ **(b)** $(y^2 + 4)^3$ **(c)** $(y + 2)^5$

  (d) $(y + 2)^6$ **(e)** None of these

6. Identify the rule of algebra which justifies the statement $(12x^2 - y) - (12x^2 - y) = 0$.

  (a) Additive Identity Property   **(b)** Multiplicative Identity Property

  (c) Additive Inverse Property   **(d)** Multiplicative Inverse Property

  (e) Distributive Property

7. Which of the following pairs of terms are *like* terms?

  (a) $14xy$ and $15x^2y$ **(b)** $2x^2y$ and $4xy^2$ **(c)** $5x^2$ and $7x^2$

  (d) $-3x^3$ and $4y^3$ **(e)** None of these

8. Which of the following statements is *true*?

  (a) $5a(a + 3) = 5a^2 + 15a$ **(b)** $5a(a - 3) = 5a - 15a$

  (c) $5a(a + 3) = 5a^2 + 15$ **(d)** $5a(a - 3) = 5a^2 - 15$

  (e) None of these

9. Simplify $2x(4y + 3) - 4(2 - xy)$.

  (a) $7xy - 5$ **(b)** $4xy + 6x - 8$ **(c)** $9xy - 5$

  (d) $12xy + 6x - 8$ **(e)** None of these

10. Simplify $2x^2y(-3xy^2)^2$.

    (a) $-18x^4y^5$ **(b)** $18x^4y^4$ **(c)** $-18x^4y^4$

    (d) $18x^4y^5$ **(e)** None of these

11. Let x and y represent numbers. Translate the following statement into a variable expression involving x and y.

    y is subtracted from 7 and the result multiplied by x.

    (a) $x(7 - y)$ **(b)** $7x - y$ **(c)** $x(y - 7)$

    (d) $xy - 7$ **(e)** None of these

12. Choose the appropriate verbal description of the following: $(5 - 4)x$.

    (a) Five times x, subtracted from four.   **(b)** Four subtracted from x, multiplied by five.

    (c) Four subtracted from the product of x and five.   **(d)** Four subtracted from five, multiplied by x.

    (e) None of these

13. Determine whether the value of x is a solution to the equation $x^2 - 2x = x + 4$.

    (a) $x = 0$ **(b)** $x = -1$ **(c)** $x = 1$ **(d)** $x = -2$ **(e)** $x = -4$

14. (-2) is a solution of:

    (a) $x^2 = 2x$ **(b)** $(-x)^2 - 2x = 0$ **(c)** $(-x)^2 = 2x$

    (d) $-x^2 = 2x$ **(e)** None of these

15. Describe the step used in transforming the given equation into the equivalent equation.

    $\frac{3}{4}x + 2 = \frac{3}{2}x - 1$ into $3x + 8 = 6x - 4$

    (a) Reduce fractions on one or both sides of the equation.

    (b) Multiply both sides of the equation by the same nonzero quantity.

    (c) Divide both sides of the equation by the same nonzero quantity.

    (d) Combine like terms.

    (e) Subtract the same quantity from both sides of the equation.

16. Match the verbal statement with the correct equation.

    Seven times the sum of a number and 4 is 91.

    (a) $7x + 4 = 91$ **(b)** $7(x + 4) = 91$ **(c)** $x + 4(7) = 91$

    (d) $x + 4 = 7(91)$ **(e)** None of these

Test Form C   **Name** _____ **Date** _____

Chapter 2   **Class** _____ **Section** _____

1. Identify the terms of the algebraic expression $7y + 3(y + 1) + 4$.

2. Evaluate $8x - 4[3x - (2x - 3)]$ when $x = 0$, $x = 1$, and $x = -2$.

3. Simplify $(-3y^3)^4$.

4. Simplify $(5x^2)^3$.

5. Use the Commutative Property of Multiplication to complete the statement
   $6(x + 2) =$ ▨ .

6. Simplify $7x(x - 6)$.

7. Simplify $\dfrac{5x}{12} - \dfrac{x}{8}$.

8. Simplify $15x + 8 - 4x - 9$.

9. Simplify $6(y - 2) - (y - 3)$.

10. Translate the phrase into an algebraic expression. (Let x represent the number.)

    Nine increased by the difference of 5 and a number.

11. A wallet contains n nickels and q quarters. Write and expression for this amount
    of money in cents.

12. A company received a 2% discount for early payment of an invoice in the amount of d
    dollars. Write an expression, in dollars, for the amount of the discounted invoice.

13. The property tax on a house valued at $50,000 is $640. Use the guess, check, and
    revise strategy to estimate the property tax on a house valued at $75,000.

14. Find the following products: $1 \cdot 2, 2 \cdot 4, 3 \cdot 6, 4 \cdot 8, 5 \cdot 10$. Make a table and
    describe a number pattern. Use your pattern to find the product of 9 and 18.

15. Write an algebraic equation for the problem. Do not solve the equation.

    A salesperson earns $400 each week, plus a year-end bonus of b dollars.
    If the total income for 1994 was $21,300, find the amount of the bonus.

16. Write an algebraic equation for the problem. Do not solve the equation.

    The sale price of a sweater is $45.50 and the list price is $54.00. Find the

Name _____ Date _____

Class _____ Section _____

1. Solve the linear equation $8x - 4 = 12$.

    (a) 1   **(b)** 2   **(c)** 8   **(d)** -2 **(e)** None of these

2. Solve the linear equation $\dfrac{x}{4} - 3 = 5$.

    (a) 2   **(b)** 8   **(c)** -8 **(d)** 32   **(e)** None of these

3. Solve the linear equation $-7x + 6 + 12x = 16$.

    (a) $\dfrac{22}{5}$ **(b)** 2   **(c)** $\dfrac{10}{19}$ **(d)** $\dfrac{22}{19}$ **(e)** None of these

4. Solve $-2(y + 5) + y = 2$.

    (a) 8   **(b)** -8 **(c)** -12 **(d)** 12   **(e)** None of these

5. Solve $\dfrac{y - 2}{3} - y = \dfrac{2y + 1}{3}$.

    (a) $-\dfrac{3}{2}$ **(b)** $-\dfrac{4}{3}$ **(c)** $-\dfrac{3}{4}$ **(d)** $-\dfrac{2}{3}$ **(e)** None of these

6. Use cross-multiplication to solve $\dfrac{5 - 2x}{4} = \dfrac{2x + 1}{3}$.

    (a) $\dfrac{5}{7}$ **(b)** $\dfrac{14}{11}$ **(c)** $\dfrac{11}{14}$ **(d)** $\dfrac{7}{5}$ **(e)** None of these

7. Change 24% to a fraction in simplest form.

    (a) $\dfrac{12}{5}$ **(b)** $\dfrac{24}{1}$ **(c)** $\dfrac{240}{1}$ **(d)** $\dfrac{6}{25}$ **(e)** None of these

8. Change the decimal 0.086 to a percent.

    (a) 8.6%   **(b)** 0.86%   **(c)** 86%   **(d)** 0.086%   **(e)** None of these

9. 6370 is 18.2% of what number?

    (a) 35,000   **(b)** 1159.34   **(c)** 115,935   **(d)** 350   **(e)** None of these

10. Find the ratio $4\frac{1}{2}$ to $3\frac{1}{4}$.

    (a) $\dfrac{18}{13}$ **(b)** $\dfrac{36}{26}$ **(c)** $\dfrac{26}{36}$ **(d)** $\dfrac{13}{18}$ **(e)** None of these

11. Solve the proportion for x: $\dfrac{16}{9} = \dfrac{64}{x}$.

    (a) $\dfrac{73}{16}$ **(b)** $\dfrac{1}{36}$ **(c)** 36   **(d)** $\dfrac{16}{73}$ **(e)** None of these

12. Solve the proportion for x: $\dfrac{x + 14}{x + 7} = -\dfrac{4}{3}$.

    (a) -1 **(b)** -10 **(c)** -2 **(d)** 2 **(e)** None of these

13. The area of a triangle is 30 square inches. If the base is 1 foot, find the height (in inches).

    (a) 5 feet   **(b)** 60 inches   **(c)** $\frac{15}{6}$ inches   **(d)** 5 inches   **(e)** None of these

14. You can cycle at a rate of 12 miles per hour. How many miles can you travel in 2 hours and 20 minutes?

    (a) 28   **(b)** 5.14   **(c)** 0.086   **(d)** $11.\overline{6}$ **(e)** None of these

15. Match the graph with the inequality.

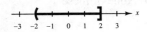

    (a) $-2 \le x \le 2$ **(b)** $-2 \le x < 2$ **(c)** $-2 < x \le 2$

    (d) $-2 < x < 2$ **(e)** None of these

16. Solve the inequality $3x + 2 > 5x - 8$.

    (a) $x < -5$ **(b)** $x > -5$ **(c)** $x < 5$ **(d)** $x > 5$ **(e)** None of these

17. Solve the inequality $15 - 5(3 - 2x) \le 4(x - 3)$.

    (a) $x \ge -2$ **(b)** $x \ge \frac{7}{4}$ **(c)** $x \le \frac{7}{4}$ **(d)** $x \le -2$ **(e)** None of these

18. Solve $|3x + 1| = 2$.

    (a) $\frac{1}{3}$ **(b)** -1 and $\frac{1}{3}$ **(c)** -1 **(d)** $-\frac{1}{3}$ and 1 **(e)** None of these

19. Write a single equation that is equivalent to the following statement.

    The distance between t and 2 is 9.

    (a) $|t - 2| = 9$ **(b)** $|t + 2| = 9$ **(c)** $|t - 9| = 2$

    (d) $|t + 9| = 2$ **(e)** None of these

20. Solve $|2 + m| < 3$.

    (a) $\{m \,|\, m < -5 \text{ or } m > 1\}$ **(b)** $\{m \,|\, m < 1 \text{ or } m > -5\}$ **(c)** $\{m \,|\, -5 < m < 1\}$

    (d) $\{m \,|\, 1 < m < -5\}$ **(e)** None of these

Test Form B
Chapter 3

Name _____   Date _____

Class _____   Section _____

1. Solve the linear equation $4x - 2 = 10$.

   (a) 2   **(b)** -3 **(c)** 3   **(d)** 8   **(e)** None of these

2. Solve the linear equation $\frac{x}{2} - 4 = 8$.

   (a) 8   **(b)** -8 **(c)** 24   **(d)** 6   **(e)** None of these

3. Solve the linear equation $-5x + 4 + 13x = 20$.

   (a) $\frac{8}{9}$ **(b)** $\frac{12}{9}$ **(c)** 3   **(d)** 2   **(e)** None of these

4. Solve $\frac{1}{4} - \frac{1}{2}x = \frac{1}{8}$.

   (a) $-\frac{1}{2}$ **(b)** $-\frac{1}{4}$ **(c)** -1 **(d**   **(e)** None of these

5. Solve $\frac{y + 2}{3} - y = \frac{3y + 1}{3}$.

   (a) $\frac{1}{5}$ **(b)** $-\frac{1}{5}$ **(c)** $\frac{1}{3}$) None of these

6. Use cross-multiplication to solve $\frac{3 + 2x}{3} = \frac{2x - 5}{4}$.

   (a) $-\frac{2}{27}$ **(b)** $\frac{17}{4}$ **(c)** $\frac{4}{17}$ **(d)**   **(e)** None of these

7. Change 32% to a fraction in simplest form.

   (a) $\frac{8}{25}$ **(b)** $\frac{32}{1}$ **(c)** $\frac{320}{1}$ **(d)** $\frac{16}{5}$ **(e)** None of these

8. Change the fraction $\frac{6}{5}$ to a percent.

   (a) 1.20%   **(b)** 12.0%   **(c)** 0.120%   **(d)** 120%   **(e)** None of these

9. 6764 is 17.8% of what number?

   (a) 380   **(b)** 1203.99   **(c)** 120,399   **(d)** 38,000   **(e)** None of these

10. Find a ratio to compare the relative sizes of 40 seconds to 5 minutes.

   (a) $\frac{8}{1}$ **(b)** $\frac{1}{8}$ **(c)** $\frac{15}{2}$ **(d)** $\frac{2}{15}$ **(e)** None of these

11. Solve the proportion for x: $\frac{4}{9} = \frac{x}{54}$.

   (a) $\frac{58}{9}$ **(b)** $\frac{9}{58}$ **(c)** $\frac{1}{24}$ **(d)** 24   **(e)** None of these

12. Solve the proportion for x: $\dfrac{x + 14}{x - 2} = -\dfrac{3}{5}$.

(a) 3   (b) -3 (c) -2 (d) -8 (e) None of these

13. You can cycle at a rate of 14 miles per hour. How many miles can you travel in 2 hours and 20 minutes?

(a) 10   (b) 6   (c) $32.\overline{6}$ (d) 0.1   (e) None of these

14. Find the selling price per pound of a blended coffee made from 8 pounds of coffee worth \$8.50 per pound and 12 pounds of coffee worth \$9.95 per pound.

(a) \$1.56   (b) \$31.17   (c) \$6.97   (d) \$7.23   (e) None of these

15. Match the graph with the inequality.

(a) $x \le -2$ (b) $x < -2$ (c) $x \ge -2$ (d) $x > -2$ (e) None of these

16. Solve the inequality $3x - 2 > 5x + 4$.

(a) $x > -3$ (b) $x < -3$ (c) $x > 3$ (d) $x < 3$ (e) None of these

17. Solve the inequality $8 - 4(3x + 5) \le 6(x - 8)$.

(a) $x \ge -\dfrac{34}{3}$ (b) $x \le -\dfrac{34}{3}$ (c) $x \ge 2$ (d) $x \le 2$ (e) None of these

18. Solve $\left|2 - \tfrac{1}{2}x\right| = 6$.

(a) -8 and 16   (b) -16 and 8   (c) -8 (d) 8   (e) None of these

19. Write a single equation that is equivalent to the following statement.

The distance between x and -3 is 8.

(a) $|x - 3| = 8$ (b) $|x - 8| = 3$ (c) $|x + 3| = 8$

(d) $|x + 8| = 3$ (e) None of these

20. Solve $|3x| \ge 12$.

(a) $\{x \mid x \ge 4 \text{ or } x \ge -4\}$ (b) $\{x \mid x \le -4 \text{ or } x \ge 4\}$ (c) $\{x \mid x \ge -4 \text{ or } x \le 4\}$

(d) $\{x \mid -4 \le x \le 4\}$ (e) None of these

Test Form C

Chapter 3

Name _____ Date _____

Class _____ Section _____

1. Solve the linear equation $7x = 16$.

2. Explain why the equation $3x - 1 = 3(x - 1)$ has no solution.

3. An engineer's consulting fee totaled $600. This included $40 for supplies and $80 for each hour of consulting. Write an equation and solve for the number of hours of consulting.

4. Solve $3(5 - x) + 5(2x - 3) = 3(2x - 1)$.

5. Solve $\dfrac{x - 3}{4} + \dfrac{5x + 1}{6} = \dfrac{19}{12}$.

6. If a number is decreased by 10, and the result is divided by 2, the answer is 15. Find the number.

7. Twenty-two is 20% of what number?

8. Two hundred forty is what percent of 200?

9. Approximately 21% of air is oxygen. Find the approximate number of liters of oxygen in a room containing 18,200 liters of air.

10. Find a ratio to compare the relative sizes of 60 grams to 3 kilograms.

11. Which product has the lower unit price: a 12.3-ounce box of cereal that sells for $3.28 or a 13-ounce box of cereal that sells for $3.36? Explain.

12. If $\frac{1}{2}$ inch represents 15 miles on a map, how many miles does $5\frac{1}{2}$ inches represent?

13. The volume of a rectangular room is 1536 cubic feet. If the height is one-half the length and the width is 12 feet, find the height and the length of the room.

14. The owner of a gift shop mixes almonds worth $4.60 per pound with 10 pounds of raisins worth $2.50 per pound. If the mixture sells for $3.20 per pound, how many pounds of almonds are needed?

15. Solve the inequality $18 - 4x \geq 2$.

16. Solve the inequality $-3 < 5x - 6 < 3$.

17. To earn a grade of B, a student must have an average of at least 80 points on five tests. A student's grades on the first four tests were 79, 83, 89, and 75. How many points must the student score on the fifth test to earn a grade of B? Write an inequality and solve for the score on the fifth test.

18. Solve $|3x - 2| = 7$.

19. Solve the inequality $|1 + 3x| < 2$.

20. An odometer on a bicycle is accurate to within 0.10 miles. If the odometer reads that you have traveled 2.37 miles, describe how far you may have actually traveled.

Test Form A
Chapter 4

Name _____ **Date** _____

Class _____ **Section** _____

1. The coordinates of point A are:

   (a) $(2, -1)$ (b) $(-2, 1)$

   (c) $(1, -2)$ (d) $(-1, 2)$

   (e) None of these

2. Which of the following ordered pairs is *not* a solution of the equation $3x - 4y = 12$?

   (a) $(-4, 0)$ (b) $(-4, -6)$ (c) $(0, -3)$ (d) $(8, 3)$ (e) None of these

3. A person's salaries for selected years are shown on the graph. Choose the best estimated value for the person's salary for 1984.

   (a) $28,000   (b) $25,000

   (c) $21,000   (d) $35,000

   (e) None of these

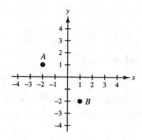

4. Match the graph with its equation.

   (a) $y = \frac{3}{2}x + 3$ (b) $y = \frac{2}{3}x + 3$

   (c) $y = -\frac{3}{2}x + 3$ (d) $y = -\frac{2}{3}x + 3$

   (e) None of these

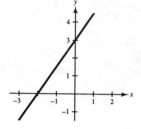

5. Match the graph with its equation.

   (a) $y - x^2 = 3$ (b) $y + x^2 = 3$

   (c) $x - y^2 = 3$ (d) $x + y^2 = 3$

   (e) None of these

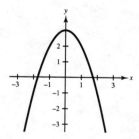

6. Use a graphing utility to graph the equation $y = |x + 2| + 1$, in a standard setting. The result resembles which of the following?

(a)

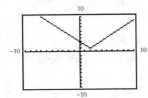

(b)

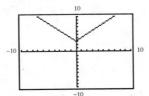

(c)

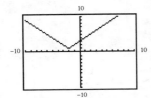

(d)

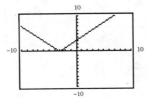

(e) None of these

7. Which of the following relations is a function?

   (a) $\{(1, 3), (2, 5), (3, 7), (4, 5)\}$ **(b)** $\{(1, 3), (2, 5), (3, 7), (1, 5)\}$

   (c) $\{(1, 3), (2, 5), (3, 7), (2, 3)\}$ **(d)** $\{(1, 3), (2, 5), (3, 7), (3, 5)\}$

   (e) None of these

8. Use the vertical line test to determine which of the following graphs represents a function of x.

(a)

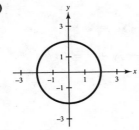

(b)

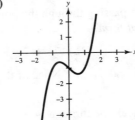

(c)

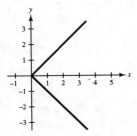

(d)

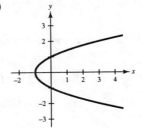

(e) None of these

9. Given $f(x) = -x^2 + 2$, evaluate $f(3)$.

   (a) 11   **(b)** -7 **(c)** -4 **(d)** 8   **(e)** None of these

10. Find the slope of the line passing through the points $(-3, -2)$ and $(1, 3)$.

   (a) $\frac{4}{5}$ **(b)** 2   **(c)** $\frac{5}{4}$ **(d)** -2 **(e)** None of these

11. The slope of the line $3x - 5y = 4$ is:

   (a) $-\frac{5}{3}$ **(b)** $\frac{5}{3}$ **(c)** $-\frac{3}{5}$ **(d)** $\frac{3}{5}$ **(e)** None of these

12. The graph of the equation $y = -\frac{1}{2}x + 2$ is:

   (a)

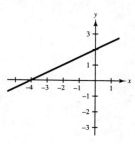

   (b)

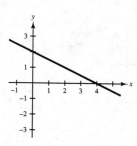

   (c)

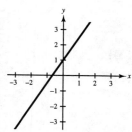

   (d)

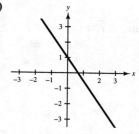

   (e) None of these

13. Write an equation of the line passing through the points $(1, -5)$ and $(3, 2)$.
   Write your answer in *general form*.

   (a) $7x - 2y - 17 = 0$ **(b)** $7x + 2y - 25 = 0$ **(c)** $2x - 7y + 8 = 0$
   (d) $2x + 7y - 20 = 0$ **(e)** None of these

14. Write an equation for a vertical line through $(4, -2)$.

   (a) $x = -2$ **(b)** $y = -2$ **(c)** $y = 4$ **(d)** $x = 4$ **(e)** None of these

15. A line is perpendicular to $3x + 2y = 8$ and passes through the point $(5, 2)$.
   Its equation is:

   (a) $y - 2 = -\frac{3}{2}(x - 5)$ **(b)** $y - 2 = \frac{2}{3}(x - 5)$ **(c)** $y - 2 = -\frac{2}{3}(x - 5)$
   (d) $y - 5 = \frac{2}{3}(x - 2)$ **(e)** None of these

16. Determine which of the following points is a solution of the linear inequality $2x - 5y < 6$.

   (a) $(0, -2)$ **(b)** $(4, 0)$ **(c)** $(2, 1)$ **(d)** $(2, -1)$ **(e)** None of these

17. Match the correct graph with the linear inequality $y \geq 2$.

(a)

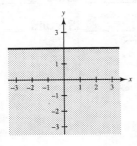

(b)

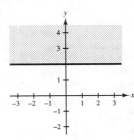

(c)

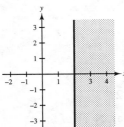

(d)

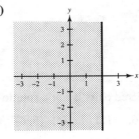

(e) None of these

18. Match the correct graph with the linear inequality $2x + 3y < 6$.

(a)

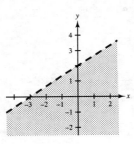

(b)

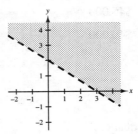

(c)

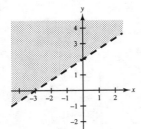

(d)

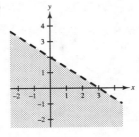

(e) None of these

Test Form B

Chapter 4

Name _____ Date _____

Class _____ Section _____

1. The coordinates of point B are:

   (a) $(2, -1)$ **(b)** $(-2, 1)$

   (c) $(1, -2)$ **(d)** $(-1, 2)$

   (e) None of these

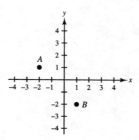

2. Which of the following ordered pairs is *not* a solution of the equation $4x - 3y = 12$?

   (a) $(0, -4)$ **(b)** $(-6, -12)$ **(c)** $(6, 4)$ **(d)** $(+3, 0)$ **(e)** None of these

   (handwritten: $(-3, -4)$)

3. A person's salaries for selected years are shown on the graph. Choose the best estimated value for the person's salary for 1990.

   (a) $35,000   **(b)** $45,000

   (c) $34,000   **(d)** $40,000

   (e) None of these

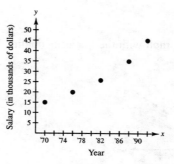

4. Match the graph with its equation.

   (a) $x + y^2 = 1$ **(b)** $x - y^2 = 1$

   (c) $y + x^2 = 1$ **(d)** $y - x^2 = 1$

   (e) None of these

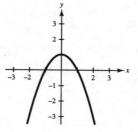

5. Match the graph with its equation.

   (a) $y = |x| + 2$ **(b)** $y = |x - 2|$

   (c) $y = |x| - 2$ **(d)** $y = |x + 2|$

   (e) None of these

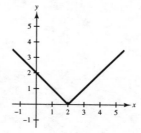

6. Use a graphing utility to graph the equation $3y - x = -6$, in a standard setting. The result resembles which of the following?

(a)

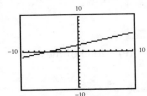

(b)

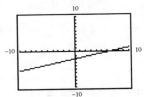

(c)

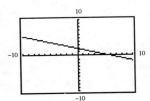

(d)

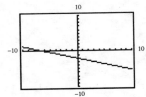

(e) None of these

7. Which of the following relations is a function?

(a) $\{(2, 5), (3, 7), (4, 9), (3, 9)\}$

(b) $\{(2, 5), (3, 7), (4, 9), (5, 11)\}$

(c) $\{(2, 5), (3, 7), (4, 9), (2, 7)\}$

(d) $\{(2, 5), (3, 7), (4, 9), (2, 9)\}$

(e) None of these

8. Use the vertical line test to determine which of the following graphs represents a function of x.

(a)

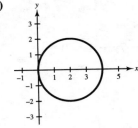

(b)

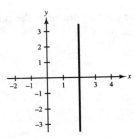

(c)

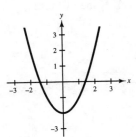

(d)

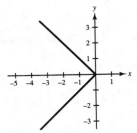

(e) None of these

9. Given $f(x) = -x^2 + 1$, evaluate $f(3)$.

(a) 10   **(b)** -5 **(c)** 7   **(d)** -8 **(e)** None of these

10. Find the slope of the line passing through the points $(-4, -1)$ and $(3, 4)$.

    (a) $\frac{5}{7}$ **(b)** 2 **(c)** $\frac{7}{5}$ **(d)** -2 **(e)** None of these

11. The slope of the line $3x + 5y = 4$ is:

    (a) $-\frac{5}{3}$ **(b)** $\frac{5}{3}$ **(c)** $-\frac{3}{5}$ **(d)** $\frac{3}{5}$ **(e)** None of these

12. The graph of the equation $y = -\frac{3}{2}x + 1$ is:

    (a)

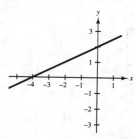

    (b)

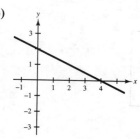

    (c)

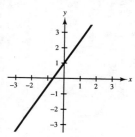

    (d)

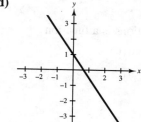

    (e) None of these

13. Write an equation of the line passing through the points $(2, -5)$ and $(5, 2)$. Write your answer in *general form.*

    (a) $7x + 3y - 41 = 0$ **(b)** $7x - 3y - 29 = 0$ **(c)** $3x - 7y - 1 = 0$

    (d) $3x + 7y - 29 = 0$ **(e)** None of these

14. Write an equation for a horizontal line through $(4, -2)$.

    (a) $x = -2$ **(b)** $y = -2$ **(c)** $y = 4$ **(d)** $x = 4$ **(e)** None of these

15. A line is perpendicular to $3x - 2y = 8$ and passes through the point $(5, 2)$. Its equation is:

    (a) $y - 2 = -\frac{3}{2}(x - 5)$ **(b)** $y - 2 = \frac{2}{3}(x - 5)$ **(c)** $y - 2 = -\frac{2}{3}(x - 5)$

    (d) $y - 5 = \frac{2}{3}(x - 2)$ **(e)** None of these

16. Determine which of the following points is a solution of the linear inequality $2x - 3y < 5$.

    (a) $(0, -3)$ **(b)** $(3, 0)$ **(c)** $(2, -1)$ **(d)** $(2, 1)$ **(e)** None of these

17. Match the correct graph with the linear inequality $x \geq 2$.

(a)

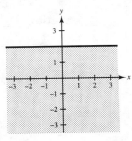

(b)

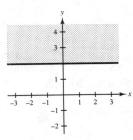

(c)

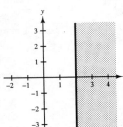

(d)

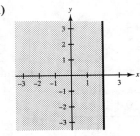

(e) None of these

18. Match the correct graph with the linear inequality $3x + 4y < 8$.

(a)

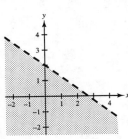

(b)

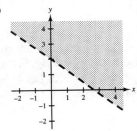

(c)

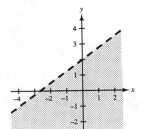

(d)

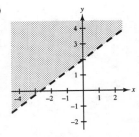

(e) None of these

Test Form C

Chapter 4

Name _____ Date _____

Class _____ Section _____

1. Plot the points $(2, 3)$, $(2, 5)$, and $(6, 3)$. Connect the points with line segments to form a triangle.

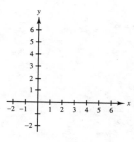

2. Complete the table and plot the results in a rectangular coordinate system.

x	-2	-1	0	1	2
$y = 4x - 2$					

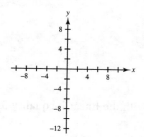

3. You park your vehicle in a parking garage which charges $3.00 for the first hour and $1.00 for each additional hour of parking. Write an equation that relates the total charge to the number of hours parked. Let C represent the total charge and let h represent the number of hours parked. Complete the table and plot the ordered pairs.

h	1	2	3	4
$C =$				

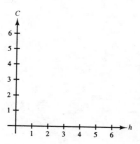

4. Complete the table and use the results to sketch the graph of the equation $x - 9 = 3y$.

x	-6	-3	0	3	6
$y =$					

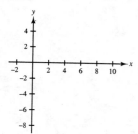

5. Complete the table and use the results to sketch the graph of the equation $x^2 + y = -4$.

x	-2	-1	0	1	2
$y =$					

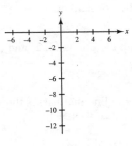

6. Find all x- and y-intercepts of the graph of the equation $y = x^2 - 9$.

7. Find the domain and the range of the relation
$\{(1975, \$420), (1980, \$450), (1985, \$420),(1990, \$425)\}$.

8. Explain why the relation is *not* a function.

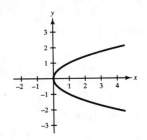

9. Use the vertical line test to determine whether y is a function of x.

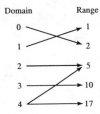

10. Find the slope of the line passing through the points $(-3, -5)$ and $(2, 4)$.

11. Write the equation of the line $5x + 2y - 8 = 0$ in *slope-intercept form.*
Use the slope and y-intercept to graph the line.

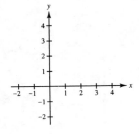

12. Determine whether the pair of lines $2x + y + 3 = 0$ and $x - 2y + 2 = 0$ are perpendicular, parallel, or neither.

13. A line passes through the points $(4, 2)$ and $(-2, 7)$. Write its equation in *slope-intercept form.*

14. Find an equation of the line that passes through the point $(3, 1)$ and is parallel to the line $x + 4y - 8 = 0$.

15. A car travels for t hours at an average speed of 65 miles per hour. Write the distance d (in miles) as a linear function of t and evaluate the function for $t = 5$.

16. Determine whether or not the point $(-5, 4)$ satisfies the linear inequality $4x + y < 12$.

17. Sketch the graph of the linear inequality $x \geq 3$.

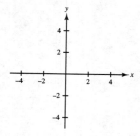

18. Write the inequality whose graph consists of all points below the x-axis.

Test Form A

Chapter 5

Name _____ Date _____

Class _____ Section _____

1. Find the sum of the polynomials and write the result in standard form:
$(2n^2 - 8n + 5) + (-3n^2 - n - 2)$.

    (a) $-n^2 - 5$

    (b) $3 - 9n - n^2$

    (c) $-n^2 - 9n + 3$

    (d) $-9n - n^2 + 3$

    (e) None of these

2. Subtract $(3x^3 + 4x^2 - 5)$ from $(x^3 - 3x + 5)$.

    (a) $-2x^3 + 4x^2 - 3x - 10$

    (b) $-2x^3 - 4x^2 - 3x + 10$

    (c) $2x^3 + 4x^2 + 3x - 10$

    (d) $2x^3 - 4x^2 + 3x - 10$

    (e) None of these

3. Subtract $(4x^3 - 7x^2 + 3)$ from $(2x^3 + 8x - 5)$.

    (a) $-2 + 8x + 7x^2 - 2x^3$

    (b) $-2x^3 + 15x - 8$

    (c) $-2x^3 + 15x^2 - 8$

    (d) $-2x^3 + 7x^2 + 8x - 8$

    (e) None of these

4. Perform the operations $2(x^2 - x - 2) - 3(x^2 - 2x + 1) + (-x^2 + x - 2)$.

    (a) $-2x^2 - 2x - 3$

    (b) $-2x^2 - 7x - 3$

    (c) $5x - 9$

    (d) $-2x^2 + 5x - 9$

    (e) None of these

5. Multiply and simplify $(2x - 7)(-3x)$.

    (a) $-6x^2 - 21x$

    (b) $-6x^2 + 21x$

    (c) $6x^2 - 21x$

    (d) $21x + 6x^2$

    (e) None of these

6. Multiply and simplify $(4x - 3)(2x + 1)$.

    (a) $8x^2 - 3$

    (b) $8x^2 + 4x - 6x - 3$

    (c) $8x^2 + 2x - 3$

    (d) $8x^2 - 2x - 3$

    (e) None of these

7. Simplify the expression $-4t(t^2 - t + 2) - t(t - 1)$.

    (a) $-4t^3 + 3t^2 - 7t$

    (b) $-4t^3 - 5t^2 - 7t$

    (c) $-4t^3 - 5t^2 + 7t$

    (d) $-4t^3 + 3t^2 + 7t$

    (e) None of these

8. Multiply and simplify $(3x - 7)^2$.

    (a) $9x^2 + 49$

    (b) $9x^2 + 42x + 49$

    (c) $9x^2 - 42x + 49$

    (d) $9x^2 - 21x + 49$

    (e) None of these

9. Rewrite $\dfrac{x^{-10}}{x^{-2}}$ with positive exponents.

    (a) $\dfrac{1}{x^8}$

    (b) x^8

    (c) $\dfrac{1}{x^5}$

    (d) x^5

    (e) None of these

10. Choose the expression which is *not* a valid rule of exponents.

    (a) $a^m \cdot a^n = a^{m+n}$
    (b) $a^0 = 1$
    (c) $(a^m)^n = a^{n+m}$

    (d) $(ab)^n = a^n b^n$
    (e) $\dfrac{a^m}{a^n} = a^{m-n}$

11. Use the rules of exponents to simplify the expression. Write your answer with only positive exponents. (Assume that no variable is zero.)

$$(-35x^5 y^{-1})^0 (2x^{-4} y^3)^{-2}$$

    (a) $\dfrac{x^8}{4y^6}$
    (b) $-\dfrac{4x^8}{y^6}$
    (c) $4x^8 y^{-6}$

    (d) $-\dfrac{35x^{13}}{4y^7}$
    (e) None of these

12. The quotient $6.4 \times 10^8 \div 1.6 \times 10^5$ is equal to:

    (a) 4.0×10^3
    (b) 4.0×10^{13}
    (c) 2.5×10^{-3}

    (d) 4.0×10^{-3}
    (e) None of these

13. If $x \neq 0$, dividing $64x^9$ by $12x^3$ gives:

    (a) $\frac{16}{3}x^6$
    (b) $\frac{16}{3}x^3$
    (c) $4x^6$
    (d) $\frac{4}{3}x^{12}$
    (e) None of these

14. Perform the division by cancellation and by subtracting exponents (Assume the denominator is not zero.): $\dfrac{6^3 x}{6^2 x^3}$.

    (a) $6x^2$
    (b) $\dfrac{x^2}{6}$
    (c) $\dfrac{6}{x^2}$
    (d) $\dfrac{1}{6x^2}$
    (e) None of these

15. Assuming $x \neq 2$, $(4x^2 - x - 8) \div (x - 2)$ gives:

    (a) $4x + 7 + \dfrac{6}{x - 2}$
    (b) $4x - 9 + \dfrac{10}{x - 2}$
    (c) $4x + 9 + \dfrac{26}{x - 2}$

    (d) $(4x + 4)$
    (e) None of these

16. Assuming $x \neq -2$, divide $(6x^3 + 16x^2 + 7x - 2)$ by $(x + 2)$.

    (a) $6x^2 - 4x - 1$
    (b) $6x^2 + 4x + 1$
    (c) $6x^2 - 4x + 1$

    (d) $6x^2 + 4x - 1$
    (e) None of these

Test Form B

Chapter 5

Name _____ Date _____

Class _____ Section _____

1. Find the sum of the polynomials and write the result in standard form:
   $(-4n^2 + 11n + 1) + (n^2 - n - 7)$.

   (a) $10n - 3n^2 - 6$ (b) $-3n^2 + 10n - 6$ (c) $-3n^2 + 5$

   (d) $-6 + 10n - 3n^2$ (e) None of these

2. Subtract $(-x^6 + 2x^4 - 2x^2 - 1)$ from $(2x^6 - 2x^4 - 2x^2 + 1)$.

   (a) $3x^6 - 4x^2$ (b) $-3x^6 + 4x^2$ (c) $3x^6 - 4x^4 + 2$

   (d) $-3x^6 + 4x^4 - 2$ (e) None of these

3. Subtract $(5x^3 - 9x + 1)$ from $(x^3 + 10x^2 - 6)$.

   (a) $-4x^3 + 10x^2 + 9x - 7$ (b) $7 + 9x + 10x^2 - 4x^3$ (c) $-4x^3 + 19x^2 - 7$

   (d) $-4x^3 + 19x - 7$ (e) None of these

4. Perform the operations $3(2 - x - 2x^2) - 2(x^2 - 3x + 1) + 3(2x + 1)$.

   (a) $-4x^2 + 2x + 8$ (b) $-8x^2 - 3x + 5$ (c) $-8x^2 + 9x + 7$

   (d) $4x^2 + 9x + 11$ (e) None of these

5. Multiply and simplify $(5x + 3)(-4x)$.

   (a) $-20x^2 + 12x$ (b) $-20x^2 + 3$ (c) $20x^2 - 12x$

   (d) $-20x^2 - 12x$ (e) None of these

6. Multiply and simplify $(5x + 1)(2x - 3)$.

   (a) $10x^2 - 3$ (b) $10x^2 + 13x - 3$ (c) $10x^2 - 13x - 3$

   (d) $10x^2 - 15x + 2x - 3$ (e) None of these

7. Simplify the expression $-6s(s^2 + s - 1) - s(s - 1)$.

   (a) $-6s^3 + 5s^2 + 7s$ (b) $-6s^3 - 7s^2 + 7s$ (c) $-6s^3 + 5s^2 - 7s$

   (d) $-6s^3 - 7s^2 - 7s$ (e) None of these

8. Multiply and simplify $(5x + 4)^2$.

   (a) $25x^2 + 20x + 16$ (b) $25x^2 + 16$ (c) $25x^2 + 20x + 4$

   (d) $25x^2 + 40x + 16$ (e) None of these

9. Rewrite $\dfrac{x^{-9}}{x^{-3}}$ with positive exponents.

   (a) x^6 (b) $\dfrac{1}{x^6}$ (c) x^3 (d) $\dfrac{1}{x^3}$ (e) None of these

10. Choose the expression which is *not* a valid rule of exponents.

(a) $a^m \cdot a^n = a^{n+m}$

(b) $(ab)^n = a^n b^n$

(c) $(a^n)^m = a^{nm}$

(d) $a^1 = 0$

(e) $\dfrac{a^m}{a^n} = a^{m-n}$

11. Use the rules of exponents to simplify the expression. Write your answer with only positive exponents. (Assume that no variable is zero.)

$$(-36x^{-1}y^6)^0(3x^{-3}y^4)^{-2}$$

(a) $-\dfrac{4x^5}{y^2}$

(b) $-6x^6 y^{-8}$

(c) $\dfrac{x^6}{9y^8}$

(d) $-\dfrac{6x^6}{y^8}$

(e) None of these

12. The product $(2.5 \times 10^7) \times (3.0 \times 10^{-3})$ is equal to:

(a) 7.5×10^{-4}

(b) 7.5×10^4

(c) 75×10^5

(d) 7.5×10^{-21}

(e) None of these

13. If $x \neq 0$, dividing $48x^{10}$ by $18x^2$ gives:

(a) $\frac{8}{3}x^5$

(b) $\frac{8}{3}x^{12}$

(c) $3x^8$

(d) $\frac{8}{3}x^8$

(e) None of these

14. Perform the division by cancellation and by subtracting exponents (Assume the denominator is not zero.): $\dfrac{7^3 x}{7^2 x^4}$.

(a) $\dfrac{7}{x^3}$

(b) $7x^3$

(c) $\dfrac{1}{7x^3}$

(d) $\dfrac{x^3}{7}$

(e) None of these

15. Assuming $x \neq -3$, $(6x^2 + 5x - 9) \div (x + 3)$ gives:

(a) $6x + 23 - \dfrac{78}{x + 3}$

(b) $(6x - 3)$

(c) $6x - 13 + \dfrac{30}{x + 3}$

(d) $6x - 23 - \dfrac{78}{x + 3}$

(e) None of these

16. Assuming $x \neq -3$, divide $(5x^3 + 18x^2 + 8x - 3)$ by $(x + 3)$.

(a) $5x^2 - 3x - 1$

(b) $5x^2 + 3x - 1$

(c) $5x^2 - 3x + 1$

(d) $5x^2 + 3x + 1$

(e) None of these

Test Form C   **Name** _____   **Date** _____

Chapter 5   **Class** _____   **Section** _____

1. Identify the degree of the polynomial $-4x^5 + 6x^3 + 3$.

2. Classify the polynomial as a monomial, binomial, or trinomial: $11 + x^2$.

3. Write the polynomial $2x + x^3 - 2x^2 - x^4$ in standard form.

4. Perform the operations $(-14x^3 + 9x^2 - 6x) - (x^3 + 9x^2 + 8) + (6x^3 - x)$.

5. Multiply and simplify $(5x^2 - 4x - 6)(x^2 - 1)$.

6. Use the square of the binomial to find the product $(3x + 5)^2$.

7. Multiply and simplify $(x + 1)^3$.

8. The length of a rectangle is $3x + 2$ and the width is $x + 3$. Find an expression for the area of the rectangle.

9. Use the rules of exponents to simplify the expression. Write your answer with only positive exponents. (Assume that no variable is zero.) $(3x^{-4}y^3)^{-4}$

10. Use the rules of exponents to simplify the expression. Write your answer with only positive exponents. (Assume that no variable is zero.) $(-7x^{-2}y^4)(6xy^{-1})$

11. Write 0.000051 in scientific notation.

12. Write 5.663×10^6 in decimal form.

13. Simplify the expression $\dfrac{-24(x^2y)^2}{16(xy^2)^2}$. (Assume the denominator is not zero.)

14. Perform the division and simplify. (Assume the denominator is not zero.)
$$\frac{m^4 + 5m - 9}{m}$$

15. Assuming $x \neq -\frac{4}{3}$, divide $(9x^2 - 16)$ by $(3x + 4)$.

16. Use the long division algorithm to find: $(4x^2 + 4x - 1) \div (2x + 1)$.

Test Form A   Name _____ Date _____

Chapter 6   Class _____ Section _____

1. Find the greatest common factor of $48n^2m^3$ and $80nm^2$.

    (a) $24nm^2$ **(b)** $16nm^2$ **(c)** $16n^2m$

    (d) $24n^2m$ **(e)** None of these

2. Factor out the greatest common monomial factor of the polynomial $28x + 56x^3$.

    (a) $7x(4 + 8x^2)$ **(b)** $4x(7 + 14x^2)$ **(c)** $14x(2 + 4x^2)$

    (d) $28x(1 + 2x^2)$ **(e)** None of these

3. Factor $2x^2 - x - 10x + 5$ by grouping.

    (a) $(x - 5)(2x - 1)^2$ **(b)** $(x + 5)(2x - 1)$ **(c)** $(x - 5)(2x - 1)$

    (d) $(x - 5)^2(2x - 1)$ **(e)** None of these

4. Find the missing factor: $x^2 + 10x - 24 = (x + 12)($ $)$.

    (a) $x - 2$ **(b)** $x + 12$ **(c)** $x - 12$ **(d)** $x + 2$ **(e)** None of these

5. Factor $x^2 + 5x - 6$.

    (a) $(x + 2)(x + 3)$ **(b)** $(x + 6)(x - 1)$ **(c)** $(x - 6)(x + 1)$

    (d) $(x - 2)(x - 3)$ **(e)** None of these

6. Factor the trinomial $2x^3 - 14x^2 + 20x$ *completely*.

    (a) $2x(x - 5)(x - 2)$ **(b)** $x(2x - 10)(x - 2)$ **(c)** $2(x^2 - 5x)(x - 2)$

    (d) $x(2x - 4)(x - 5)$ **(e)** None of these

7. Factor $8x^2 - 14x + 3$.

    (a) $(2x - 3)(4x - 1)$ **(b)** $(4x - 3)(2x - 1)$ **(c)** $(8x - 3)(x - 1)$

    (d) $(8x - 1)(x - 3)$ **(e)** None of these

8. Factor $-6x^2 + 7x - 2$.

    (a) $-(2x + 1)(3x + 2)$ **(b)** $-(2x + 2)(3x + 1)$ **(c)** $-(2x - 1)(3x - 2)$

    (d) $-(2x - 2)(3x - 1)$ **(e)** None of these

9. Factor $6x^2 + 15x - 9$ *completely*.

    (a) $3(2x + 3)(x - 1)$ **(b)** $3(2x - 1)(x + 3)$ **(c)** $3(2x - 3)(x + 1)$

    (d) $3(2x + 1)(x - 3)$ **(e)** None of these

10. Factor $(x + 3)^2 - 25$ and simplify.

    (a) $(x + 8)(x - 2)$ **(b)** $(x + 2)(x - 8)$ **(c)** $(x - 2)(x - 2)$

    (d) $(x + 4)(x - 4)$ **(e)** None of these

11. Factor the binomial *completely* $a^4 - 625$.

    (a) $(a^2 + 25)(a - 5)(a - 5)$ **(b)** $(a^2 + 25)(a - 5)(a + 5)$ **(c)** $(a + 5)(a + 5)(a + 5)(a - 5)$

    (d) $(a^2 + 25)(a^2 - 25)$ **(e)** None of these

12. Identify which of the following polynomials is a perfect square trinomial.

    (a) $4x^2 + 12x + 9$ **(b)** $4x^2 + 20x + 9$ **(c)** $4x^2 + 37x + 9$

    (d) $4x^2 + 13x + 9$ **(e)** None of these

13. Find the solutions of $x^2 + 2x = 8$.

    (a) $x = 6$ and $x = 8$ **(b)** $x = -4$ and $x = 2$ **(c)** $x = -2$ and $x = 4$

    (d) $x = -2$ and $x = 8$ **(e)** None of these

14. Find the solutions of $(x + 2)(x - 2) = 5$.

    (a) $x = 3$ and $x = 7$ **(b)** $x = 3$ only   **(c)** $x = -3$ and $x = 3$

    (d) $x = -3$ only   **(e)** None of these

15. Find the solutions of $x^3 = 3x^2 + 18x$.

    (a) $x = -3$ and $x = 6$ **(b)** $x = -6$ and $x = 0$ **(c)** $x = -6, x = 0$, and $x = 3$

    (d) $x = -3, x = 0$, and $x = 6$ **(e)** None of these

Test Form B

Chapter 6

Name _____   Date _____

Class _____   Section _____

1. Find the greatest common factor of $54c^3d^2$ and $90c^2d$.

   (a) $18cd^2$

   (b) $27cd^2$

   (c) $27c^2d$

   (d) $18c^2d$

   (e) None of these

2. Factor out the greatest common monomial factor of the polynomial $32x + 64x^3$.

   (a) $8x(4 + 8x^2)$

   (b) $32x(1 + 2x^2)$

   (c) $16x(2x + 4x^2)$

   (d) $4x(8x + 16x^2)$

   (e) None of these

3. Factor $3x^2 - x - 12x + 4$ by grouping.

   (a) $(x - 4)(3x - 1)^2$

   (b) $(x - 4)^2(3x - 1)$

   (c) $(x + 4)(3x - 1)$

   (d) $(x - 4)(3x - 1)$

   (e) None of these

4. Find the missing factor: $x^2 + 9x - 36 = (x + 12)(\quad)$.

   (a) $x - 24$
   (b) $x + 24$
   (c) $x + 3$
   (d) $x - 3$
   (e) None of these

5. Factor $x^2 - 5x - 6$.

   (a) $(x + 6)(x - 1)$

   (b) $(x + 2)(x + 3)$

   (c) $(x - 2)(x - 3)$

   (d) $(x - 6)(x + 1)$

   (e) None of these

6. Factor the trinomial $2x^3 - 14x^2 + 24x$ *completely.*

   (a) $2(x^2 - 4x)(x - 3)$

   (b) $x(2x - 6)(x - 4)$

   (c) $2x(x - 4)(x - 3)$

   (d) $x(2x - 4)(x - 3)$

   (e) None of these

7. Factor $8x^2 - 14x + 5$.

   (a) $(8x - 5)(x - 1)$

   (b) $(4x - 1)(2x - 5)$

   (c) $(2x - 1)(4x - 5)$

   (d) $(8x - 1)(x - 5)$

   (e) None of these

8. Factor $-6x^2 + 11x - 3$.

   (a) $-(3x + 3)(2x + 1)$

   (b) $-(3x - 1)(2x - 3)$

   (c) $-(3x + 1)(2x + 3)$

   (d) $-(3x - 3)(2x - 1)$

   (e) None of these

9. Factor $6x^2 + 10x - 4$ *completely.*

   (a) $2(3x + 1)(x - 2)$

   (b) $2(3x - 2)(x + 1)$

   (c) $2(3x + 2)(x - 1)$

   (d) $2(3x - 1)(x + 2)$

   (e) None of these

10. Factor $(x + 4)^2 - 25$ and simplify.

   (a) $(x + 1)(x - 9)$ **(b)** $(x + 3)(x - 3)$ **(c)** $(x + 9)(x - 1)$

   (d) $(x - 1)(x - 1)$ **(e)** None of these

11. Factor the binomial *completely* $a^4 - 81$.

   (a) $(a + 3)(a + 3)(a + 3)(a - 3)$ **(b)** $(a^2 + 9)(a^2 - 9)$ **(c)** $(a^2 + 9)(a + 3)(a - 3)$

   (d) $(a^2 + 9)(a - 3)(a - 3)$ **(e)** None of these

12. Identify which of the following polynomials is a perfect square trinomial.

   (a) $4x^2 + 101x + 25$ **(b)** $4x^2 + 25x + 25$ **(c)** $4x^2 + 29x + 25$

   (d) $4x^2 + 20x + 25$ **(e)** None of these

13. Find the solutions of $x^2 + 3x = 10$.

   (a) $x = -2$ and $x = 5$ **(b)** $x = 7$ and $x = 10$ **(c)** $x = -3$ and $x = 10$

   (d) $x = -5$ and $x = 2$ **(e)** None of these

14. Find the solutions of $(x + 1)(x - 1) = 3$.

   (a) $x = -2$ and $x = 2$ **(b)** $x = 2$ and $x = 4$ **(c)** $x = -2$ only

   (d) $x = 2$ only   **(e)** None of these

15. Find the solutions of $x^3 = 4x^2 + 12x$.

   (a) $x = -3$ and $x = 0$ **(b)** $x = -2, x = 0$, and $x = 6$ **(c)** $x = -6, x = 0$, and $x = 2$

   (d) $x = -2$, and $x = 6$ **(e)** None of these

Test Form C

Chapter 6

Name _____ Date _____

Class _____ Section _____

1. Factor the polynomial $27x^7 + 45x^2 - 54x$.

2. Factor out a negative common monomial factor: $-10y^3 + 25y^2 + 5y$.

3. Complete the factorization: $8y(y^2 + 1) - (y^2 + 1) = (y^2 + 1)(\quad)$.

4. Factor $x^2 - 7x + 12$.

5. Factor $n^2 - nm - 30m^2$.

6. Find the missing factor: $3x^2 + 33x - 36 = 3(x - 1)(\quad)$.

7. Factor $9x^2 + 18x + 5$.

8. Find the missing factor: $-4x^2 - 13x - 3 = -(4x + 1)(\quad)$.

9. Rewrite the middle term of the trinomial $6x^2 + 23x + 15$ so that the trinomial can be factored by grouping.

10. Factor the polynomial $\frac{1}{36}n^2 - \frac{1}{25}$.

11. Factor $5y^4 - 45y^2$ *completely*.

12. Factor $16x^2 - 40x + 25$ and write the result as the square of a binomial.

13. Write the polynomial equation $y^2 - 6y = 7$ in standard form.

14. Solve the equation $(x + 1)(x - 4) = 14$.

15. The product of two consecutive negative integers is 80. Write a polynomial equation and solve for the integers.

Test Form A

Chapter 7

Name _____ Date _____

Class _____ Section _____

1. Use a graphing utility to determine which ordered pair is a solution of the system of equations.

$$2x + y = 1$$
$$-x + 2y = 7$$

   (a) $(1, -1)$ (b) $(-1, 3)$ (c) $(-9, -1)$ (d) $(-1, 4)$ (e) None of these

2. Solve the system of equations by the method of substitution.

$$x^2 + 2y = 6$$
$$2x + y = 3$$

   (a) $(4, -5)$ (b) $(2, 1)$ (c) $(0, 3)$

   (d) $(0, 3)$ and $(4, -5)$ (e) None of these

3. Solve the system by the method of substitution.

$$0.1x - 0.3y = 1.2$$
$$3x - 2y = 71$$

   (a) $(5, 27)$ (b) $(a, 5a)$ (c) $(27, 5)$ (d) $\left(\frac{61}{3}, 5\right)$ (e) None of these

4. A bag contains 85 coins, all dimes and quarters. Find the number of dimes and the number of quarters if the value of the coins is $12.25.

   (a) 40 dimes and 45 quarters   (b) 45 dimes and 40 quarters   (c) 60 dimes and 25 quarters

   (d) 25 dimes and 60 quarters   (e) None of these

5. Use the method of elimination to find the value of y in the solution of the system of equations.

$$5x + 2y = -1$$
$$-15x + 8y = 10$$

   (a) $\frac{1}{2}$ (b) $\frac{9}{10}$ (c) $\frac{9}{14}$ (d) 0 (e) None of these

6. Use a graphing utility to graph the lines in the system of equations.

$$2x + 4y = 7$$
$$3x + 6y = 5$$

   Use the graph to determine which choice describes the solution.

   (a) Consistent, exactly one solution   (b) Consistent, infinitely many solutions

   (c) Inconsistent

7. Solve the system of linear equations.

$$x - y + z = 5$$
$$3x + 2y - z = -2$$
$$2x + y + 3z = 10$$

  (a) $(1, -1, 3)$ **(b)** $(2, -5, -2)$ **(c)** $(-1, 7, 13)$

  (d) $(3, -9, -7)$ **(e)** No solution

8. Solve the system of linear equations.

$$x - y + z = 2$$
$$2x + 3y + z = 7$$
$$3x + 2y + 2z = -8$$

  (a) $(1, 0, 1)$ **(b)** $(6, 4, 4)$ **(c)** $(1, 2, 3)$

  (d) No solution   **(e)** None of these

9. The sum of three positive numbers is 19. Find the second number if the third is three times the first and the second is one more than twice the first.

  (a) 7   **(b)** 13   **(c)** 1   **(d)** 9   **(e)** None of these

10. Fill in the box by using elementary row operations to form a row-equivalent matrix.

$$\begin{bmatrix} 1 & 2 & -5 \\ -3 & 2 & 1 \end{bmatrix} \quad \begin{bmatrix} 1 & 2 & -5 \\ 0 & 8 & \blacksquare \end{bmatrix}$$

  (a) -14 **(b)** 16   **(c)** -8 **(d)** -4 **(e)** None of these

11. Form the augmented matrix of the system of equations.

$$y - 3z = 5$$
$$2x + z = -1$$
$$4x - y = 0$$

  (a) $\begin{bmatrix} 1 & -3 \\ 2 & 1 \\ 4 & -1 \end{bmatrix}$ **(b)** $\begin{bmatrix} 1 & -3 & \vdots & 5 \\ 2 & 1 & \vdots & -1 \\ 4 & -1 & \vdots & 0 \end{bmatrix}$ **(c)** $\begin{bmatrix} 0 & 1 & -3 \\ 2 & 0 & 1 \\ 4 & -1 & 0 \end{bmatrix}$

  (d) $\begin{bmatrix} 0 & 1 & -3 & \vdots & 5 \\ 2 & 0 & 1 & \vdots & -1 \\ 4 & -1 & 0 & \vdots & 0 \end{bmatrix}$ **(e)** None of these

12. The fraction $\dfrac{x^2 - x + 2}{x^3 - x^2 + x - 1}$ can be written as the sum of two fractions as follows.

$$\frac{x^2 - x + 2}{x^3 - x^2 + x - 1} = \frac{A}{x - 1} + \frac{Bx + C}{x^2 + 1}$$

where A, B, and C are the solutions of the system

$$A + B = 1$$
$$-B + C = -1$$
$$A - C = 2.$$

Solve the system.

(a) $A = -1, B = 1, C = 0$ (b) $A = 1, B = 0, C = -1$ (c) $A = 1, B = -1, C = 2$

(d) $A = 1, B = -1, C = 0$ (e) $A = 0, B = 0, C = -2$

13. Evaluate the determinant of the matrix.

$$\begin{bmatrix} 3 & 1 & -2 \\ 0 & 2 & 3 \\ 1 & -2 & -2 \end{bmatrix}$$

(a) 13   (b) 5   (c) -31 (d) 9   (e) None of these

14. Use a graphing utility to evaluate the determinant of the matrix.

$$\begin{bmatrix} 0 & 2 & 3 \\ 1 & -1 & 4 \\ 3 & 0 & 2 \end{bmatrix}$$

(a) 9   (b) 19   (c) 29   (d) 0   (e) None of these

15. Use a graphing utility and Cramer's Rule to find the value of y in the solution of the system of equations.

$$2x - 3y = 5$$
$$2x + 3y = -3$$

(a) $\frac{1}{2}$ (b) $-\frac{3}{4}$ (c) $-\frac{4}{3}$ (d) $\frac{4}{3}$ (e) None of these

Test Form B

Chapter 7

Name _____ Date _____

Class _____ Section _____

1. Use a graphing utility to determine which ordered pair is the solution of the system of equations.

   $$5x + y = 11$$
   $$3x - 2y = 4$$

   (a) $\left(\frac{15}{13}, \frac{68}{13}\right)$ (b) $(2, 21)$ (c) $(2, 1)$ (d) $(-1, 16)$ (e) None of these

2. Solve the system of equations by the method of substitution.

   $$x^2 + 2y = -6$$
   $$x - y = 3$$

   (a) $(-2, -5)$ (b) $(0, -3)$ (c) $(-2, -5)$ and $(0, -3)$

   (d) $(4, 1)$ (e) None of these

3. Solve the system by the method of substitution.

   $$\frac{1}{3}x - \frac{3}{5}y = -2$$
   $$2x - y = 14$$

   (a) $\left(\frac{136}{23}, \frac{50}{23}\right)$ (b) $(12, 10)$ (c) $(12, -38)$ (d) No solution   (e) None of these

4. A bag contains 85 coins, all dimes and quarters. Find the number of dimes and the number of quarters if the value of the coins is $17.50.

   (a) 40 dimes and 45 quarters   (b) 45 dimes and 40 quarters   (c) 60 dimes and 25 quarters

   (d) 25 dimes and 60 quarters   (e) None of these

5. Use the method of elimination to find the value of x in the solution of the system of equations.

   $$7x + y = 3$$
   $$21x + 5y = 11$$

   (a) 1   (b) $\frac{2}{7}$ (c) $-\frac{3}{7}$ (d) -2 (e) None of these

6. Use a graphing utility to graph the lines in the system of equations.

   $$6x - 5y = 4$$
   $$3x + 2y = 1$$

   Use the graph to determine which choice describes the solution.

   (a) Consistent, exactly one solution   (b) Consistent, infinitely many solutions

   (c) Inconsistent

7. Solve the system of linear equations.

$$x + y + 3z = 0$$
$$2x - y - 3z = -9$$
$$x + 2y + 3z = 1$$

(a) $\left(-3a, a, \dfrac{2a}{3}\right)$ **(b)** $\left(-1, 2, -\dfrac{1}{3}\right)$ **(c)** $\left(-3, 1, \dfrac{2}{3}\right)$

(d) No solution   **(e)** None of these

8. Solve the system of linear equations.

$$2x + y - z = 3$$
$$x - 3y + z = 7$$
$$3x + 5y - 3z = 0$$

(a) $\left(a, \dfrac{3a - 10}{2}, \dfrac{7a - 16}{2}\right)$ **(b)** $\left(\dfrac{3a + 10}{3}, a, 6a - 21\right)$ **(c)** $(2, -2, -1)$

(d) No solution   **(e)** None of these

9. The sum of three positive numbers is 180. Find the first number if the third is four times the first and the second is thirty-six less than the third.

(a) 12   **(b)** 36   **(c)** 24   **(d)** 60   **(e)** None of these

10. Find the number that belongs in the box by using elementary row operations to form a row-equivalent matrix.

$$\begin{bmatrix} 1 & -3 & 4 \\ -2 & 7 & 1 \end{bmatrix} \quad \begin{bmatrix} 1 & -3 & 4 \\ 0 & 1 & \blacksquare \end{bmatrix}$$

(a) 5   **(b)** -7 **(c)** 8   **(d)** 0   **(e)** None of these

11. Form the augmented matrix of the system of equations.

$$x + 2z = 7$$
$$y - z = -5$$
$$3x - y = 2$$

(a) $\begin{bmatrix} 1 & 2 & \vdots & 7 \\ 1 & -1 & \vdots & -5 \\ 3 & -1 & \vdots & 2 \end{bmatrix}$ **(b)** $\begin{bmatrix} 1 & 0 & 2 \\ 0 & 1 & -1 \\ 3 & -1 & 0 \end{bmatrix}$ **(c)** $\begin{bmatrix} 1 & 0 & 2 & \vdots & 7 \\ 0 & 1 & -1 & \vdots & -5 \\ 3 & -1 & 0 & \vdots & 2 \end{bmatrix}$

(d) $\begin{bmatrix} 1 & 2 \\ 1 & -1 \\ 3 & -1 \end{bmatrix}$ **(e)** None of these

12. The fraction $\dfrac{16x}{x^3 - 10x^2}$ can be written as the sum of three fractions as follows.

$$\frac{16x}{x^3 - 10x^2} = \frac{A}{x} + \frac{B}{x^2} + \frac{C}{x - 10}$$

where A, B, and C are the solutions of the system

$$\begin{aligned} A + \quad C &= 0 \\ -10A + \quad B &= 16 \\ -10B &= 0. \end{aligned}$$

Solve the system.

(a) $A = 0, B = 16, C = 0$ **(b)** $A = -\dfrac{8}{5}, B = 0, C = 0$ **(c)** $A = 0, B = -\dfrac{8}{5}, C = \dfrac{8}{5}$

(d) $A = \dfrac{8}{5}, B = \dfrac{8}{5}, C = -\dfrac{8}{5}$ **(e)** $A = -\dfrac{8}{5}, B = 0, C = \dfrac{8}{5}$

13. Evaluate the determinant of the matrix.

$$\begin{bmatrix} -2 & 1 & 3 \\ 3 & 0 & -1 \\ 4 & -2 & 1 \end{bmatrix}$$

(a) 7   **(b)** -21 **(c)** 0   **(d)** 21   **(e)** None of these

14. Use a graphing utility to evaluate the determinant of the matrix.

$$\begin{bmatrix} 0 & -1 & 2 \\ 3 & 5 & 0 \\ 1 & -1 & 3 \end{bmatrix}$$

(a) 25   **(b)** -25 **(c)** 7   **(d)** -7 **(e)** None of these

15. Use a graphing utility and Cramer's Rule to find the value of x in the solution of the system of equations.

$$\begin{aligned} 2x - y &= 6 \\ 2x + 2y &= -9 \end{aligned}$$

(a) 2   **(b)** $\frac{1}{2}$ **(c)** -5 **(d)** $\frac{21}{2}$ **(e)** None of these

Test Form C

Chapter 7

Name _____ **Date** _____

Class _____ **Section** _____

1. Use a graphing utility to solve the system.

    $3x + 4y = 2$

    $2x + \ y = 3$

2. Solve the system by the method of substitution.

    $x + \ y = \quad 1$

    $x^2 + 3y^2 = 21$

3. Use a graphing utility to determine the solution to the system of equations.

    $x^2 - 4x + y = 0$

    $x - y = 0$

4. A 20 pound mixture of two kinds of candy sells for \$30.52. One kind of candy in the mixture sells for \$1.35 per pound. The other kind sells for \$1.79 per pound. How much of the cheaper candy is in the mixture?

5. Solve the system of linear equations.

    $0.02x - 0.05y = -0.38$

    $0.03x + 0.04y = \quad 1.04$

6. Use a graphing utility to graph the lines in the system of equations. Use the graphs to determine whether the solution is consistent of inconsistent. If it is consistent, determine the number of solutions.

    $\frac{1}{3}x - \frac{3}{5}y = -2$

    $2x - \ y = \ 14$

7. Solve the system of linear equations.

    $x - \ y - z = 0$

    $2x + 4y + z = 0$

    $3x + \ y - z = 0$

8. Solve the system of linear equations.

    $x - 2y - \ z = 7$

    $-3x + 6y + 3z = 0$

9. Find an equation of the parabola $y = ax^2 + bx + c$ that passes through the points $(1, 4), (-1, 0)$, and $(2, -3)$.

10. Use the variables x, y, and z to write the system of linear equations represented by the augmented matrix.

$$\begin{bmatrix} 2 & -1 & 0 & \vdots & 4 \\ 0 & 3 & 1 & \vdots & -2 \\ 1 & -3 & 1 & \vdots & 1 \end{bmatrix}$$

11. Find the solution to the system of linear equations with the augmented matrix.

$$\begin{bmatrix} 1 & 2 & -1 & \vdots & 4 \\ 0 & 2 & 1 & \vdots & -3 \\ 0 & 0 & 2 & \vdots & -4 \end{bmatrix}$$

12. The fraction $\dfrac{3x + 4}{x^3 - 2x - 4}$ can be written as the sum of two fractions as follows.

$$\frac{3x + 4}{x^3 - 2x - 4} = \frac{A}{x - 2} + \frac{Bx + C}{x^2 + 2x + 2}$$

where A, B, and C are the solutions of the system

$$\begin{aligned} A + B &= 0 \\ 2A - 2B + C &= 3 \\ 2A - 2C &= 4. \end{aligned}$$

Solve the system.

13. Find the determinant of the matrix.

$$\begin{bmatrix} 3 & -1 & 6 \\ 2 & 0 & 4 \\ 1 & 6 & 2 \end{bmatrix}$$

14. Use a graphing utility to evaluate the determinant of the matrix.

$$\begin{bmatrix} 2 & 3 & -1 \\ 0 & 5 & 0 \\ -1 & 1 & 2 \end{bmatrix}$$

15. Use a graphing utility and Cramer's Rule to find the value of x in the solution of the system of equations.

$$\begin{aligned} 2x - 3y &= 5 \\ 2x + 3y &= -3 \end{aligned}$$

Test Form A

Chapter 8

Name _____ Date _____

Class _____ Section _____

1. Find the domain: $\dfrac{x + 4}{(x + 4)(x - 1)}$.

(a) $(-\infty, -4) \cup (-4, \infty)$

(b) $(-\infty, 1) \cup (1, \infty)$

(c) $(-\infty, -4) \cup (-4, 1) \cup (1, \infty)$

(d) $(-\infty, \infty)$

(e) None of these

2. Simplify: $\dfrac{1 - 2x}{2x^2 + 5x - 3}$.

(a) $\dfrac{1}{6x - 3}$

(b) $\dfrac{1}{x + 3}$

(c) $\dfrac{1 - 2x}{2x^2 + 5x - 3}$

(d) $\dfrac{-1}{x + 3}$

(e) None of these

3. Simplify: $\dfrac{\left(\dfrac{3}{x - 1}\right)}{\left(\dfrac{x}{x^2 - 1}\right)}$.

(a) 4

(b) $\dfrac{3(x + 1)}{x}$

(c) $\dfrac{3x}{(x - 1)(x^2 - 1)}$

(d) 3

(e) None of these

4. Use a graphing utility to graph the equation $y_1 = \dfrac{6x}{4 - x^2} \cdot \dfrac{(x - 2)^2}{x^2 - 2x}$. Then graph each of the choices for y_2 and use the results to decide which is equivalent to y_1.

(a) $y_2 = 6(2 - x)$

(b) $y_2 = \dfrac{6x}{2 - x}$

(c) $y_2 = \dfrac{-6}{x + 2}$

(d) $y_2 = \dfrac{6}{x + 2}$

(e) $y_2 = \dfrac{6x}{x - 2}$

5. Add and simplify: $\dfrac{x}{x - 1} + \dfrac{3x}{x^2 - 1}$.

(a) $-4x$

(b) $\dfrac{4 - x}{x - 1}$

(c) $\dfrac{4x}{x^2 - 1}$

(d) $\dfrac{x^2 + 4x}{x^2 - 1}$

(e) None of these

6. Simplify: $\dfrac{\left(1 + \dfrac{1}{x}\right)}{\left(1 - \dfrac{1}{x}\right)}$.

(a) $\dfrac{x + 1}{x - 1}$ (b) $\dfrac{x - 1}{x + 1}$ (c) 1 (d) -1 (e) None of these

7. Find $\dfrac{f(2 + h) - f(2)}{h}$ for the function $f(x) = \dfrac{1}{1 + x}$.

(a) $\dfrac{-1}{3(3 + h)}$ (b) -1 (c) $\dfrac{1}{3(3 + h)}$ (d) $\dfrac{1}{3 + h}$ (e) $\dfrac{1}{3h(3 + h)}$

8. Find the vertical asymptote(s): $f(x) = \dfrac{1}{(x + 2)(x - 5)}$.

(a) $x = 2, x = -5$ (b) $y = 0$ (c) $x = -2, x = 5$
(d) $y = 1$ (e) None of these

9. Find the horizontal asymptote (if any): $f(x) = \dfrac{5x}{x - 1}$.

(a) $x = 1$ (b) $x = 0$ (c) $y = 0$ (d) $y = 5$ (e) None of these

10. Use a graphing utility to match the graph with the correct function.

(a) $f(x) = \dfrac{x - 3}{x}$ (b) $f(x) = \dfrac{x + 3}{x}$

(c) $f(x) = \dfrac{x - 3}{x - 1}$ (d) $f(x) = \dfrac{x}{x - 3}$

(e) None of these

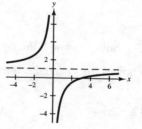

11. Solve: $\dfrac{1}{x - 2} + \dfrac{1}{x + 2} = \dfrac{4}{x^2 - 4}$.

(a) 2 (b) -2 (c) $2, -2$ (d) 4 (e) None of these

12. Use a graphing utility to determine the x-intercepts of the graph of the equation $y = \dfrac{9}{x - 5} + \dfrac{6}{x}$.

(a) $(3, 0)$ (b) $(0, 3)$ (c) $(0, 0)$ (d) $(2, 0)$ (e) There are none

13. Write a mathematical model for the statement
   "A varies jointly with x and the square of y."

   (a) $A = k(x + y^2)$ **(b)** $A = kxy^2$ **(c)** $A = kx\sqrt{y}$

   (d) $A = \dfrac{kx}{y^2}$ **(e)** None of these

14. Find the value of the constant of proportionality for a mathematical model that
   relates S and t if S varies inversely as t and $S = 12$ when $t = \frac{3}{2}$.

   (a) 18   **(b)** 8   **(c)** $\frac{1}{8}$ **(d)** $\frac{1}{18}$ **(e)** None of these

15. F varies jointly as x and y. F equals $\frac{1}{6}$ when $x = \frac{3}{8}$ and $y = \frac{5}{12}$. Find the value of F
   when $x = \frac{3}{4}$ and $y = \frac{5}{8}$.

   (a) 2   **(b)** $\frac{8}{9}$ **(c)** $\frac{9}{8}$ **(d)** $\frac{1}{2}$ **(e)** None of these

Test Form B

Chapter 8

Name _____ Date _____

Class _____ Section _____

1. Find the domain: $\dfrac{x + 3}{(x + 3)(x - 1)}$.

   (a) $(-\infty, -3) \cup (-3, 1) \cup (1, \infty)$

   (b) $(-\infty, 1) \cup (1, \infty)$

   (c) $(-\infty, \infty)$

   (d) $(-\infty, -3) \cup (-3, \infty)$

   (e) None of these

2. Simplify: $\dfrac{3 - 2x}{2x^2 - x - 3}$.

   (a) 1

   (b) $-\dfrac{1}{x^2}$

   (c) $-\dfrac{1}{x + 1}$

   (d) $\dfrac{3 - 2x}{2x^2 - x - 3}$

   (e) None of these

3. Simplify: $\dfrac{\left(\dfrac{x^2}{x^2 - 1}\right)}{\left(\dfrac{3x}{x + 1}\right)}$.

   (a) $-\dfrac{1}{3}$

   (b) $\dfrac{3x^3}{(x^2 - 1)(x + 1)}$

   (c) $\dfrac{x}{3(x - 1)}$

   (d) $\dfrac{1}{x(x - 1)}$

   (e) None of these

4. Use a graphing utility to graph the equation $y_1 = \dfrac{x^2 + x - 12}{x^2 + x - 6} \cdot \dfrac{x - 1}{x + 4}$. Then graph each of the choices for y_2 and use the results to decide which is equivalent to y_1.

   (a) $y_2 = \dfrac{x + 4}{x - 3}$

   (b) $y_2 = \dfrac{x - 1}{x + 4}$

   (c) $y_2 = \dfrac{x + 4}{x - 1}$

   (d) $y_2 = \dfrac{x + 4}{x + 2}$

   (e) $y_2 = \dfrac{(x - 3)^2(x + 4)}{(x - 1)(x + 2)^2}$

5. Add and simplify: $\dfrac{5}{x + 2} + \dfrac{3}{x - 1}$.

   (a) $\dfrac{8x + 1}{(x - 1)(x + 2)}$

   (b) $\dfrac{8x + 5}{(x - 1)(x + 2)}$

   (c) $\dfrac{8}{(x - 1)(x + 2)}$

   (d) $\dfrac{8x - 3}{(x - 1)(x + 2)}$

   (e) None of these

6. Simplify: $\dfrac{\left(2 - \dfrac{1}{x}\right)}{x}$.

(a) 1

(b) $\dfrac{2x - 1}{x^2}$

(c) $\dfrac{2x - 1}{x}$

(d) $2x - 1$

(e) None of these

7. Find $\dfrac{f(2 + h) - f(2)}{h}$ for the function $f(x) = \dfrac{1}{x + 2}$.

(a) -1

(b) $\dfrac{1}{4 + h}$

(c) $\dfrac{-1}{4(4 + h)}$

(d) $\dfrac{-1}{4h(4 + h)}$

(e) $\dfrac{1}{4(4 + h)}$

8. Find the vertical asymptote(s): $f(x) = \dfrac{x}{(x + 1)^2}$.

(a) $x = 0$

(b) $x = -1, x = 1$

(c) $x = -1$

(d) $y = 0$

(e) None of these

9. Find the horizontal asymptote (if any): $f(x) = \dfrac{2x + 7}{3 - x}$.

(a) $x = 3$

(b) $y = \dfrac{2}{3}$

(c) $y = -2$

(d) $x = -\dfrac{7}{2}$

(e) None of these

10. Use a graphing utility to match the graph with the correct function.

(a) $f(x) = \dfrac{x - 2}{x + 1}$

(b) $f(x) = \dfrac{2}{x^2 + 1}$

(c) $f(x) = \dfrac{-2}{x^2 + 1}$

(d) $f(x) = \dfrac{-2}{x^2 - 1}$

(e) $f(x) = \dfrac{x + 2}{x - 1}$

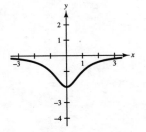

11. Solve: $\dfrac{1}{x - 2} + \dfrac{1}{x + 3} = \dfrac{5}{x^2 + x - 6}$.

(a) 2

(b) -3

(c) 3

(d) $2, -3$

(e) None of these

12. Use a graphing utility to determine the x-intercepts of the graph of the equation $y = \dfrac{1}{x - 6} + \dfrac{2}{x}$.

(a) $(0, 0)$

(b) $(4, 0)$

(c) $\left(\dfrac{1}{2}, 0\right)$

(d) $\left(0, \dfrac{1}{2}\right)$

(e) $(0, 4)$

13. Write a mathematical model for the statement
"*W* varies directly with the square root of *x*."

    (a) $W = k\sqrt{x}$ **(b)** $W = kx^2$ **(c)** $W = k + x^2$

    (d) $W = \dfrac{k}{\sqrt{x}}$ **(e)** None of these

14. Find the value of the constant of proportionality for a mathematical model that relates *S* and *t* if *S* varies inversely as the square of *t* and $S = 12$ when $t = \frac{3}{2}$.

    (a) 18   **(b)** 27   **(c)** $\frac{16}{3}$ **(d)** $\frac{1}{18}$ **(e)** None of these

15. *G* varies jointly as *x* and *y*. *G* equals $\frac{2}{3}$ when $x = \frac{1}{2}$ and $y = \frac{1}{3}$. Find the value of *G* when $x = \frac{3}{2}$ and $y = \frac{1}{4}$.

    (a) $\frac{4}{9}$ **(b)** $\frac{2}{3}$ **(c)** $\frac{3}{2}$ **(d)** $\frac{3}{32}$ **(e)** None of these

Test Form C Name _____ Date _____

Chapter 8 Class _____ Section _____

1. Find the domain: $\dfrac{x + 3}{x^2 + 3x}$.

2. Simplify: $\dfrac{12 - 5x - 2x^2}{4x^2 - 9}$.

3. Divide and simplify: $\dfrac{3x^2 - x - 2}{x^2 - 8x + 16} \div \dfrac{3x^2 + 2x}{x^3 - 64}$.

4. Use a graphing utility to graph the two equations in the same viewing rectangle. Use the graphs to determine whether the expressions are equivalent.

$$y_1 = \dfrac{2 - x}{x + 2} \cdot \dfrac{x + 3}{x^2 - 4} \cdot \dfrac{(x + 2)^2}{3 - x} \quad \text{and} \quad y_2 = \dfrac{x - 3}{x + 3}$$

5. Simplify: $\dfrac{\left(2 - \dfrac{4}{3 - x}\right)}{\dfrac{6}{x}}$.

6. Find and simplify the expression $\dfrac{f(2 + h) - f(2)}{h}$ for the function $f(x) = \dfrac{x}{x + 1}$.

7. Combine and simplify: $\dfrac{2}{x^2 + x} + \dfrac{3}{x^2 - 1} - \dfrac{5}{x^2 - x}$.

8. Find the vertical asymptote(s): $f(x) = \dfrac{2x + 1}{x - 3}$.

9. Find the horizontal asymptote (if any): $f(x) = \dfrac{2x - 5}{1 - 3x}$.

10. Sketch the graph of the rational function $f(x) = \dfrac{2}{4 - x}$. Find intercepts, vertical asymptotes, and horizontal asymptotes.

11. Determine a number that can be added to its reciprocal to obtain $\frac{41}{20}$.

12. Use a graphing utility to determine the x-intercepts of the graph of the equation $y = x - 3 + \dfrac{2}{x}$.

13. Write a mathematical model for the statement,
"*A* is inversely proportional to the square root of *x*."

14. *I* varies jointly as *P* and *t*, $I = 22.5$ when $P = 1500$ and $t = \frac{1}{4}$. Find the value of *I* when $P = 3000$ and $t = \frac{5}{12}$.

15. The power *P* generated by a wind turbine varies directly as the cube of the wind speed ω.

  (a) Write a mathematical model for this statement.

  (b) Find the constant of proportionality if $P = 800$ watts when $\omega = 20$ miles-per-hour.

  (c) Find the power when the wind speed is 30 miles per hour.

  (d) Find the wind speed when the power is 12.5 watts.

Test Form A

Chapter 9

Name _____ Date _____

Class _____ Section _____

1. Evaluate without using a calculator: $(49)^{3/2}$.

   (a) 343   **(b)** $\sqrt[3]{2401}$ **(c)** 800   **(d)** $\frac{147}{2}$ **(e)** None of these

2. Evaluate without using a calculator: $\sqrt{3}\sqrt{27}$.

   (a) 81   **(b)** $\frac{81}{2}$ **(c)** 3   **(d)** 9   **(e)** None of these

3. Combine: $\sqrt{72y} - \sqrt{8y}$.

   (a) $4\sqrt{2y}$ **(b)** $8\sqrt{y}$ **(c)** $8y$ **(d)** $2\sqrt{2y}$ **(e)** None of these

4. Evaluate without using a calculator: $81^{-3/4}$.

   (a) -27 **(b)** $\frac{1}{27}$ **(c)** $-\frac{243}{4}$ **(d)** $\frac{4}{\sqrt[3]{81}}$ **(e)** None of these

5. Simplify: $x^{1/2} \cdot x^{1/3}$.

   (a) $x^{1/6}$ **(b)** x^6 **(c)** $x^{5/6}$ **(d)** $x^{1/5}$ **(e)** None of these

6. Evaluate without a calculator: $\sqrt{100 - 4(3)(-8)}$.

   (a) 2   **(b)** 4   **(c)** 8.485   **(d)** 14   **(e)** 196

7. Simplify: $\sqrt[5]{\dfrac{x^{10}}{32y^5}}$.

   (a) $\dfrac{x^5}{2}$ **(b)** $\dfrac{x^{10}}{32}$ **(c)** $\dfrac{x^2}{2\sqrt{2y}}$ **(d)** $\dfrac{x^2}{2y}$ **(e)** None of these

8. Rationalize the denominator and simplify: $\dfrac{6}{\sqrt{12}}$.

   (a) $\sqrt{3}$ **(b)** $\dfrac{1}{\sqrt{2}}$ **(c)** $\dfrac{\sqrt{3}}{2}$ **(d)** 1   **(e)** None of these

9. Find the length of the hypotenuse of the right triangle.

   (a) 8   **(b)** $2\sqrt{13}$ **(c)** $5\sqrt{2}$

   (d) 52   **(e)** 7

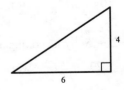

10. Multiply and simplify: $\left(2 - \sqrt{x}\right)^2$.

    (a) $4 - x$ **(b)** $4 + x$ **(c)** $4 - 2\sqrt{x} + x$

    (d) $4 - 4\sqrt{x} + x$ **(e)** None of these

11. Rationalize the denominator and simplify: $\dfrac{1}{1 + \sqrt{2}}$.

(a) $\sqrt{2} - 1$

(b) $\dfrac{1}{3}$

(c) $\dfrac{1}{3 + 2\sqrt{2}}$

(d) $\dfrac{1 + \sqrt{2}}{3 + 2\sqrt{2}}$

(e) None of these

12. Find $f\left(2 + \sqrt{3}\right)$ for the function $f(x) = x^2 - 2x - 1$.

(a) $1 + \sqrt{3}$ (b) $4\sqrt{3}$ (c) $2 + 2\sqrt{3}$ (d) $12 + 6\sqrt{3}$ (e) $2 + 4\sqrt{3}$

13. Use a graphing utility to graph $y_1 = \dfrac{1}{3 - \sqrt{x}}$. Then graph each of the choices for y_2 and determine which is equivalent to y_1.

(a) $y_2 = 3 + \sqrt{x}$

(b) $y_2 = \dfrac{3 + \sqrt{x}}{3 - \sqrt{x}}$

(c) $y_2 = \dfrac{1 + \sqrt{x}}{3 - x}$

(d) $y_2 = \dfrac{3 + \sqrt{x}}{9 + x}$

(e) $y_2 = \dfrac{3\sqrt{x}}{9 + x}$

14. Find s when $t = 3$ in the equation $t = \dfrac{\sqrt{1350 - s}}{4}$.

(a) 9175   (b) 1206   (c) 1494   (d) 1338   (e) None of these

15. Solve: $\sqrt{x + 4} + 2 = x$.

(a) $\dfrac{-1 \pm \sqrt{33}}{2}$ (b) 5   (c) 0, 5   (d) 0, 1   (e) None of these

16. Use a graphing utility to graph both sides of the equation $\sqrt{x^2 + 9} + \sqrt{x^2 - 7} = 8$ on the same screen. Then use the graphs to determine the number of solutions.

(a) 0   (b) 1   (c) 2   (d) 3   (e) 4

17. Simplify: $(3 - 2i) + (-4 + 4i) - \left(1 + \sqrt{-4}\right)$.

(a) $-2 + 4i$ (b) 0   (c) -2 (d) $4i$ (e) None of these

18. Divide: $(3 + 4i) \div (2 - i)$.

(a) $\frac{3}{2} - 4i$ (b) $10 + 5i$ (c) $2 + i$ (d) $\frac{2}{5} + \frac{11}{5}i$ (e) None of these

19. Multiply the number $-2 + 5i$ by its conjugate.

(a) -21 (b) -29 (c) $-21 - 20i$ (d) $29 - 20i$ (e) 29

20. Perform the indicated operation and write the result in standard form: $\dfrac{2}{(3 - i)^2}$.

(a) $\dfrac{4}{25} + \dfrac{3}{25}i$ (b) $\dfrac{1}{4 - 3i}$ (c) $8 - 6i$ (d) $\dfrac{1}{4} - \dfrac{1}{3}i$ (e) None of these

Test Form B   Name _____ Date _____

Chapter 9   Class _____ Section _____

1. Evaluate without using a calculator: $\left(\dfrac{1}{8}\right)^{2/3}$.

   (a) 4   **(b)** $\dfrac{1}{12}$ **(c)** $\dfrac{1}{4}$ **(d)** $\dfrac{1}{\sqrt{512}}$ **(e)** None of these

2. Evaluate without using a calculator: $\sqrt[3]{5}\,\sqrt[3]{25}$.

   (a) $\sqrt[6]{125}$ **(b)** 5   **(c)** $\sqrt[9]{125}$ **(d)** $\frac{125}{3}$ **(e)** None of these

3. Combine: $\sqrt{27a} - \sqrt{75a}$.

   (a) $-\sqrt{48a}$ **(b)** $-16\sqrt{3a}$ **(c)** $-2\sqrt{3a}$ **(d)** $-4\sqrt{3a}$ **(e)** None of these

4. Evaluate without using a calculator: $64^{-2/3}$.

   (a) -16 **(b)** $-\frac{1}{16}$ **(c)** $-\frac{128}{3}$ **(d)** $\frac{1}{16}$ **(e)** None of these

5. Simplify: $x^{2/3} \cdot x^{3/4}$.

   (a) $x^{1/2}$ **(b)** $\dfrac{1}{x^{1/12}}$ **(c)** $x^{5/7}$ **(d)** $x^{17/12}$ **(e)** None of these

6. Evaluate without a calculator: $\sqrt{1 - 4(2)(-21)}$.

   (a) 12.124   **(b)** 169   **(c)** 13   **(d)** 11.225   **(e)** Not a real number

7. Simplify: $\sqrt{\dfrac{81x^3}{y^6}}$.

   (a) $\dfrac{9x^2}{y^3}$ **(b)** $\dfrac{9x^2}{y^4}$ **(c)** $\dfrac{9x\sqrt{x}}{y^3}$ **(d)** $\dfrac{9x}{y^3}$ **(e)** None of these

8. Rationalize the denominator and simplify: $\dfrac{8}{\sqrt{18}}$.

   (a) $\dfrac{2}{3}$ **(b)** $\dfrac{4\sqrt{2}}{3}$ **(c)** $\sqrt{2}$ **(d)** $\dfrac{4}{3}$ **(e)** None of these

9. Find the length of the hypotenuse of the right triangle shown.

   (a) $4\sqrt{5}$ **(b)** 80   **(c)** 12

   (d) 10   **(e)** 9

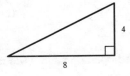

10. Multiply and simplify: $\left(\sqrt{x} + 2\right)^2$.

   (a) $x + 4$ **(b)** $x + 2\sqrt{x} + 4$ **(c)** $4x$

   (d) $x + 4\sqrt{x} + 4$ **(e)** None of these

11. Rationalize the denominator and simplify: $\dfrac{2}{1 - \sqrt{3}}$.

   (a) -2 (b) $-1 + \sqrt{3}$ (c) $\dfrac{2}{2 - \sqrt{3}}$ (d) $-1 - \sqrt{3}$ (e) None of these

12. Find $f\left(1 - \sqrt{2}\right)$ for the function $f(x) = 1 - x^2$.

   (a) $-2 + 2\sqrt{2}$ (b) 2 (c) $4 + 2\sqrt{2}$ (d) $6\sqrt{2}$ (e) $2 - 2\sqrt{2}$

13. Use a graphing utility to graph $y_1 = \dfrac{\sqrt{x}}{1 + \sqrt{x}}$. Then graph each of the choices for y_2 and determine which is equivalent to y_1.

   (a) $y_2 = \dfrac{-\sqrt{x}}{1 - x}$ (b) $y_2 = \dfrac{\sqrt{x}}{x - 1}$ (c) $y_2 = \dfrac{\sqrt{x} - x}{1 - x}$

   (d) $y_2 = \dfrac{2\sqrt{x}}{1 - x}$ (e) $y_2 = \dfrac{\sqrt{x} + x}{1 - x}$

14. Find x when $y = 4$ in the equation $\sqrt{2x} = \dfrac{y}{3}$.

   (a) $\dfrac{8}{9}$ (b) $\dfrac{2}{3}$ (c) $\dfrac{2\sqrt{2}}{3}$ (d) $\dfrac{8}{3}$ (e) None of these

15. Solve: $3x + 5 = \sqrt{2 - 2x}$.

   (a) $-\frac{23}{9}, -1$ (b) $-\frac{23}{9}$ (c) $0, -1$ (d) -1 (e) None of these

16. Use a graphing utility to graph both sides of the equation $\sqrt{5x - 4} = 2 - \sqrt{5x}$ on the same screen. Then use the graphs to determine the number of solutions.

   (a) 0 (b) 1 (c) 2 (d) 3 (e) 4

17. Simplify: $(5 - 3i) + (-2 - i) - \left(2 + \sqrt{-9}\right)$.

   (a) $1 - 7i$ (b) $1 - i$ (c) $5 - 7i$ (d) $1 - i$ (e) None of these

18. Divide: $(3 + 4i) \div (2 + i)$.

   (a) $\frac{3}{2} + 4i$ (b) $2 + i$ (c) $\frac{2}{5} + i$ (d) $3 + 4i$ (e) None of these

19. Multiply the number $3 - 5i$ by its conjugate.

   (a) -16 (b) 34 (c) 16 (d) $-16 - 30i$ (e) $25 - 15i$

20. Perform the indicated operation and write the result in standard form: $\dfrac{(2 - i)(3 + 4i)}{2 + i}$.

   (a) $\dfrac{31}{5} - \dfrac{32}{5}i$ (b) 10 (c) $10 + 5i$ (d) 5 (e) None of these

Test Form C

Chapter 9

Name _____ Date _____

Class _____ Section _____

1. Evaluate without using a calculator: $\left(\frac{1}{16}\right)^{3/4}$.

2. Evaluate without using a calculator: $\sqrt{4}\sqrt{64}$.

3. Combine: $\sqrt{5}\sqrt{15x} + \sqrt{48x} - \sqrt{3x}$.

4. Evaluate without using a calculator: $(-27)^{5/3}$.

5. Evaluate without a calculator: $\sqrt{1 - 4(3)(-2)}$.

6. **a.** Use a graphing utility to graph $y = x^{2/3}$.

   b. Explain why the range is $y \geq 0$.

7. Simplify: $\sqrt{32} - \sqrt{50}$.

8. Rationalize the denominator and simplify: $\dfrac{9x^6}{\sqrt{3x}}$.

9. Find the length of the hypotenuse of the right triangle.

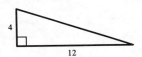

10. Rationalize the denominator and simplify: $\dfrac{\sqrt{3}}{\sqrt{2} - 1}$.

11. Rationalize the denominator: $\dfrac{1}{\sqrt{x + h + 1} - \sqrt{x + 1}}$.

12. Find $f\left(5 + \sqrt{2}\right)$ for the function $f(x) = x^2 - 3x - 4$.

13. Use a graphing utility to determine whether y_1 and y_2 are equivalent.

$$y_1 = \frac{4 - x}{2 + \sqrt{x}}, \quad y_2 = 2 - \sqrt{x}$$

14. Solve: $\dfrac{3}{\sqrt{2 - x}} = 4$.

15. Find C when $x = 3$ in the equation $x = \dfrac{4 + \sqrt{16 - 4C}}{2}$.

16. Use a graphing utility to graph both sides of the equation $\sqrt{x^2 + 11} - \sqrt{x^2 - 9} = 2$ on the same screen. Then use the graphs to determine the number of solutions and to approximate the solution(s). Check your approximations algebraically.

17. Perform the operations and write your answer in standard form:
$(-4 - 3i) + (2 + 5i) - \left(-2 - \sqrt{-9}\right)$.

18. Multiply and write your answer in standard form: $(2 + 5i)(4 - i)$.

19. Divide and write your answer in standard form: $(2 + 5i) \div (4 - i)$.

20. Multiply the number $-4 + 3i$ by its conjugate.

Test Form A

Chapter 10

Name _____ Date _____

Class _____ Section _____

1. Solve by extracting square roots: $4(x - 1)^2 + 3 = 0$.

   (a) $1 + \dfrac{\sqrt{3}}{2}, 1 - \dfrac{\sqrt{3}}{2}$

   (b) $\dfrac{1}{2} + \dfrac{\sqrt{3}}{2}i, -\dfrac{1}{2} + \dfrac{\sqrt{3}}{2}i$

   (c) $1 + \dfrac{\sqrt{3}}{2}i, 1 - \dfrac{\sqrt{3}}{2}i$

   (d) $1 + \sqrt{7}i, 1 - \sqrt{7}i$

   (e) None of these

2. Use a graphing utility to approximate the solutions of the equation $(2x + 7)^2 = 4$.

   (a) -5 and -3

   (b) $-\dfrac{9}{2}$ and $-\dfrac{5}{2}$

   (c) $-\dfrac{7}{2}$

   (d) $\dfrac{5}{2}$ and $\dfrac{9}{2}$

   (e) There are none.

3. Solve the equation: $2\left(\dfrac{x + 1}{x}\right)^2 - 5\left(\dfrac{x + 1}{x}\right) - 12 = 0$.

   (a) $-\dfrac{3}{2}$ and 4

   (b) $-\dfrac{2}{5}$ and $\dfrac{1}{3}$

   (c) $-\dfrac{2}{3}$ and $\dfrac{1}{4}$

   (d) $-\dfrac{3}{5}$ and $-\dfrac{4}{3}$

   (e) 2 and $-\dfrac{1}{3}$

4. Find the real number c such that $x^2 - \dfrac{2}{3}x + c$ is a perfect square trinomial.

   (a) $\dfrac{4}{9}$

   (b) 4

   (c) $-\dfrac{4}{9}$

   (d) $\dfrac{1}{9}$

   (e) $\dfrac{1}{3}$

5. Solve the equation $4x^2 + 5x - 2 = 0$ by completing the square and use a calculator to estimate the solutions to two decimal places.

   (a) $-5.94, -4.06$

   (b) $-6.27, 1.27$

   (c) $-0.63 \pm 0.33i$

   (d) $-1.57, 0.32$

   (e) $-2.5 \pm 1.32i$

6. Solve by using the Quadratic Formula: $3x^2 - 6x + 2 = 0$.

   (a) $\dfrac{3 - \sqrt{3}}{3}, \dfrac{3 + \sqrt{3}}{3}$

   (b) $1 - \sqrt{3}, 1 + \sqrt{3}$

   (c) $\dfrac{3 - \sqrt{15}}{3}, \dfrac{3 + \sqrt{15}}{3}$

   (d) $\dfrac{1}{3}, 2$

   (e) None of these

7. Use a calculator to solve: $2.5x^2 + 3.267x - 8.97 = 0$. Round your answer to three decimal places.

   (a) $-6.643, 3.376$

   (b) $-5.271, -1.263$

   (c) $-8.276, 1.742$

   (d) $-2.657, 1.350$

   (e) None of these

8. Use a graphing utility to determine the type of solutions of the equation
$4.6x^2 - 5.8x + 3.3 = 0$ by graphing the function $y = 4.6x^2 - 5.8x + 3.3$.

    (a) Two distinct real   **(b)** Two distinct complex

    (c) One rational repeated   **(d)** No solutions

9. Find the length of the hypotenuse of a right triangle if the two sides measure
39 cm and 52 cm.

    (a) 34.39 cm   **(b)** 9.54 cm   **(c)** 60 cm   **(d)** 65 cm   **(e)** None of these

10. An open box is to be constructed from a square piece of material by cutting a
3-inch square from each corner. Use a calculator to find the dimensions of the
square piece of material if the box is to have a volume of 363 cubic inches.

    (a) 14″ by 14″   **(b)** 17″ by 17″   **(c)** 20″ by 20″   **(d)** 23″ by 23″   **(e)** 11″ by 11″

11. Solve: $\dfrac{2}{x - 1} < 5$.

    (a) $(-\infty, 1)$ **(b)** $\left(\frac{7}{5}, \infty\right)$ **(c)** $\left(-\infty, -\frac{3}{5}\right) \cup \left(\frac{7}{5}, \infty\right)$

    (d) $(-\infty, 1) \cup \left(\frac{7}{5}, \infty\right)$ **(e)** None of these

12. Use a graphing utility to solve the inequality $x^2 - x \le 6$.

    (a) $[-2, 3]$ **(b)** $(-\infty, -2] \cup [3, \infty)$ **(c)** $[-3, 2]$

    (d) $(-\infty, 3]$ **(e)** $(-\infty, \infty)$

13. Find the domain of the function $f(x) = \sqrt{36 - x^2}$.

    (a) $[-6, 6]$ **(b)** $(-\infty, -6] \cup [6, \infty)$ **(c)** $(-6. 6)$

    (d) $(-\infty, -6) \cup (6, \infty)$ **(e)** $(-\infty, \infty)$

14. Use the standard form of the parabola $y = -x^2 - 6x + 2$ to find the vertex.

    (a) $(3, -25)$ **(b)** $(-3, -25)$ **(c)** $(3, -7)$

    (d) $(-3, 11)$ **(e)** None of these

15. Write a quadratic function for the parabola shown.

    (a) $y = (x - 3)^2 + 1$

    (b) $y = -x^2 + 6x + 2$

    (c) $y = -(x - 3)^2 + 1$

    (d) $y = -(x - 3)^2 + 2$

    (e) None of these

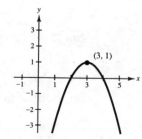

Test Form B

Chapter 10

Name _____ Date _____

Class _____ Section _____

1. Solve by extracting square roots: $9(x - 2)^2 + 1 = 0$.

   (a) $\dfrac{5}{3}, \dfrac{7}{3}$

   (b) $2 - 2\sqrt{2}, 2 + 2\sqrt{2}$

   (c) $2 - \sqrt{10}i, 2 + \sqrt{10}i$

   (d) $2 - \dfrac{i}{3}, 2 + \dfrac{i}{3}$

   (e) None of these

2. Use a graphing utility to approximate the solutions of the equation: $(x - 5)^2 = 121$.

   (a) -6

   (b) 5

   (c) -5

   (d) There are none

   (e) -6 and 16

3. Solve the equation: $2x^{2/3} - x^{1/3} - 6 = 0$.

   (a) $\dfrac{3}{2}$ and 2

   (b) $\dfrac{9}{4}$ and 4

   (c) $\dfrac{3}{2}$ and -2

   (d) $-\dfrac{27}{8}$ and 8

   (e) $\dfrac{27}{8}$ and -8

4. Find the real number c such that $x^2 + \dfrac{4}{5}x + c$ is a perfect square trinomial.

   (a) $\dfrac{4}{25}$

   (b) $\dfrac{16}{25}$

   (c) $\dfrac{2}{5}$

   (d) $-\dfrac{16}{25}$

   (e) $\dfrac{64}{25}$

5. Solve the equation $3x^2 - x - 3 = 0$ by completing the square and use a calculator to estimate the solutions to two decimal places.

   (a) $-2.54, 3.54$

   (b) $-2.04, 4.04$

   (c) $-0.85, 1.18$

   (d) $-0.01, 2.01$

   (e) $0.16 \pm 0.99i$

6. Solve by using the Quadratic Formula: $x^2 + 4x + 2 = 0$.

   (a) $-2 - 2\sqrt{2}, -2 + 2\sqrt{2}$

   (b) $-2 - \sqrt{2}, -2 + \sqrt{2}$

   (c) $-2 - \sqrt{6}, -2 + \sqrt{6}$

   (d) $-4 - \sqrt{2}, -4 + \sqrt{2}$

   (e) None of these

7. Use a calculator to solve: $1.37x^2 - 2.4x - 5.41 = 0$. Round your answer to three decimal places.

   (a) $0.228, 4.572$

   (b) $-1.296, 3.048$

   (c) $-1.775, 4.175$

   (d) $-5.720, 2.432$

   (e) None of these

8. Use a graphing utility to determine the type of solutions of the equation $-0.6x^2 + 2.9x + 2.1 = 0$ by graphing the function $y = -0.6x^2 + 2.9x + 2.1$.

   (a) Two distinct real   **(b)** Two distinct complex

   (c) One rational repeated   **(d)** No solutions

9. Find the length of the leg of a right triangle if the hypotenuse measures 7 inches and the one leg measures 2 inches.

   (a) $\sqrt{53}$ **(b)** $3\sqrt{5}$ **(c)** 5   **(d)** $\sqrt{47}$ **(e)** None of these

10. An open box is to be constructed from a square piece of material by cutting a 4-inch square from each corner. Use a calculator to find the dimensions of the square piece of material if the box is to have a volume of 961 cubic inches.

   (a) 23.5″ by 23.5″   **(b)** 31″ by 31″   **(c)** 19.5″ by 19.5″

   (d) 15.5″ by 15.5″   **(e)** 17.5″ by 17.5″

11. Solve: $\dfrac{2}{x+1} \geq 5$.

   (a) $(-\infty, -1) \cup \left[-\frac{3}{5}, \infty\right)$ **(b)** $\left(-\infty, -\frac{3}{5}\right]$ **(c)** $\left(-1, -\frac{3}{5}\right]$

   (d) $\left(-\infty, \frac{1}{5}\right]$ **(e)** None of these

12. Use a graphing utility to solve the inequality: $x - x^2 < -12$.

   (a) $[-3, 4]$ **(b)** $(-\infty, -3) \cup (4, \infty)$ **(c)** $(-3, 4)$

   (d) $(-4, 3)$ **(e)** $(-\infty, \infty)$

13. Find the domain of the function: $f(x) = \sqrt{9x^2 - 169}$.

   (a) $\left(-\frac{13}{3}, \frac{13}{3}\right)$ **(b)** $\left[-\frac{13}{3}, \frac{13}{3}\right]$ **(c)** $\left(-\infty, -\frac{13}{3}\right] \cup \left[\frac{13}{3}, \infty\right)$

   (d) $\left(-\infty, -\frac{13}{3}\right) \cup \left(\frac{13}{3}, \infty\right)$ **(e)** $(-\infty, \infty)$

14. Use the standard form of the parabola $y = 4x^2 - 16x + 3$ to find the vertex.

   (a) $(-2, 51)$ **(b)** $(2, -13)$ **(c)** $(4, 3)$

   (d) $(0, 3)$ **(e)** None of these

15. Write a quadratic function for the parabola shown.

   (a) $y = (x + 2)^2 - 2$

   (b) $y = (x - 2)^2 - 2$

   (c) $y = -(x + 2)^2 + 2$

   (d) $y = (x - 2)^2 + 2$

   (e) None of these

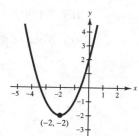

Test Form C   Name _____   **Date** _____

Chapter 10   Class _____   **Section** _____

1. Solve by extracting square roots: $9\left(x + \frac{1}{2}\right)^2 + 5 = 0$.

2. Use a graphing utility to approximate the solutions of the equation: $(2x - 3)^2 = 4$.

3. Solve the equation: $\left(\sqrt{x} + 1\right)^2 - \left(\sqrt{x} + 1\right) - 6 = 0$.

4. Find the real number c such that $x^2 - \frac{8}{3}x + c$ is a perfect square trinomial.

5. Solve the equation $3x^2 - 5x - 4 = 0$ by completing the square and use a calculator to estimate the solutions to two decimal places.

6. Solve by using the Quadratic Formula: $2x^2 - 2x - 1 = 0$.

7. Use a calculator to solve the equation $1.36x^2 - 5.21x - 2.82 = 0$. Round your answer to three decimal places.

8. Use a graphing utility to determine the type of solutions of the equation $3.4x^2 + 27.2x + 54.4 = 0$ by graphing the function $y = 3.4x^2 + 27.2x + 54.4$.

9. The daily profit in dollars P of producing x items is given by the quadratic equation $P = x^2 - 300x + 23{,}500$ where x is the number of items produced. Use a calculator to find how many items are produced if the daily profit is \$3025.

10. Find the larger of two consecutive positive integers m and n such that $m^2 - n^2 = 35$.

11. Solve the inequality $\dfrac{5}{x + 3} \le 1$ and graph the solution on the real number line.

12. Use a graphing utility to solve the inequality: $x^2 + 1 \ge 0$.

13. Find the domain of the function: $f(x) = \sqrt{x^2 - 7x - 8}$.

14. Write the equation of the parabola $y = -2x^2 + 4x$ in standard form and find the vertex.

15. If the graph of $f(x) = x^2$ is shifted two units to the left and one unit downward, write its new equation.

Test Form A Name _____ Date _____

Chapter 11 Class _____ Section _____

1. Use a calculator to find the amount of an investment of $1000 invested at a rate of 9% for three years if the interest is compounded monthly.

   (a) $270 **(b)** $1270 **(c)** $1309.96 **(d)** $1308.65 **(e)** None of these

2. A certain population decreases according to the equation $y = 300 - 5e^{0.2t}$. Use a calculator to find the population (to the nearest integer) when $t = 10$.

   (a) 295 **(b)** 293 **(c)** 263 **(d)** 37 **(e)** None of these

3. Let $f(x) = \sqrt{x - 4}$ and $g(x) = 9 - 8x - x^2$. Find $g(f(4))$.

   (a) $(9 - 8x - x^2)\left(\sqrt{x - 4}\right)$ **(b)** 0 **(c)** 9

   (d) $-9, 1$ **(e)** None of these

4. Given $f(x) = 3x^3 - 1$, use a graphing utility to determine which function is f^{-1}.

   (a) $\dfrac{1}{3x^3 - 1}$ **(b)** $3x^{-3} - 1$ **(c)** $3(x + 1)$

   (d) $\sqrt[3]{\dfrac{x + 1}{3}}$ **(e)** None of these

5. Find the inverse of the function: $f(x) = \dfrac{2}{3x + 1}$.

   (a) $\dfrac{3x - 1}{2}$ **(b)** $\dfrac{2 - x}{3x}$ **(c)** $\dfrac{3x + 1}{2}$

   (d) $\dfrac{1 - x}{2}$ **(e)** None of these

6. Evaluate $\log_{27} 3$ without the aid of a calculator.

   (a) 9 **(b)** $\frac{1}{9}$ **(c)** 3 **(d)** $\frac{1}{3}$ **(e)** None of these

7. Evaluate: $\ln e^4$.

   (a) $\frac{1}{4}$ **(b)** e^{-4} **(c)** 4 **(d)** -4 **(e)** $-\frac{1}{4}$

8. Use the properties of logarithms to expand $\log_{10}\left(\dfrac{2x\sqrt{y}}{z^2}\right)$ as a sum, difference, or multiple of logarithms.

   (a) $\log_{10} 2x + \log_{10}\sqrt{y} + \log_{10} z^2$

   (b) $\log_{10} 2 + \log_{10}x + \dfrac{1}{2}\log_{10} y + 2\log_{10} z$

   (c) $\log_{10} 2 + \log_{10} x + \dfrac{1}{2}\log_{10} y - 2\log_{10} z$

   (d) $\left(\log_{10} 2\right)\left(\log_{10} x\right)\left(\dfrac{1}{2}\log_{10} y\right) / \left(2\log_{10} z\right)$

   (e) None of these

9. Use the properties of logarithms to condense $\ln(x + 1) + 4 \ln x$ into a logarithm of a single quantity.

   (a) $\ln(x + 1 + x^4)$ **(b)** $\ln[x^4(x + 1)]$ **(c)** $\ln(5x + 1)$

   (d) $\ln\left(\dfrac{x + 1}{x^4}\right)$ **(e)** None of these

10. Simplify $\ln\left(e^{x^2 + 1}\right)$.

    (a) $x^2 + 1$ **(b)** $\ln e^{x^2} + \ln e$ **(c)** $(\ln e^{x^2})(\ln e)$ **(d)** $\ln e^{x^2}$ **(e)** None of these

11. Solve without using a calculator: $\log_{10}(2x + 5) = 0$.

    (a) 1 **(b)** $-\dfrac{5}{2}$ **(c)** -2 **(d)** -2.3219 **(e)** None of these

12. Solve $10^{x/2} = 76$. Use a calculator and round your answer to four decimal places.

    (a) 15.2 **(b)** 8.6615 **(c)** 577.2 **(d)** 3.7616 **(e)** None of these

13. Solve $100e^{0.06t} = 152$. Use a calculator and round your answer to four decimal places.

    (a) 1.4315 **(b)** 7.8373 **(c)** 3.2321 **(d)** 6.9785 **(e)** None of these

14. A savings account had a balance of $2000 five years ago and has a balance of $2760.84 today. Use a calculator to find the annual percentage rate if the interest is compounded quarterly.

    (a) 5.83% **(b)** 6.50% **(c)** 6.27% **(d)** 6.63% **(e)** None of these

15. A deposit of $1000 is made into a fund with an annual interest rate of 10%. Find the time (in years) necessary for the investment to double if the interest is compounded continuously. Round your answer to two decimal places.

    (a) 10 years   **(b)** 7.23 years   **(c)** 6.93 years   **(d)** 20 years   **(e)** None of these

Test Form B

Chapter 11

Name _____ Date _____

Class _____ Section _____

1. Use a calculator to find the amount of an investment of $1000 invested at a rate of 11% for two years if the interest is compounded quarterly.

   (a) $220   (b) $1242.38   (c) $1220   (d) $1246.08   (e) None of these

2. A certain population decreases according to the equation $y = 40e^{0.025t}$. Use a calculator to find the population (to the nearest integer) when $t = 50$.

   (a) 140   (b) 2051   (c) 45   (d) 50   (e) None of these

3. Let $f(x) = \sqrt{x + 4}$ and $g(x) = 9 - 8x - x^2$. Find $f(g(1))$.

   (a) $\sqrt{13 - 8x - x^2}$ (b) $4 - 8\sqrt{5}$ (c) $-2, 2$

   (d) 2   (e) None of these

4. Given $f(x) = 2x^5$, use a graphing utility to determine which function is f^{-1}.

   (a) $\sqrt[5]{\dfrac{x}{2}}$ (b) $\dfrac{1}{2}\sqrt[5]{x}$ (c) $\dfrac{1}{2x^5}$

   (d) $\dfrac{2}{x^5}$ (e) None of these

5. Find the inverse of the function: $f(x) = \dfrac{7}{x + 2}$.

   (a) $f(x)$ has no inverse   (b) $\dfrac{x + 2}{7}$ (c) $\dfrac{7 - 2x}{x}$

   (d) $-\dfrac{7}{x + 2}$ (e) None of these

6. Evaluate $\log_2 \frac{1}{16}$ without the use of a calculator.

   (a) -4 (b) $\frac{1}{4}$ (c) 8   (d) $\frac{1}{8}$ (e) None of these

7. Evaluate: $\ln \dfrac{1}{e^2}$.

   (a) e^{-2} (b) 2   (c) $\frac{1}{2}$ (d) -2 (e) $-\frac{1}{2}$

8. Use the properties of logarithms to expand $\ln\left(\dfrac{x^2 y}{2\sqrt{z}}\right)$ as a sum, difference, or multiple of logarithms.

   (a) $2\ln x + \ln y - \ln 2 + \frac{1}{2}\ln z$ (b) $2\ln x + \ln y - \ln 2 - \dfrac{1}{2}\ln z$

   (c) $(2\ln x)(\ln y)/(\ln 2)\left(\dfrac{1}{2}\ln z\right)$ (d) $2\ln x + 2\ln y - \ln 2 - \dfrac{1}{2}\ln z$

   (e) None of these

9. Use the properties of logarithms to condense $2 \log_{10} x - \dfrac{1}{2} \log_{10} z$ into a logarithm of a single quantity.

(a) $\log_{10}\left(x^2 - \sqrt{z}\right)$

(b) $\log_{10}\left(\dfrac{x}{z}\right)$

(c) $\log_{10} \dfrac{x^2}{\sqrt{z}}$

(d) $\log_{10}\left(\dfrac{4x}{z}\right)$

(e) None of these

10. Simplify: $e^{\ln (x^2 + 1)}$.

(a) $e^{\ln x^2} + e^{\ln 1}$

(b) $x^2 + 1$

(c) $\left(e^{\ln x^2}\right)\left(e^{\ln 1}\right)$

(d) $\dfrac{1}{x^2 + 1}$

(e) None of these

11. Solve without using a calculator: $\log_{10}(2x + 5) = 1$.

(a) $\frac{5}{2}$

(b) -2

(c) $\frac{15}{2}$

(d) 10

(e) None of these

12. Solve $10^{x/3} = 29$. Use a calculator and round your answer to four decimal places.

(a) 8.7

(b) 4.3872

(c) 10.1019

(d) 0.4875

(e) None of these

13. Solve $100e^{0.07t} = 152$. Use a calculator and round your answer to four decimal places.

(a) 3.0780

(b) 7.9832

(c) 5.9816

(d) -0.1575

(e) None of these

14. A savings account had a balance of $2000 five years ago and has a balance of $2835.25 today. Use a calculator to find the annual percentage rate if the interest is compounded quarterly.

(a) 5.83%

(b) 8.35%

(c) 7.00%

(d) 6.85%

(e) None of these

15. A deposit of $6000 is made into a fund with an annual interest rate of 10%. Find the time (in years) necessary for the investment to triple if the interest is compounded continuously. Round your answer to two decimal places.

(a) 30 years

(b) 15 years

(c) 10.99 years

(d) 11.12 years

(e) None of these

Test Form C
Chapter 11

Name _____ Date _____

Class _____ Section _____

1. Let $f(x) = 2^{-x}$. Find:

   (a) $f(0)$ (b) $f(-3)$ (c) $f(5)$

2. If \$2000 is invested at $8\frac{1}{2}\%$ interest compounded daily, use a calculator to find the balance after 10 years. (Assume a non-leap year.)

3. Let $f(x) = x - 2$ and $g(x) = \dfrac{x+5}{3}$. Find $(f \circ g)(x)$.

4. Given $f(x) = x^2 + 1$ for $x \geq 0$, use a graphing utility to determine which function is f^{-1}.

   (a) $\dfrac{1}{x^2 + 1}$ (b) $\sqrt{x-1}$ (c) $\sqrt{x} - 1$ (d) $1 - \sqrt{x}$ (e) None of these

5. Evaluate $\log_2 \frac{1}{16}$ without the aid of a calculator.

6. Use a calculator to evaluate $\ln \frac{3}{4}$. Round your answer to 4 decimal places.

7. Evaluate: $\ln \dfrac{1}{e^{\sqrt{2}}}$.

8. Use the properties of logarithms to expand $\ln \dfrac{x}{yz}$.

9. Simplify: $\ln \left(\dfrac{e^{x^2+1}}{e} \right)$.

10. Use the properties of logarithms to expand and simplify: $\log_{10} \sqrt{\dfrac{10}{t}}$.

11. Use a calculator to solve: $\left(1 + \dfrac{0.07}{4} \right)^{4t} = 3$. Round your answer to two decimal places.

12. Solve: $\ln \sqrt{3 - x} = 1$.

13. Solve without using a calculator: $\ln x - \ln(x + 1) = 1$.

14. Use a calculator to find the constant k so that the exponential function $y = 2e^{kt}$
passes through the points given on the graph.

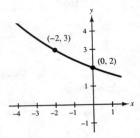

15. On the Richter Scale, the magnitude R of an earthquake intensity I is given by
$R = \log_{10} I$. Use a calculator to find the intensity per unit of area for the
earthquake in Yugoslavia in 1979 which measured $R = 7.2$.

Test Form A
Chapter 12

Name _____ Date _____

Class _____

Section _____

1. Find the fifth term of the sequence whose nth term is given by $a_n = 2(3^{n-1})$. (Begin with $n = 1$.)

   (a) 486   (b) -486 (c) $\frac{1}{162}$ (d) 162   (e) None of these

2. Find the partial sum S_5 for the sequence whose nth term is $a_n = n^2 - 1$. (Assume n begins with 1.)

   (a) 10   (b) 50   (c) 25   (d) 40   (e) 52

3. Use a graphing utility to evaluate $\sum_{i=1}^{4} (1 - i)$.

   (a) -3 (b) -6 (c) 6   (d) -5 (e) None of these

4. Use sigma notation to write the sum: $\frac{2}{1} + \frac{3}{2} + \frac{4}{3} + \cdots + \frac{7}{6}$.

   (a) $\sum_{n=1}^{7} \frac{n}{n-1}$ (b) $\sum_{n=1}^{6} \frac{n+1}{n}$ (c) $\sum_{n=1}^{7} \frac{n}{n+1}$

   (d) $\sum_{n=2}^{n} \frac{n}{n+1}$ (e) None of these

5. Find the ninth term of the arithmetic sequence with the first term $a_1 = 4$ and common difference $d = 10$.

   (a) 94   (b) 84   (c) 46   (d) 49   (e) None of these

6. Find the sum of the first 18 terms of the arithmetic sequence whose nth term is $a_n = 3n - 1$.

   (a) 495   (b) 53   (c) 459   (d) 445   (e) None of these

7. Write the first five terms of the arithmetic sequence defined recursively.

   $$a_1 = -3$$
   $$a_{k+1} = a_k + 5$$

   (a) $-3, -2, -1, 0, 1$ (b) $-3, -1, 1, 3, 5$ (c) $-3, 0, 3, 6, 9$

   (d) $-3, 2, 7, 12, 17$ (e) $5, 10, 15, 20, 25$

8. A person buys a \$100,000 term life insurance policy. During the next five years the value of the policy will depreciate at the rate of 4% per year. (That is, at the end of each year, the depreciated value is 96% of what it was at the beginning of the year.) Find the depreciated value of the policy at the end of five full years.

   (a) \$88,000   (b) \$84,934.66   (c) \$81,537.27   (d) \$78,275.78   (e) None of these

9. Find the 20th term of the geometric sequence with $a_1 = 5$ and $r = 1.1$.

   (a) 1.1665   **(b)** 37.0012   **(c)** 33.6375   **(d)** 30.5795   **(e)** None of these

10. Use a calculator to find the sum: $\sum_{n=0}^{10} 2\left(\frac{3}{5}\right)^n$. Round your answer to four decimal places.

   (a) 4.9690   **(b)** 5.0000   **(c)** 4.9819   **(d)** 55.0000   **(e)** None of these

11. Use the Binomial Theorem to find the x^4 term in the expression of $(x + 2y)^7$.

   (a) $35x^4y^3$ **(b)** $8x^4y^3$ **(c)** $1680x^4y^3$ **(d)** $280x^4y^3$ **(e)** None of these

12. Use Pascal's Triangle to evaluate the complex number $(2 - i)^4$.

   (a) 17   **(b)** $-7 - 24i$ **(c)** $13 + 6i$ **(d)** 15   **(e)** None of these

13. Use a graphing utility to evaluate $_{25}C_{17}$.

   (a) 1,081,575   **(b)** 2,042,975   **(c)** 0   **(d)** 480,700   **(e)** 3.85×10^{20}

14. An auto license plate is made using two letters followed by three digits. Find the number of plates possible.

   (a) 676,000   **(b)** 468,000   **(c)** 492,804   **(d)** 1,757,600   **(e)** None of these

15. A random number generator selects an integer from 1 to 20. Find the number of ways in which a number that is a multiple of three can be selected.

   (a) 6   **(b)** 720   **(c)** 5   **(d)** 120   **(e)** None of these

16. An organization consisting of 54 members is going to elect four officers. No person may hold more than one office. How many different outcomes are possible?

   (a) 354,294   **(b)** 8,503,056   **(c)** 316,251   **(d)** 7,590,024   **(e)** None of these

17. Find the probability of choosing an E when selecting a letter at random from those in the word COLLEGE.

   (a) $\frac{2}{7}$ **(b)** $\frac{1}{5}$ **(c)** $\frac{2}{5}$ **(d)** $\frac{1}{7}$ **(e)** None of these

18. If the probability of getting a rotten apple in a basket of apples is 12%, what is the probability of getting 3 good apples choosing one from each of three different baskets? Round your answer to four decimal places.

   (a) 0.9983   **(b)** 0.0017   **(c)** 0.8800   **(d)** 0.6815   **(e)** None of these

19. If the probability that an event will occur is $\frac{6}{11}$, find the probability that the event will not occur.

   (a) 0   **(b)** 1   **(c)** $\frac{6}{11}$ **(d)** $\frac{5}{11}$ **(e)** 5

20. Find the sum: $\sum_{n=0}^{\infty} 5\left(-\frac{2}{3}\right)^n$.

   (a) -2 **(b)** $\frac{3}{5}$ **(c)** 3   **(d)** $\frac{10}{3}$ **(e)** $-\frac{10}{3}$

Test Form B
Chapter 12

Name _____ **Date** _____

Class _____ **Section** _____

1. Find the tenth term of the sequence whose nth term is given by $a_n = \dfrac{2n + 1}{5 + 3(n - 1)}$. (Begin with $n = 1$.)

   (a) $\dfrac{21}{32}$ (b) $\dfrac{21}{72}$ (c) $\dfrac{22}{32}$ (d) $\dfrac{19}{29}$ (e) None of these

2. Find the partial sum S_3 for the sequence whose nth term is $a_n = \dfrac{(-1)^n}{n}$. (Assume n begins with 1.)

   (a) $-\dfrac{1}{3}$ (b) $-\dfrac{1}{6}$ (c) $-\dfrac{2}{3}$ (d) $-\dfrac{5}{6}$ (e) $\dfrac{5}{6}$

3. Use a graphing utility to evaluate: $\displaystyle\sum_{i=1}^{4}(2i - 1)$.

   (a) $8i - 2$ (b) 16   (c) 7   (d) 6   (e) None of these

4. Use sigma notation to write the sum: $\dfrac{3}{1} + \dfrac{3}{4} + \dfrac{3}{9} + \dfrac{3}{16} + \dfrac{3}{25}$.

   (a) $\displaystyle\sum_{i=1}^{5}\dfrac{1}{i^2}$ (b) $\displaystyle\sum_{i=1}^{5}\dfrac{3}{4i}$ (c) $\displaystyle\sum_{i=1}^{6}\dfrac{3}{i^2}$

   (d) $\displaystyle\sum_{i=1}^{5}\dfrac{3}{i^2}$ (e) None of these

5. Find the eighth term of the arithmetic sequence with the first term $a_1 = 5$ and common difference $d = 8$.

   (a) 69   (b) 48   (c) 61   (d) 104   (e) None of these

6. Find the sum of the first 20 terms of the arithmetic sequence whose nth term is $a_n = 3n - 1$.

   (a) 570   (b) 610   (c) 59   (d) 551   (e) None of these

7. Write the first five terms of the arithmetic sequence defined recursively.

   $a_1 = 42$

   $a_{k+1} = a_k - 6$

   (a) 42, 48, 54, 60, 66   (b) $-6, 0, 6, 12, 18$ (c) 42, 41, 40, 39, 38

   (d) 42, 43, 44, 45, 46   (e) 42, 36, 30, 24, 18

8. A person buys a $100,000 term life insurance policy. During the next five years the value of the policy will depreciate at the rate of 3% per year. (That is, at the end of each year, the depreciated value is 97% of what it was at the beginning of the year.) Find the depreciated value of the policy at the end of five full years.

  (a) $88,529.28   **(b)** $85,873.40   **(c)** $83,297.20   **(d)** $85,000   **(e)** None of these

9. Find the 23rd term of the geometric sequence with $a_1 = -23$ and $r = \sqrt{2}$.

  (a) $-47,104\sqrt{2}$ **(b)** $-2048\sqrt{2}$ **(c)** -2048

  (d) $-47,104$ **(e)** None of these

10. Use a calculator to find the sum: $\sum_{j=0}^{40} 3(1.05)^j$. Round your answer to two decimal places.

  (a) 383.52   **(b)** 362.40   **(c)** 984   **(d)** 22.18   **(e)** None of these

11. Use the Binomial Theorem to find the x^4 term in the expression of $(2x + y)^7$.

  (a) $35x^4y^3$ **(b)** $560x^4y^3$ **(c)** $16x^4y^3$ **(d)** $280x^4y^3$ **(e)** None of these

12. Use Pascal's Triangle to evaluate the complex number $(2 + i)^4$.

  (a) $-7 - 24i$ **(b)** $7 - 24i$ **(c)** $13 + 6i$ **(d)** $-7 + 24i$ **(e)** 17

13. Use a graphing utility to evaluate $_{18}C_{12}$.

  (a) 8568   **(b)** 0   **(c)** 18,564   **(d)** 125,970   **(e)** 6.03×10^{13}

14. Determine the number of possible five digit zip codes.

  (a) 120   **(b)** 90,000   **(c)** 3,628,800   **(d)** 100,000   **(e)** None of these

15. A random number generator selects an integer from 1 to 20. Find the number of ways in which a number that is a multiple of three can be selected.

  (a) 6   **(b)** 720   **(c)** 5   **(d)** 120   **(e)** None of these

16. A class of 9 students line up single file for lunch. How many different ways can this occur if the 6 boys in the class must line up first?

  (a) 18   **(b)** 60,480   **(c)** 4320   **(d)** 504   **(e)** None of these

17. Find the probability of choosing an A, B, or N when selecting a letter at random from those in the word BANANA.

  (a) $\frac{1}{26}$ **(b)** 0   **(c)** 1   **(d)** $\frac{3}{7}$ **(e)** None of these

18. Two integers from 0 to 9 inclusive are chosen by a random number generator. What is the probability of choosing the number 2 both times?

    (a) $\frac{1}{10}$ **(b)** $\frac{1}{100}$ **(c)** $\frac{1}{50}$ **(d)** $\frac{4}{5}$ **(e)** None of these

19. If the probability that an event will occur is 0.47, find the probability that the event will not occur.

    (a) 0.63   **(b)** 1   **(c)** 0   **(d)** 0.47   **(e)** 0.53

20. Find the sum: $\sum_{n=0}^{\infty} 3\left(-\frac{3}{4}\right)^n$.

    (a) $\frac{4}{7}$ **(b)** $-\frac{3}{7}$ **(c)** $-\frac{9}{7}$ **(d)** 12   **(e)** $\frac{12}{7}$

Test Form C   **Name** _____ **Date** _____

Chapter 12   **Class** _____ **Section** _____

1. Write the first five terms of the sequence whose nth term is $a_n = \dfrac{n!}{(n+2)!}$. (Assume that n begins with 0.)

2. Find the partial sum S_4 for the sequence whose nth term is $a_n = (-1)^{n+1}n$. (Assume that n begins with 1.)

3. Use a graphing utility to find the sum: $\displaystyle\sum_{i=0}^{8} i!$.

4. Use sigma notation to write the sum: $\frac{1}{2} + \frac{2}{6} + \frac{3}{24} + \frac{4}{120} + \frac{5}{720}$.

5. Find a formula for a_n for the arithmetic sequence with $a_2 = 15$ and $d = \frac{3}{2}$. (Begin with $n = 1$.)

6. Find the sum of the first 50 positive integers that are multiples of 3.

7. Write the first five terms of the arithmetic sequence defined recursively.

$$a_1 = 21$$
$$a_{k+1} = a_k - 4$$

8. Determine whether the sequence $-2, \frac{4}{3}, -\frac{8}{9}, \frac{16}{27}, \ldots$ is geometric. If it is, find its common ratio.

9. Find a formula for the nth term of the geometric sequence with first term $a_1 = 5$ and common ratio $r = \frac{2}{3}$. (Begin with $n = 1$.)

10. Find the first five terms of the geometric sequence with $a_1 = 3$ and $r = \frac{3}{2}$.

11. Find the coefficient of x^3y^5 in the expansion of $(3x + 2y)^8$.

12. Use Pascal's Triangle to evaluate the complex number $(3 - i)^3$.

13. Use a graphing utility to evaluate $_{81}C_{59}$.

14. How many ways can 4 girls be picked from a group of 30 girls?

15. In how many ways can 7 people be seated in a row of 7 chairs?

16. Use a graphing utility to evaluate $_{24}C_{19}$.

17. In an experiment in which 2 six-sided dice are tossed, what is the probability of not getting a sum of 10?

18. A die is tossed 3 times. What is the probability that a 2 will come up all three times?

19. If the probability that an event will occur is $\frac{13}{17}$, find the probability that the event will not occur.

20. Find the sum: $\sum\limits_{n=0}^{\infty} 2\left(-\frac{2}{5}\right)^n$.

Answers to Chapter 1 Tests

TEST FORM A

1. c	**2.** d	**3.** d	**4.** c	**5.** d
6. a	**7.** b	**8.** a	**9.** c	**10.** b
11. c	**12.** d	**13.** b	**14.** b	**15.** c
16. a				

TEST FORM B

1. d	**2.** a	**3.** a	**4.** a	**5.** b
6. c	**7.** b	**8.** e, Division by 0 is not defined.		
9. c	**10.** b	**11.** b	**12.** c	**13.** a
14. d	**15.** d	**16.** b		

TEST FORM C

1. $-\frac{3}{2}$ **2.** $>$ **3.** -9

4. 128 **5.** 42 **6.** 15

7. $2 \cdot 2 \cdot 2 \cdot 2 \cdot 3$ **8.** 12 **9.** 84

10. $\frac{15}{32}$ **11.** $-\frac{13}{24}$ **12.** $\frac{19}{18}$

13. 3^5 **14.** 26 **15.** 220.99

16. $4(-15 + x)$

Answers to Chapter 2 Tests

TEST FORM A

1. b	**2.** b	**3.** d	**4.** b	**5.** c
6. c	**7.** d	**8.** b	**9.** d	**10.** d
11. b	**12.** c	**13.** c	**14.** a	**15.** b
16. a				

TEST FORM B

1. c	**2.** c	**3.** a	**4.** e	**5.** d
6. c	**7.** c	**8.** a	**9.** d	**10.** d
11. a	**12.** d	**13.** b	**14.** d	**15.** b
16. b				

TEST FORM C

1. $7y, 3(y + 1), 4$

2. $-12, -8, -20$

3. $81y^{12}$

4. $125x^6$

5. $(x + 2)6$

6. $7x^2 - 42x$

7. $\dfrac{7x}{24}$

8. $11x - 1$

9. $5y - 9$

10. $9 + (5 - x)$

11. $5n + 25q$

12. $d - 0.02d = 0.98d$

13. Approximately $960

14. The pattern is a product of two and a perfect square. The product of 9 and 18 is $2 \cdot 9^2 = 162$.

Numbers	$1 \cdot 2$	$2 \cdot 4$	$3 \cdot 6$	$4 \cdot 8$	$5 \cdot 10$
Products	2	8	18	32	50

15. $400(52) + b = 21{,}300$

16. $d = 54.00 - 45.50$

Answers to Chapter 3 Tests

TEST FORM A

1. b	**2.** d	**3.** b	**4.** c	**5.** c
6. c	**7.** d	**8.** a	**9.** a	**10.** a
11. c	**12.** b	**13.** d	**14.** a	**15.** c
16. c	**17.** d	**18.** b	**19.** a	**20.** c

TEST FORM B

1. c	**2.** c	**3.** d	**4.** d	**5.** a
6. d	**7.** a	**8.** d	**9.** d	**10.** d
11. d	**12.** d	**13.** c	**14.** c	**15.** b
16. b	**17.** c	**18.** a	**19.** c	**20.** b

TEST FORM C

1. $\frac{16}{7}$

2. $3x - 1 \neq 3x - 3$ for any value of x.

3. $80n + 40 = 600$; $n = 7$ where n represents the number of hours.

4. -3

5. 2

6. 40

7. 110

8. 120%

9. ≈ 3822 liters

10. $\frac{1}{50}$

11. The 13-ounce box of cereal has the lower unit price of $0.258 per ounce. The 12.3 ounce box has the higher unit price of $0.2\overline{6}$ per ounce.

12. 165 miles

13. height $= 8$ feet, length $= 16$ feet

14. 5

15. $x \leq 4$

16. $\frac{3}{5} < x < \frac{9}{5}$

17. $\frac{79 + 83 + 89 + 75 + x}{5} \geq 80$; $x \geq 74$

18. $-\frac{5}{3}$ and 3

19. $\left\{x \mid -1 < x < \frac{1}{3}\right\}$

20. You have traveled somewhere between 2.27 and 2.47 miles.

Answers to Chapter 4 Tests

TEST FORM A

1. b	**2.** a	**3.** a	**4.** a	**5.** b
6. c	**7.** a	**8.** b	**9.** b	**10.** c
11. d	**12.** b	**13.** a	**14.** d	**15.** b
16. c	**17.** b	**18.** d		

TEST FORM B

1. c	**2.** d	**3.** d	**4.** c	**5.** b
6. b	**7.** b	**8.** c	**9.** d	**10.** a
11. c	**12.** d	**13.** b	**14.** b	**15.** c
16. d	**17.** c	**18.** a		

TEST FORM C

1.

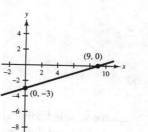

2. $-10, -6, -2, 2, 6$

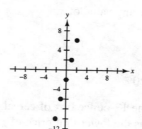

3. $C = 3 + 1(h - 1); 3, 4, 5, 6$

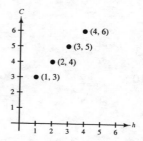

4. $y = \frac{1}{3}x - 3; -5, -4, -3, -2, -1$

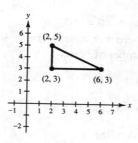

5. $y = -x^2 - 4; -8, -5, -4, -5, -8$

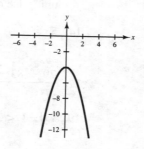

6. $(3, 0)$ and $(-3, 0); (0, -9)$

7. $D = \{1975, 1980, 1985, 1990\}$ and $R = \{\$420, \$425, \$450\}$

8. 4 is paired with two different second components, 5 and 17.

9. No, y is not a function of x.

10. $\frac{9}{5}$

11. $y = -\frac{5}{2}x + 4$

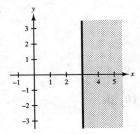

12. Perpendicular

13. $y = -\frac{5}{6}x + \frac{16}{3}$

14. $y = -\frac{1}{4}x + \frac{7}{4}$

15. $d = 65t$; 325

16. It does.

17.

18. $y < 0$

Answers to Chapter 5 Tests

TEST FORM A

1. c	**2.** b	**3.** d	**4.** d	**5.** b
6. d	**7.** a	**8.** c	**9.** a	**10.** c
11. a	**12.** a	**13.** a	**14.** c	**15.** a
16. d				

TEST FORM B

1. b	**2.** c	**3.** a	**4.** c	**5.** d
6. c	**7.** b	**8.** d	**9.** b	**10.** d
11. c	**12.** b	**13.** d	**14.** a	**15.** c
16. b				

TEST FORM C

1. 5

2. binomial

3. $-x^4 + x^3 - 2x^2 + 2x$

4. $-9x^3 - 7x - 8$

5. $5x^4 - 4x^3 - 11x^2 + 4x + 6$

6. $(3x)^2 + 2(3x)(5) + (5)^2 = 9x^2 + 30x + 25$

7. $x^3 + 3x^2 + 3x + 1$

8. $(3x + 2)(x + 3)$ or $3x^2 + 11x + 6$

9. $\dfrac{x^{16}}{81y^{12}}$

10. $\dfrac{-42y^3}{x}$

11. 5.1×10^{-5}

12. 5,663,000

13. $\dfrac{-3x^2}{2y^2}$

14. $m^3 + 5 - \dfrac{9}{m}$

15. $3x - 4$

16. $(2x + 1) - \dfrac{2}{2x + 1}$

Answers to Chapter 6 Tests

TEST FORM A

1. b　　**2.** d　　**3.** c　　**4.** a　　**5.** b

6. a　　**7.** a　　**8.** c　　**9.** b　　**10.** a

11. b　　**12.** a　　**13.** b　　**14.** c　　**15.** d

TEST FORM B

1. d　　**2.** b　　**3.** d　　**4.** d　　**5.** d

6. c　　**7.** c　　**8.** b　　**9.** d　　**10.** c

11. c　　**12.** d　　**13.** d　　**14.** a　　**15.** b

TEST FORM C

1. $9x(3x^6 + 5x - 6)$　　**2.** $-5y(2y^2 - 5y - 1)$　　**3.** $(8y - 1)$

4. $(x - 3)(x - 4)$　　**5.** $(n - 6m)(n + 5m)$　　**6.** $x + 12$

7. $(3x + 5)(3x + 1)$　　**8.** $x + 3$　　**9.** $23x = 18x + 5x$

10. $\left(\frac{1}{6}n + \frac{1}{5}\right)\left(\frac{1}{6}n - \frac{1}{5}\right)$　　**11.** $5y^2(y + 3)(y - 3)$　　**12.** $(4x - 5)^2$

13. $y^2 - 6y - 7 = 0$　　**14.** $x = -3, x = 6$　　**15.** $x(x + 2) = 80$; $x = -10$ and $x = -8$

Answers to Chapter 7 Tests

TEST FORM A

1. b	**2.** d	**3.** c	**4.** c	**5.** a
6. c	**7.** a	**8.** d	**9.** a	**10.** a
11. d	**12.** b	**13.** a	**14.** c	**15.** c

TEST FORM B

1. c	**2.** c	**3.** b	**4.** d	**5.** b
6. a	**7.** c	**8.** d	**9.** c	**10.** e
11. c	**12.** e	**13.** b	**14.** d	**15.** b

TEST FORM C

1. $(2, -1)$

2. $\left(-\frac{3}{2}, \frac{5}{2}\right)$ and $(3, -2)$

3. $(0, 0)$ and $(3, 3)$

4. 12 pounds

5. $(16, 14)$

6. Consistent, one solution

7. $(a, -a, 2a)$ where a is any real number

8. No solution

9. $y = -3x^2 + 2x + 5$

10.
$$\begin{aligned} 2x - y &= 4 \\ 3y + z &= -2 \\ x - 3y + z &= 1 \end{aligned}$$

11. $\left(3, -\frac{1}{2}, -2\right)$

12. $A = 1$, $B = -1$, and $C = -1$

13. 0

14. 15

15. $\frac{1}{2}$

Answers to Chapter 8 Tests

TEST FORM A

1. c	**2.** d	**3.** b	**4.** c	**5.** d
6. a	**7.** a	**8.** c	**9.** d	**10.** a
11. e	**12.** d	**13.** b	**14.** a	**15.** d

TEST FORM B

1. a	**2.** c	**3.** c	**4.** c	**5.** a
6. b	**7.** c	**8.** c	**9.** c	**10.** c
11. e	**12.** b	**13.** a	**14.** b	**15.** c

TEST FORM C

1. $(-\infty, -3) \cup (-3, 0) \cup (0, \infty)$

2. $-\dfrac{x + 4}{2x + 3}$

3. $\dfrac{(x^2 + 4x - 16)(x - 1)}{x(x - 4)}$

4. $y_1 \neq y_2$

5. $\dfrac{x - x^2}{3(3 - x)}$

6. $\dfrac{\dfrac{2 + h}{(2 + h) + 1} - \dfrac{2}{3}}{h} = \dfrac{1}{3(3 + h)}$

7. $-\dfrac{7}{x(x^2 - 1)}$

8. $x = 3$

9. $y = \frac{3}{2}$

10. Intercept: $\left(0, \frac{1}{2}\right)$

Vertical asymptote: $x = 4$

Horizontal asymptote: $y = 0$

11. $\frac{4}{5}$ or $\frac{5}{4}$

12. $(1, 0)$ and $(2, 0)$

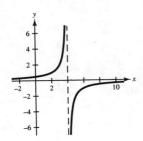

13. $A = \dfrac{k}{\sqrt{x}}$

14. 75

15. **a.** $P = k\omega^3$

b. $\frac{1}{10}$

c. 2700 watts

d. 5 mph

Answers to Chapter 9 Tests

TEST FORM A

1. a	**2.** d	**3.** a	**4.** b	**5.** c
6. d	**7.** d	**8.** a	**9.** b	**10.** d
11. a	**12.** c	**13.** d	**14.** b	**15.** b
16. c	**17.** c	**18.** d	**19.** e	**20.** a

TEST FORM B

1. c	**2.** b	**3.** c	**4.** d	**5.** d
6. c	**7.** c	**8.** b	**9.** a	**10.** d
11. d	**12.** a	**13.** c	**14.** a	**15.** d
16. b	**17.** a	**18.** b	**19.** b	**20.** d

TEST FORM C

1. $\frac{1}{8}$ **2.** 16   **3.** $8\sqrt{3x}$ **4.** -243 **5.** 5

6. a.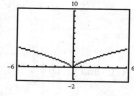

   b. $y = x^{2/3} = (x^{1/3})^2$

   $y \geq 0$ because y is a squared quantity for any value of x.

7. $-\sqrt{2}$ **8.** $3x^5\sqrt{3x}$ **9.** $4\sqrt{10}$

10. $\sqrt{3}(\sqrt{2} + 1)$ **11.** $\dfrac{\sqrt{x + h + 1} + \sqrt{x + 1}}{h}$ **12.** $8 - 7\sqrt{2}$

13. $y_1 = y_2$ **14.** $\frac{23}{16}$ **15.** 3

16. -5 and 5   **17.** $4 - i$ **18.** $13 + 18i$

19. $\frac{3}{17} + \frac{22}{17}i$ **20.** 25

Answers to Chapter 10 Tests

TEST FORM A

1. c	**2.** b	**3.** b	**4.** d	**5.** d
6. a	**7.** d	**8.** b	**9.** d	**10.** b
11. d	**12.** a	**13.** a	**14.** d	**15.** c

TEST FORM B

1. d	**2.** e	**3.** d	**4.** a	**5.** c
6. b	**7.** b	**8.** a	**9.** b	**10.** a
11. c	**12.** b	**13.** c	**14.** b	**15.** a

TEST FORM C

1. $-\dfrac{1}{2} \pm \dfrac{\sqrt{5}}{3}i$

2. $\dfrac{1}{2}$ and $\dfrac{5}{2}$

3. 4

4. $\dfrac{16}{9}$

5. $\dfrac{5 + \sqrt{73}}{6} \approx 2.26$

$\dfrac{5 - \sqrt{73}}{6} \approx -0.59$

6. $\dfrac{1 \pm \sqrt{3}}{2}$

7. $-0.481, 4.312$

8. One rational repeated

9. 195

10. 18

11. $(-\infty, -3) \cup [2, \infty)$

12. $(-\infty, \infty)$

13. $(-\infty, -1] \cup [8, \infty)$

14. $y = -2(x - 1)^2 + 2; (1, 2)$

15. $y = (x - 2)^2 + 1$

Answers to Chapter 11 Tests

TEST FORM A

1. d	**2.** c	**3.** c	**4.** d	**5.** b
6. d	**7.** c	**8.** c	**9.** b	**10.** a
11. c	**12.** d	**13.** d	**14.** b	**15.** c

TEST FORM B

1. b	**2.** a	**3.** d	**4.** a	**5.** c
6. a	**7.** d	**8.** b	**9.** c	**10.** b
11. a	**12.** b	**13.** c	**14.** c	**15.** c

TEST FORM C

1. a. 1

  b. 8

  c. $\frac{1}{32}$

2. $4678.83

3. $\dfrac{x-1}{3}$

4. b

5. -4

6. -0.2877

7. $-\sqrt{2}$

8. $\ln x - \ln y - \ln z$

9. x^2

10. $\frac{1}{2} - \frac{1}{2}\log_{10} t$

11. 15.83

12. $3 - e^2$

13. $\dfrac{e}{1-e}$

14. $-\dfrac{1}{2}\ln\dfrac{3}{2} \approx -0.2027$

15. 15,848,931.92

Answers to Chapter 12 Tests

TEST FORM A

1. d	**2.** b	**3.** b	**4.** b	**5.** b
6. a	**7.** d	**8.** c	**9.** d	**10.** c
11. d	**12.** b	**13.** a	**14.** a	**15.** a
16. d	**17.** a	**18.** d	**19.** d	**20.** c

TEST FORM B

1. a	**2.** d	**3.** b	**4.** d	**5.** c
6. b	**7.** e	**8.** b	**9.** d	**10.** a
11. b	**12.** d	**13.** c	**14.** d	**15.** b
16. c	**17.** c	**18.** b	**19.** e	**20.** e

TEST FORM C

1. $\frac{1}{2}, \frac{1}{6}, \frac{1}{12}, \frac{1}{20}, \frac{1}{30}$

2. -2

3. 46,234

4. $\sum_{n=1}^{5} \frac{n}{(n+1)!}$

5. $a_n = \frac{3}{2}n + 12$

6. 3825

7. 21, 17, 13, 9, 5

8. Yes, $r = -\frac{2}{3}$

9. $5\left(\frac{2}{3}\right)^{n-1}$

10. $3, \frac{3}{2}, \frac{27}{4}, \frac{81}{8}, \frac{243}{16}$

11. 48,384

12. $18 - 26i$

13. 3.72×10^{19}

14. 27,405

15. $7! = 5040$

16. 42,504

17. $\frac{11}{12}$

18. $\frac{1}{216}$

19. $\frac{4}{17}$

20. $\frac{10}{5}$

Final Exam
Multiple-Choice Version

Name _____ Date _____

Class _____ Section _____

1. Simplify: $(s^2t^2)^3(s^3t)$.

   (a) s^5t^3 (b) s^8t^6 (c) s^9t^7 (d) $s^{18}t^6$ (e) None of these

2. Solve: $0.3x - 4 = 2$.

   (a) 2   (b) $\frac{9}{5}$ (c) 20   (d) $-\frac{20}{3}$ (e) None of these

3. 52 is 13% of what number?

   (a) 6.76   (b) 400   (c) 25   (d) 676   (e) None of these

4. A bookstore advertises 20% off the regular price of all paperback books. Find the sale price of a paperback book that lists for $11.95.

   (a) $2.39   (b) $14.34   (c) $9.56   (d) $9.95   (e) None of these

5. Solve the inequality: $-1 < \dfrac{2x + 2}{3} < 2$.

   (a) $-\dfrac{5}{2} < x < 3$ (b) $-\dfrac{5}{2} < x < 4$ (c) $-5 < x < 2$

   (d) $x > -\dfrac{3}{2}$ (e) $-\dfrac{5}{2} < x < 2$

6. Suppose the figure shown is shifted 2 units down and 3 units to the left. Find the coordinates of the vertex in the new location that corresponds to the vertex $(-3, 2)$.

   (a) $(-1, -1)$ (b) $(-5, -1)$

   (c) $(-1, 0)$ (d) $(-6, 0)$

   (e) $(2, -1)$

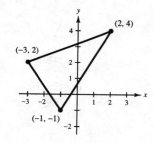

7. Find the y-intercept of the graph of the equation $2x + 3y - 6 = 0$.

   (a) $(0, 2)$ (b) $(2, 0)$ (c) $(3, 0)$ (d) $(3, 2)$ (e) None of these

8. Determine the slope of the line passing through the points $(2, -3)$ and $(-1, 5)$.

   (a) 2   (b) $-\frac{8}{3}$ (c) $-\frac{3}{8}$ (d) -5 (e) None of these

9. Use the graph of $y = |x|$ to write an equation for the transformation shown.

(a) $y = |x - 2|$ (b) $y = |x| + 2$

(c) $y = |x + 2|$ (d) $y = |x| - 2$

(e) None of these

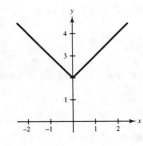

10. Multiply and simplify: $(4x)^2 - (8x - 1)(2x - 3)$.

(a) $-12x^2 + 26x - 3$ (b) $13x - 3$ (c) $26x - 3$

(d) $26x + 3$ (e) None of these

11. Factor completely: $24x^4 + 3x$.

(a) $3x(2x + 1)^3$ (b) $3x(2x + 1)(4x^2 + 4x + 1)$

(c) $3x(2x + 1)(4x^2 - 2x + 1)$ (d) $3x(2x + 1)(4x^2 + 2x + 1)$

(e) None of these

12. Find all values of b for which the polynomial $9x^2 + bx + 4$ is a perfect square trinomial.

(a) 6 and -6 (b) 2 and -2 (c) 10 and -10

(d) 12 and -12 (e) $\frac{2}{3}$

13. Solve: $x^3 = 4x$.

(a) $-2, 2$ (b) $-2, 0, 2$ (c) 2

(d) $0, 2$ (e) None of these

14. Divide: $\dfrac{x^3 + 8}{x + 2}$.

(a) $x^2 - 2x + 4$ (b) $x^2 + 4$ (c) $x^2 + 2x + 4$

(d) $x^2 + 2x - 4$ (e) None of these

15. Use a graphing utility to match the graph with the correct function.

(a) $f(x) = \dfrac{0}{x^2 + 1}$

(b) $f(x) = \dfrac{3}{x^2 + 1}$

(c) $f(x) = \dfrac{x - 3}{x^2 + 1}$

(d) $f(x) = \dfrac{3}{x^2 + 1}$

(e) None of these

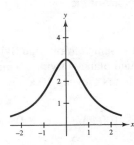

16. The markup for an item that sells for $560 is given by

$$\text{Markup rate} = \frac{560}{C} - 1$$

where C is the wholesale cost. Find the wholesale cost if the markup rate is 75%.

(a) $224   (b) $73.68   (c) $320   (d) $319.43   (e) None of these

17. Determine a number that can be added to its reciprocal to obtain $\frac{34}{15}$.

(a) $\frac{5}{3}$ (b) $\frac{16}{15}$ (c) $\frac{15}{9}$ (d) $\frac{17}{15}$ (e) $\frac{33}{15}$

18. Evaluate: $(-2^2)^{-3}$.

(a) $\frac{1}{64}$ (b) 32 (c) $-\frac{1}{32}$ (d) $-\frac{1}{64}$ (e) None of these

19. Multiply and simplify: $\left(2 - \sqrt{3}\right)\left(5 + \sqrt{3}\right)$.

(a) $7 - 3\sqrt{3}$ (b) $4 - 3\sqrt{3}$ (c) $7 + \sqrt{3}$ (d) 7 (e) None of these

20. Solve: $\sqrt{2 - 5x} = 5x$.

(a) $\frac{1}{5}$ (b) $-\frac{2}{5}$ (c) $\frac{1}{5}, -\frac{2}{5}$ (d) $\frac{1}{10}$ (e) None of these

21. Perform the indicated operation and write the result in standard form: $\dfrac{2}{1 + i}$.

(a) $2 + \dfrac{2}{i}$ (b) $1 - i$ (c) $2 + 2i$ (d) 1 (e) None of these

22. Use a calculator to find the real number c so that $s^2 - 1.7s + c$ is a perfect square trinomial. Then write the trinomial as a binomial squared.

(a) $(s - 1.7)^2$ (b) $(s - 0.7225)^2$ (c) $(s - 0.85)^2$

(d) $(s + 0.85)^2$ (e) $(s - 1.3)^2$

23. Solve: $\dfrac{1}{x} - \dfrac{1}{x + 1} = 1$.

(a) $0, -1$ (b) $\dfrac{-1 - \sqrt{5}}{2}, \dfrac{-1 + \sqrt{5}}{2}$ (c) $-1 - \dfrac{\sqrt{5}}{2}, -1 + \dfrac{\sqrt{5}}{2}$

(d) $\dfrac{-1 - \sqrt{3}i}{2}, \dfrac{1 + \sqrt{3}i}{2}$ (e) None of these

24. Two airplanes leave simultaneously from the same airport, one flying due east, and the other flying due north. The eastbound plane is flying 50 miles per hour slower than the northbound one. If after 4 hours they are 1000 miles apart, how fast is the northbound plane traveling?

(a) 150 mph   (b) 200 mph   (c) 100 mph   (d) 300 mph   (e) None of these

25. Solve: $2x^2 + 3x \geq 5$.

(a) $\left[-\frac{5}{2}, 1\right]$

(b) $\left[-\frac{5}{2}, \infty\right)$

(c) $\left(-\infty, -\frac{5}{2}\right] \cup [1, \infty)$

(d) $\left(-\infty, -\frac{3}{2}\right] \cup [5, \infty)$

(e) None of these

26. Find an equation of the line that passes through $(-4, 1)$ and is perpendicular to the line $x = 3$.

(a) $3x - y + 13 = 0$

(b) $3x - y + 11 = 0$

(c) $x = -4$

(d) $y = 1$

(e) None of these

27. Find the standard form of the equation of the parabola with vertex $(-1, 3)$ and passing through the point $(2, 1)$.

(a) $y = \frac{4}{9}(x + 1)^2 + 3$

(b) $y = -2x^2 - 4x - 2$

(c) $y = -2(x - 1)^2 + 3$

(d) $y = -\frac{2}{9}(x + 1)^2 + 3$

(e) None of these

28. Write the equation of the parabola in standard form: $x^2 - 2y + 6x + 7 = 0$.

(a) $2y + 2 = (x + 3)^2$

(b) $2(y + 1) = (x + 3)^2$

(c) $y = \frac{1}{2}(x + 3)^2 - 1$

(d) $y = (x + 3)^2 - 1$

(e) None of these

29. y is directly proportional to x and $y = 2.4$ when $x = 15$. Find the linear model that relates to y and x.

(a) $y = 0.16x$

(b) $y = 0.625x$

(c) $y = 6.25x$

(d) $y = 1.6x$

(e) None of these

30. If the total cost of running a business is given by the equation $C = 450x + 1000$ and the revenue is given by the equation $R = 500x$, find the sales necessary to break even.

(a) 220

(b) 11

(c) 20

(d) 2000

(e) None of these

31. Use Gaussian elimination to solve the system of equations.

$$\begin{aligned} x - 6y + z &= 1 \\ -x + 2y - 4z &= 3 \\ 7x - 10y + 3z &= -25 \end{aligned}$$

(a) $(5, 1, 2)$

(b) $(-5, -1, 0)$

(c) $(-1, 3, 1)$

(d) No solution

(e) None of these

32. Find the value of the determinant of the coefficient matrix of the system.

$$\begin{aligned} x - 4y &= 1 \\ 3x + 2y &= 10 \end{aligned}$$

(a) 3

(b) 42

(c) 14

(d) -10

(e) None of these

33. Use Cramer's Rule to find the value of x for the solution of the system of equations.

$$x - 4y = 1$$
$$3x + 2y = 10$$

(a) 3   (b) $\frac{1}{2}$ (c) 14   (d) 1   (e) None of these

34. Let $f(x) = \dfrac{1}{\sqrt{x}}$ and $g(x) = 1 - x^2$. Find $(g \circ f)(x)$.

(a) $\dfrac{1 - x^2}{\sqrt{x}}$ (b) $\dfrac{1}{\sqrt{1 - x^2}}$ (c) $1 - \dfrac{1}{x}$

(d) $\dfrac{1}{\sqrt{x}} + 1 - x^2$ (e) None of these

35. Write in exponential form: $\log_x 81 = 4$.

(a) $4^x = 81$ (b) $x^4 = 81$ (c) $81^x = 4$ (d) $81^4 = x$ (e) None of these

36. Solve: $3 \ln x = 7$. Use a calculator and round your answer to four decimal places.

(a) 10.3123   (b) 365.5444   (c) 0.8473   (d) 0.6486   (e) None of these

37. The number of bacteria N in a culture is given by the model $N = 100e^{kt}$ where t is the time in hours. When $t = 5$, $N = 300$. Use a calculator to find the number of hours it takes for the population to double its size ($N = 200$). Round your answer to four decimal places.

(a) 1.6667   (b) 3.1546   (c) 10   (d) 2.3671   (e) None of these

38. On the Richter Scale, the magnitude R of an earthquake intensity I is given by $R = \log_{10} I$. Find the magnitude R of an earthquake of intensity $I = 100,000,000$.

(a) 8   (b) 9   (c) 10   (d) 18.42   (e) None of these

39. Find the sum of the first six terms of the geometric sequence for which $a_1 = 2$ and $a_2 = -4$.

(a) -42 (b) $\frac{130}{3}$ (c) 42   (d) $-\frac{62}{3}$ (e) None of these

40. A multiple choice test question has five possible choices. Find the probability of randomly selecting the correct answer.

(a) $\frac{1}{4}$ (b) $\frac{1}{2}$ (c) $\frac{1}{5}$ (d) $\frac{4}{5}$ (e) None of these

Final Exam

Open-Ended Version

Name _____   Date _____

Class _____   Section _____

1. Evaluate the expression $x^2 - xy + 2y^2$ when $x = 1$ and $y = -2$.

2. Solve: $\dfrac{2x + 1}{5} - \dfrac{x + 1}{3} = \dfrac{1}{15}$.

3. 36 is 90% of what number?

4. Find the sales tax rate if an appliance that lists for $695 costs $743.65 including tax.

5. Solve the inequality: $3 < \dfrac{2x - 1}{5} < 7$.

6. Plot the points $(2, 1), (-1, 2), (-2, -1), (1, -2)$ and connect them with line segments to form a square. Verify that the figure is a square.

7. Use a graphing utility to graph the equation $y = x^3 - 9x$. Use the graph to find the x-intercept(s).

8. A line with slope $m = \frac{2}{3}$ passes through the points $(2, -2)$ and $(x, 6)$. Find the unknown coordinate x.

9. The perimeter of a rectangle is 80 meters.

   a. Use a graphing utility to graph the function for the area of the rectangle, $A = x(40 - x)$.

   b. Use the graph to determine what value of x yields the largest value of A.

   c. Find the area of the largest rectangle.

10. Multiply and simplify: $2x(x - 4) - (x + 2)(x - 1)$.

11. Factor $256 - 81y^4$ completely.

12. Find a real number c so that the polynomial $t^2 - 26t + c$ is a perfect square trinomial.

13. The length of a rectangular room is two feet less that three times its width. If the area of the room is 176 square feet, write an algebraic equation to model this problem and solve it to find the dimensions of the room.

14. Simplify the compounded fraction: $\dfrac{\left(\dfrac{1}{x} - \dfrac{1}{y}\right)}{\left(\dfrac{x - y}{x^3 + x^2y}\right)}$.

15. Divide: $\dfrac{x^3 + x^2 - 8}{x - 2}$.

16. Use the graph of $f(x) = \dfrac{1}{x}$ to sketch the graph of $g(x) = \dfrac{1}{x} - 1 = \dfrac{1 - x}{x}$.

17. The sum of 3 times a number and 2 times its reciprocal is $\frac{55}{3}$. Find the number.

18. Rewrite the expression using only positive exponents and simplify: $\dfrac{x^{-2}y^2}{3x^2y^{-3}}$.

19. Divide and simplify: $\left(\sqrt{x} + 3\right) \div \left(\sqrt{x} + 2\right)$.

20. Solve: $\sqrt{5x - 3} = 4$.

21. Multiply the number $6 - 3i$ by its conjugate.

22. Solve the equation $2x^2 - 4x + 1 = 0$ by completing the square and use a calculator to estimate the solutions to two decimal places.

23. Solve: $\sqrt{3x - 2} + 1 = x$.

24. The daily profit in dollars P of producing x items is given by the quadratic equation $P = x^2 - 300x + 23{,}500$ where x is the number of items produced. Use a calculator to find how many items are produced if the daily profit is $1000.

25. Solve: $3x^2 + 2x \le 5$.

26. Write the general form of the equation for the line that passes through the point $(1, 3)$ and is perpendicular to the line given by $2x + 3y + 5 = 0$.

27. Write an equation of the parabola shown in the figure.

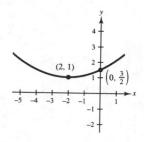

28. Write an equation for the line which is parallel to $7x - 12y - 4 = 0$ and passes through the point $(2, -1)$.

29. Determine whether the variation model is of the form $y = kx$ or $y = \dfrac{k}{x}$ and find k.

x	10	20	30	40	50
y	2.5	5	7.5	10	12.5

30. Solve the system by the method of substitution.

$$2x^2 - y = -2$$
$$x - y = -2$$

31. Find a, b, and c for the quadratic equation $f(x) = ax^2 + bx + c$, such that $f(1) = -2, f(-2) = 19,$ and $f(3) = 4$.

32. Use matrices to solve the system of linear equations.

$$x + 2y + z = 5$$
$$2x - y - 3z = 5$$
$$-2x + 3y + z = -11$$

33. Use Cramer's Rule to solve the system of equations.

$$5x + 3y = 9$$
$$2x - 4y = 14$$

34. Let $f(x) = x - 2$ and $g(x) = \dfrac{x + 5}{3}$. Find $(g \circ f)(x)$.

35. Evaluate: $\ln \dfrac{e^4}{e^5}$.

36. Solve: $\ln x^4 = 7$.

37. The population P in a certain town is given by the model $P = 50{,}000e^{kt}$ where t is the time in years. When $t = 2$, $P = 60{,}000$. Use a calculator to find the number of years it will take for the population to double its size ($P = 100{,}000$). Round your answer to four decimal places.

38. The pH of a solution is determined by pH $= -\log_{10}[\text{H}^+]$ when pH is a measure of the hydrogen ion concentration $[\text{H}^+]$, measured in moles per liter. Find the pH of a solution for which $[\text{H}^+] = 7.61 \times 10^{-6}$.

39. Find the 30th term of the arithmetic sequence with $a_1 = -5$ and $d = \frac{1}{3}$. (Begin with $n = 1$.)

40. In a group of ten children, three have blond hair and seven have brown hair. If a child is chosen at random, what is the probability that child will have brown hair?

Answers to Final Exam

MULTIPLE-CHOICE VERSION

1. c	**2.** c	**3.** b	**4.** c	**5.** e
6. d	**7.** a	**8.** b	**9.** b	**10.** c
11. c	**12.** d	**13.** b	**14.** a	**15.** b
16. c	**17.** a	**18.** d	**19.** a	**20.** a
21. b	**22.** c	**23.** b	**24.** b	**25.** c
26. d	**27.** d	**28.** c	**29.** a	**30** c
31. b	**32.** c	**33.** a	**34.** c	**35.** b
36. a	**37.** b	**38.** a	**39.** a	**40.** c

OPEN-ENDED VERSION

1. 11   **2.** 3   **3.** 40   **4.** 7%   **5.** $8 < x < 18$

6.

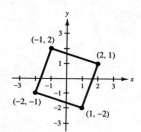

7. $(-3, 0)(0, 0)$, and $(3, 0)$ **8.** 14

The length of each side is $\sqrt{10}$. The slopes of adjacent sides are 3 and $-\frac{1}{3}$; hence, adjacent sides are perpendicular.

9. a.

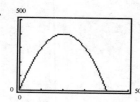

10. $x^2 - 9x + 2$ **11.** $(4 - 3y)(4 + 3y)(16 + 9y^2)$

b. $x = 20$

c. $A = 400$ square meters

12. 169   **13.** $x(3x - 2) = 176$; 8 feet by 22 feet

14. $-\dfrac{x(x + y)}{y}$ **15.** $x^2 + 3x + 6 + \dfrac{4}{x - 2}$

16.

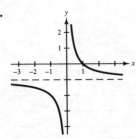

17. 6 or $\dfrac{1}{9}$

18. $\dfrac{y^5}{3x^4}$

19. $\dfrac{x + \sqrt{x} - 6}{x - 4}$

20. $\dfrac{19}{5}$

21. 45

22. $\dfrac{2 + \sqrt{2}}{2} \approx 1.71$

$\dfrac{2 - \sqrt{2}}{2} \approx 0.29$

23. $\dfrac{5 \pm \sqrt{13}}{2}$

24. 150

25. $\left[-\dfrac{5}{3}, 1 \right]$

26. $3x - 2y + 3 = 0$

27. $y = \frac{1}{8}x^2 + \frac{1}{2}x + \frac{3}{2}$

28. $7x - 12y - 26 = 0$

29. $y = kx$ and $k = \frac{1}{4}$

30. $(0, 2)$ and $\left(\frac{1}{2}, \frac{5}{2}\right)$

31. $a = 2, b = -5, c = 1$

32. $(5, -1, 2)$

33. $(3, -2)$

34. $\dfrac{x + 3}{3}$

35. -1

36. $\pm e^{7/4}$

37. 7.6036

38. 5.12

39. $\frac{14}{3}$

40. $\frac{7}{10}$

Transparency Masters

TITLE	Section	Page	Reference
Endowment Funds	1.2	26	Exercise 139
Find the Total Area	1.4	52	Exercise 125
Company Expenses	1.4	53	Exercise 127
Total Area	2.2	81	Exercise 70
Area of a Trapezoid	2.3	83	Exercise 157
Raising a Weight	3.2	136	Exercise 82
Office Vists to Physicians	3.3	147	Exercise 101
Photo Enlarged	3.3	148	Exercise 105
Photo Enlarged	3.3	148	Exercise 106
Floor Plan	3.5	170	Exercise 25
Label the Points	4.1	209	Exercise 11
Personal Income	4.1	212	Exercises 71-74
Percents of Gross Domestic Product Spent on Health Care	4.1	212	Exercises 75-76
Net Sales for Walmart	4.4	245	Exercise 89
Find the Area of the Shaded Portion	5.1	282	Exercises 103-106
The Trinomial $x^2 + 3x + 2 = (x + 1)(x + 2)$ Shown Graphically	6.2	336	Exercises 77-80
Constructing a Box	6.5	365	Exercise 91
Are They Parallel?	7.1	387	Exercise 78
Identify Each Line with the Proper Equation	7.2	395	Exercise 5
Identify Each Line with the Proper Equation	7.2	395	Exercise 7
Cost of Medicare	8.1	453	Exercises 95-96
Working Together	8.4	483	Exercises 85-86
Match the Rational Function with its Graph	8.5	492	Exercises 29-32
Health Care in the United States	10.1	575	Exercises 135-136
Find the Transformations of $f(x) = x^2$ Given by the Graph	10.4	601	Exercises 91-94
Distance Traveled	10.5	611	Exercise 35
Match the Exponential Function with its Graph	11.1	639	Exercises 51-58
Sketch f^{-1}	11.2	653	Exercise 106
Match the Functions to its Graph	11.3	664	Exercises 63-68
Area	12.3	731	Exercise 124

ENDOWMENT FUNDS

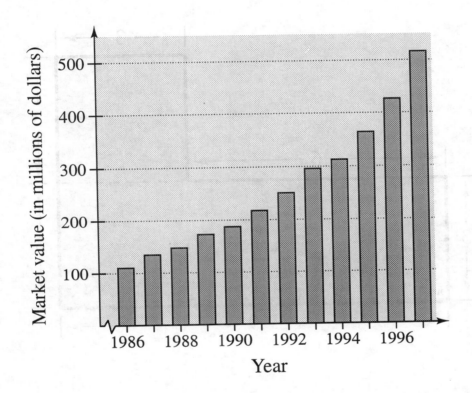

FIND THE TOTAL AREA

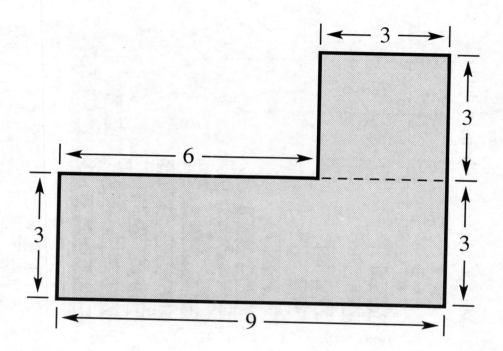

COMPANY EXPENSES

Company Expenses

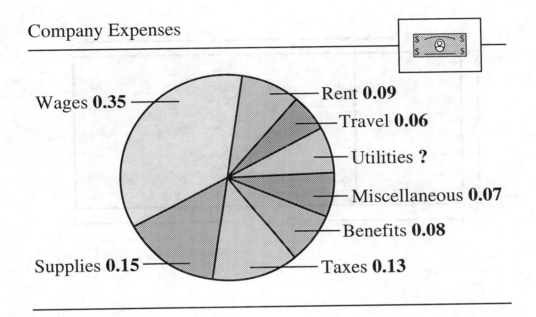

Wages **0.35**

Rent **0.09**

Travel **0.06**

Utilities **?**

Miscellaneous **0.07**

Benefits **0.08**

Supplies **0.15**

Taxes **0.13**

TOTAL AREA

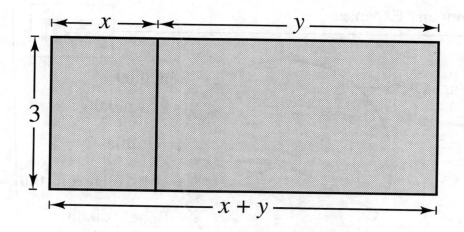

AREA OF A TRAPEZOID

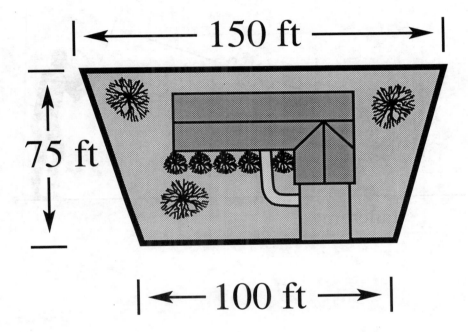

Elementary and Intermediate Algebra: A Combined Course, Third Edition, Larson/Hostetler
Copyright © 2000 by Houghton Mifflin Company

RAISING A WEIGHT

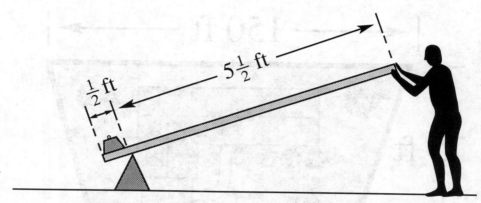

Fulcrum

OFFICE VISITS TO PHYSICIANS

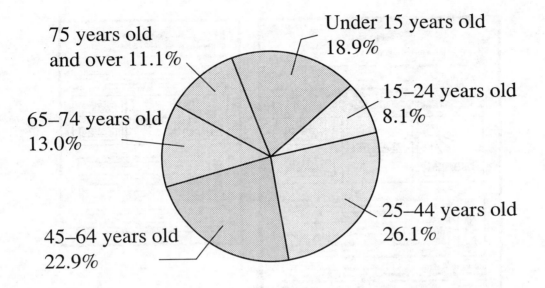

75 years old and over 11.1%

Under 15 years old 18.9%

15–24 years old 8.1%

65–74 years old 13.0%

25–44 years old 26.1%

45–64 years old 22.9%

PHOTO ENLARGED

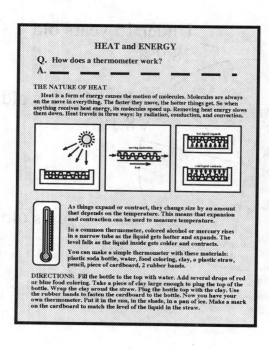

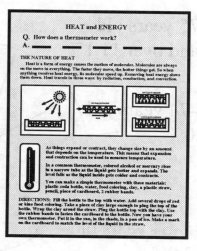

PHOTO ENLARGED

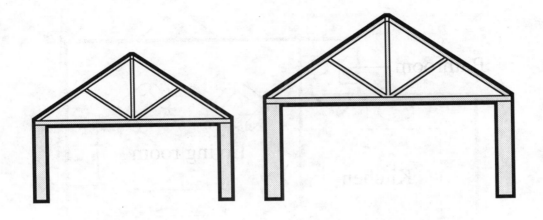

FLOOR PLAN

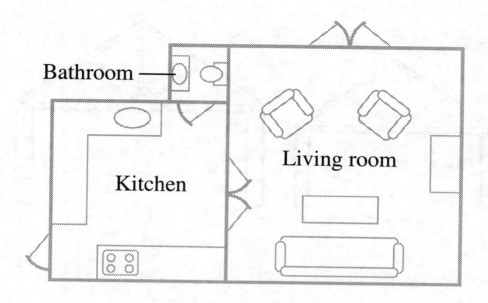

Bathroom

Kitchen

Living room

LABEL THE POINTS

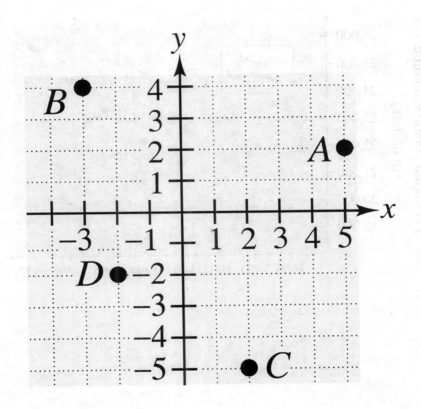

PERSONAL INCOME

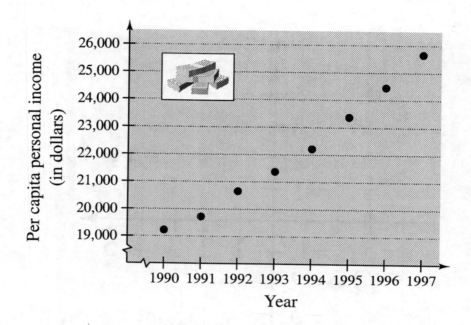

PERCENTS OF GROSS DOMESTIC PRODUCT SPENT ON HEALTH CARE

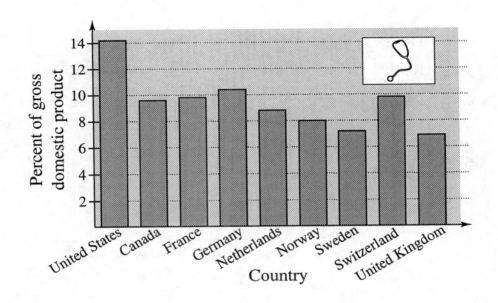

NET SALES FOR WALMART

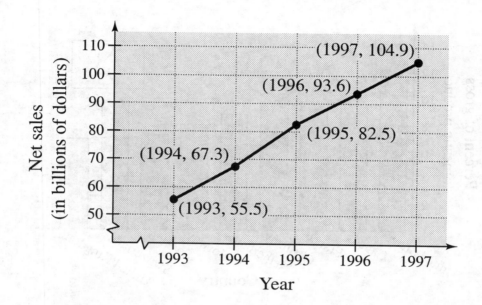

FIND THE AREA OF THE SHADED PORTION

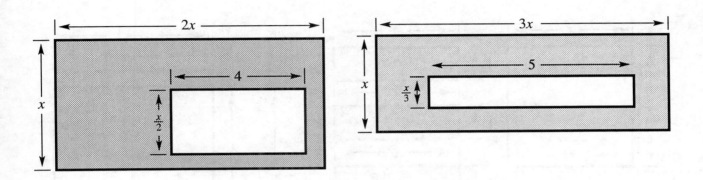

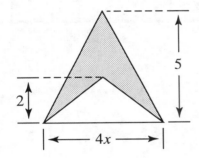

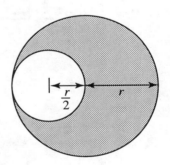

Elementary and Intermediate Algebra: A Combined Course, Third Edition, Larson/Hostetler
Copyright © 2000 by Houghton Mifflin Company

THE TRINOMIAL $x^2 + 3x + 2 = (x + 1)(x + 2)$
SHOWN GRAPHICALLY

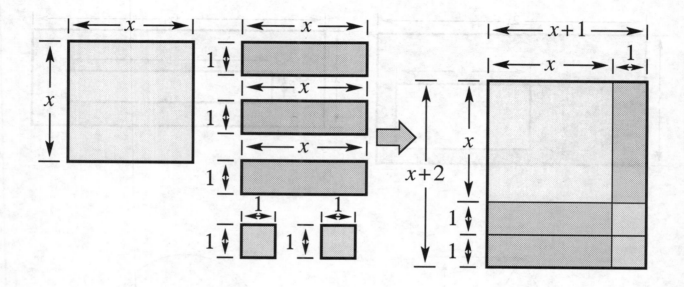

CONSTRUCTING A BOX

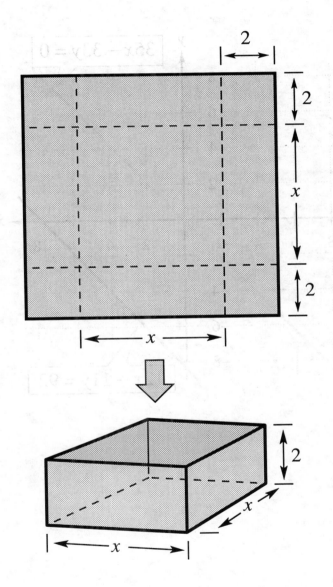

ARE THEY PARALLEL?

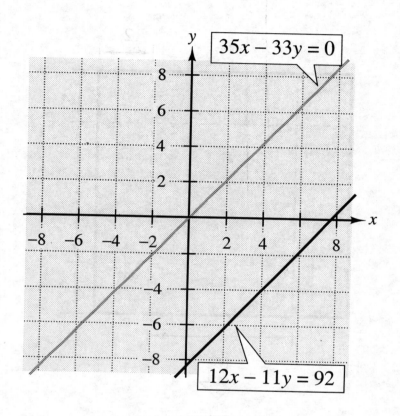

$35x - 33y = 0$

$12x - 11y = 92$

IDENTIFY EACH LINE WITH THE PROPER EQUATION

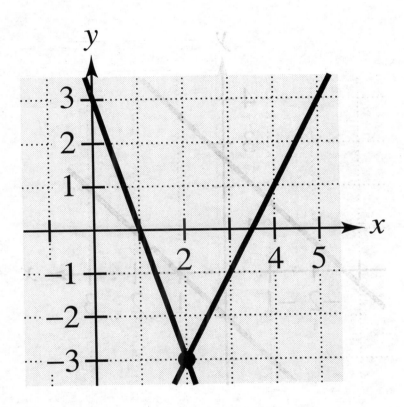

IDENTIFY EACH LINE WITH THE PROPER EQUATION

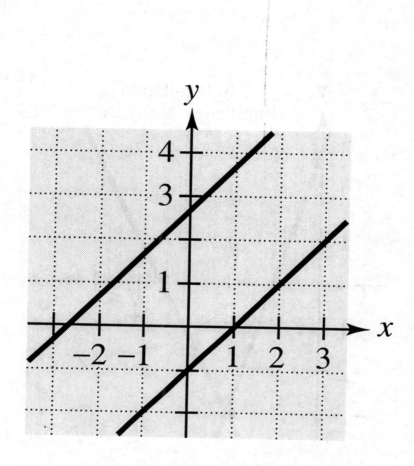

COST OF MEDICARE

U.S. Population Enrolled in Medicare

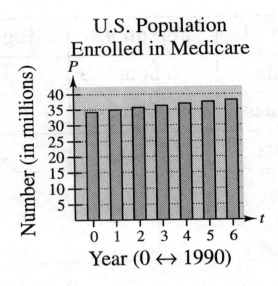

Cost of Medicare

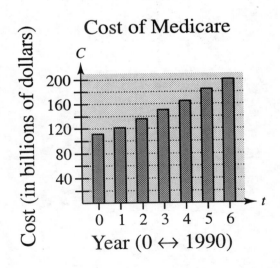

WORKING TOGETHER

Person #1	Person #2	Together
6 hours	6 hours	
3 minutes	5 minutes	
5 hours	$2\frac{1}{2}$ hours	

MATCH THE RATIONAL FUNCTION WITH ITS GRAPH

(a)

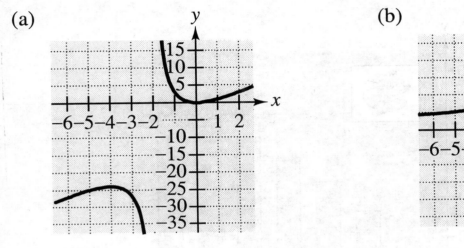

(b)

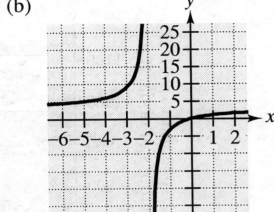

(c)

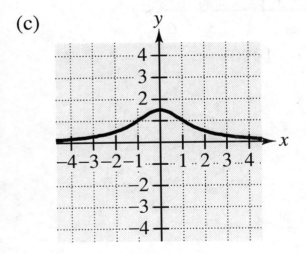

(d)

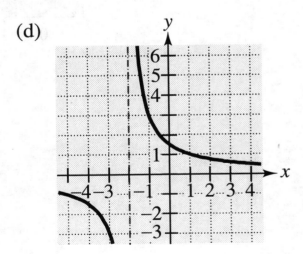

HEALTH CARE IN THE UNITED STATES

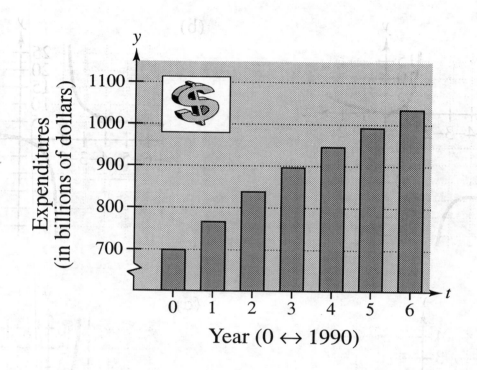

FIND THE TRANSFORMATIONS OF $f(x) = x^2$ GIVEN BY THE GRAPH

91.

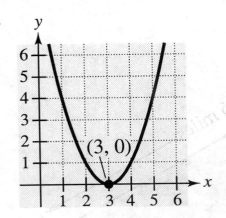

92.

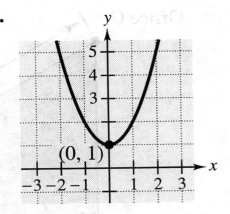

93.

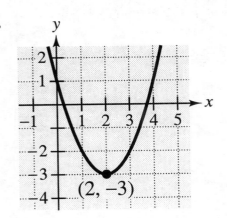

94.

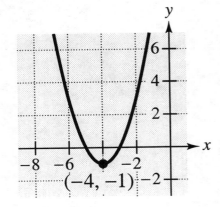

DISTANCE TRAVELED

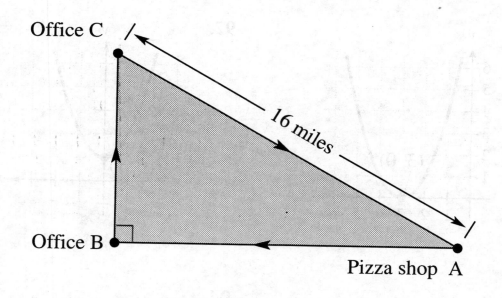

Office C

16 miles

Office B

Pizza shop A

MATCH THE EXPONENTIAL FUNCTION WITH ITS GRAPH

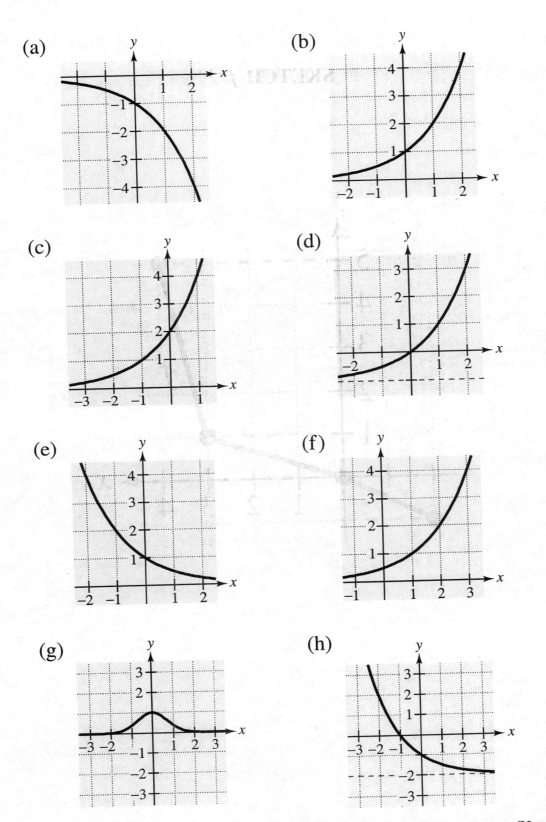

SKETCH f^{-1}

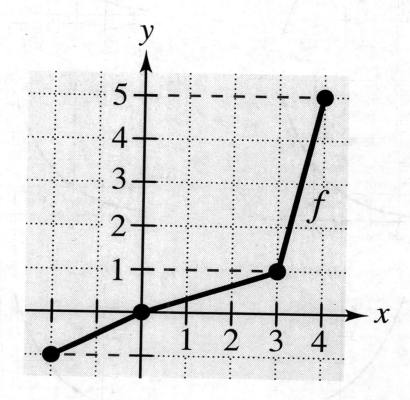

MATCH THE FUNCTION TO ITS GRAPH

(a)

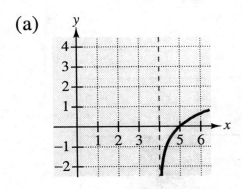

(b)

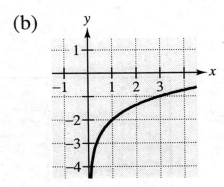

(c)

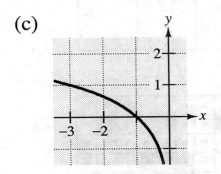

(d)

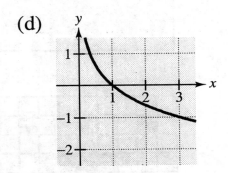

(e)

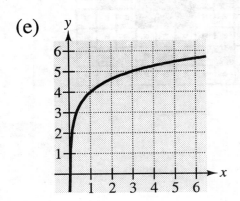

(f)

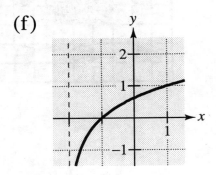

AREA

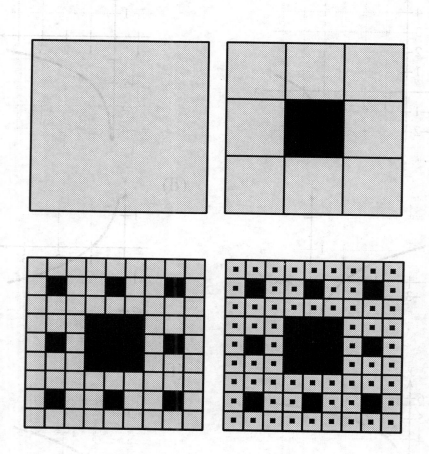